CW00797048

Mechanical vibration analysis and computation

The author's companion book *Random Vibrations and Spectral Analysis* is also published by Longman

Mechanical vibration analysis and computation

D. E. Newland

Professor of Engineering
University of Cambridge

Copublished in the United States with
John Wiley & Sons, Inc., New York

Longman Scientific and Technical
Longman Group UK Limited
Longman House, Burnt Mill, Harlow
Essex CM20 2JE, England
and Associated Companies throughout the world

Copublished in the United States with
John Wiley & Sons, Inc., 605 Third Avenue, New York, NY 10158

First published 1989

British Library Cataloguing in Publication Data
Newland D. E. (David Edward), 1936–
  Mechanical vibration analysis and computation
  1. Mechanical vibration. Analysis
  I. Title
  620.3

ISBN 0-582-02744-6

Library of Congress Cataloging in Publication Data
Newland, D. E. (David Edward)
  Mechanical vibration analysis and computation/D. E. Newland.
    p. cm.
  Bibliography: p.
  Includes index.
  ISBN 0-470-21388-4 (Wiley)
  1. Vibration. I. Title.
  TA355.N49 1989
  620.3–dc19   88-22017
                                                                              CIP

Set in 10/12 Times Roman

Produced by Longman Singapore Publishers (Pte) Ltd.
Printed in Singapore

Contents

Preface

This book has arisen from my experience as a teacher and consultant in mechanical vibrations. It is intended for senior undergraduates in mechanical engineering and the applied sciences and for postgraduates who are concerned with vibration problems. It is also designed to be a practical handbook for those who need to carry out vibration calculations; I hope that it will be useful for many engineers in industry.

Mechanical Vibration Analysis and Computation is a companion for my other book *Random Vibrations and Spectral Analysis* (second edition, Longman, 1984). Although each can be read separately, the two books go together and, where appropriate, topics in this book are cross-referenced to those in *Random Vibrations*. Taken together, the two books cover the whole field of mechanical vibration analysis, including random and non-linear vibrations and digital data analysis. Although the subject is a mathematical one, and in this new book there is a considerable amount of matrix analysis, I have tried to keep the mathematics as simple as possible; the emphasis is on practical applications of the theory in computation, rather than on rigorous proofs of theoretical results.

Although most readers will probably have had some preliminary introduction to vibration analysis, the basic ideas of single degree-of-freedom vibration theory are reviewed in Chapter 1. This is followed, in Chapter 2, by a detailed study of the frequency response of linear systems. The emphasis is on the interpretation of a system's frequency response in terms of its eigenvalues. In Chapter 3 more general response properties are considered, including alternative measures of damping, and the time for resonant oscillations to build up. These three chapters serve as a background for Chapter 4 which introduces the main ideas of matrix analysis, including the expression of a general linear vibration problem in terms of a set of first-order differential equations. This transformation is necessary in order to use modern computational methods which are organized for sets of first-order equations.

The physical interpretation of natural frequencies and mode shapes is discussed at length in Chapter 5 which includes applications to three major practical problems: the bending vibrations of self-supporting chimneys and

masts, the torsional vibrations of a diesel-electric generator system, and the
hunting oscillations of a railway vehicle. The general theory of linear
vibration is usually developed on the assumption that the eigenvalues of
the vibrating system are all different. Sometimes this assumption is not
valid, and then there may no longer be a full set of independent modes.
Such problems are considered in Chapter 6, and the analysis is illustrated
by a torsional vibration problem which has three zero eigenvalues.

Most practical problems of vibration analysis require the application of
computer routines to extract eigenvalues and eigenvectors, and Chapter 7
is about how these programs work. The numerical procedures for computing the eigenvalues of a real, unsymmetric matrix by the QR method are
explained in detail and corresponding logical flow diagrams are given in
the appendices. Although many workers will use library programs for
vibration analysis, it is helpful to know how these programs operate and
what their shortcomings are. These matters are discussed in detail in
Chapter 7. The accompanying flow diagrams will allow those readers who
wish to prepare their own programs to do so in whatever language is most
convenient.

Chapters 8, 9 and 10 are about methods of numerical calculation for the
vibration response of large linear systems. In Chapter 8, the frequency-
response function matrix and impulse-response function matrix are expressed in general form in terms of the mass, stiffness and damping matrices. In
Chapter 9 these functions are used to generate general input-output
relations for a multi-degree-of-freedom linear system. In Chapter 10
methods of discrete calculation are described, including discrete calculations in both the frequency domain and the time domain, discrete
finite-difference calculations, and response calculations by numerical integration. The numerical integration section deals with the fourth-order
Runge–Kutta method, and a logical flow diagram for one integration step
is given in Appendix 7.

When the mass and stiffness matrices of an undamped system are
symmetric matrices, the general frequency-response and impulse-response
equations are simplified. Chapter 11 is a detailed analysis of such a system.
The analysis applies for the general case when there is no restriction on the
eigenvalues, and so applies when there are repeated eigenvalues as well as
when all the eigenvalues are distinct. Many structural vibration problems
have symmetric matrices and the method of modal truncation that can be
applied to problems in this class has important practical applications.

Chapters 12 and 13 are concerned with the analysis and vibration
properties of continuous systems. General series solutions for frequency-
response functions and impulse-response functions are derived and their
application is illustrated by the analysis of the longitudinal vibration of an
elastic column subjected to displacement inputs at one end. Beam and
plate vibrations are considered in detail, including the vibration of beams
when the effects of rotary inertia and shear deformation are included.

There is also a careful consideration of the application of Rayleigh's principle. This principle is used to calculate the whirling speed of a rotating cantilever shaft of variable area when subjected to external pressure. It is a problem with no known exact solution. The corollaries of Rayleigh's principle give some extremely useful practical results and they are explained carefully. These corollaries are not as well known as they deserve to be.

Finally, Chapter 14 is about parametric and nonlinear vibrations. It begins with the theory of the Mathieu equation and the exact calculation of stability boundaries, first without damping and then in the presence of damping. This leads to a consideration of autoparametric systems and the phenomenon of internal resonance. The Mathieu analysis is also used to investigate the stability of the forced periodic vibration of systems with nonlinear stiffness. This introduces nonlinear jump behaviour, when a periodic response suddenly jumps from one steady amplitude to another steady amplitude.

When a system with large nonlinearity is subjected to large-amplitude excitation, there may be conditions under which periodic motion is impossible. The system then undergoes chaotic motion which never repeats itself. This behaviour is illustrated by a typical time history computed by numerical integration of the equations of motion. However, for weakly nonlinear systems, the main engineering interest is in their periodic response, and several methods of finding the forced periodic response of weakly nonlinear systems are discussed. To illustrate how these methods may be applied, Galerkin's method is used to calculate the forced response of a system with a centrifugal pendulum vibration absorber.

In order to help readers who are studying the subject in detail for the first time and to guide lecturers who may be using the book, a suggested choice of topics for a first course on vibration analysis and computation is given after this preface.

The book includes a detailed list of references, and interested readers will be able to use these references to pursue many of the topics that are discussed here. Also there is a set of specially chosen problems intended to illustrate the theoretical ideas and methods in each chapter. The author hopes that teachers and students will find these problems helpful. Where possible, answers are given at the end of the problems, but in some cases the answers are too complicated or too lengthy (for example a graph or a numerical output from a computer calculation) so that it has not been practicable to print all the results here. A solutions manual is being prepared and it is hoped that this will be available shortly after the book is published. Details can be obtained from the author.

Lastly, it is necessary to say that no warranty is given that the calculation methods and procedures are free from error. The reader's attention is drawn particularly to the legal disclaimer printed below. In solving any new problem, it is always desirable to begin with special cases for which solutions are known and work up progressively to the full problem. Also, test calculations should be carried out on the full problem using extreme sets of parameter values (for example very large masses or very small stiffnesses) to test that the calculation procedure works properly on asymptotic cases of the full problem. It is possible that major errors will be found in the book and certain that there will be minor ones. The author will be most grateful for the notification of all of these and will be very pleased to hear from readers who care to write with their comments and with suggestions for improving later editions.

Cambridge University Engineering Department
Trumpington Street   D. E. NEWLAND
Cambridge, CB2 1PZ   November, 1988
England

Disclaimer of warranty

Selected topics for a first course on vibration analysis and computation

All of Chapters 1, 2, 3 and 4.

All of Chapter 5. The intention is to illustrate the properties of eigenvalues and eigenvectors without requiring detailed knowledge of the examples.

Chapter 6 deals with the special properties of singular and defective matrices, and the details may be omitted on first reading. However, the reader should understand that a matrix cannot necessarily be diagonalized if its eigenvalues are repeated and should know the form of the Jordan matrix.

Chapter 7 describes numerical methods for the extraction of eigenvalues and related calculations. The details may be omitted other than to see in general terms how eigenvalues are computed.

All of Chapter 8 is needed except for the following sections:

Frequency-response functions when the eigenvector matrix is defective.
Example 8.2: Frequency-response function for a system with repeated eigenvalues.
Impulse-response functions when the eigenvector matrix is defective.
Use of the matrix exponential function.
Application to the general response equation.

All of Chapter 9.

The discrete response methods in Chapter 10 should be included if time permits because they are the basis of practical calculations of vibration behaviour. However, the whole of this chapter may be omitted without interfering with the rest of the course.

Chapter 11 includes Lagrange's equations and a detailed analysis of the properties of systems with symmetric matrices, which are extremely important in structural vibration and in many mechanical problems. It is possible to begin reading at the section entitled 'Alternative proof of orthogonality when the eigenvalues are distinct' and to omit all the earlier part of this chapter if time does not allow the detailed analysis in the first part of the chapter to be absorbed.

All of Chapter 12 except the last section on general response equations.

Chapter 13 contains standard results on beams and plates in its first four sections, and the sections on Rayleigh's method are extremely important. The following sections may be omitted on a first reading:

Timoshenko beam.
 Effect of rotary inertia only.
 Effect of rotary inertia and shear together.
 Beam with a travelling load.
Example of the whirling of a shaft subjected to external pressure.

Chapter 14 includes much important material but time may prevent all of it being studied in detail. In that case, the sections to be included are:

Autoparametric systems.
Internal resonance.
Nonlinear jump phenomena.
Stability of forced vibration with numerical stiffness.
Numerical integration: chaotic response.

These can be studied alone provided that the equations of motion in the section 'Autoparametric systems' are derived by applying Newton's laws rather than by applying Lagrange's equations. There is reference back to the stability charts for the Mathieu equation, but if these are accepted without proof the material in the sections listed may be followed without further explanation.

A syllabus for a course based on this selection of material is given below together with the numbers of some appropriate problems selected from the list at the back of the book.

Response properties

	Chapter	Problems
Introduction	1	1.1–1.4
Frequency response; expansion in partial fractions; composite systems	2	2.1–2.6
Receptance and mobility graphs; measures of damping; forced vibration with hysteretic damping	3	3.1–3.4
Time for resonant oscillations to build up; acceleration through resonance	3	

00410000000004000000041000

Parametric and nonlinear effects

Acknowledgements

The first draft of this book grew out of my teaching notes for a final-year undergraduate course in vibrations at Cambridge. Several of my colleagues have been involved with this and other vibrations courses, particularly Dr R. W. Gregory, Dr J. D. Smith, Mr J. J. Thwaites and Dr J. Woodhouse, and I am grateful for their indirect contributions to this book. Dr Woodhouse kindly reviewed the final manuscript and made many helpful suggestions. Four of my former graduate students have also contributed significantly. The development of the subject-matter into the computational field stemmed from research done when I was at Imperial College with Mr W. Nelson Caldwell. Later this work was continued at Sheffield with Dr R. W. Aylward; more recently I have had the help of Dr David Cebon and Dr Hugh E. M. Hunt at Cambridge. I am very grateful to all of them. Also, I wish to mention particularly my secretary, Mrs Margaret Margereson, who prepared numerous typed drafts. She shouldered this extra burden with a ready smile however boring the work and however heavy her daily work schedule.

I should not have been able to complete this book without the opportunities provided by two spells of sabbatical leave from my job in Cambridge: a year during 1983–84 and a term in 1986. Without these opportunities to devote myself single-mindedly to the task, it would certainly not be finished now.

It would also not be finished had I not had the interest and support throughout of my wife, Tricia. The mental application that is required for writing a theoretical textbook can only be achieved by eschewing other more routine duties. I have been especially fortunate that Tricia has encouraged me throughout the endeavour and enabled me to bring this project to a successful conclusion.

D.E.N.

The Author and publishers are indebted to the following for permission to reproduce copyright material: the American Society of Mechanical Engineers for Fig. 5.16 which is based on Fig. 3 and for Fig. P5.6 which is Fig. 2 of the author's paper 'Steering a flexible railway truck on curved track', *J. Engng for Ind.*, Trans. Am. Soc. Mech. Engrs, Series B, Vol. 91, 908–18, 1969; the Institute of Marine Engineers for Figs 6.1 and 8.2 which are based on Fig. 9 of the author's contribution in Trans. Inst. Mar. Engrs, Vol. 91 (TM), 119–21, 1979; the Council of the Institution of Mechanical Engineers for Fig. 13.3 which is Fig. 7 of the author's paper 'Whirling of a cantilever elastic shaft subjected to external pressure', *J. Mech. Engng Sci.*, Vol. 14, 11–18, 1972; the American Society of Mechanical Engineers for Figs 14.11, 14.12 and P14.10 which are Figs 1, 2 and 10 of the author's paper 'Nonlinear aspects of the performance of centrifugal pendulum vibration absorbers', *J. Engng for Ind.*, Trans. Am. Soc. Mech. Engrs, Vol. 86, Series B, 257–63, 1964.

Chapter 1

Fundamental concepts

General solution for one degree of freedom

The vibration behaviour of many real systems can be approximated by a physical model with one degree of freedom defined by

$$m\frac{d^2y}{dt^2} + c\frac{dy}{dt} + ky = x \tag{1.1}$$

where $x \equiv x(t)$ is the excitation and $y \equiv y(t)$ is the response, which are both functions of time, t. The constants m, c and k represent the mass, viscous damping and stiffness of the system, which is shown in Fig. 1.1. If there is no excitation, so that $x(t) = 0$, this has the general solution

$$y(t) = C_1 e^{\lambda_1 t} + C_2 e^{\lambda_2 t} \tag{1.2}$$

where C_1 and C_2 are arbitrary constants determined by the initial conditions and the *eigenvalues* λ_1, λ_2 are the two roots of the *characteristic equation*

$$m\lambda^2 + c\lambda + k = 0 \tag{1.3}$$

which we assume are distinct so that $\lambda_1 \neq \lambda_2$. When $x(t)$ is not zero, the

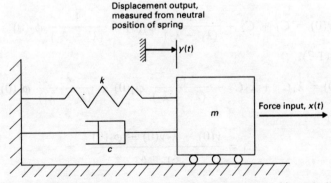

Fig. 1.1 Single-degree-of-freedom system with force input $x(t)$ and displacement output $y(t)$

solution from $y(t)$ can be written in the form

$$y(t) = \left[C_1 + \frac{1}{(\lambda_1 - \lambda_2)} \, \phi_1(t) \right] e^{\lambda_1 t} + \left[C_2 + \frac{1}{(\lambda_2 - \lambda_1)} \, \phi_2(t) \right] e^{\lambda_2 t} \quad (1.4)$$

where $\phi_1(t)$ and $\phi_2(t)$ are the indefinite integrals

$$\phi_1(t) = \int e^{-\lambda_1 t} \, \frac{x(t)}{m} \, dt \qquad (1.5)$$

$$\phi_2(t) = \int e^{-\lambda_2 t} \, \frac{x(t)}{m} \, dt. \qquad (1.6)$$

Each integral introduces an arbitrary constant of integration; in (1.4) these are given by the constants C_1 and C_2, which must be chosen to satisfy the initial conditions.

In Chapter 4 we shall derive the solution (1.4) from first principles, but the reader can check that the answer given is correct by differentiating (1.4) to obtain $\dot{y}$ and $\ddot{y}$ and then substituting these expressions into the left-hand side of (1.1). The result for $\dot{y}$ is

$$\dot{y}(t) = \left[C_1 + \frac{1}{(\lambda_1 - \lambda_2)} \, \phi_1(t) \right] \lambda_1 e^{\lambda_1 t} + \left[C_2 + \frac{1}{(\lambda_2 - \lambda_1)} \, \phi_2(t) \right] \lambda_2 e^{\lambda_2 t}$$

$$(1.7)$$

as may be verified from Problem 1.1. On first inspection it appears that (1.7) cannot be the result of differentiating (1.4) because the functions $\phi_1(t)$ and $\phi_2(t)$ do not appear to have been differentiated. However, because of the form of (1.5) and (1.6),

$$\dot{\phi}_1(t) \, e^{\lambda_1 t} = \frac{x(t)}{m} = \dot{\phi}_2(t) \, e^{\lambda_2 t} \qquad (1.8)$$

and so these terms cancel out in (1.7).

If, at time $t = 0$, the initial conditions are $y(0)$ and $\dot{y}(0)$, and the integrals in (1.5) and (1.6) have the values $\phi_1(0)$ and $\phi_2(0)$, then, from (1.4),

$$y(0) = C_1 + C_2 + \frac{1}{(\lambda_1 - \lambda_2)} \, \phi_1(0) + \frac{1}{(\lambda_2 - \lambda_1)} \, \phi_2(0) \qquad (1.9)$$

and, from (1.7),

$$\dot{y}(0) = \lambda_1 C_1 + \lambda_2 C_2 + \frac{\lambda_1}{(\lambda_1 - \lambda_2)} \, \phi_1(0) + \frac{\lambda_2}{(\lambda_2 - \lambda_1)} \, \phi_2(0) \qquad (1.10)$$

from which

$$C_1 = \frac{\dot{y}(0) - \lambda_2 y(0) - \phi_1(0)}{\lambda_1 - \lambda_2} \qquad (1.11)$$

and

$$C_2 = \frac{\dot{y}(0) - \lambda_1 y(0) - \phi_2(0)}{\lambda_2 - \lambda_1}. \qquad (1.12)$$

On substituting in (1.4) for C_1 and C_2 from (1.11) and (1.12), we find that the general solution for $y(t)$ can be written in the form

$$y(t) = \frac{1}{(\lambda_1 - \lambda_2)} [\dot{y}(0) - \lambda_2 y(0) + \phi_1(t) - \phi_1(0)] e^{\lambda_1 t}$$

$$+ \frac{1}{(\lambda_2 - \lambda_1)} [\dot{y}(0) - \lambda_1 y(0) + \phi_2(t) - \phi_2(0)] e^{\lambda_2 t} \quad (1.13)$$

and, from (1.7), $\dot{y}(t)$ can be written as

$$\dot{y}(t) = \frac{\lambda_1}{(\lambda_1 - \lambda_2)} [\dot{y}(0) - \lambda_2 y(0) + \phi_1(t) - \phi_1(0)] e^{\lambda_1 t}$$

$$+ \frac{\lambda_2}{(\lambda_2 - \lambda_1)} [\dot{y}(0) - \lambda_1 y(0) + \phi_2(t) - \phi_2(0)] e^{\lambda_2 t}. \quad (1.14)$$

Equations (1.13) and (1.14) give the general solution of the single-degree-of-freedom system defined by (1.1) where λ_1, λ_2 are its two eigenvalues given, from (1.3), by

$$\lambda_1, \lambda_2 = \frac{-c \pm \sqrt{c^2 - 4mk}}{2m} \quad (1.15)$$

and $\phi_1(t)$, $\phi_2(t)$ are the two integrals defined by (1.5) and (1.6). These results do not apply for the special case when $\lambda_1 = \lambda_2$ when the denominators in (1.13) and (1.14) become zero, and we shall consider this limiting case separately later in this chapter.

Steady-state harmonic response

If we assume that there is steady-state harmonic excitation at angular frequency ω, then the excitation can be written as

$$x(t) = x_0 e^{i\omega t} \quad (1.16)$$

where x_0 is a constant and, from the theory of complex numbers,

$$e^{i\omega t} = \cos \omega t + i \sin \omega t. \quad (1.17)$$

The use of the complex exponential function $e^{i\omega t}$ to represent the physical excitation in a real system implies that we mean that the excitation defined by (1.16) is

$$x(t) = \text{Re}\{x_0 e^{i\omega t}\} = x_0 \cos \omega t \quad (1.18)$$

(when x_0 is real) or, alternatively, that it is

$$x(t) = \text{Im}\{x_0 e^{i\omega t}\} = x_0 \sin \omega t. \quad (1.19)$$

It does not matter which is used, Re or Im for 'the real part of' or 'the imaginary part of' provided that the same meaning is adopted throughout. Because of this, it is customary not to say which convention is being adopted. Of course, the interpretation of a complex response, whether represented physically by its real part or by its imaginary part, must be consistent with the interpretation that has been placed on the corresponding complex excitation.

For the harmonic excitation defined by (1.16), the equation of motion for one degree of freedom is, from (1.1),

$$m\ddot{y} + c\dot{y} + ky = x_0 e^{i\omega t} \tag{1.20}$$

and, when the starting transients have had time to decay away, the steady-state solution is also harmonic and we will assume that it can be represented by

$$y(t) = H(i\omega)x_0 e^{i\omega t} \tag{1.21}$$

where $H(i\omega)$ is the (complex) *frequency-response function* for the system. On substituting (1.21) into (1.20) we find that

$$\{m(i\omega)^2 + c(i\omega) + k\}H(i\omega) = 1 \tag{1.22}$$

and so

$$H(i\omega) = \frac{1}{m(i\omega)^2 + c(i\omega) + k}. \tag{1.23}$$

If the undamped natural frequency is ω_N defined by

$$\omega_N^2 = \frac{k}{m} \tag{1.24}$$

and the damping ratio is ζ defined by

$$2\zeta\omega_N = \frac{c}{m} \tag{1.25}$$

then $H(i\omega)$ can be written as

$$H(i\omega) = \frac{1}{m[(i\omega)^2 + 2\zeta\omega_N(i\omega) + \omega_N^2]}. \tag{1.26}$$

The output/input amplitude ratio is given by

$$|H(i\omega)| = \frac{1}{m\omega_N^2 \left[\left(2\zeta \dfrac{\omega}{\omega_N}\right)^2 + \left(1 - \dfrac{\omega^2}{\omega_N^2}\right)^2\right]^{1/2}} \tag{1.27}$$

and the output lags behind the input by angle θ where

$$\tan\theta = \frac{2\zeta \dfrac{\omega}{\omega_N}}{\left(1 - \dfrac{\omega^2}{\omega_N^2}\right)} \tag{1.28}$$

(see problem 1.2). These relationships (1.27) and (1.28) are plotted in Fig. 1.2(a) and 1.2(b). Fig. 1.2(a) shows the non-dimensional amplitude ratio $k|H(i\omega)|$ plotted against the ratio of forcing frequency to natural frequency, ω/ω_N; Fig. 1.2(b) shows the angle of phase lag θ plotted against ω/ω_N. In both cases, curves are plotted for several different (constant) values for the damping ratio ζ.

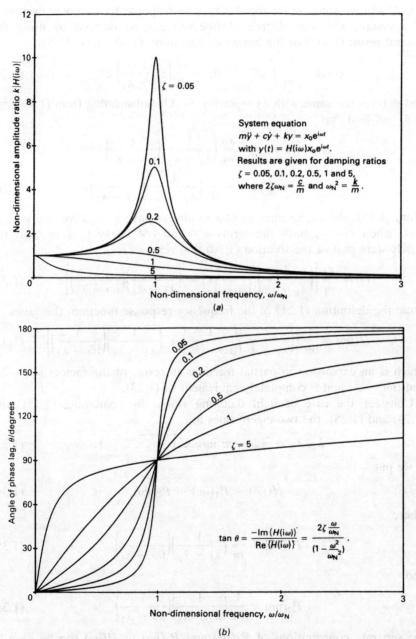

Fig. 1.2 (*a*) Magnitude of the frequency response function for the displacement of the single-degree-of-freedom system in Fig. 1.1. (*b*) Angle of phase lag of the displacement response behind the harmonic force excitation for the single-degree-of-freedom system in Fig. 1.1

Expansion of the frequency-response function in partial fractions

An alternative solution for the steady-state response to harmonic excitation of a system with one degree of freedom can be derived by using the general result (1.4). For the harmonic excitation (1.16), from (1.5),

$$\phi_1(t) = \frac{x_0}{m} \int e^{(i\omega - \lambda_1)t} \, dt = \frac{x_0}{m} \left(\frac{1}{i\omega - \lambda_1} \right) e^{(i\omega - \lambda_1)t} \qquad (1.29)$$

and $\phi_2(t)$ is the same with λ_2 replacing λ_1. On substituting from (1.29) into (1.4), we find that

$$y(t) = C_1 e^{\lambda_1 t} + \frac{x_0}{m} \left(\frac{1}{\lambda_1 - \lambda_2} \right)\left(\frac{1}{i\omega - \lambda_1} \right) e^{i\omega t}$$
$$+ C_2 e^{\lambda_2 t} + \frac{x_0}{m} \left(\frac{1}{\lambda_2 - \lambda_1} \right)\left(\frac{1}{i\omega - \lambda_2} \right) e^{i\omega t}. \qquad (1.30)$$

From (1.15), the eigenvalues λ_1 and λ_2 always have a negative real part so that, when $t \to \infty$, both the terms $e^{\lambda_1 t}$ and $e^{\lambda_2 t}$ decay to zero, and the steady-state part of the solution (1.30) that remains is

$$y(t) = \frac{x_0}{m} \left[\left(\frac{1}{\lambda_1 - \lambda_2} \right)\left(\frac{1}{i\omega - \lambda_1} \right) + \left(\frac{1}{\lambda_2 - \lambda_1} \right)\left(\frac{1}{i\omega - \lambda_2} \right) \right] e^{i\omega t}. \qquad (1.31)$$

From the definition (1.21) of the frequency-response function, this gives

$$H(i\omega) = \frac{1}{m} \left[\left(\frac{1}{\lambda_1 - \lambda_2} \right)\left(\frac{1}{i\omega - \lambda_1} \right) + \left(\frac{1}{\lambda_2 - \lambda_1} \right)\left(\frac{1}{i\omega - \lambda_2} \right) \right] \qquad (1.32)$$

which is an expansion in partial fractions in terms of the factors $(i\omega - \lambda_1)$ and $(i\omega - \lambda_2)$ and is completely equivalent to (1.23).

Consider the case of light damping when, by combining (1.15) with (1.24) and (1.25), the two eigenvalues are

$$\lambda_1, \lambda_2 = -\zeta\omega_N \pm i\omega_N \sqrt{1 - \zeta^2}, \zeta < 1. \qquad (1.33)$$

If we put

$$H(i\omega) = P_1(i\omega) + P_2(i\omega) \qquad (1.34)$$

where

$$P_1(i\omega) = \frac{1}{m} \left(\frac{1}{\lambda_1 - \lambda_2} \right)\left(\frac{1}{i\omega - \lambda_1} \right) \qquad (1.35)$$

and

$$P_2(i\omega) = \frac{1}{m} \left(\frac{1}{\lambda_2 - \lambda_1} \right)\left(\frac{1}{i\omega - \lambda_2} \right) \qquad (1.36)$$

the separate contributions of $P_1(i\omega)$ and $P_2(i\omega)$ to $H(i\omega)$ can be seen by plotting the real and imaginary parts of $P_1(i\omega)$ against ω in Fig. 1.3(a) and the real and imaginary parts of $P_2(i\omega)$ against ω in Fig. 1.3(b), for a typical value of $\zeta = 0.1$. In Fig. 1.3(c), the combinations of $P_1(i\omega)$ and

$P_2(i\omega)$ to give the real and imaginary parts of $H(i\omega)$ are plotted against ω; the right-hand halves of these diagrams correspond to the same results plotted a different way in Figs 1.2(*a*) and (*b*).

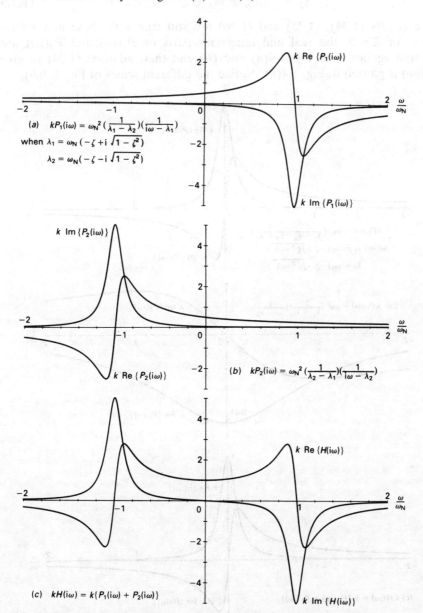

(*a*) $kP_1(i\omega) = \omega_N^2\left(\dfrac{1}{\lambda_1 - \lambda_2}\right)\left(\dfrac{1}{i\omega - \lambda_1}\right)$

when $\lambda_1 = \omega_N(-\zeta + i\sqrt{1-\zeta^2})$

  $\lambda_2 = \omega_N(-\zeta - i\sqrt{1-\zeta^2})$

(*b*) $kP_2(i\omega) = \omega_N^2\left(\dfrac{1}{\lambda_2 - \lambda_1}\right)\left(\dfrac{1}{i\omega - \lambda_2}\right)$

(*c*) $kH(i\omega) = k\{P_1(i\omega) + P_2(i\omega)\}$

Fig. 1.3 Real and imaginary parts of the frequency response function for the single-degree-of-freedom system in Fig. 1.1 as a function of frequency, for the case $\zeta = 0.1$. (*a*) Partial fraction corresponding to the factor $(i\omega - \lambda_1)$. (*b*) Partial fraction corresponding to the factor $(i\omega - \lambda_2) = (i\omega - \lambda_1^*)$. (*c*) Addition of these partial fractions to give $H(i\omega)$

If the damping ratio ζ is greater than unity, then the eigenvalues λ_1, λ_2 are both real and (1.33) becomes

$$\lambda_1, \lambda_2 = -\zeta\omega_N \pm \omega_N\sqrt{\zeta^2 - 1}, \ \zeta > 1. \tag{1.37}$$

The results (1.34), (1.35) and (1.36) are still true with these new values and, for $\zeta = 5$, the real and imaginary parts of $P_1(i\omega)$ and $P_2(i\omega)$ are plotted against ω in Figs 1.4(a) and (b) and their addition (1.34) to give $H(i\omega)$ is plotted in Fig. 1.4(c). Notice the different scales of Fig. 1.4(b).

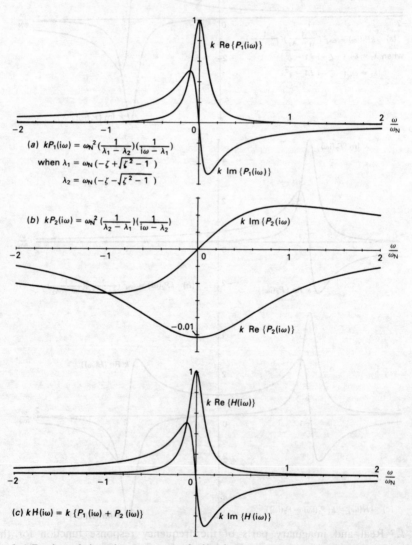

Fig. 1.4 Real and imaginary parts of the frequency response function for the single-degree-of-freedom system in Fig. 1.1 as a function of frequency, for the case $\zeta = 5$, when both the eigenvalues λ_1 and λ_2 are real

We shall see later that the frequency-response functions for systems with many degrees of freedom can always be expanded in a series of partial fractions like that in (1.32). The influence of each eigenvalue on the harmonic response is represented by functions like those in Fig. 1.3(a) and (b), for $\zeta < 1$, and like those in Fig. 1.4(a) and (b), for $\zeta > 1$.

Negative frequencies

The frequency axis in Figs 1.3 and 1.4 runs from $-\infty$ to $+\infty$. When harmonic excitation is defined in complex exponential notation (1.16), the expression for negative frequencies, with

$$\omega = -\Omega, \tag{1.38}$$

Ω positive, is

$$x(t) = x_0 e^{-i\Omega t}, \tag{1.39}$$

x_0 assumed real, and from (1.21), the corresponding response is

$$y(t) = H(-i\Omega)x_0 e^{-i\Omega t}. \tag{1.40}$$

If $e^{i\Omega t}$ and $e^{-i\Omega t}$, Ω positive, are drawn on an Argand diagram, they appear as shown on Fig. 1.5(a). A positive frequency gives a line OQ_1 rotating counter-clockwise at angular speed Ω; a negative frequency gives a line OQ_2 rotating clockwise at angular speed Ω. If we assume that $H(-i\Omega)$ has a positive real part $H_r(-i\Omega)$ and a positive imaginary part $iH_i(-i\Omega)$, as shown in Fig. 1.4(b), then the result of multiplying together the two complex numbers $H(-i\Omega)$ and $e^{-i\Omega t}$ is shown in Fig. 1.5(c). From the theory of complex numbers

$$|OQ_4| = |OQ_2|.|OQ_3| \tag{1.41}$$

and OQ_4 lags OQ_2 by angle θ, where θ is defined in Fig. 1.5(b). We conclude from (1.40) that the ratio

$$\frac{\text{amplitude of response}}{\text{amplitude of excitation}} = |H(-i\Omega)| \tag{1.42}$$

since $|e^{-i\Omega t}| = 1$ and that the response lags the excitation by angle θ where

$$\tan \theta = \frac{\text{Im}\{H(-i\Omega)\}}{\text{Re}\{H(-i\Omega)\}}. \tag{1.43}$$

For positive frequencies, the corresponding angle of phase lag is (see Problem 1.2)

$$\tan \theta = \frac{-\text{Im}\{H(i\Omega)\}}{\text{Re}\{H(i\Omega)\}} \tag{1.44}$$

This is consistent with (1.43) because the only way that $i = \sqrt{-1}$ appears in $H(i\Omega)$ is in the product $i\Omega$. If Ω changes sign then so do all the products $i\Omega$, which is the same as if i had changed sign with Ω unchanged.

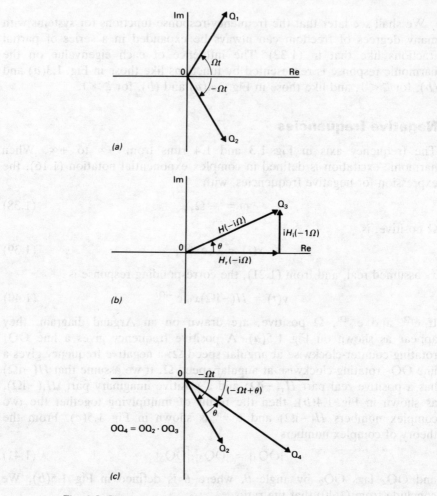

Fig. 1.5 Geometrical interpretation of negative frequencies

Therefore

$$H(-i\Omega) = H^*(i\Omega) \tag{1.45}$$

where the asterisk means the complex conjugate of $H(i\Omega)$. Hence, in (1.43),

$$\mathrm{Re}\{H(-i\Omega)\} = \mathrm{Re}\{H^*(i\Omega)\} = \mathrm{Re}\{H(i\Omega)\} \tag{1.46}$$

and

$$\mathrm{Im}\{H(-i\Omega)\} = \mathrm{Im}\{H^*(i\Omega)\} = -\mathrm{Im}\{H(i\Omega)\} \tag{1.47}$$

so that (1.43) and (1.44) are in agreement.

For the $H(i\omega)$ defined by (1.26) (or, in its alternative form by (1.34) with (1.35) and (1.36)), Figs 1.6(*a*) and (*b*), and 1.7(*a*) and (*b*) show output/input amplitude ratio and phase angle plotted against the full range of ω, positive and negative, for the two cases $\zeta = 0.1$ in Fig. 1.6 and $\zeta = 5$ in Fig. 1.7.

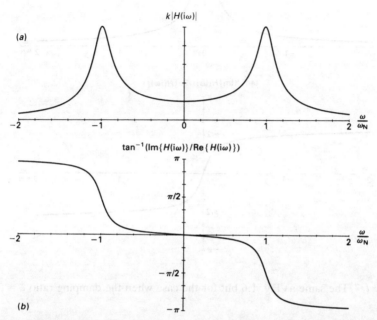

Fig. 1.6 (*a*) Magnitude of the frequency response function, and (*b*) angle of phase difference between output and·input, for the system in Fig. 1.1 with force input and displacement output when subjected to steady-state harmonic excitation at frequency ω, for the case when the damping ratio $\zeta = 0.1$

Root locus diagram

The response of the single-degree-of-freedom system described by (1.1) is determined by its eigenvalues λ_1, λ_2 which are the roots of the system's characteristic equation (1.3). The dependence of these roots on the system's damping can be illustrated on a root locus diagram. This is an Argand diagram showing the loci of movement of the eigenvalues as the system's damping changes. In Fig. 1.8, the values of λ_1, λ_2 defined by (1.33) and (1.37) are plotted for changing damping ratio ζ (with the system's undamped natural frequency ω_N held constant). For zero damping, λ_1, $\lambda_2 = \pm i\omega_N$, so that the loci start on the imaginary axis. As ζ is increased, λ_1, λ_2 move about the origin in a circular path, converging on the negative real axis when $\zeta = 1$. Thereafter, both λ_1 and λ_2 remain real and negative, with λ_1 approaching zero and λ_2 approaching minus infinity as $\zeta \rightarrow \infty$.

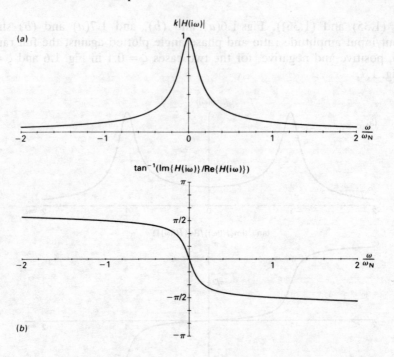

Fig. 1.7 The same as Fig. 1.6 but for the case when the damping ratio $\zeta = 5$

When $\zeta \to \infty$, there is a very large amount of damping present. From (1.2), the general response for no excitation has one term which dies away very slowly because λ_1 becomes a very small negative quantity, and a second term which dies away extremely quickly because λ_2 becomes a very large negative quantity. The first term is the result of the very viscous damping allowing only a very slow return to static equilibrium after a disturbance. The second term is due to the high viscous force rapidly destroying the momentum of the moving mass and reducing the mass's velocity to almost zero in a very short time.

Impulse response

We now consider the transient response of the system (1.1) in greater detail by calculating its response to an impulsive input applied at $t = 0$. Using the delta-function nomenclature, we put

$$x(t) = \delta(t) \qquad (1.48)$$

which means that $x(t)$ is zero everywhere except at $t = 0$ where it is infinite in such a way that

$$\int_{-\infty}^{\infty} x(t)\, \mathrm{d}t = 1. \qquad (1.49)$$

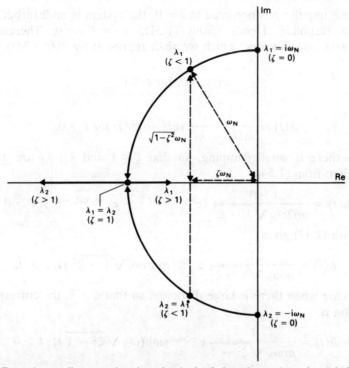

Fig. 1.8 Root locus diagram showing the loci of the eigenvalues (roots) λ_1, λ_2 of the system in Fig. 1.1 as the damping ratio ζ is increased from 0 to ∞

The analogy is with a mechanical impulse, which is a very large force acting for a very short time, and which has sufficient magnitude to cause a unit change of momentum.

For the general solution (1.4), we need the functions $\phi_1(t)$ and $\phi_2(t)$ defined by (1.5) and (1.6). On substituting for $x(t)$ from (1.48) into (1.5) and evaluating the integral, we find that

$$\phi_1(t) = 0, \text{ for } t < 0$$

$$= \frac{1}{m}, \text{ for } t > 0$$

$$(1.50)$$

since the exponential function $e^{-\lambda_1 t}$ is unity at $t = 0$ which is the only time when $x(t) \neq 0$. Similarly, $\phi_2(t)$ is the same as $\phi_1(t)$, and so (1.4) gives

$$y(t) = C_1 e^{\lambda_1 t} + C_2 e^{\lambda_2 t}, \text{ for } t < 0$$

$$(1.51)$$

and

$$y(t) = \left(C_1 + \frac{1}{m(\lambda_1 - \lambda_2)}\right) e^{\lambda_1 t} + \left(C_2 + \frac{1}{m(\lambda_2 - \lambda_1)}\right) e^{\lambda_2 t}, \text{ for } t > 0.$$

$$(1.52)$$

Before the impulse has occurred at $t = 0$, the system is undisturbed and so has zero response. Hence, from (1.51), $C_1 = C_2 = 0$. Therefore the *impulse-response function*, which we shall represent by $y(t) = h(t)$ is given by

$$h(t) = 0, \text{ for } t < 0 \tag{1.53}$$

and by

$$h(t) = \frac{1}{m(\lambda_1 - \lambda_2)} (e^{\lambda_1 t} - e^{\lambda_2 t}), \text{ for } t > 0. \tag{1.54}$$

When there is small damping, so that $\zeta < 1$ and λ_1, λ_2 are given by (1.33), then from (1.54)

$$h(t) = \frac{e^{-\zeta\omega_N t}}{mi2\omega_N\sqrt{1 - \zeta^2}} (e^{i\omega_N\sqrt{(1 - \zeta^2)}t} - e^{-i\omega_N\sqrt{(1 - \zeta^2)}t}), t > 0 \tag{1.55}$$

which with (1.17) gives

$$h(t) = \frac{1}{m\omega_N\sqrt{1 - \zeta^2}} e^{-\zeta\omega_N t} \sin(\omega_N\sqrt{1 - \zeta^2}\, t), t > 0. \tag{1.56}$$

For the case when there is large damping, so that $\zeta > 1$, the corresponding expression is

$$h(t) = \frac{1}{m\omega_N\sqrt{\zeta^2 - 1}} e^{-\zeta\omega_N t} \sinh(\omega_N\sqrt{\zeta^2 - 1}\, t), t > 0 \tag{1.57}$$

since

$$\sinh\theta = \frac{1}{2}(e^\theta - e^{-\theta}). \tag{1.58}$$

In Fig. 1.9, $h(t)$ is plotted against t for three different values of the damping ratio ζ. For $\zeta = 0.1$, there is an oscillatory transient, while, for $\zeta = 5$, there is no oscillation. The initial slope of both graphs is the same because the initial velocity is the same for the same unit impulse at $t = 0$.

The form of the response for $\zeta = 1$ can be found by taking the limiting case when

$$\zeta = 1 - \varepsilon \tag{1.59}$$

in (1.56) and letting $\varepsilon \to 0$ (Problem 1.3). When this is done, the result for $\zeta = 1$ is

$$h(t) = \frac{t}{m} e^{-\omega_N t}, t > 0 \tag{1.60}$$

which is plotted as the third graph on Fig. 1.9.

Special case of repeated eigenvalues

The general response of the single-degree-of-freedom system (1.1) for the case when $\zeta = 1$ can be derived from (1.4) by putting

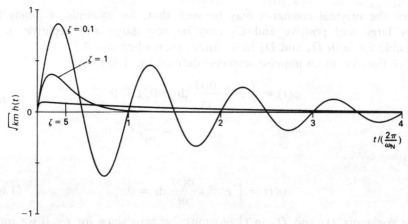

Fig. 1.9 Impulse-response functions for the system in Fig. 1.1 for the three cases $\zeta = 0.1$, 1 and 5

$$\lambda_1, \lambda_2 = \lambda \pm \varepsilon \qquad (1.61)$$

and letting $\varepsilon \to 0$. From (1.5), we have

$$\phi_1(t) = \int e^{-(\lambda+\varepsilon)t} \frac{x(t)}{m} \, dt$$

$$= \int e^{-\lambda t} (1 - \varepsilon t + \ldots) \frac{x(t)}{m} \, dt$$

$$= \phi(t) - \varepsilon\psi(t) + 0(\varepsilon^2) - \ldots \qquad (1.62)$$

where

$$\psi(t) = \int e^{-\lambda t} \, t \, \frac{x(t)}{m} \, dt \qquad (1.63)$$

and $0(\varepsilon^2)$ means terms of order ε^2 and smaller. The expression for $\phi_2(t)$ is the same as (1.62) except that the minus sign becomes a plus sign. Substituting these results into (1.4) gives

$$y(t) = \left\{ C_1 + \frac{1}{2\varepsilon} [\phi(t) - \varepsilon\psi(t) + 0(\varepsilon^2)] \right\} e^{\lambda t} (1 + \varepsilon t + \ldots)$$

$$+ \left\{ C_2 - \frac{1}{2\varepsilon} [\phi(t) + \varepsilon\psi(t) + 0(\varepsilon^2)] \right\} e^{\lambda t} (1 - \varepsilon t + \ldots) \qquad (1.64)$$

and to order ε this simplifies to

$$y(t) = [(C_1 + C_2) + \varepsilon(C_1 - C_2)t - \psi(t) + t\phi(t)] e^{\lambda t} \qquad (1.65)$$

with the other terms involving ε cancelling. On replacing $(C_1 + C_2)$ and $\varepsilon(C_1 - C_2)$ by new constants D_1 and D_2, the final result for $\zeta = 1$ is that

$$y(t) = [D_1 + tD_2 - \psi(t) + t\phi(t)] e^{\lambda t}. \qquad (1.66)$$

Since the original constants may be such that, for example, C_1 may be very large and positive and C_2 may be very large and negative, it is possible for both D_1 and D_2 to be finite, even when $\varepsilon \to 0$.

For the case of an impulse response defined by (1.48)

$$\phi(t) = \int e^{-\lambda t} \frac{\delta(t)}{m} \, dt = 0, \, t < 0$$

$$= \frac{1}{m}, \, t > 0 \tag{1.67}$$

and

$$\psi(t) = \int e^{-\lambda t} t \frac{\delta(t)}{m} \, dt = 0. \tag{1.68}$$

The constants D_1 and D_2 in (1.66) must be zero since for $t < 0$ we must have $y(t) = 0$ because there is no response before the impulse has occurred. With (1.67) and (1.68), the impulse response for $\zeta = 1$ is therefore

$$h(t) = y(t) = \frac{t}{m} e^{\lambda t}, \, t > 0 \tag{1.69}$$

which agrees with (1.60) since, from (1.33),

$$\lambda_1, \lambda_2 = -\omega_N \tag{1.70}$$

when $\zeta = 1$.

In Problem 1.4, the general result (1.66) is used to calculate the frequency-response function $H(i\omega)$ of the system (1.1) when $\lambda_1 = \lambda_2 = \lambda = -\omega_N$. The result is that

$$H(i\omega) = \frac{1}{m(i\omega + \omega_N)^2} \tag{1.71}$$

which is in agreement with (1.26) for the case when $\zeta = 1$.

Chapter 2

Frequency response of linear systems

General form of the frequency-response function

Equation (1.1) defines the response of the single-degree-of-freedom system shown in Fig. 1.1. For a more complicated system, with an output or response $y(t)$ responding to a single input or excitation $x(t)$, input and output will be assumed to be related by a general linear differential equation of the form

$$a_n \frac{d^n y}{dt^n} + a_{n-1} \frac{d^{n-1} y}{dt^{n-1}} + \ldots + a_1 \frac{dy}{dt} + a_0 y$$

$$= b_m \frac{d^m x}{dt^m} + b_{m-1} \frac{d^{m-1} x}{dt^{m-1}} + \ldots + b_1 \frac{dx}{dt} + b_0 x. \quad (2.1)$$

The output $y(t)$ and all its derivatives, up to the highest derivative involved, which is the nth derivative, occur once only in the l.h.s. of (2.1). Also, the input $x(t)$ and all its derivatives, up to the mth derivative, occur once only in the r.h.s. of (2.1). There are no nonlinear terms like y^2 or

$$y \frac{dy}{dt}$$

and the a's and b's are all independent of y and x. Although the system would still be linear if these coefficients were functions of time, t, we shall assume that they are constant so that the system's characteristics do not change with time. Because the system is linear, the principle of superposition applies and the response to two different inputs is just the result of adding together the response due to each input acting alone.

We shall assume also that (2.1) describes a passive system for which, if there is no input, after a sufficiently long period of time there will be negligible output. This means that the damping is always positive so that transient motions die away eventually.

Obviously, (1.1) is a special case of (2.1) with all the a's zero except $a_0 = k$, $a_1 = c$ and $a_2 = m$ and with all the b's zero except $b_0 = 1$.

The frequency-response function $H(i\omega)$ for a steady-state harmonic input defined by (1.16) and a corresponding steady-state harmonic output defined by (1.21) can be found by substituting into (2.1) to give

$$H(i\omega) = \frac{b_m(i\omega)^m + b_{m-1}(i\omega)^{m-1} + \ldots + b_1(i\omega) + b_0}{a_n(i\omega)^n + a_{n-1}(i\omega)^{n-1} + \ldots + a_1(i\omega) + a_0}$$

$$= \frac{B(i\omega)}{A(i\omega)} \tag{2.2}$$

where

$$A(i\omega) = a_n(i\omega)^n + a_{n-1}(i\omega)^{n-1} + \ldots + a_1(i\omega) + a_0 \tag{2.3}$$

and

$$B(i\omega) = b_m(i\omega)^m + b_{m-1}(i\omega)^{m-1} + \ldots + b_1(i\omega) + b_0. \tag{2.4}$$

Example 1

For the system in Fig. 1.1, instead of the output being the displacement $y(t)$, let it be the velocity $v(t) = \dot{y}(t)$. The input remains the force $x(t)$. Find $H(i\omega)$.

By differentiating (1.1), we find that, in terms of v,

$$m\frac{d^2v}{dt^2} + c\frac{dv}{dt} + kv = \frac{dx}{dt}.$$

Substituting

$$x(t) = e^{i\omega t} \text{ and } v(t) = H(i\omega) e^{i\omega t} \tag{2.5}$$

then gives

$$H(i\omega) = \frac{i\omega}{m(i\omega)^2 + c(i\omega) + k}. \tag{2.6}$$

This differs from the displacement frequency-response function (1.23) by the factor $(i\omega)$ in the numerator.

The same result can be obtained by noting that, if $H_y(i\omega)$ is the displacement frequency response so that

$$y(t) = H_y(i\omega) e^{i\omega t} \tag{2.7}$$

and if $H_v(i\omega)$ is the velocity frequency-response function so that

$$v(t) = H_v(i\omega) e^{i\omega t}, \tag{2.8}$$

then (2.8) can be obtained by differentiating (2.7), to give

$$v(t) = \frac{d}{dt} y(t) = (i\omega)H_y(i\omega) e^{i\omega t}$$

and hence

$$H_v(i\omega) = (i\omega)H_y(i\omega). \tag{2.9}$$

When defining the steady-state harmonic input in (2.5), we have chosen the amplitude of $x(t)$ to be unity, rather than the arbitrary value x_0 included previously in (1.16). This is merely a convenient choice for x_0, which cancels anyway because the response of a linear system is independent of amplitude.

Example of vibration isolation

An important application of frequency-response functions occurs in the subject of vibration isolation. In the system of Fig. 1.1, a vibrating force $x(t)$ is acting to shake the mass m. Suppose that it is desired to prevent the disturbance caused by $x(t)$ from being felt at the boundary wall to which the spring and damper are connected. If the force transmitted to this wall is $p(t)$, then

$$p(t) = c \frac{dy}{dt} + ky \tag{2.10}$$

since the wall feels the damper force and the spring force acting together. We can obtain a differential equation relating this force $p(t)$, which we regard as our new output, to the input force $x(t)$ as follows. Differentiate (1.1) throughout with respect to t, and multiply the resulting equation by c. Add this new equation to a second equation obtained by multiplying (1.1) by k. The result is

$$m \left(c \frac{d^3y}{dt^3} + k \frac{d^2y}{dt^2} \right) + c \left(c \frac{d^2y}{dt^2} + k \frac{dy}{dt} \right) + k \left(c \frac{dy}{dt} + ky \right) = c \frac{dx}{dt} + kx \tag{2.11}$$

which, on substituting from (2.10), gives

$$m \frac{d^2p}{dt^2} + c \frac{dp}{dt} + kp = c \frac{dx}{dt} + kx. \tag{2.12}$$

If we now define $H_{px}(i\omega)$ to be the frequency-response function relating output force $p(t)$ to input force $x(t)$ so that, if

$$x(t) = e^{i\omega t}$$

then

$$\tag{2.13}$$

$$p(t) = H_{px}(i\omega) e^{i\omega t},$$

we find, on substituting from (2.13) into (2.12), that

$$H_{px}(i\omega) = \frac{c(i\omega) + k}{m(i\omega)^2 + c(i\omega) + k}. \tag{2.14}$$

The magnitude of $H_{px}(i\omega)$ gives the ratio of the amplitude of the output force (at the wall) to the amplitude of the input force (on the mass), which is called the *transmissibility*. The ratio of the imaginary part of $H_{px}(i\omega)$ to its real part gives the tangent of the phase angle between the two forces, with the output force lagging behind the input force if this is a negative angle.

The same frequency-response function applies for the inverse case when the input is the harmonic displacement of the wall and the output is the displacement of the mass, Fig. 2.1. In terms of the input $z(t)$ and output $y(t)$ of Fig. 2.1, the equation of motion is

$$m \frac{d^2y}{dt^2} = c\left(\frac{dz}{dt} - \frac{dy}{dt}\right) + k(z - y) \tag{2.15}$$

giving

$$m \frac{d^2y}{dt^2} + c \frac{dy}{dt} + ky = c \frac{dz}{dt} + kz. \tag{2.16}$$

For steady-state harmonic vibration with

$$z(t) = e^{i\omega t}$$

and (2.17)

$$y(t) = H_{yz}(i\omega)\, e^{i\omega t},$$

(2.16) gives

$$H_{yz}(i\omega) = \frac{c(i\omega) + k}{m(i\omega)^2 + c(i\omega) + k}, \tag{2.18}$$

which is the same as $H_{px}(i\omega)$.

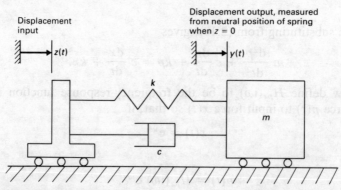

Displacement input

$z(t)$

Displacement output, measured from neutral position of spring when $z = 0$

$y(t)$

k

m

c

Fig. 2.1 Single-degree-of-freedom system with displacement input $z(t)$ and displacement output $y(t)$

In Fig. 2.2(a), the transmissibility, $|H_{px}(i\omega)| = |H_{yz}(i\omega)|$ is plotted as a function of frequency for several different (constant) damping values and, in Fig. 2.2(b), the angle of phase lag of the output behind the input is plotted for the same damping values.

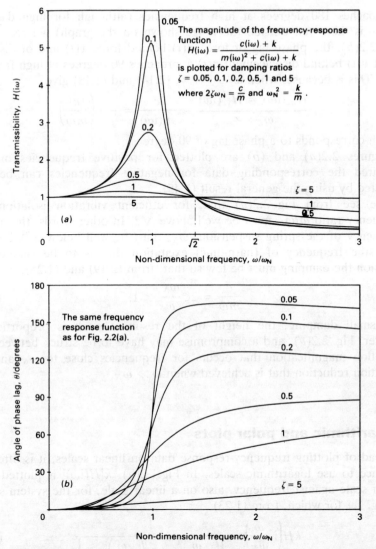

The magnitude of the frequency-response function
$$H(i\omega) = \frac{c(i\omega) + k}{m(i\omega)^2 + c(i\omega) + k}$$
is plotted for damping ratios $\zeta = 0.05, 0.1, 0.2, 0.5, 1$ and 5 where $2\zeta\omega_N = \dfrac{c}{m}$ and $\omega_N^2 = \dfrac{k}{m}$.

The same frequency response function as for Fig. 2.2(a).

Fig. 2.2 (a) Transmissibility plotted against frequency, for force transmission to the wall in the case of the system in Fig. 1.1, and for displacement transmission to the mass in the case of the system in Fig. 2.1. (b) Angle of phase lag corresponding to the transmissibility plotted in Fig. 2.2(a)

By comparing the curves in Fig. 2.2(a) with those in Fig. 1.2(a), an important difference in the two sets of response curves becomes apparent. In Fig. 2.2(a), the response curves cross over each other at $\omega/\omega_N = \sqrt{2}$. Above this frequency, greater damping gives greater transmissibility. This is because of the transmission path through the viscous dashpot, which becomes stronger when the damping is increased. Fig. 1.2(b) the phase lag approaches 180 degrees at high frequencies (although for high damping ω/ω_N is then well outside the range shown on the graph) whereas, from Fig. 2.2(b), the phase lag of force $p(t)$ behind force $x(t)$ and of displacement $y(t)$ behind displacement $z(t)$ approaches 90 degrees at high frequencies. This is because, when $\omega/\omega_N \to \infty$, (2.14) and (2.18) give

$$\underbrace{H_{px}(i\omega) = H_{yz}(i\omega)}_{\omega \to \infty} \to \frac{c}{m(i\omega)} = -i\left(\frac{c}{m\omega}\right) \qquad (2.19)$$

which corresponds to a phase lag of 90 degrees.

Figures 2.2(a) and (b) are plotted for positive frequencies only; if required the corresponding data for negative frequencies can be constructed by using the general result (1.45).

We see from Fig. 2.2(a) that, for efficient vibration isolation, the frequency ratio ω/ω_N must be well above $\sqrt{2}$. In other words, the natural frequency of the spring suspension, ω_N, must be well below $\omega/\sqrt{2}$ where ω is the frequency of (harmonic) excitation that is to be isolated. In addition the damping must be low so that, from (2.19) and (1.25),

$$\frac{c}{m\omega} = 2\zeta\,\frac{\omega_N}{\omega} \ll 1. \qquad (2.20)$$

For small damping, the height of the resonant peak is proportionally greater, Fig. 2.2(a), and a compromise may have to be struck between the vibration magnification that occurs for frequencies close to ω_N and the vibration reduction that is achieved when $\omega \gg \omega_N$.

Logarithmic and polar plots

Instead of plotting frequency-response data on linear scales, it is often the practice to use logarithmic scales. In Fig.1.2(a), $k|H(i\omega)|$ is plotted on a linear scale against frequency, also on a linear scale, for the system shown in Fig. 1.1 for which, from (1.23),

$$kH\left(i\,\frac{\omega}{\omega_N}\right) = \frac{1}{\left[\left(i\,\dfrac{\omega}{\omega_N}\right)^2 + 2\zeta\left(i\,\dfrac{\omega}{\omega_N}\right) + 1\right]}. \qquad (2.21)$$

For the case when $\zeta = 0.1$, $k|H(i\omega)|$ for the same system is plotted to log scales in Fig. 2.3(a). The curve starts at 0 dB when $k|H(i\omega)| = 1$, reaches its peak value just below $\omega/\omega_N = 1$, at which frequency

$$20\log_{10}\left[k\left|H\left(i\,\frac{\omega}{\omega_N}\right)\right|\right] = 20\log_{10}5 = 14 \text{ dB (approx.)}, \qquad (2.22)$$

and then decays, finally decaying linearly on the log scales as $\omega/\omega_N \to \infty$. When $\omega/\omega_N \to \infty$, from (2.21),

$$20\log_{10}\left[k\left|H\left(i\,\frac{\omega}{\omega_N}\right)\right|\right] \simeq 20\log_{10}\left[\frac{1}{(\omega/\omega_N)^2}\right] = -40\log_{10}\left(\frac{\omega}{\omega_N}\right), \qquad (2.23)$$

so that the downwards slope of the right-hand part of the curve in Fig. 2.3(a) is constant at − 40 dB per decade.

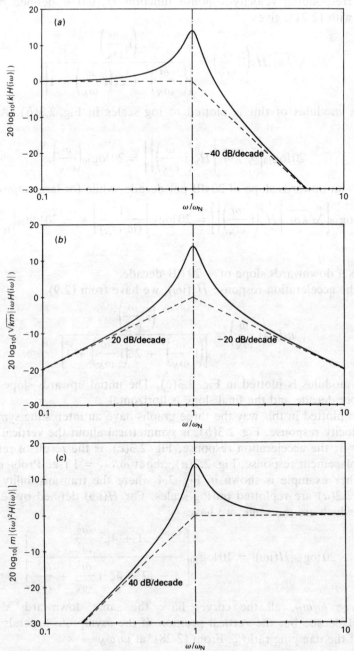

Fig. 2.3 Graphs of the moduli of (a) the displacement, (b) the velocity, and (c) the acceleration response functions for the system in Fig. 1.1, plotted to log scales. The damping ratio for all the graphs is $\zeta = 0.1$

The frequency-response function defined by (2.21) is for the displacement response of the system in Fig. 1.1 when subjected to force excitation. The corresponding velocity-response function $H_v(i\omega)$ is defined by (2.9) which, with (2.21), gives

$$\sqrt{km}\ H_v\left(i\,\frac{\omega}{\omega_N}\right) = \frac{\left(i\,\dfrac{\omega}{\omega_N}\right)}{\left[\left(i\,\dfrac{\omega}{\omega_N}\right)^2 + 2\zeta\left(i\,\dfrac{\omega}{\omega_N}\right) + 1\right]} \tag{2.24}$$

and the modulus of this is plotted to log scales in Fig. 2.3(*b*). At small ω/ω_N

$$20\log_{10}\left[\sqrt{km}\ \left|H_v\left(i\,\frac{\omega}{\omega_N}\right)\right|\right] \simeq 20\log_{10}\left(\frac{\omega}{\omega_N}\right), \tag{2.25}$$

which is an upwards slope of 20 dB per decade, while for large ω/ω_N

$$20\log_{10}\left[\sqrt{km}\ \left|H_v\left(i\,\frac{\omega}{\omega_N}\right)\right|\right] \simeq 20\log_{10}\left[\frac{1}{(\omega/\omega_N)}\right] = -20\log_{10}\left(\frac{\omega}{\omega_N}\right), \tag{2.26}$$

which is a downwards slope of -20 dB/decade.

For the acceleration response $H_a(i\omega)$, we have from (2.9)

$$mH_a\left(i\,\frac{\omega}{\omega_N}\right) = \frac{\left(i\,\dfrac{\omega}{\omega_N}\right)^2}{\left[\left(i\,\dfrac{\omega}{\omega_N}\right)^2 + 2\zeta\left(i\,\dfrac{\omega}{\omega_N}\right) + 1\right]} \tag{2.27}$$

and its modulus is plotted in Fig. 2.3(*c*). The initial upwards slope is now 40 dB per decade and the final slope is horizontal.

When plotted in this way the three graphs have an interesting symmetry. The velocity response, Fig. 2.3(*b*), is symmetrical about the vertical axis at $\omega/\omega_N = 1$; the acceleration response, Fig. 2.3(*c*), is the result of reflecting the displacement response, Fig. 2.3(*a*), about $\omega/\omega_N = 1$ (see Problem 2.1).

Another example is shown in Fig. 2.4 where the transmissibility curves of Fig. 2.2(*a*) are replotted on log scales. For $H(i\omega)$ defined by (2.14) or (2.18), which are the same, we have

$$20\log_{10}|H(i\omega)| = 10\log_{10}\left[\frac{1 + 4\zeta^2\,\dfrac{\omega^2}{\omega_N^2}}{1 - (2 - 4\zeta^2)\,\dfrac{\omega^2}{\omega_N^2} + \dfrac{\omega^4}{\omega_N^4}}\right]. \tag{2.28}$$

For large ω/ω_N, all the curves have the same downwards slope of -20 dB/decade but the vertical position of the asymptote depends on the value of the damping ratio ζ. From (2.28), at $\omega/\omega_N \to \infty$

$$20\log_{10}|H(i\omega)| \simeq 10\log_{10}(4\zeta^2) - 20\log_{10}\left(\frac{\omega}{\omega_N}\right). \tag{2.29}$$

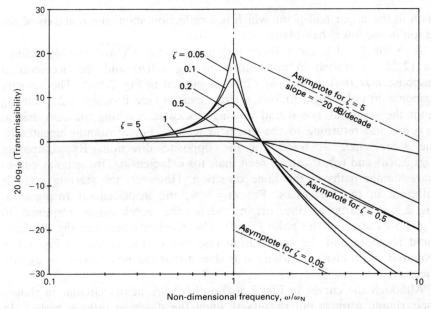

Fig. 2.4 The same graph as Fig. 2.2(*a*) but plotted to log scales

For illustration, the position of this asymptote is shown on Fig. 2.4 for three of the cases, $\zeta = 0.05$, 0.5 and 5.

The same frequency-response data may also be plotted on polar graph paper, with both modulus and phase angle shown on the same graph. For the displacement frequency-response function defined by (2.21), if we put

$$kH(i\omega) = R\, e^{i\theta} \qquad (2.30)$$

then, from (2.21)

$$R \equiv R(\omega) = k|H(i\omega)| = \frac{1}{\left[\left(1 - \dfrac{\omega^2}{\omega_N^2}\right)^2 + \left(2\zeta\dfrac{\omega}{\omega_N}\right)^2\right]^{1/2}} \qquad (2.31)$$

and

$$\theta \equiv \theta(\omega) = \tan^{-1}\frac{2\zeta\left(\dfrac{\omega}{\omega_N}\right)}{\left(\dfrac{\omega^2}{\omega_N^2} - 1\right)}. \qquad (2.32)$$

In Fig. 1.6, R and θ are shown plotted against ω/ω_N for the case when $\zeta = 0.1$. The corresponding polar graph is Fig. 2.5(*a*). At zero frequency, $\omega = 0$, the graph starts on the real axis at $R = 1$. For increasing ω, it follows an almost circular path in a clockwise direction, passing through resonance at $\theta \simeq -\pi/2$, and continuing until it converges on the origin at $\omega \to \infty$. For ω decreasing from zero, the graph follows a corresponding path in the upper half-plane which is a reflection about the real axis of the graph in the lower half-plane.

Also for $\zeta = 0.1$, the velocity-response function $\sqrt{km}\,H_v(i\omega)$ defined by (2.24) is plotted in polar form in Fig. 2.5(b) and the acceleration response $mH_a(i\omega)$ defined by (2.27) is plotted in Fig. 2.5(c). The velocity response in polar form follows a circle exactly (see Problem 2.2), starting from the origin at $\omega = 0$ and moving clockwise reaching the real axis at $\omega = \omega_N$ and returning to the origin at $\omega = \infty$. For ω running negatively, the same circle is traced in the opposite direction. By comparing Figs 2.5(a) and (c), it can be seen that, for ω increasing, these polar curves trace similar paths in the same direction. However, the starting point is different in the two cases. For $\omega = -\infty$, the displacement response in Fig. 2.5(a) starts at the origin, while the acceleration response in Fig. 2.5(c) starts at the point (1, i0). This similarity between the displacement response and the acceleration response of the system in Fig. 1.1 is explored in Problem 2.2 where it is shown that the two curves are exactly the same.

Although the curves in Figs 2.5(a) and (c) are nearly circular in shape, their simple form is not preserved when the damping ratio is higher. In Figs 2.6(a), (b) and (c) the displacement response is shown in polar form for the three cases $\zeta = 0.5$, 1 and 5. By comparing these with Fig. 2.5(a), which is the corresponding case for $\zeta = 0.1$ (drawn to a different scale), the double circle for the light damping case deforms nearly to the two semi-circles in Fig. 2.6(c) as ζ increases to 5. In the limiting case when $\zeta \to \infty$, Fig. 2.6(c) becomes a perfect circle of radius $\frac{1}{2}$ and with its centre at the point $(\frac{1}{2}, i0)$ (see Problem 2.3).

General expansion in partial fractions

Now we return to the general case and equation (2.1). For no excitation, the response $y(t)$ satisfies

$$a_n \frac{d^n y}{dt^n} + a_{n-1} \frac{d^{n-1} y}{dt^{n-1}} + \ldots + a_1 \frac{dy}{dt} + a_0 y = 0 \qquad (2.33)$$

and there is a general solution

$$y = e^{\lambda t} \qquad (2.34)$$

where, by substituting for y from (2.34) into (2.33), λ must satisfy the characteristic equation

$$a_n \lambda^n + a_{n-1} \lambda^{n-1} + \ldots + a_1 \lambda + a_0 = 0. \qquad (2.35)$$

The n solutions for λ from (2.35) are the n eigenvalues of the system which we shall denote by λ_j, $j = 1$ to n. We shall assume at first that all the λ_j are distinct, i.e. that they are all different, and will leave the special case of repeated eigenvalues until later.

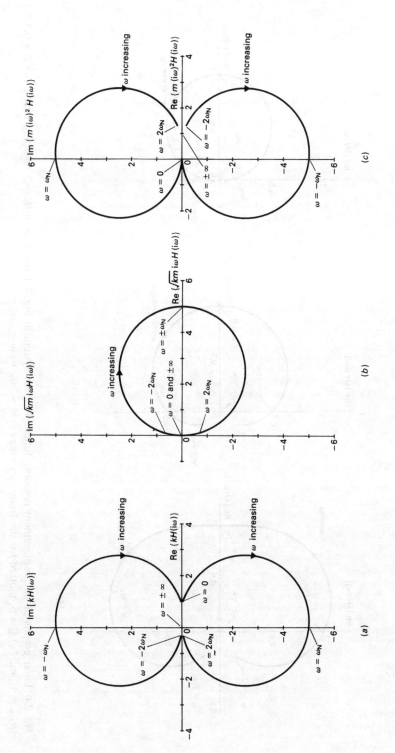

Fig. 2.5 Polar graphs of (*a*) the displacement, (*b*) the velocity, and (*c*) the acceleration response functions of the system in Fig. 1.1 for the case when the damping ratio $\zeta = 0.1$. In (*a*) and (*c*) the curves from $|\omega| = 2\omega_N$ to $|\omega| = \infty$ are not drawn

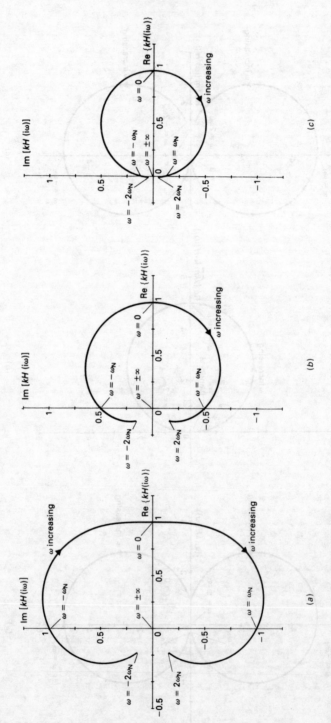

Fig. 2.6 Polar graphs of the displacement response function of the system in Fig. 1.1 for three different damping ratios, (a) $\zeta = 0.5$, (b) $\zeta = 1$, and (c) $\zeta = 5$, plotted for the frequency range $\omega = -2\omega_N$ to $\omega = 2\omega_N$

If $\lambda = \lambda_j$ is a solution of (2.35), then $(\lambda - \lambda_j)$ must be a factor of the l.h.s. of (2.35), so that an alternative form of (2.35) is

$$a_n(\lambda - \lambda_1)(\lambda - \lambda_2) \ldots (\lambda - \lambda_j) \ldots (\lambda - \lambda_n) = 0. \qquad (2.36)$$

The repeated product of factors can be represented by the symbol Π, and in this notation (2.36) becomes

$$a_n \prod_{j=1}^{n} (\lambda - \lambda_j) = 0. \qquad (2.37)$$

By comparing (2.35) with (2.3), we see that the function $A(i\omega)$ defined by (2.3) is the l.h.s. of (2.35) with $i\omega$ replacing λ. It follows from (2.37) that an alternative expression for $A(i\omega)$ is

$$A(i\omega) = a_n \prod_{j=1}^{n} (i\omega - \lambda_j). \qquad (2.38)$$

With this result, our general expression (2.2) for the frequency response function $H(i\omega)$ becomes

$$H(i\omega) = \frac{B(i\omega)}{a_n \prod_{j=1}^{n} (i\omega - \lambda_j)} \qquad (2.39)$$

where $B(i\omega)$ is still given by (2.4).

We shall now consider how $H(i\omega)$ may be expanded in a series of partial fractions each term of which has the form $p_j/(i\omega - \lambda_j)$, where p_j is a constant (which may be complex). To do this we shall assume that the order m of the numerator in (2.2) is less than the order n of the denominator. The reason for this restriction on the form of (2.1) can be seen as follows. If

$$H(i\omega) = \frac{p_1}{i\omega - \lambda_1} + \frac{p_2}{i\omega - \lambda_2} \qquad (2.40)$$

then, by taking a common denominator,

$$H(i\omega) = \frac{i\omega(p_1 + p_2) - (\lambda_2 p_1 + \lambda_1 p_2)}{(i\omega)^2 - i\omega(\lambda_1 + \lambda_2) + \lambda_1\lambda_2} \qquad (2.41)$$

and the order of the numerator in $(i\omega)$ is one less than the order of the denominator. The same conclusion holds for the case when there are more terms in the expansion (2.40). So an expansion of the form

$$H(i\omega) = \sum_{j=1}^{n} \frac{p_j}{i\omega - \lambda_j} \qquad (2.42)$$

is only possible if $m < n$. Most physical problems are found to satisfy this condition, and implementation of the expansion (2.42) is then a great help in understanding their behaviour.

For a problem for which $m \geqslant n$ in (2.1), the simple expansion (2.42) does not apply. In that case, in theory the numerator can be factorized so that

$$B(i\omega) = C(i\omega).D(i\omega) \qquad (2.43)$$

where the order of $C(i\omega)$ is $n - 1$ and the order of $D(i\omega)$ is $m - n + 1$, and then, although $H(i\omega)$ cannot be expanded in the simple form (2.42), $H(i\omega)/D(i\omega)$ can be. Then it may still be possible to exploit the advantages of the expanded form (2.42).

We shall now assume that $m < n$ so that the expansion (2.42) applies and find an expression for the constants p_j, $j = 1$ to n. This is obtained by the usual procedure for developing an expansion in partial fractions. If we multiply both sides of (2.42) by the factor $(i\omega - \lambda_j)$ and then take the limit when $i\omega = \lambda_j$, we find that

$$\underbrace{H(i\omega)(i\omega - \lambda_j) = p_j}_{\text{Limit } i\omega = \lambda_j} \qquad (2.44)$$

because all the terms on the r.h.s. of (2.42) are multiplied by zero and only the jth term with $(i\omega - \lambda_j)$ in its denominator is not zero. The term on the l.h.s. of (2.44) is called the residuc of $H(i\omega)$ at $i\omega = \lambda_j$. By substituting for $H(i\omega)$ from (2.39) into (2.44), and taking the limit, we obtain the following expression for the coefficient p_j

$$p_j = \frac{B(\lambda_j)}{a_n \prod\limits_{\substack{k=1 \\ k \neq j}}^{n} (\lambda_j - \lambda_k)}, \, j = 1 \text{ to } n. \qquad (2.45)$$

Example 2

Expand the frequency-response function

$$H(i\omega) = \frac{1}{m(i\omega - \lambda_1)(i\omega - \lambda_2)(i\omega - \lambda_3)}$$

in a series of partial fractions. From (2.42)

$$H(i\omega) = \frac{p_1}{i\omega - \lambda_1} + \frac{p_2}{i\omega - \lambda_2} + \frac{p_3}{i\omega - \lambda_3}$$

where, from (2.45),

$$p_j = \frac{1}{m \prod\limits_{k \neq j} (\lambda_j - \lambda_k)}, \, j = 1 \text{ to } 3,$$

since $B(i\omega) = 1$. Hence we find that

$$p_1 = \frac{1}{m(\lambda_1 - \lambda_2)(\lambda_1 - \lambda_3)}$$

$$p_2 = \frac{1}{m(\lambda_2 - \lambda_1)(\lambda_2 - \lambda_3)}$$

$$p_3 = \frac{1}{m(\lambda_3 - \lambda_1)(\lambda_3 - \lambda_2)}$$

and the expanded form of $H(i\omega)$ can be written

$$H(i\omega) =$$

$$\frac{1}{m(\lambda_1 - \lambda_2)(\lambda_2 - \lambda_3)(\lambda_3 - \lambda_1)} \left(\frac{\lambda_3 - \lambda_2}{i\omega - \lambda_1} + \frac{\lambda_1 - \lambda_3}{i\omega - \lambda_2} + \frac{\lambda_2 - \lambda_1}{i\omega - \lambda_3} \right).$$

Expansion for complex eigenvalues

In Chapter 1 we saw that if the two eigenvalues of a second-order system have imaginary parts, they form a complex-conjugate pair. If the coefficients a_r, $r = 1$ to n, of the characteristic polynomial (2.35) are all real, the same conclusion applies for a general nth-order system. If $\lambda = \alpha + i\beta$ is an eigenvalue (α, β real), then so must $\lambda = \alpha - i\beta$ be an eigenvalue. This is because, on substituting $\lambda = \alpha + i\beta$ into (2.35), both the real part and the imaginary part of the resulting expression must separately be zero. Changing the sign of the $i\beta$ term does not alter the real part of the expression (which contains $(i\beta)^2$, $(i\beta)^4$ and higher even powers of $i\beta$) and only changes the sign of the imaginary part (which contains odd powers of $i\beta$). Since both real and imaginary parts of (2.35) are zero when $\lambda = \alpha + i\beta$, it follows that they are also zero when $\lambda = \alpha - i\beta$. Therefore, if they are complex, the eigenvalues will always occur in complex-conjugate pairs.

We shall now consider the special case of the expression (2.42) when n is even and all the eigenvalues occur in complex-conjugate pairs, so that

$$\lambda_1^* = \lambda_2, \lambda_3^* = \lambda_4, \ldots, \lambda_{n-1}^* = \lambda_n. \tag{2.46}$$

This would represent a multi-degree-of-freedom system with small damping, which is an important practical case. We shall find the coefficients p_j, p_{j+1} for the partial fractions $p_j/(i\omega - \lambda_j)$ and $p_{j+1}/(i\omega - \lambda_{j+1})$ where λ_j, λ_{j+1} form a complex-conjugate pair so that

$$\lambda_j^* = \lambda_{j+1}. \tag{2.47}$$

First we note that, for the function $B(i\omega)$ defined by (2.4),

$$B(\lambda_{j+1}) = B(\lambda_j^*) = B^*(\lambda_j) \tag{2.48}$$

because changing the sign of the imaginary part of λ_j changes the sign of the imaginary part of the expression $B(\lambda_j)$. Hence, from (2.45),

$$p_j = \frac{B(\lambda_j)}{a_n(\lambda_j - \lambda_1)(\lambda_j - \lambda_1^*) \ldots (\lambda_j - \lambda_j^*) \ldots (\lambda_j - \lambda_{n-1})(\lambda_j - \lambda_{n-1}^*)}$$
$$(2.49)$$

and

$$p_{j+1} = \frac{B^*(\lambda_j)}{a_n(\lambda_j^* - \lambda_1)(\lambda_j^* - \lambda_1^*) \ldots (\lambda_j^* - \lambda_j) \ldots (\lambda_j^* - \lambda_{n-1})(\lambda_j^* - \lambda_{n-1}^*)}.$$
$$(2.50)$$

The factor that would be zero in the denominators is omitted in both cases. Hence we conclude that

$$p_j^* = p_{j+1}, \, j = 1, 3, \ldots, n - 1. \tag{2.51}$$

The partial fraction expansion (2.42) may therefore be written in the form

$$H(i\omega) = \sum_{j=1,3\ldots,n-1} \left(\frac{p_j}{i\omega - \lambda_j} + \frac{p_j^*}{i\omega - \lambda_j^*} \right)$$

$$= \sum_{j \text{ odd}} \left[\frac{(p_j + p_j^*)(i\omega) - (p_j\lambda_j^* + p_j^*\lambda_j)}{(i\omega)^2 - (\lambda_j + \lambda_j^*)(i\omega) + \lambda_j\lambda_j^*} \right]. \tag{2.52}$$

For a passive system, which we have assumed is the case, the real parts of all the eigenvalues must be negative, otherwise the transient response of the system will not decay to zero after the excitation is removed. Hence the sum $\lambda_j + \lambda_j^*$ will be a negative real constant. Also, $p_j + p_j^*$ will be a real constant and, because $p_j^*\lambda_j$ is the complex conjugate of $p_j\lambda_j^*$, the sum $p_j\lambda_j^* + p_j^*\lambda_j$ will also be a real constant. Therefore, we can define real constants ω_j, ζ_j, α_j and β_j by

$$\omega_j^2 = \lambda_j\lambda_j^* \tag{2.53}$$

$$2\zeta_j\omega_j = -(\lambda_j + \lambda_j^*) \tag{2.54}$$

$$\alpha_j = -(p_j\lambda_j^* + p_j^*\lambda_j) \tag{2.55}$$

$$\beta_j = p_j + p_j^* \tag{2.56}$$

where ω_j and ζ_j are always positive. With these definitions (2.52) can be written

$$H(i\omega) = \sum_{j \text{ odd}} \left[\frac{\beta_j(i\omega) + \alpha_j}{(i\omega)^2 + 2\zeta_j\omega_j(i\omega) + \omega_j^2} \right]. \tag{2.57}$$

The general frequency-response function for a lightly damped system of order n, with n even, is expressed as a sum of $n/2$ *modal responses*. When $\beta_j = 0$, the jth term in (2.57) is similar to the displacement response of the system in Fig. 1.1. When $\alpha_j = 0$ but β_j is not zero, the jth term in (2.57) is similar to the velocity response of the system in Fig. 1.1. The overall frequency response is therefore represented as the sum of the responses of

$n/2$ lightly damped oscillators like that in Fig. 1.1. Each oscillator describes the behaviour of a vibrational *mode* and ω_j and ζ_j are the *modal natural frequency* and *modal damping ratio* for the $(j + 1)/2$th mode.

Numerical examples

To illustrate the previous theory we shall consider a sample calculation for a system with three degrees of freedom, see Fig. 2.7. If $y_1(t)$, $y_2(t)$ and $y_3(t)$ give the displacements of the three masses from static equilibrium as a result of force $x(t)$ acting on m_1, the equations of motion for the three masses are

$$m\ddot{y}_1 = k(y_2 - 2y_1) + x \tag{2.58}$$

$$m\ddot{y}_2 = k(y_3 - 2y_2 + y_1) - c\dot{y}_2 \tag{2.59}$$

$$m\ddot{y}_3 = k(-2y_3 + y_2). \tag{2.60}$$

For steady-state response to harmonic excitation defined by

$$x(t) = e^{i\omega t} \tag{2.61}$$

we have

$$y_1(t) = H_1(i\omega)\,e^{i\omega t}$$
$$y_2(t) = H_2(i\omega)\,e^{i\omega t} \tag{2.62}$$
$$y_3(t) = H_3(i\omega)\,e^{i\omega t}$$

and, on substituting this solution into the equations of motion and eliminating $H_2(i\omega)$ and $H_3(i\omega)$, the reader can check that the following result is obtained for $H_1(i\omega)$

$$H_1(i\omega) =$$

$$\frac{m^2(i\omega)^4 + mc(i\omega)^3 + 4mk(i\omega)^2 + 2ck(i\omega) + 3k^2}{m^3(i\omega)^6 + m^2c(i\omega)^5 + 6m^2k(i\omega)^4 + 4mck(i\omega)^3 + 10mk^2(i\omega)^2 + 4ck^2(i\omega) + 4k^3}. \tag{2.63}$$

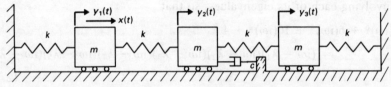

Fig. 2.7 A three-degree-of-freedom oscillator with force input $x(t)$ and displacement outputs $y_1(t)$, $y_2(t)$ and $y_3(t)$

Example 2.1 Undamped response

Consider first the case of zero damping, with a set of data

$$m = 1 \text{ kg}$$
$$c = 0 \tag{2.64}$$
$$k = 1 \text{ N/m}.$$

Then (2.63) gives

$$H_1(i\omega) = \frac{(i\omega)^4 + 4(i\omega)^2 + 3}{(i\omega)^6 + 6(i\omega)^4 + 10(i\omega)^2 + 4} \tag{2.65}$$

with the units being displacement/force = m/N. From (2.35), the eigenvalues are the solution of

$$\lambda^6 + 6\lambda^4 + 10\lambda^2 + 4 = 0 \tag{2.66}$$

which can be factorized into

$$(\lambda^2 + 2)(\lambda^4 + 4\lambda^2 + 2) = 0 \tag{2.67}$$

and again into

$$(\lambda^2 + 2)(\lambda^2 + 2 + \sqrt{2})(\lambda^2 + 2 - \sqrt{2}) = 0 \tag{2.68}$$

from which we can see that the 6 eigenvalues for the undamped case are

$$\lambda_{1,2} = \pm i(2 - \sqrt{2})^{1/2} = \pm i\, 0.765$$
$$\lambda_{3,4} = \pm i\sqrt{2} = \pm i\, 1.414 \tag{2.69}$$
$$\lambda_{5,6} = \pm i(2 + \sqrt{2})^{1/2} = \pm i\, 1.848$$

the units being s^{-1}.

In order to expand $H_1(i\omega)$ in the form (2.57), we need the partial fraction coefficients p_j, $j = 1$ to 6. Consider p_1, corresponding to $\lambda_1 = i\,(2 - \sqrt{2})^{1/2}$, for which $\lambda_1^2 = -(2 - \sqrt{2})$ and $\lambda_1^4 = 6 - 4\sqrt{2}$. Then the numerator of (2.65) with λ_1 replacing $i\omega$ is

$$B(\lambda_1) = 6 - 4\sqrt{2} + 4(-2 + \sqrt{2}) + 3 = 1. \tag{2.70}$$

The denominator of (2.65) can be expressed as the product of factors involving each of its eigenvalues, so that

$$(i\omega)^6 + 6(i\omega)^4 + 10(i\omega)^2 + 4$$
$$= (i\omega - \lambda_1)(i\omega - \lambda_2)(i\omega - \lambda_3)(i\omega - \lambda_4)(i\omega - \lambda_5)(i\omega - \lambda_6). \tag{2.71}$$

On replacing $i\omega$ by λ_1 and omitting the first factor (which would be zero) we obtain

$$\prod_{k=2}^{6} (\lambda_1 - \lambda_k) =$$

$$i\, 2(2 - \sqrt{2})^{1/2}\, [(2 - \sqrt{2})^{1/2} - \sqrt{2}][(2 - \sqrt{2})^{1/2} + \sqrt{2}] \times$$
$$\times [(2 - \sqrt{2})^{1/2} - (2 + \sqrt{2})^{1/2}][(2 - \sqrt{2})^{1/2} + (2 + \sqrt{2})^{1/2}]$$
$$= i\, 8(2 - \sqrt{2})^{1/2}. \tag{2.72}$$

Hence, from (2.45), the coefficient p_1 is given by

$$p_1 = \frac{B(\lambda_1)}{\displaystyle\prod_{k=2}^{6} (\lambda_1 - \lambda_k)} = \frac{-i}{8(2 - \sqrt{2})^{1/2}} = -i\, 0.1633 \tag{2.73}$$

and, from (2.51),

$$p_2 = p_1^* = \frac{i}{8(2 - \sqrt{2})^{1/2}} = i\, 0.1633. \tag{2.74}$$

Similarly, the other coefficients are

$$p_3 = p_4^* = -\frac{i}{4\sqrt{2}} = -i\, 0.1768 \tag{2.75}$$

and

$$p_5 = p_6^* = -\frac{i}{8(2 + \sqrt{2})^{1/2}} = -i\, 0.0676. \tag{2.76}$$

Then, by using (2.53), (2.54), (2.55) and (2.56), we obtain

$$\omega_1^2 = 2 - \sqrt{2} \qquad \omega_3^2 = 2 \qquad \omega_5^2 = 2 + \sqrt{2}$$
$$2\zeta_1\omega_1 = 0 \qquad 2\zeta_3\omega_3 = 0 \qquad 2\zeta_5\omega_5 = 0$$
$$\alpha_1 = 1/4 \qquad \alpha_3 = 1/2 \qquad \alpha_5 = 1/4 \tag{2.77}$$
$$\beta_1 = 0 \qquad \beta_3 = 0 \qquad \beta_5 = 0$$

and therefore the expansion (2.57) becomes for this example

$$H_1(i\omega) = \frac{\frac{1}{4}}{(i\omega)^2 + (2 - \sqrt{2})} + \frac{\frac{1}{2}}{(i\omega)^2 + 2} + \frac{\frac{1}{4}}{(i\omega)^2 + (2 + \sqrt{2})}$$
$$= \frac{0.25}{(i\omega)^2 + (0.7654)^2} + \frac{0.5}{(i\omega)^2 + (1.414)^2} + \frac{0.25}{(i\omega)^2 + (1.848)^2} \tag{2.78}$$

where ω is (angular) frequency measured in rad/s. There are three modes with natural frequencies $(2 - \sqrt{2})^{1/2} = 0.765$ rad/s, $\sqrt{2} = 1.414$ rad/s and $(2 + \sqrt{2})^{1/2} = 1.848$ rad/s. In (2.78), the frequency-response function for the displacement of the left-hand mass in Fig. 2.7 when subjected to harmonic excitation applied to this mass is expressed as the sum of its three *modal responses*. This result is illustrated in Fig. 2.8 where the magnitudes of each of the three terms in (2.78) are plotted on the same graph as the magnitude of their summation, $|H_1(i\omega)|$. All the terms are made non-dimensional by multiplying by $\frac{4}{3}k$ in order to make $H_1(i\omega) = 1$ when $\omega = 0$ (see (2.63)). When the excitation frequency is close to a natural frequency, the corresponding modal response can be seen to dominate the response graph; the other two modal responses then contribute relatively little to the total response.

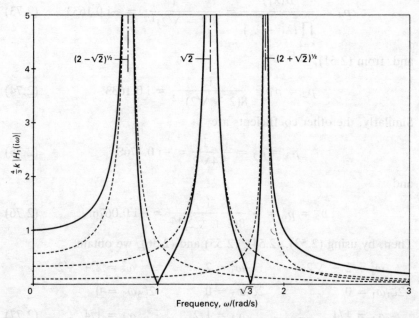

Fig. 2.8 Displacement response for the left-hand mass in Fig. 2.7 for the undamped case, when the parameter values are $m = 1$ kg, $c = 0$, and $k = 1$ N/m. The broken lines give the modal responses; the solid line gives their summation according to (2.78)

For excitation frequencies between the natural frequencies, we see from Fig. 2.8 that the total response is less than the modal responses alone. This is because of the different phases of the modal responses. For $\omega = 1$ rad/s and $\omega = \sqrt{3} = 1.732$ rad/s, the left-hand mass in Fig. 2.7 has no motion at all. At these frequencies, the other two masses serve as vibration absorbers for the left-hand mass and ensure that the left-hand mass is a *node* or *nodal point* for the system. This is because the numerator of (2.65) is zero for $\omega = 1$ and $\omega = \sqrt{3}$; these frequencies are called the *zeros* or *zero frequencies* of the frequency-response function.

Note that, in equations (2.77), the second mode is identified by subscript 3 and the third mode by subscript 5. This is because, in (2.69), we have associated mode 1 with its two eigenvalues λ_1, $\lambda_2 = \lambda_1^*$, mode 2 with its eigenvalues λ_3, $\lambda_4 = \lambda_3^*$, and mode 3 with its eigenvalues λ_5, $\lambda_6 = \lambda_5^*$. Therefore mode 1 is really mode 1, 2; mode 2 is mode 3, 4, etc. In the fundamental equation (2.57), the modal summation is for index j having odd values only. If, instead, the modes are numbered $k = 1, 2, 3, \ldots$, then in (2.57) the corresponding values of j are $j = 2k - 1$.

Example 2.2 Undamped mode shapes

The ratio of the amplitudes of harmonic motion at each coordinate $y_1(t)$, $y_2(t)$, $y_3(t)$ can be obtained from the equations of motion. If at frequency ω we put

$$y_1(t) = Y_1 e^{i\omega t}$$
$$y_2(t) = Y_2 e^{i\omega t} \qquad (2.79)$$
$$y_3(t) = Y_3 e^{i\omega t}$$

then (2.59) gives, for zero damping, $c = 0$,

$$[m(i\omega)^2 + 2k]\, Y_2 = kY_3 + kY_1 \qquad (2.80)$$

and (2.60) gives

$$[m(i\omega)^2 + 2k]\, Y_3 = kY_2. \qquad (2.81)$$

On eliminating Y_3 between (2.80) and (2.81), we obtain

$$\frac{Y_2}{Y_1} = \frac{mk(i\omega)^2 + 2k}{m^2(i\omega)^4 + 4mk(i\omega)^2 + 3k^2} \qquad (2.82)$$

and, combining (2.81) with (2.82),

$$\frac{Y_3}{Y_1} = \frac{k^2}{m^2(i\omega)^4 + 4mk(i\omega)^2 + 3k^2}. \qquad (2.83)$$

For the numerical data in (2.64), these ratios become

$$\frac{Y_2}{Y_1} = \frac{(i\omega)^2 + 2}{(i\omega)^4 + 4(i\omega)^2 + 3} \qquad (2.84)$$

and

$$\frac{Y_3}{Y_1} = \frac{1}{(i\omega)^4 + 4(i\omega)^2 + 3}. \qquad (2.85)$$

By substituting, in turn, the three natural frequencies into (2.84) and (2.85), we obtain the results given in Table 2.1 for the amplitude ratios in free undamped vibration. These undamped modes are illustrated in Fig. 2.9 where the (real) amplitudes of the coordinates are illustrated graphically for free vibration at the corresponding natural frequencies. The amplitudes Y_1, Y_2, Y_3 are drawn as horizontal lines of appropriate length and, to illustrate the 'mode shape', the ends of these lines are joined together. The vertical spacing between the horizontal lines is arbitrary.

Table 2.1 Undamped natural frequencies and mode shapes for the system in Fig. 2.7

Mode	Natural frequency	Y_2/Y_1	Y_3/Y_1
1	$(2 - \sqrt{2})^{1/2}$	$\sqrt{2}$	1
2	$\sqrt{2}$	0	-1
3	$(2 + \sqrt{2})^{1/2}$	$-\sqrt{2}$	1

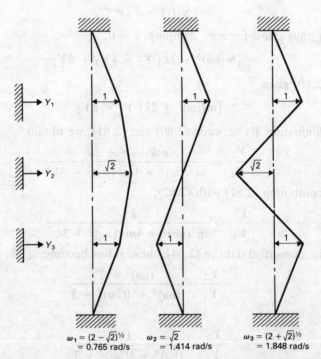

$\omega_1 = (2 - \sqrt{2})^{1/2}$ $= 0.765$ rad/s $\omega_2 = \sqrt{2}$ $= 1.414$ rad/s $\omega_3 = (2 + \sqrt{2})^{1/2}$ $= 1.848$ rad/s

Fig. 2.9 Undamped natural modes of the system shown in Fig. 2.7 when $m = 1$ kg, $c = 0$ and $k = 1$ N/m

For steady harmonic excitation, each of the three modes contributes to the total response. In Problem 2.4, the expressions corresponding to (2.78) for the displacement responses of the other two masses in Fig. 2.7 are calculated and shown to be

$$H_2(i\omega) = \frac{\frac{1}{4}\sqrt{2}}{(i\omega)^2 + (2 - \sqrt{2})} - \frac{\frac{1}{4}\sqrt{2}}{(i\omega)^2 + (2 + \sqrt{2})} \qquad (2.86)$$

$$H_3(i\omega) = \frac{\frac{1}{4}}{(i\omega)^2 + (2 - \sqrt{2})} - \frac{\frac{1}{2}}{(i\omega)^2 + 2} + \frac{\frac{1}{4}}{(i\omega)^2 + (2 + \sqrt{2})}. \qquad (2.87)$$

It is interesting to see that, for forced vibration, the corresponding numerators in each modal fraction in (2.78), (2.86) and (2.87) are in the same proportions as the amplitudes in free vibration: for example, in the first fraction in each equation the proportions are $H_2/H_1 = \sqrt{2}$ and $H_3/H_1 = 1$, in agreement with the first row of Table 2.1. We note that $H_2(i\omega)$ has no response in its second mode because this mode has a node at the middle mass.

Next we examine how these results are modified by the addition of damping.

Example 2.3 Damped response

Consider the case when the damping is no longer zero and, instead of (2.64), the parameter values are

$$m = 1 \text{ kg}$$
$$c = 0.3 \text{ Ns/m} \qquad (2.88)$$
$$k = 1 \text{ N/m}.$$

Then (2.63) gives

$$H_1(i\omega) =$$

$$\frac{(i\omega)^4 + 0.3(i\omega)^3 + 4(i\omega)^2 + 0.6(i\omega) + 3}{(i\omega)^6 + 0.3(i\omega)^5 + 6(i\omega)^4 + 1.2(i\omega)^3 + 10(i\omega)^2 + 1.2(i\omega) + 4} \qquad (2.89)$$

instead of the simpler expression (2.65). As before, the eigenvalues λ_j, $j = 1$ to 6, are the solutions obtained by replacing $i\omega$ by λ in the denominator of (2.89) and finding the values of λ which make this zero. The eigenvalues are therefore the solutions of

$$\lambda^6 + 0.3\lambda^5 + 6\lambda^4 + 1.2\lambda^3 + 10\lambda^2 + 1.2\lambda + 4 = 0. \qquad (2.90)$$

Since the second mode has a node at the middle mass (see Fig. 2.9), which is where the damper acts, there will still be an undamped mode given by

$$\lambda_{3,4} = \pm i\sqrt{2} \qquad (2.91)$$

and so $(\lambda^2 + 2)$ is again a factor of (2.90) which may be written

$$(\lambda^2 + 2)(\lambda^4 + 0.3\lambda^3 + 4\lambda^2 + 0.6\lambda + 2) = 0. \qquad (2.92)$$

Later we shall be dealing with the numerical calculation of eigenvalues, so we shall not take time to do this now, and will just state that (2.92) can be factorized further to

$$(\lambda^2 + 2)(\lambda^2 + 0.1512\lambda + 0.5905)(\lambda^2 + 0.1488\lambda + 3.3871) = 0$$

$$(2.93)$$

which result the reader can check by multiplying together the terms in the brackets in (2.93) and verifying that (2.92) is then regained. The six eigenvalues of the damped system are the solutions of (2.93), which are

$$\lambda_{1,2} = -0.0756 \pm i\,0.765$$

$$\lambda_{3,4} = \pm i\,1.414 \qquad (2.94)$$

$$\lambda_{5,6} = -0.0744 \pm i\,1.839$$

with the units of s^{-1}. These results may be compared with (2.69) for the undamped case. The frequency of the first mode, although the same to three significant figures, is slightly less for the damped case, being reduced from $0.7654\,\text{rad/s}$ for the undamped case to $0.7647\,\text{rad/s}$ when there is the damping specified in (2.88). The modal damping ratios are given, from (2.54), by

$$2\zeta_1\omega_1 = 0.1512, \quad \text{where } \omega_1^2 = 0.5905$$

$$2\zeta_3\omega_3 = 0, \qquad \text{where } \omega_3^2 = 2 \qquad (2.95)$$

$$2\zeta_5\omega_5 = 0.1488, \quad \text{where } \omega_5^2 = 3.3871$$

so that

$$\zeta_1 = 0.098, \; \zeta_3 = 0, \; \zeta_5 = 0.040. \qquad (2.96)$$

Therefore the lowest frequency mode is the most heavily damped, the middle frequency mode has no damping (for the reason mentioned previously), and the highest frequency mode has an intermediate level of damping.

We shall now express the frequency-response function $H_1(i\omega)$ defined by (2.89) in the expanded form of (2.57). To do this we have to calculate the coefficients α_j and β_j, $j = 1, 3, 5$, in (2.57) by using the formulae (2.55) and (2.56). These in turn need the partial fraction coefficients p_j, $j = 1$ to 6, which are found by using (2.45) and (2.51).

We shall calculate p_1, p_3 and p_5 from (2.45). From (2.94), we have

$$\lambda_1 = -0.0756 + i\,0.765 = \lambda_2^*$$

$$\lambda_3 = i\,1.414 = \lambda_4^* \qquad (2.97)$$

$$\lambda_5 = -0.0744 + i\,1.839 = \lambda_6^*$$

and, with $B(i\omega)$ being the numerator of (2.89),

$$B(\lambda_1) = 1, \ B(\lambda_3) = -1, \ B(\lambda_5) = 1. \tag{2.98}$$

The reason for two of the results in (2.98) can be seen by inspection by comparing the form of $B(\lambda)$ with the form of the second factor in (2.92). Since the second factor in (2.92) differs from $B(\lambda)$ by unity and this factor is zero when $\lambda = \lambda_1$ and $\lambda = \lambda_5$, it follows that $B(\lambda) = 1$ for $\lambda = \lambda_1$ and $\lambda = \lambda_5$.

The products

$$\prod_{\substack{k=1 \\ k \neq j}}^{6} (\lambda_1 - \lambda_k), \text{ for } j = 1, 3, 5$$

which are needed for the denominators in (2.45), can be calculated by hand using the values in (2.97), or more easily by computer, and yield the results that

$$\prod_{k=2}^{6} (\lambda_1 - \lambda_k) = 0.4986 + i \, 6.078$$

$$\prod_{\substack{k=1 \\ k \neq 3}}^{6} (\lambda_3 - \lambda_k) = -i \, 5.657$$

$$\tag{2.99}$$

$$\prod_{\substack{k=1 \\ k \neq 5}}^{6} (\lambda_5 - \lambda_k) = -2.792 + i \, 14.158.$$

On substituting these results into (2.45) we find, since the coefficient a_6 in the denominator of (2.89) is unity,

$$p_1 = 0.0134 - i \, 0.1634 = p_2^*$$
$$p_3 = -i \, 0.1768 = p_4^* \tag{2.100}$$
$$p_5 = -0.0134 - i \, 0.0680 = p_6^*$$

and then, from the definitions in (2.53), (2.54), (2.55) and (2.56),

$\omega_1^2 = 0.5905$	$\omega_3^2 = 2$	$\omega_5^2 = 3.387$
$2\zeta_1\omega_1 = 0.1512$	$2\zeta_3\omega_3 = 0$	$2\zeta_5\omega_5 = 0.1488$
$\alpha_1 = 0.252$	$\alpha_3 = 0.5$	$\alpha_5 = 0.248$
$\beta_1 = 0.027$	$\beta_3 = 0$	$\beta_5 = -0.027$

$$\tag{2.101}$$

and the expanded form of $H_1(i\omega)$ is given by

$$H_1(i\omega) = \frac{0.027(i\omega) + 0.252}{(i\omega)^2 + 0.151(i\omega) + (0.7647)^2} +$$

$$+ \frac{0.5}{(i\omega)^2 + (1.414)^2} + \frac{-0.027(i\omega) + 0.248}{(i\omega)^2 + 0.149(i\omega) + (1.839)^2}$$

$$(2.102)$$

within the accuracy of the significant figures shown. As before, the units of $H_1(i\omega)$ are m/N.

Figure 2.10 shows the magnitude of the three modal responses plotted on the same graph as the magnitude of the total response, $|H_1(i\omega)|$. The results are again normalized by first multiplying through by $\frac{4}{3}k$, with $k = 1$ N/m in this example, so that the results are non-dimensional and $H_1(i\omega) = 1$ when $\omega = 0$. Because the middle mass (see Fig. 2.7) has no motion in the second mode (see Fig. 2.9), damping applied to the middle mass does not affect the second mode. Therefore the second mode remains undamped whatever the value of c in Fig. 2.7 and the response at $\omega = 2$ rad/s is infinite.

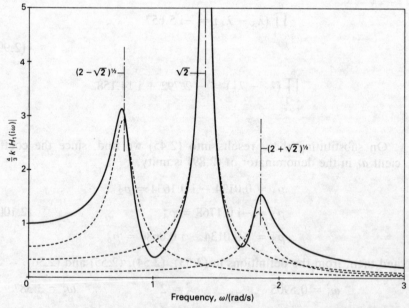

Fig. 2.10 The same as Fig. 2.8 except that the damping $c = 0.3$ N s/m. $H_1(i\omega)$ is now given by (2.102)

Now that damping has been included, the response no longer falls to zero between the natural frequencies. This is because there is now no real value of frequency ω for which the numerator of (2.89) is zero. The magnitude of the overall response at $\omega = (2 - \sqrt{2})^{1/2}$ and

$(2 + \sqrt{2})^{1/2}$ rad/s exceeds slightly the corresponding modal peak because of the contributions from the other modes. Also, we note that the height of the peak of the high-frequency mode is about half the height of the peak of the low-frequency mode. This is despite the damping ratio for the high-frequency mode being less than half that of the low-frequency mode (see equations 2.96). The explanation can be seen from equations (2.101) and (2.102). From (2.101), the products $\zeta \omega_N$ are approximately the same for the two modes. From (2.102), the magnitude of the peak value of a modal response is approximately proportional to $1/2\zeta\omega_N^2$ and, because of its higher natural frequency, the high-frequency mode accordingly has a lower height at its peak than does the low-frequency mode. In the next chapter we shall consider how the widths of the modal peaks depend on their corresponding modal damping ratios and how the relative heights of the peaks change when velocity-response and acceleration-response functions are plotted.

Example 2.4 Logarithmic and polar plots of the damped response

In Fig. 2.11 the magnitude of the (non-dimensional) displacement frequency-response function for this example, $\frac{4}{3}k\, H_1(i\omega)$, is plotted to log scales. For the undamped case, plotted as the thin continuous line, $H_1(i\omega)$ is given by (2.65) or by its equivalent modal expansion (2.78). For the damped case, plotted as the thick continuous line, $H_1(i\omega)$ is given by (2.89) or its equivalent modal expansion (2.102). The undamped case is the same as that plotted as the continuous line in Fig. 2.8; the damped case is the same as that plotted as the continuous line in Fig. 2.10.

As $\omega \to 0$, the curves become asymptotic to the 0 dB line, while as $\omega \to \infty$, the asymptotic slope is -40 dB/decade. This is the same behaviour as in Fig. 2.3(a) for the single-degree-of-freedom system in Fig. 1.1. In Fig. 2.11 a 'skeleton' is shown as the broken line. At its left-hand end this skeleton is the 0 dB line; at its right-hand end it is a line at -40 dB/decade which is defined, from (2.65), by

$$20 \log_{10}\left[\frac{4}{3}\, k|H_1(i\omega)|\right] \simeq 20 \log_{10}\left[\frac{4}{3\omega^2}\right]$$

$$= 20 \log_{10}\frac{4}{3} - 40 \log_{10}\omega$$

$$= 2.5 - 40 \log_{10}\omega. \qquad (2.103)$$

We shall investigate the skeletal properties of logarithmic plots in the next chapter, where it will be shown that, in between the two outer natural frequencies, the skeleton is continuous and that it switches between sloping and horizontal segments, with the slope always being -40 dB/decade.

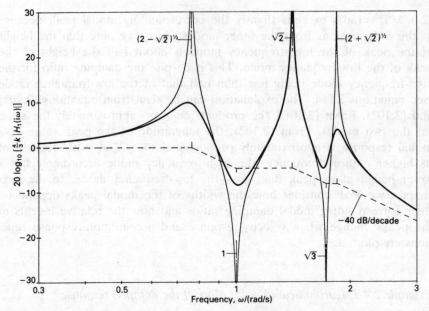

Fig. 2.11 Magnitude of the displacement response functions for the left-hand mass in Fig. 2.7 plotted to log scales. For the undamped case, given by equation 2.78, the parameter values are $m = 1$ kg, $c = 0$, $k = 1$ N/m. For the damped case, given by equation (2.102), they are $m = 1$ kg, $c = 0.3$ Ns/m, $k = 1$ N/m. The position of the 'skeleton', shown by the broken line, is located as explained in Chapter 3

In Fig. 2.12 the real and imaginary parts of $\frac{4}{3}kH_1(i\omega)$ for this example with $m = 1$ kg, $c = 0.3$ N s/m, $k = 1$ N/m are plotted for frequency values in the range 0 to ∞ to give a polar graph. This may be compared with the graph in the lower half of Fig. 2.5(a). At $\omega = 0$, the graph in Fig. 2.12 begins on the real axis at the point (1, i0) and follows a generally circular path, reaching its lowest point at a frequency close to the lowest (undamped) natural frequency of $(2 - \sqrt{2})^{1/2}$ rad/s before returning to a position close to the real axis. The graph then moves away to the right as it starts to form a second circle which has infinite radius. This corresponds to the undamped second mode whose natural frequency is $\sqrt{2}$ rad/s. The graph returns to the diagram from its left-hand margin and then completes a final loop whose lowest point is reached at a frequency near the highest natural frequency of $(2 + \sqrt{2})^{1/2}$ rad/s before converging on the origin of the diagram as $\omega \to \infty$. This behaviour is typical of the displacement response of a multi-degree-of-freedom system.

Partial-fraction expansion when there are repeated eigenvalues

We return now to the general partial fraction expansion of the frequency-

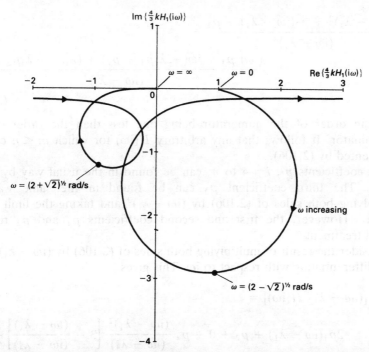

Fig. 2.12 Polar graph of the (non-dimensional) displacement response function, $(4/3)kH_1(i\omega)$, of the left-hand mass in Fig. 2.7, when $m = 1$ kg, $c = 0.3$ N s/m, $k = 1$ N/m. The graph is drawn from equation (2.102) for positive frequencies only

response function $H(i\omega)$. Beginning with $H(i\omega)$ in the form of equation (2.2), with the order of the numerator m less than the order of the denominator n, we have seen that it is always possible to expand $H(i\omega)$ in a series of its partial fractions to give

$$H(i\omega) = \sum_{j=1}^{n} \frac{p_j}{i\omega - \lambda_j} \qquad (2.104)$$

provided that the eigenvalues λ_j, $j = 1$ to n, are all distinct. When two or more of the λ_j are the same, these λs are said to be repeated eigenvalues or, alternatively, multiple eigenvalues. In that case (2.104) is no longer true. Suppose that λ_1 is repeated twice so that

$$\lambda_3 = \lambda_2 = \lambda_1 \qquad (2.105)$$

and that the remaining λ_j, $j = 4$ to n are distinct. Then, instead of (2.104), the corresponding expansion is

$$H(i\omega) = \frac{p_1}{i\omega - \lambda_1} + \frac{p_2}{(i\omega - \lambda_1)^2} + \frac{p_3}{(i\omega - \lambda_1)^3} + \sum_{j=4}^{n} \frac{p_j}{i\omega - \lambda_j}. \qquad (2.106)$$

On combining the first three fractions on the r.h.s. of (2.106), these give

$$\frac{p_1(i\omega - \lambda_1)^2 + p_2(i\omega - \lambda_1) + p_3}{(i\omega - \lambda_1)^3} =$$

$$\frac{(i\omega)^2 p_1 + i\omega(-2\lambda_1 p_1 + p_2) + (\lambda_1^2 p_1 - \lambda_1 p_2 + p_3)}{(i\omega - \lambda_1)^3}$$

$$(2.107)$$

with the order of the numerator being one less than the order of the denominator. It follows that any arbitrary $H(i\omega)$ for which $m < n$ can be represented by (2.106).

The coefficients p_j, $j = 4$ to n, can be found in the usual way by using (2.44). The third coefficient p_3 can be found in the same way by multiplying both sides of (2.106) by $(i\omega - \lambda_1)^3$ and taking the limit when $i\omega = \lambda_1$. However, the first and second coefficients p_1 and p_2 require special treatment.

Consider the result of multiplying both sides of (2.106) by $(i\omega - \lambda_1)^3$ and then differentiating with respect to $i\omega$. This gives

$$\frac{d}{d(i\omega)} [(i\omega - \lambda_1)^3 H(i\omega)] =$$

$$2p_1(i\omega - \lambda_1) + p_2 + 0 + p_4 \frac{(i\omega - \lambda_1)^2}{(i\omega - \lambda_4)} \left[3 - \frac{(i\omega - \lambda_1)}{(i\omega - \lambda_4)} \right] + \ldots$$

$$(2.108)$$

and, in the limit when $i\omega = \lambda_1$ we have

$$\underbrace{\frac{d}{d(i\omega)} [(i\omega - \lambda_1)^3 H(i\omega)]}_{\text{Limit } i\omega = \lambda_1} = p_2 \qquad (2.109)$$

which gives the unknown coefficient p_2. On differentiating (2.108) a second time with respect to $i\omega$ and taking the limit, we get

$$\underbrace{\frac{d^2}{d(i\omega)^2} [(i\omega - \lambda_1)^3 H(i\omega)]}_{\text{Limit } i\omega = \lambda_1} = 2p_1 \qquad (2.110)$$

which gives the other unknown coefficient p_1.

When an eigenvalue is repeated twice (so that it occurs three times), two derivatives of $(i\omega - \lambda_1)^3 H(i\omega)$ have to be calculated to find p_1 and p_2. If an eigenvalue is repeated j times (so that it occurs $(j + 1)$ times), then j derivatives of $(i\omega - \lambda_1)^{j+1} H(i\omega)$ have to be calculated to obtain all the coefficients $p_1, p_2, \ldots, p_{j+1}$ in the partial fraction expansion.

In practice, as we shall see in Chapter 8, it is not necessary to make such calculations, because the general form of the frequency-response function automatically generates the required coefficients of the partial-fraction expansion. In Example 8.2 a typical calculation is given for a torsional system with two zero eigenvalues. Its frequency-response function is

$$H(i\omega) = \frac{(1/3)(i\omega)^2 + 5(i\omega)^2 + (400/9)(i\omega) + 500/3}{(i\omega)^5 + 15(i\omega)^4 + 200(i\omega)^3 + 1500(i\omega)^2}. \tag{2.111}$$

The denominator factorizes to

$$(i\omega)^2(i\omega + 10)(i\omega + 2.5 - i\,11.99)(i\omega + 2.5 + i\,11.99) \tag{2.112}$$

and the partial-fraction expansion of (2.111) is shown in Example 8.2 to be

$$H(i\omega) = 1/3\left[\frac{0.0444}{i\omega} + \frac{0.3333}{(i\omega)^2} - \frac{0.0167}{(i\omega + 10)} - \frac{(0.0139 + i\,0.0180)}{(i\omega + 2.5 - i\,11.99)}\right.$$
$$\left. - \frac{(0.0139 - i\,0.0180)}{(i\omega + 2.5 + i\,11.99)}\right]. \tag{2.113}$$

Frequency response of composite systems

When a dynamic system is composed of a number of identifiable parts or sub-systems, and their manner of connection is known, it is possible to calculate the frequency-response functions of the composite system by combining the frequency-response functions of the sub-systems.

For any linear, time-invariant passive system with input $x(t)$ and output $y(t)$, if there is a steady-state harmonic input

$$x(t) = X(i\omega)\,e^{i\omega t} \tag{2.114}$$

where $X(i\omega)$ is the (possibly complex) amplitude, then the steady-state output will be

$$y(t) = Y(i\omega)\,e^{i\omega t} \tag{2.115}$$

where, from the definition of the frequency-response function $H(i\omega)$,

$$Y(i\omega) = H(i\omega)X(i\omega). \tag{2.116}$$

If there are two inputs and two outputs as shown in Fig. 2.13(a), then (2.116) becomes

$$\begin{bmatrix} Y_1(i\omega) \\ Y_2(i\omega) \end{bmatrix} = \begin{bmatrix} H_{11}(i\omega) & H_{12}(i\omega) \\ H_{21}(i\omega) & H_{22}(i\omega) \end{bmatrix} \begin{bmatrix} X_1(i\omega) \\ X_2(i\omega) \end{bmatrix} \tag{2.117}$$

and there are four frequency-response functions defined so that $H_{jk}(i\omega)$ gives the response at output j to unit harmonic excitation at input k.

Consider two mechanical sub-systems A and B, Fig. 2.13(b), which are joined together as shown in Fig. 2.13(c). At position 1 there is a general input $x_1(t)$, and a general output $y_1(t)$, both of which are unspecified as to their nature. For example, $x_1(t)$ could be an applied moment in a specified direction and $y_1(t)$ could be a linear velocity in a different direction. However, at the point where the two sub-systems are connected, the inputs $x_{2A}(t)$, $x_{2B}(t)$ are both forces in the same direction and the outputs $y_{2A}(t)$,

$y_{2B}(t)$ are both displacements (or both velocities or accelerations) in the same direction. The method of connection must be such that deflection of B can only react on A by causing a force in the reference direction, and vice versa. Deflections and forces do not need to be collinear to satisfy this condition, but generally that will be the case.

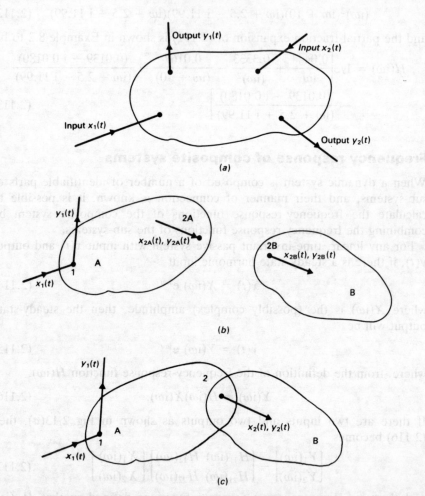

Fig. 2.13 Illustrating frequency-response calculations for a composite system. (*a*) Single system with two inputs and two outputs. (*b*) Two separate sub-systems which are joined to form the composite system (*c*)

When the two sub-systems are connected, we use $x_2(t)$ to denote the input and $y_2(t)$ to denote the output of the composite system at the coupling point. For geometrical compatibility

$$y_2(t) = y_{2A}(t) = y_{2B}(t) \qquad (2.118)$$

and for force equilibrium

$$x_2(t) = x_{2A}(t) + x_{2B}(t). \tag{2.119}$$

In terms of the complex amplitudes for steady-state harmonic motion, these equations give

$$Y_2(i\omega) = Y_{2A}(i\omega) = Y_{2B}(i\omega) \tag{2.120}$$

and

$$X_2(i\omega) = X_{2A}(i\omega) + X_{2B}(i\omega). \tag{2.121}$$

If the frequency-response functions for the A sub-system are defined so that

$$\begin{bmatrix} Y_1(i\omega) \\ Y_{2A}(i\omega) \end{bmatrix} = \begin{bmatrix} A_{11}(i\omega) & A_{12}(i\omega) \\ A_{21}(i\omega) & A_{22}(i\omega) \end{bmatrix} \begin{bmatrix} X_1(i\omega) \\ X_{2A}(i\omega) \end{bmatrix} \tag{2.122}$$

and for the B sub-system so that

$$Y_{2B}(i\omega) = B_{22}(i\omega)X_{2B}(i\omega) \tag{2.123}$$

we have six equations relating eight parameters, the four input amplitudes and the four output amplitudes. There are two equations in (2.120), two in (2.122) and one each in (2.121) and (2.123). Four of the equations can be used to eliminate $X_{2A}(i\omega)$, $X_{2B}(i\omega)$, $Y_{2A}(i\omega)$ and $Y_{2B}(i\omega)$ to leave two equations for $Y_1(i\omega)$ and $Y_2(i\omega)$ in terms of $X_1(i\omega)$ and $X_2(i\omega)$. The best method is to substitute for $X_{2A}(i\omega)$ and $Y_{2A}(i\omega)$ in (2.122) in terms of $X_2(i\omega)$ and $Y_2(i\omega)$ from (2.120), (2.121) and (2.123). The reader can check that the result is

$$\begin{bmatrix} Y_1(i\omega) \\ Y_2(i\omega) \end{bmatrix} = \begin{bmatrix} \dfrac{A_{11}A_{22} - A_{12}A_{21} + A_{11}B_{22}}{A_{22} + B_{22}} & \dfrac{A_{12}B_{22}}{A_{22} + B_{22}} \\[4mm] \dfrac{A_{21}B_{22}}{A_{22} + B_{22}} & \dfrac{A_{22}B_{22}}{A_{22} + B_{22}} \end{bmatrix} \begin{bmatrix} X_1(i\omega) \\ X_2(i\omega) \end{bmatrix} \tag{2.124}$$

where the arguments $(i\omega)$ have been omitted from the As and Bs for brevity. The four frequency-response functions of the composite system are expressed in terms of the frequency-response functions of its two sub-systems. If $H_{11}(i\omega)$, $H_{12}(i\omega)$, $H_{21}(i\omega)$ and $H_{22}(i\omega)$ denote the frequency-response functions for the composite system then, from (2.124),

$$H_{11}(i\omega) = \frac{A_{11}(i\omega)A_{22}(i\omega) - A_{12}(i\omega)A_{21}(i\omega) + A_{11}(i\omega)B_{22}(i\omega)}{A_{22}(i\omega) + B_{22}(i\omega)} \tag{2.125}$$

$$H_{12}(i\omega) = \frac{A_{12}(i\omega)B_{22}(i\omega)}{A_{22}(i\omega) + B_{22}(i\omega)} \tag{2.126}$$

$$H_{21}(i\omega) = \frac{A_{21}(i\omega)B_{22}(i\omega)}{A_{22}(i\omega) + B_{22}(i\omega)} \qquad (2.127)$$

$$H_{22}(i\omega) = \frac{A_{22}(i\omega)B_{22}(i\omega)}{A_{22}(i\omega) + B_{22}(i\omega)}. \qquad (2.128)$$

Example

Find an expression for the frequency-response function $H_{11}(i\omega)$ for the composite torsional system shown in Fig. 2.14(a), where the input is torque x_1 and the output is angular deflection y_1.

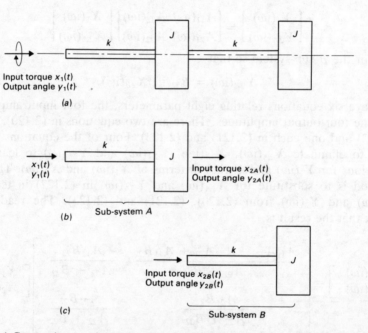

(a)

(b)   Sub-system A

(c)   Sub-system B

Fig. 2.14 Composite torsional system for frequency-response analysis in sub-systems A and B by using equation (2.124)

Consider a single wheel–shaft pair, sub-system A in Fig. 2.14(b). The equations of motion are

$$x_1 = k(y_1 - y_{2A}) \qquad (2.129)$$

and

$$x_1 + x_{2A} = J\ddot{y}_{2A}. \qquad (2.130)$$

Hence, if

$$y_1(t) = A_{11}(i\omega)\,e^{i\omega t} \quad \text{and} \quad y_{2A}(t) = A_{21}(i\omega)\,e^{i\omega t} \qquad (2.131)$$

when

$$x_1(t) = e^{i\omega t} \quad \text{and} \quad x_{2A}(t) = 0, \tag{2.132}$$

we have, on substituting into (2.129) and (2.130),

$$1 = k(A_{11} - A_{21}) \tag{2.133}$$

and

$$1 = -J\omega^2 A_{21} \tag{2.134}$$

giving

$$A_{11}(i\omega) = \frac{1}{k} - \frac{1}{J\omega^2}; \quad A_{21}(i\omega) = -\frac{1}{J\omega^2}. \tag{2.135}$$

Similarly, putting

$$y_1(t) = A_{12}(i\omega)\, e^{i\omega t} \quad \text{and} \quad y_{2A}(t) = A_{22}(i\omega)\, e^{i\omega t} \tag{2.136}$$

when

$$x_1(t) = 0 \quad \text{and} \quad x_{2A}(t) = e^{i\omega t} \tag{2.137}$$

we find that

$$A_{12}(i\omega) = A_{22}(i\omega) = -\frac{1}{J\omega^2}. \tag{2.138}$$

For sub-system B, Fig. 2.14(c),

$$B_{22}(i\omega) = A_{11}(i\omega) = \frac{1}{k} - \frac{1}{J\omega^2}. \tag{2.139}$$

Hence for the composite system, from (2.125),

$$
\begin{aligned}
H_{11}(i\omega) &= A_{11}(i\omega) - \frac{A_{12}(i\omega)A_{21}(i\omega)}{A_{22}(i\omega) + B_{22}(i\omega)} \\[2mm]
&= \left(\frac{1}{k} - \frac{1}{J\omega^2} \right) - \frac{\left(-\dfrac{1}{J\omega^2} \right)\left(-\dfrac{1}{J\omega^2} \right)}{-\dfrac{1}{J\omega^2} + \left(\dfrac{1}{k} - \dfrac{1}{J\omega^2} \right)} \\[2mm]
&= \frac{1}{k} \left[1 - \frac{k}{J\omega^2} - \frac{k}{J\omega^2 \left(\dfrac{J\omega^2}{k} - 2 \right)} \right].
\end{aligned}
\tag{2.140}
$$

The analysis can be extended to more shaft–wheel pairs in the same way.

The form of (2.124) depends on the specification that, at the point where the sub-systems are joined, the input variable is a force and the output variable is a displacement, velocity or acceleration, so that (2.118) and (2.119) apply. In Problem 2.6(a), we consider the case where the input at point 2 (see Fig. 2.13c) is the displacement there (displacement forcing) and the output at 2 is the force required to cause this displacement. In that case the equivalent expression to (2.124) has a completely different appearance.

The analysis in this section involves sub-systems joined at a single coordinate. Cases may occur where sub-systems are linked at two (or more) coordinates, for example the connection of a moving mass to a beam. The geometrical output coordinates are then linear deflection and angular rotation, and the corresponding inputs are the shear force and bending moment at the connecting position. The analysis of composite systems joined at more than one coordinate is similar in principle to the analysis given above, although the algebra is a good deal more involved (see Problem 2.6(b)).

Natural frequencies of composite systems

Since $H_{jk}(\omega)$ is the complex ratio of amplitudes for output j/input k, peak response at output j for harmonic input k occurs when $|H_{jk}(i\omega)|$ is a maximum or, conversely, when $|1/H_{jk}(i\omega)|$ is a minimum. If $H_{jk}(i\omega)$ is infinite, then there will be an infinite response, which is the condition for a natural frequency of the undamped system. For composite systems, this condition can be interpreted in terms of the frequency-response functions for the sub-systems.

For the case we have considered, with two sub-systems joined at a single displacement coordinate at which there is force equilibrium, we know from (2.124) that all the frequency-response functions $H_{jk}(i\omega)$, j, $k = 1$ or 2, will have a zero denominator when

$$A_{22}(i\omega) + B_{22}(i\omega) = 0. \tag{2.141}$$

Unless the numerator of $H_{jk}(i\omega)$ is also zero, output j will then be infinite and, in general, all outputs will be simultaneously infinite at natural frequencies defined by (2.141). The exception is when the numerator of $H_{jk}(i\omega)$ is also zero. This may occur when either output j or input k happens to be at a nodal point for the mode in question. When the output is at a node, there is zero response; when the input (but not the output) is at a node there is a finite response but not an infinite response. The reader can demonstrate this latter result for the system in Fig. 2.7 by calculating $H_{12}(i\omega)$ for output at the left-hand mass 1 and input at the middle mass 2. At the natural frequency $\omega = \sqrt{2k/m}$ for which the middle mass is a node, $H_{12}(i\omega) = -1/2k$.

Another way in which some or all of the elements of the frequency-response function matrix in (2.124) can be infinite is for some or all of the $A(i\omega)$'s and for $B_{22}(i\omega)$ to be simultaneously infinite. For example, if $A_{22}(i\omega)$ and $B_{22}(i\omega)$ are both infinite, then

$$H_{22}(i\omega) = \frac{A_{22}(i\omega)B_{22}(i\omega)}{A_{22}(i\omega) + B_{22}(i\omega)} \qquad (2.142)$$

will also be infinite. This would occur if both (undamped) sub-systems had the same natural frequency for harmonic force excitation at point 2; then the combined system would have the same natural frequency as its sub-systems.

Example

Use the result of the previous example to find the natural frequencies of the torsional system in Fig. 2.15(*a*).

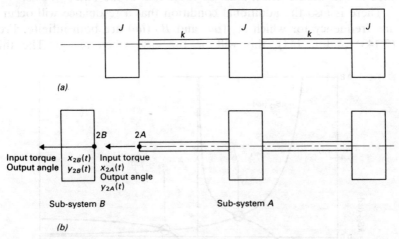

Fig. 2.15 Composite torsional system for frequency-response analysis in sub-systems *A* and *B* by using equation (2.141)

Let the system be divided into two sub-systems *A* and *B* as shown in Fig. 2.15(*b*). The frequency-response function for sub-system *B* is

$$B_{22}(i\omega) = -\frac{1}{J\omega^2}. \qquad (2.143)$$

Sub-system *A* consists of the two shafts and two wheels shown in Fig. 2.14(*a*) for which, from the previous example (from (2.140)),

$$A_{22}(i\omega) = \frac{1}{k}\left[1 - \frac{k}{J\omega^2} - \frac{k}{J\omega^2(J\omega^2/k - 2)}\right]. \qquad (2.144)$$

Hence, from (2.141), the frequency equation is

$$\frac{k}{J\omega^2} = 1 - \frac{k}{J\omega^2} - \frac{k/J\omega^2}{(J\omega^2/k - 2)} \qquad (2.145)$$

or, after rearrangement,

$$(\omega^2 - 3k/J)(\omega^2 - k/J) = 0. \tag{2.146}$$

Therefore there are two natural frequencies

$$\omega_1 = \sqrt{k/J} \text{ and } \omega_2 = \sqrt{3k/J}. \tag{2.147}$$

Since the three wheels have the same inertia J and the two shafts have the same stiffness k, the mode shapes can be found by inspection. At ω_1 the two outer wheels vibrate through the same amplitude but in anti-phase, with the middle wheel stationary. At ω_2 the two outer wheels move in phase through the same amplitude with the middle wheel vibrating through a larger amplitude in anti-phase to the outer wheels. For the conservation of angular momentum, the amplitude of the middle wheel must be twice that of the outer wheels.

There is also the additional condition that a resonance will occur at any frequency for which $A_{22}(i\omega)$ and $B_{22}(i\omega)$ are both infinite. From (2.143) and (2.144), this will be the case when $\omega = 0$. The third

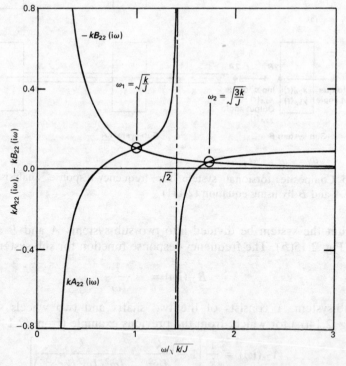

Fig. 2.16 Graph of the frequency-response functions (angular displacement output/torque input) $A_{22}(i\omega)$ and $B_{22}(i\omega)$ for sub-system A (two wheels and two shafts) and sub-system B (one wheel) of the composite torsional system of three wheels and two shafts in Fig. 2.15. The torsional stiffness of each shaft is k and the inertia of each wheel is J. The graph is made non-dimensional by plotting $kA_{22}(i\omega)$ and $-kB_{22}(i\omega)$ against $\omega/\sqrt{k/J}$

natural frequency is therefore

$$\omega_0 = 0 \qquad\qquad (2.148)$$

at which rigid-body rotation of the complete system occurs.

These results can be illustrated graphically by sketching $A_{22}(i\omega)$ and $-B_{22}(i\omega)$ versus ω on the same graph, Fig. 2.16.

Chapter 3

General response properties

Terminology

There are a variety of different names for the frequency-response function and its inverse. We have mentioned already that the term *complex frequency-response function* is sometimes used and that subscripts are often attached to indicate which is the output and which the input: for example, $H_{jk}(i\omega)$ is the complex ratio of output j to input k. Also, as an abbreviation, some authors use the initials frf or FRF (in capitals) instead of the full name.

We saw in Chapter 2 that, for a system with mass and stiffness, the displacement frequency response differs significantly from the corresponding velocity frequency response, which in turn differs from the acceleration frequency response. The term *receptance* is a synonym for the displacement frequency-response function for a mechanical system with force excitation, and is now used quite widely. Alternative names for the same function are *mechanical compliance, mechanical admittance* and *dynamic flexibility* but these are much less popular. The term *mobility* or, sometimes, *mechanical mobility* has become a synonym for the velocity frequency-response function of a mechanical system, and *inertance* and *accelerance* are alternative names for the acceleration frequency-response function.

Instead of the excitation being a force, it may also be a prescribed displacement, velocity or acceleration. When the input is a displacement and the output is the force required to generate that displacement the frequency response function is called the *dynamic stiffness*. When the input is a prescribed velocity and the output is the force required to generate that velocity, the frf is called the *mechanical impedance* (or just *impedance*, for short). When the input is a prescribed acceleration and the output is the force required to generate that acceleration, then the frf is called the *apparent mass*.

When there is only one input and one output, the dynamic stiffness is the inverse of the displacement frf (or receptance), the mechanical impedance is the inverse of the velocity frf (mobility) and the apparent mass is the inverse of the acceleration frf (inertance). However, for multiple input and output systems these reciprocal relationships no longer apply. This is because, for a system with multiple inputs and outputs, it is necessary to prescribe all the inputs before any one output is determined. In calculating the displacement frf for a force applied at one input position and an output displacement measured at the same or another position, it is understood by the definition that the output concerned arises only from the prescribed input, with all the other possible inputs being zero. In other words, the system is force-free everywhere except at the one input position that is receiving the prescribed force. In the case of dynamic stiffness, a different situation exists. A prescribed displacement is applied at one input position and the force required to generate this displacement is measured at another position. Although not stated explicitly, it is implied by the definition of dynamic stiffness that all the other input positions have zero displacement. In other words they are fixed. Therefore, in the case of a multiple input and output system the system for which the displacement frf is calculated is a different system from the system for which the dynamic stiffness is calculated. In the former case, the system is force-free except for a single input force; in the latter case, the system is clamped at all its input positions except the one to which a prescribed displacement is applied. This means that essentially different dynamic systems are involved and that the receptance associated with stations j and k is generally not the inverse of the dynamic stiffness associated with the same stations.

In Chapter 8 we shall develop results for all the frequency response functions for a general system with M inputs and M outputs. The M-dimensional vector of outputs is determined from the M-dimensional vector of inputs by multiplying by a square matrix of order $M \times M$. Each of the elements of this matrix is a separate frequency-response function and element j, k in row j and column k is the frequency-response function relating output j to input k. It follows from the laws of matrix algebra that the vector of inputs can be obtained from the vector of outputs by multiplying by the inverse of the frequency-response function matrix. Therefore, for such a system with the same number of inputs and outputs, the matrix of dynamic stiffnesses is the inverse of the *matrix* of receptances (although in general corresponding elements of the two matrices are not reciprocals). It is similarly true that the matrix of impedances is the inverse of the matrix of mobilities and the matrix of apparent masses is the inverse of the matrix of inertances.

For mechanical and structural systems, there are practical advantages in using velocity as the response parameter that is measured. This is because the dynamic range required for a velocity measurement over a band of frequencies is usually less than the dynamic range required for a corresponding displacement or acceleration measurement (see, for example, the ranges of the graphs in Figs 3.7(a) and (b)). Therefore in practice mobilities (velocity frequency-response functions) are used quite frequently.

Returning to the general frequency response function $H_{jk}(i\omega)$, if $i\omega$ is replaced by the Laplace operator s, then $H_{jk}(s)$ is the *transfer function* between input k and output j defined by

$$H_{jk}(s) = \frac{\text{transformed output } j}{\text{transformed input } k}.$$

The terminology is confused here because another name for the general transfer function is the *admittance function*, and the term impedance function is sometimes used for the inverse of $H_{jk}(s)$. These names may conflict with the definitions of admittance and impedance given above for a mechanical system where they are restricted to displacement output for admittance and velocity output for impedance with force inputs in both cases. To avoid confusion, we shall not use the term admittance and will only use impedance for the frequency-response function for which there is a prescribed velocity input and the output is the force which is a consequence of that prescribed velocity.

In the literature on receptances, lower-case Greek letters are often used for receptances, but the capital H notation is now more common and will usually be used here.

Properties of logarithmic response diagrams

Figure 2.3 shows the displacement, velocity and acceleration frequency-response functions plotted to log scales for a single-degree-of-freedom mechanical system with force excitation. In this section we shall consider how these diagrams can be generalized for the case of a multiple-degree-of-freedom system whose response is represented by the expansion (2.57).

Consider an undamped system of masses and springs with N degrees of freedom. The system's position is then defined by N independent displacement coordinates. We shall be concerned initially with the receptance of the system for displacement response at one coordinate when the excitation is a force applied to one of the masses. Because there is no damping, the system's $2N$ eigenvalues will be purely imaginary and occur in N complex conjugate pairs. We shall assume that the N pairs of eigenvalues are all distinct (different) so that the N natural frequencies of the system are all different. Also, we shall assume that the displacement response is always exactly in phase or exactly in anti-phase with the force excitation, so that the receptance $H(i\omega)$ is always real. In Chapter 11 we shall prove that this is the case, but for the moment it is a necessary assumption for further progress.

Since the eigenvalues λ_j are purely imaginary, it follows that the product

$$\prod_{j=1}^{2N} (i\omega - \lambda_j)$$

in (2.38) is always real (because the product involves an even number of terms each of which is imaginary). Hence we see from (2.38) that the denominator $A(i\omega)$ of $H(i\omega)$ is always real, and therefore, since $H(i\omega)$ is real, the numerator $B(i\omega)$ of $H(i\omega)$ is also always real.

In order to use the expansion (2.57), we need the constants ω_j, ζ_j, α_j and β_j. These are defined in terms of the eigenvalues λ_j and the coefficients p_j by (2.53) to (2.56). From (2.49), we see that p_j is always imaginary when $\lambda_j = i\omega_j$. This is because there is an odd number of imaginary factors in the denominator, while the numerator remains always real. Therefore, from (2.54), the damping ratios ζ_j are all zero since $\lambda_j + \lambda_j^*$ is always zero (because the λ_j are imaginary) and, from (2.56), the coefficients β_j in the numerator of (2.57) are always zero (because the p_j are imaginary).

Receptance graphs

We conclude that for an undamped mechanical system with N degrees of freedom, the general receptance function $H(i\omega)$ expressed by (2.57) can be written in the simplified form

$$H(i\omega) = \sum_{j \text{ odd}} \left[\frac{\alpha_j}{(i\omega)^2 + \omega_j^2} \right] \tag{3.1}$$

where $j = 1, 3, 5, \ldots, 2N - 1$. In terms of a new integer k defined by

$$k = \frac{j + 1}{2} \tag{3.2}$$

this becomes

$$H(i\omega) = \sum_{k=1}^{N} \left[\frac{\alpha_k}{(i\omega)^2 + \omega_k^2} \right] \tag{3.3}$$

where ω_k, $k = 1$ to N, are the N natural frequencies of the system and α_k, $k = 1$ to N, are N real coefficients.

We shall now investigate the general shape of a graph of $\log|H(i\omega)|$ plotted against $\log \omega$. For convenience we shall use logarithms to base 10 and express the result in decibels by calculating $20\log_{10}|H(i\omega)|$, which we plot against $\log_{10} \omega$. The expansion (3.3) can be written

$$H(i\omega) = \frac{\alpha_1}{\omega_1^2 - \omega^2} + \frac{\alpha_2}{\omega_2^2 - \omega^2} + \ldots + \frac{\alpha_N}{\omega_N^2 - \omega^2} \tag{3.4}$$

or, taking a common denominator, as

$$H(i\omega) = \frac{c_0 + c_1\omega^2 + c_2\omega^4 + \ldots + c_{N-1}\omega^{2(N-1)}}{(\omega_1^2 - \omega^2)(\omega_2^2 - \omega^2) \ldots (\omega_N^2 - \omega^2)} \tag{3.5}$$

where the coefficients c_0, c_1, c_2, etc. may be positive or negative or zero depending on the values of the α's in (3.4). There will generally be a number of real values of ω for which the numerator in (3.5) is zero. For these values of frequency there is no output displacement and the receptance is zero. They are called *zero frequencies* or *anti-resonant frequencies*. There may be any number of anti-resonances up to $N - 1$.

Example

Find expressions for the receptances $H_1(i\omega)$ and $H_2(i\omega)$ of the two-degree-of-freedom system shown in Fig. 3.1 where, for force excitation,

$$x(t) = e^{i\omega t} \tag{i}$$

the displacement response is

$$y_1(t) = H_1(i\omega)\, e^{i\omega t}$$
$$y_2(t) = H_2(i\omega)\, e^{i\omega t}. \tag{ii}$$

The equations of motion are:

$$m\ddot{y}_1 + 2ky_1 - ky_2 = x$$
$$m\ddot{y}_2 - ky_1 + ky_2 = 0. \tag{iii}$$

On substituting $x(t)$, $y_1(t)$ and $y_2(t)$ from (i) and (ii) into (iii) then gives

$$(-m\omega^2 + 2k)H_1(i\omega) - kH_2(i\omega) = 1 \tag{iv}$$

$$-kH_1(i\omega) + (-m\omega^2 + k)H_2(i\omega) = 0 \tag{v}$$

and eliminating $H_2(i\omega)$ between these last two equations we obtain

$$H_1(i\omega) = \frac{(k - m\omega^2)}{(k^2 - 3km\omega^2 + m^2\omega^4)} \tag{vi}$$

and, from (v),

$$H_2(i\omega) = \frac{k}{(k^2 - 3km\omega^2 + m^2\omega^4)}. \tag{vii}$$

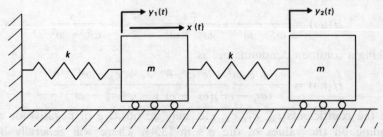

Fig. 3.1 Undamped two-degree-of-freedom system for calculation of the receptance and mobilities plotted in Fig. 3.2

To put these results in the standard form (3.5), we can define

$$\omega_1^2 = \frac{k}{m}\left(\frac{3 - \sqrt{5}}{2}\right)$$

$$\omega_2^2 = \frac{k}{m}\left(\frac{3 + \sqrt{5}}{2}\right) \tag{viii}$$

$$\Omega_1^2 = \frac{k}{m}$$

and then we have

$$H_1(i\omega) = \frac{(\Omega_1^2 - \omega^2)}{m(\omega_1^2 - \omega^2)(\omega_2^2 - \omega^2)} \tag{ix}$$

and

$$H_2(i\omega) = \frac{\Omega_1^2}{m(\omega_1^2 - \omega^2)(\omega_2^2 - \omega^2)}. \tag{x}$$

In the case of the *direct receptance* $H_1(i\omega)$, there is an anti-resonant frequency at

$$\omega = \Omega_1 = \sqrt{\frac{k}{m}}.$$

At this frequency the right-hand mass acts as a perfect vibration absorber for the left-hand mass and there is no movement at y_1. For the *cross-receptance* $H_2(i\omega)$, there is no anti-resonant frequency and y_2 shows some measure of response at all frequencies.

We shall assume in the following analysis that there are M anti-resonant frequencies given by Ω_r, $r = 1$ to M, where $M < N$, and that (3.5) can then be written as

$$H(i\omega) = \frac{c(\Omega_1^2 - \omega^2)(\Omega_2^2 - \omega^2) \ldots (\Omega_M^2 - \omega^2)}{(\omega_1^2 - \omega^2)(\omega_2^2 - \omega^2) \ldots (\omega_N^2 - \omega^2)} \tag{3.6}$$

where c is a positive (real) constant. At zero frequency

$$H(i\omega)_{\omega = 0} = \frac{c\Omega_1^2\Omega_2^2 \ldots \Omega_M^2}{\omega_1^2\omega_2^2 \ldots \omega_N^2} \tag{3.7a}$$

and so if K is defined as the static stiffness for displacement output y as a result of force input x

$$K = \frac{1}{H(i\omega)_{\omega = 0}} = \frac{\omega_1^2\omega_2^2 \ldots \omega_N^2}{c\Omega_1^2\Omega_2^2 \ldots \Omega_M^2}. \tag{3.7b}$$

As a specific example, consider a two-degree-of-freedom system whose receptance is given by

$$H(i\omega) = \frac{(\Omega_1^2 - \omega^2)}{(\omega_1^2 - \omega^2)(\omega_2^2 - \omega^2)} \tag{3.8}$$

where $\omega_1 < \Omega_1 < \omega_2$. The log magnitude of $H(i\omega)$ is plotted against $\log \omega$ in Fig. 3.2(a) as the broken curve. The curve starts from the level marked A at $\omega = 0$, goes to infinity at $\omega = \omega_1$, falls to zero at $\omega = \Omega_1$ and goes to infinity again at $\omega = \omega_2$ before becoming asymptotic to a line sloping downwards at 40 dB/decade (which is about 12 dB per octave) as $\omega \to \infty$. The final asymptote passes through the level marked B at $\omega = \omega_2$.

The curve is drawn with a 'skeleton' of straight-line segments shown as the solid line in Fig. 3.2(a). The skeleton begins as the horizontal line at level L_A, where

$$L_A = 20 \log_{10} |H(i\omega)|_{\omega = 0} = 20 \log_{10} \frac{\Omega_1^2}{\omega_1^2 \omega_2^2}. \tag{3.9}$$

It finishes as the final asymptote, which is a line defined by

$$20 \log_{10} |H(i\omega)|_{\omega \to \infty} = 20 \log_{10} \frac{1}{\omega^2} = -40 \log_{10} \omega \tag{3.10}$$

and which begins at level L_B at $\omega = \omega_2$ where, from (3.10),

$$L_B = -40 \log_{10} \omega_2. \tag{3.11}$$

In between ω_1 and ω_2, the skeleton has two other segments: a line sloping downwards at 40 dB/decade from $\omega = \omega_1$ to $\omega = \Omega_1$ and a horizontal line at level L_B from $\omega = \Omega_1$ to $\omega = \omega_2$.

We can see that this skeleton is continuous because the change of level between ω_1 and Ω_1 will be

$$-40 \log_{10} \frac{\Omega_1}{\omega_1}$$

for a -40 dB/decade slope, in which case

$$L_B - L_A = -40 \log_{10} \frac{\Omega_1}{\omega_1}. \tag{3.12}$$

Hence, if L_A is given by (3.9),

$$L_B = 40 \log_{10} \frac{\Omega_1}{\omega_1 \omega_2} - 40 \log_{10} \frac{\Omega_1}{\omega_1}$$

$$= 40(\log_{10} \Omega_1 - \log_{10} \omega_1 - \log_{10} \omega_2 - \log_{10} \Omega_1 + \log_{10} \omega_1)$$

$$= -40 \log_{10} \omega_2 \tag{3.13}$$

which is in agreement with (3.11).

Properties of the skeleton

A skeletal backbone can be drawn through the corresponding graph for N degrees of freedom in the same way as in the previous section. A plot of

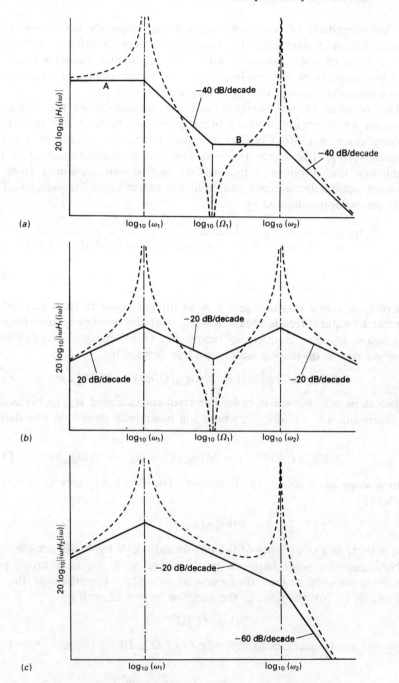

Fig. 3.2 Log magnitude of (*a*) the direct receptance, (*b*) the direct mobility, and (*c*) the cross-mobility of a two-degree-of-freedom system such as that in Fig. 3.1, plotted against log frequency, showing the 'skeleton' of each graph

the log magnitude of receptance against log frequency has N *resonances* where, for zero damping, the receptance becomes infinite, and up to $N - 1$ zeros or *anti-resonances* where the receptance becomes zero. The skeleton consists of straight-line segments which change direction every time a natural frequency or a zero frequency is crossed.

The position of the skeleton and the magnitude of the change of direction which occurs at every break point can be found by considering limiting cases of (3.6). Consider the skeleton in the vicinity of a natural frequency, ω_k. The factor $(\omega_k^2 - \omega^2)$ in the denominator of (3.6) then dominates the response. Suppose that ω_k is well separated from the adjacent natural frequencies and from the nearest zero frequencies. Then (3.6) can be approximated by

$$\underset{\omega \simeq \omega_k}{H(i\omega)} \simeq \frac{c(-\omega^2)(-\omega^2) \dots (\Omega_M^2)}{(-\omega^2)(-\omega^2) \dots (-\omega^2)(\omega_k^2 - \omega^2)(\omega_{k+1}^2) \dots (\omega_N^2)}$$

$$= \frac{C}{\omega^{2r}(\omega_k^2 - \omega^2)} \tag{3.14}$$

where C is a new constant and r is an integer equal to the excess of the number of natural frequencies below ω_k over the number of zero frequencies below ω_k. For frequencies below ω_k, (3.14) becomes asymptotic to $C/\omega^{2r}\omega_k^2$ which, on the log scales, is a line defined by

$$20 \log_{10}(C/\omega^{2r}\omega_k^2) = 20 \log_{10}(C/\omega_k^2) - 40r \log_{10} \omega \tag{3.15}$$

whose slope is $- 40r$ dB/decade. For frequencies above ω_k, (3.14) becomes asymptotic to $- C/\omega^{2(r+1)}$, whose log magnitude plots as a line defined by

$$20 \log_{10}(C/\omega^{2(r+1)}) = 20 \log_{10} C - 40(r + 1) \log_{10} \omega \tag{3.16}$$

with a slope of $- 40(r + 1)$ dB/decade. The two lines meet at $\omega = \omega_k$ at the level

$$20 \log_{10}(C/\omega_k^{2(r+1)})$$

where there is a steepening of the downwards slope by 40 dB/decade.

Now consider what happens to the skeleton if the next break point above $\omega = \omega_k$ is a zero frequency at $\omega = \Omega_k$. According to the line defined by (3.16), the level of the skeleton at $\omega = \Omega_k$ will be

$$20 \log_{10}(C/\Omega_k^{2(r+1)}).$$

However for frequencies in the vicinity of Ω_k, $H(i\omega)$ changes from (3.14) to

$$\underset{\omega \simeq \Omega_k}{H(i\omega)} = - \frac{C}{\omega^{2(r+1)}} \left(1 - \frac{\omega^2}{\Omega_k^2}\right) \tag{3.17}$$

subject to assumptions similar to those for (3.14). The asymptotes on either side of Ω_k are given by a repeat of (3.16) for $\omega < \Omega_k$ and by

$$20\log_{10}(C/\omega^{2r}\Omega_k^2) = 20\log_{10}(C/\Omega_k^2) - 40r\log_{10}\omega \qquad (3.18)$$

when $\omega > \Omega_k$. These asymptotes intersect at the break frequency Ω_k and there is now a $+40$ dB/decade change of slope at the break, as the skeleton's equation changes from (3.16) to (3.18). Since the equation for the skeleton on the right side of ω_k is the same as that for the skeleton on the left side of Ω_k, both being given by (3.16), the skeleton is a continuous graph.

Although (3.14) and (3.17) have been derived as limiting cases of the frequency-response function equation (3.6), they are used to define the skeleton whether ω_k and Ω_k are well separated from each other and from other natural frequencies and zero frequencies, or not. The skeleton of the logarithmic response diagram is therefore a continuous sequence of straight lines which indicates the overall trend of the response level, without showing resonant peaks or troughs, and which becomes asymptotic to the response curve at its two extremes: at very low frequencies and at very high frequencies. At every break point there is a 40 dB/decade (12 dB/octave) change of slope. If the break frequency is a natural frequency, the slope decreases by 40 dB/decade. If it is a zero frequency, the slope increases by 40 dB/decade.

For the three-degree-of-freedom system of masses and springs in Fig. 2.7, the receptance at the left-hand mass (where the force is applied) is plotted to log scales in Fig. 2.11. In this case there are two anti-resonant frequencies such that $\omega_1 < \Omega_1 < \omega_2 < \Omega_2 < \omega_3$ so the skeleton begins horizontally (where motion is controlled by the static stiffness of the system) and then has segments alternately sloping downwards at 40 dB/decade and running horizontally, with the break points occurring at ω_1, Ω_1, ω_2, Ω_2 and ω_3, successively, as frequency is increased.

Mobility graphs

The velocity frequency-response function, or mobility, can be calculated from the corresponding displacement frequency-response function, or receptance, by using (2.9). In this case, corresponding to (3.3), we have

$$i\omega H(i\omega) = \sum_{k=1}^{N} \frac{i\omega\alpha_k}{(i\omega)^2 + \omega_k^2} \qquad (3.19)$$

and, corresponding to (3.6),

$$i\omega H(i\omega) = \frac{i\omega c(\Omega_1^2 - \omega^2)(\Omega_2^2 - \omega^2)\ldots(\Omega_M^2 - \omega^2)}{(\omega_1^2 - \omega^2)(\omega_2^2 - \omega^2)\ldots(\omega_N^2 - \omega^2)}. \qquad (3.20)$$

For the two-degree-of-freedom system whose receptance is given by (3.8), the corresponding mobility is

$$i\omega H(i\omega) = \frac{i\omega(\Omega_1^2 - \omega^2)}{(\omega_1^2 - \omega^2)(\omega_2^2 - \omega^2)} \qquad (3.21)$$

and in Fig. 3.2(*b*)

$$20\log_{10}|i\omega H(i\omega)| = 20\log_{10}\left|\frac{\omega(\Omega_1^2 - \omega^2)}{(\omega_1^2 - \omega^2)(\omega_2^2 - \omega^2)}\right| \qquad (3.22)$$

is plotted against $\log_{10}\omega$ as the broken line. The graph's skeleton is drawn as the solid line. In this case, the skeleton consists only of sloping segments, with the initial asymptote being

$$20\log_{10}|i\omega H(i\omega)|_{\omega\to 0} = 20\log_{10}\frac{\omega\Omega_1^2}{\omega_1^2\omega_2^2} \qquad (3.23)$$

with a positive slope of 20 dB/decade (approximately 6 dB/octave), and the final asymptote being

$$20\log_{10}|i\omega H(i\omega)|_{\omega\to\infty} = 20\log_{10}\frac{1}{\omega} \qquad (3.24)$$

with a negative slope of 20 dB/decade. In between ω_1 and ω_2 there are two further segments, as shown in Fig. 3.2(*b*), with the same slopes: -20 dB/decade from ω_1 to Ω_1, and $+20$ dB/decade from Ω_1 to ω_2. As for the receptance case, the skeleton is continuous and it has the same property of a -40 dB/decade change in slope every time a natural frequency is reached and a $+40$ dB/decade change in slope every time a zero frequency is reached.

If there is not a zero frequency between ω_1 and ω_2, the mobility graph becomes like Fig. 3.2(*c*). This is a graph of $20\log_{10}|i\omega H(i\omega)|$, where

$$i\omega H(i\omega) = \frac{i\omega\Omega_1^2}{(\omega_1^2 - \omega^2)(\omega_2^2 - \omega^2)} \qquad (3.25)$$

instead of (3.21). This may be compared with equation (x) (on p. 61) for the two-degree-of-freedom system in Fig. 3.1 (see the example calculation in the previous section). It represents the *cross-mobility* or *transfer-mobility* for the output velocity $\dot{y}_2(t)$ of the right-hand mass in Fig. 3.1 in response to an input force $x(t)$ on the left-hand mass. The skeleton begins with a $+20$ dB/decade slope, as for Fig. 3.2(b), there is a -40 dB/decade change in slope at ω_1 and a further -40 dB/decade change at ω_2, so that the skeleton has a downwards slope of 60 dB/decade on the right-hand side of the graph.

For the three-degree-of-freedom system in Fig. 2.7, the *direct mobility* (velocity at the mass to which the force is applied) is plotted in Fig. 3.3 which may be compared with the corresponding *direct receptance* in Fig. 2.11. There are break points at the three natural frequencies and at the two zero frequencies, with the skeleton starting with a 20 dB/decade upwards slope, and then switching by ± 40 dB/decade at every break. For this velocity response, the third resonance at $\omega_3 = (2 + \sqrt{2})^{1/2}$ rad/s now has a higher peak than the first resonance at $\omega_1 = (2 - \sqrt{2})^{1/2}$ rad/s, which is the opposite of the case for the displacement response in Fig. 2.11.

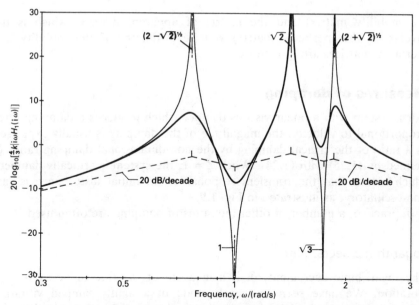

Fig. 3.3 Magnitude of the mobility of the left-hand mass in Fig. 2.7 plotted to log scales. This is a re-plot of Fig. 2.11, except that the velocity response function is plotted instead of the displacement response function. For the undamped case, $m = 1$ kg, $c = 0$ and $k = 1$ N/m. For the damped case, $m = 1$ kg, $c = 0.3$ N s/m and $k = 1$ N/m

Reciprocity relations

For many linear systems, it will be shown in Chapter 11 that cross-receptances, cross-mobilities and cross-inertances occur in corresponding pairs, with $H_{jk}(i\omega)$ being the same as $H_{kj}(i\omega)$ in each case. The conditions for this reciprocal relationship to be true in general are discussed in Chapter 11. Apart from the requirement of linearity (which usually means that only small amplitude vibrations can take place) the most important condition is that the inputs and outputs cannot be mixed. For example, all the inputs must be forces and all the outputs must be displacements, or vice versa. Reciprocity does not apply if some of the outputs are displacements and some are velocities, or if some of the inputs are forces and some are displacements. For most problems of structural small-amplitude vibration and many other mechanical problems, the upshot is that the matrices of receptances, mobilities and inertances are all symmetric matrices.

From the theory of matrix algebra, we know that if a matrix is symmetric, its inverse will also be symmetric (see, for example, Gantmacher [33]). Therefore if the matrix of receptances is symmetric, it follows that its inverse, which is the matrix of dynamic stiffnesses, will also be symmetric. Similarly, the matrix of impedances (which is the inverse of the mobility matrix) and the matrix of apparent masses (which is the inverse of the inertance matrix) will be symmetric if the mobility and inertance matrices are symmetric.

Measures of damping

For a system with a linear viscous damper which produces a damping force proportional to velocity, the magnitude of the damping is usually expressed as a ratio of the critical damping by the non-dimensional damping ratio, ζ, defined by (1.25) with (1.24). When $\zeta = 1$, the system is critically damped, which means that the transient response to an initial disturbance is just non-oscillatory, as illustrated in Fig. 1.9.

In practice, a number of other measures of damping are often used.

Logarithmic decrement

The logarithmic decrement, δ, is a measure of the rate of decay of free vibration. We have seen that each mode of a lightly-damped vibrating system is characterized by its complex-conjugate pair of eigenvalues λ_j, $\lambda_{j+1} = \lambda_j^*$, where, from (2.53) and (2.54),

$$\lambda_j, \lambda_{j+1} = -\zeta_j\omega_j \pm i\omega_j\sqrt{1 - \zeta_j^2}. \tag{3.26}$$

Free motion in this mode (alone) is then given, from (2.34), by

$$y(t) = N_j\,e^{\lambda_j t} + N_{j+1}\,e^{\lambda_{j+1} t} \tag{3.27}$$

where N_j and N_{j+1} are constants. On substituting for the λ's from (3.26), we have

$$
\begin{aligned}
y_j(t) &= e^{-\zeta_j\omega_j t}[N_j e^{i\omega_j\sqrt{(1 - \zeta_j^2)}t} + N_{j+1}\,e^{-i\omega_j\sqrt{(1 - \zeta_j^2)}t}] \\
&= e^{-\zeta_j\omega_j t}[(N_j + N_{j+1})\cos\omega_j\sqrt{1 - \zeta_j^2}\,t \\
&\quad + i(N_j - N_{j+1})\sin\omega_j\sqrt{1 - \zeta_j^2}\,t].
\end{aligned}
\tag{3.28}
$$

Because, by definition, the response $y_j(t)$ is real, the constants N_j and N_{j+1} must be complex conjugates so that both $(N_j + N_{j+1})$ and $i(N_j - N_{j+1})$ are real. Then (3.28) can also be written as

$$y_j(t) = e^{-\zeta_j\omega_j t}C\cos[\omega_j\sqrt{1 - \zeta_j^2}\,t - \phi] \tag{3.29}$$

where C and ϕ are both real constants.

When one mode only of a passive system is excited and then allowed to decay freely, a typical coordinate has the decaying response (3.29). The logarithmic decrement (or log dec, for short) of mode j is defined by

$$\delta_j = \log_e\left[\frac{y_j(t)}{y_j(t + \tau_j)}\right] \tag{3.30}$$

where τ_j is the corresponding period for the free vibration of mode j given, from (3.29), by

$$\tau_j = \frac{2\pi}{\omega_j \sqrt{1 - \zeta_j^2}}.$$　(3.31)

This definition is illustrated in Fig. 3.4(*a*). For small damping, the decay rate is slow enough for individual cycles to be identified and we can talk of the amplitude of a single cycle. In that case, the log dec is just the logarithm to base e of the ratio of the amplitudes of successive cycles.

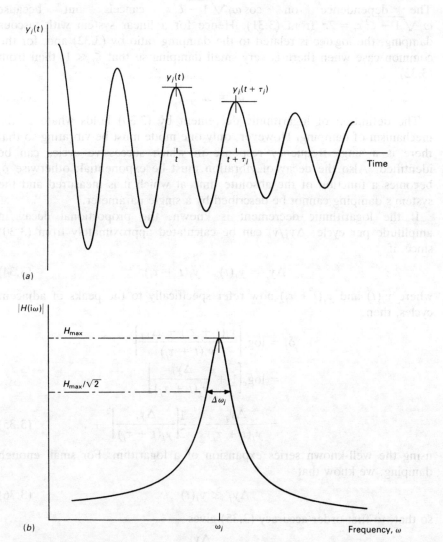

Fig. 3.4 Calculation of (*a*) the logarithmic decrement in free vibration, and (*b*) the bandwidth of steady-state forced vibration

On substituting for y_j from (3.29) into (3.30), we find that

$$\delta_j = \log_e[e^{-\zeta_j\omega_j t}/e^{-\zeta_j\omega_j(t+\tau_j)}]$$

$$= \log_e[e^{\zeta_j\omega_j\tau_j}]$$

$$= \zeta_j\omega_j\tau_j$$

$$= 2\pi\frac{\zeta_j}{\sqrt{1-\zeta_j^2}}. \tag{3.32}$$

The dependence on $\cos\omega_j\sqrt{1-\zeta_j^2}\,t$ cancels out because $\omega_j\sqrt{1-\zeta_j^2}\,\tau_j = 2\pi$ from (3.31). Hence for a linear system with viscous damping, the log dec is related to the damping ratio by (3.32) and, for the common case when there is very small damping so that $\zeta_j \ll 1$, then from (3.32)

$$\delta_j \simeq 2\pi\zeta_j. \tag{3.33}$$

The definition of logarithmic decrement by (3.30) holds whatever the mechanism of damping. However, only one mode must be vibrating so that there is a single-frequency response in which successive cycles can be identified. Also the decay of vibration must be exponential; otherwise δ_j becomes a function of the absolute time at which it is measured and the system's damping cannot be described by a single parameter.

If the logarithmic decrement is known, the proportional decay in amplitude per cycle, $\Delta y_j/y_j$ can be calculated approximately from (3.30) since, if

$$\Delta y_j = y_j(t) - y_j(t + \tau_j) \tag{3.34}$$

where $y_j(t)$ and $y_j(t + \tau_j)$ now refer specifically to the peaks of adjacent cycles, then

$$\delta_j = \log_e\left[\frac{y_j(t + \tau_j) + \Delta y_j}{y_j(t + \tau_j)}\right]$$

$$= \log_e\left[1 + \frac{\Delta y_j}{y_j(t + \tau_j)}\right]$$

$$= \frac{\Delta y_j}{y_j(t + \tau_j)} - \frac{1}{2}\left[\frac{\Delta y_j}{y_j(t + \tau_j)}\right]^2 + \cdots \tag{3.35}$$

using the well-known series expansion of a logarithm. For small enough damping, we know that

$$\Delta y_j \ll y_j(t) \tag{3.36}$$

so that, to first-order accuracy (3.35) gives

$$\delta_j \simeq \frac{\Delta y_j}{y_j} \tag{3.37}$$

where $\Delta y_j/y_j$ is the proportional loss of amplitude per cycle. The subscript

j refers to mode j, and different modes will have different decrements and different decay rates.

For a linear system an alternative definition of a mode's logarithmic decrement can be written directly in terms of the mode's eigenvalues λ_j, $\lambda_{j+1} = \lambda_j^*$. From (3.26)

$$\text{Re}\{\lambda_j\} = -\zeta_j\omega_j$$
$$\text{Im}\{\lambda_j\} = \pm\,\omega_j\sqrt{1 - \zeta_j^2} \tag{3.38}$$

so that (3.32) can be written in the alternative form

$$\delta_j = 2\pi\,\frac{-\text{Re}\{\lambda_j\}}{|\text{Im}\{\lambda_j\}|}. \tag{3.39}$$

For a linear system, this is a completely equivalent alternative definition of the log dec which is expressed directly in terms of the ratio of the real to the imaginary part of (either of) the mode's eigenvalues.

Bandwidth

Another measure of damping is the bandwidth of a steady-state harmonic response curve. Provided that the damping is small and that the natural frequencies are sufficiently separated, then, if the excitation frequency is close to a natural frequency, one mode only will dominate the response (we assume that the point of excitation does not happen to be close to a node for the mode in question). Then one term in the series expansion (2.57) predominates and

$$H(i\omega) \underset{\omega \simeq \omega_j}{\simeq} \frac{\beta_j(i\omega) + \alpha_j}{(i\omega)^2 + 2\zeta_j\omega_j(i\omega) + \omega_j^2}. \tag{3.40}$$

If $H(i\omega)$ represents a receptance (displacement output for force input) then we have shown earlier in this chapter that, for zero damping, β_j and ζ_j are both zero and (3.40) is one term in the expansion (3.1). Alternatively, if $H(i\omega)$ represents a mobility (velocity output for force input) then, for zero damping, α_j and ζ_j in (3.40) are both zero. We shall now investigate the dependence on damping of the bandwidth of the resonant peak defined by (3.40), on the assumptions that

$$\zeta \ll 1 \tag{3.41}$$

but that α_j, β_j and ω_j in (3.40) are not small.

We shall define the 'bandwidth' of a resonant peak as the frequency interval between opposite sides of the peak at a level $1/\sqrt{2}$ times the maximum value of the peak, as shown in Fig. 3.4(b). When the damping ratio ζ is very small, the maximum value occurs very close to $\omega = \omega_j$ so that, from (3.40),

$$H_{\max} \simeq \frac{|i\,\beta_j\omega_j + \alpha_j|}{|i\,2\zeta_j\omega_j^2|}. \tag{3.42}$$

To a close approximation, the resonant peak is symmetrical about the vertical axis $\omega = \omega_j$. If the maximum height of the peak is H_{max}, then $\Delta\omega_j$ is such that at frequency $\omega = \omega_j + \Delta\omega_j/2$ the response level has reduced to $H_{max}/\sqrt{2}$. Hence, from (3.40),

$$\frac{|\beta_j \, i(\omega_j + \Delta\omega_j/2) + \alpha_j|}{|-(\omega_j + \Delta\omega_j/2)^2 + i \, 2\zeta_j\omega_j(\omega_j + \Delta\omega_j/2) + \omega_j^2|} = \frac{H_{max}}{\sqrt{2}} \quad (3.43)$$

and, on eliminating H_{max} between (3.42) and (3.43),

$$\frac{|i \, \beta_j\omega_j(1 + \Delta\omega_j/2\omega_j) + \alpha_j|}{|-(1 + \Delta\omega_j/2\omega_j)^2 + i \, 2\zeta_j(1 + \Delta\omega_j/2\omega_j) + 1|} = \frac{|i \, \beta_j\omega_j + \alpha_j|}{2\sqrt{2} \, \zeta_j}. \quad (3.44)$$

We shall prove shortly that, if $\zeta \ll 1$, then the bandwidth $\Delta\omega_j$ is much less than the centre frequency ω_j, so that

$$\frac{\Delta\omega_j}{\omega_j} \ll 1. \quad (3.45)$$

If we assume this result, it is possible to simplify (3.44) by neglecting all terms which are of second order in the quantities ζ and $\Delta\omega/\omega_j$, and so obtain

$$\frac{2\sqrt{2}\zeta_j|i \, \beta_j\omega_j + \alpha_j|}{|-\Delta\omega_j/\omega_j + i \, 2\zeta_j|} \simeq |i \, \beta_j\omega_j + \alpha_j|. \quad (3.46)$$

On cancelling the common factor, this gives

$$2\sqrt{2}\zeta_j \simeq |-\Delta\omega_j/\omega_j + i \, 2\zeta_j| \quad (3.47)$$

or

$$8\zeta_j^2 \simeq (\Delta\omega_j/\omega_j)^2 + 4\zeta_j^2 \quad (3.48)$$

and so

$$\frac{\Delta\omega_j}{\omega_j} \simeq 2\zeta_j \quad (3.49)$$

thereby confirming the assumption that if (3.41) is true then so is (3.45) true. The proportional bandwidth of the resonant peak of a lightly damped mode of a linear system is therefore equal to twice the mode's damping ratio. This result is true both for a receptance peak and for a mobility peak as well as for the more general case when the numerator in (3.40) has both α_j and β_j terms which are not small.

The proportional bandwidth $\Delta\omega_j/\omega_j$ is an independent measure of the damping of any kind of resonant system, whatever the mechanism by which damping acts. In electrical engineering, its inverse $\omega_j/\Delta\omega_j$ is used to measure the peakiness of a resonance curve and is called the quality factor or *Q-factor* of the curve. For a linear system with small viscous damping, from (3.49),

$$Q_j = \frac{\omega_j}{\Delta \omega_j} \simeq \frac{1}{2\zeta_j}. \tag{3.50}$$

Energy dissipation

The rate of energy dissipation during vibration is another measure of the level of damping present. If there is force excitation $x(t)$ at a single point and if the velocity of this point in the direction of the force is $v(t)$, then the instantaneous power $\Pi(t)$ which enters the system is

$$\Pi(t) = x(t)v(t). \tag{3.51}$$

For steady-state harmonic excitation such that

$$x(t) = x_0 e^{i\omega t} \tag{3.52}$$

where x_0 is real, the corresponding velocity response can be written as

$$v(t) = V(i\omega) x_0 e^{i\omega t} \tag{3.53}$$

where $V(i\omega)$ is the direct mobility of the vibrating system for excitation at the point in question. We can now substitute from (3.52) and (3.53) into (3.51). Before doing so we must take account of the meaning implied by (3.52) and (3.53) that the l.h.s. is equal to the real part (or the imaginary part) of the r.h.s. in each case. We must identify which meaning we want, and in this case we shall choose (arbitrarily) 'the imaginary part'. Then (3.51) becomes

$$\begin{aligned}
\Pi(t) &= \text{Im}\{x_0 e^{i\omega t}\} \, \text{Im}\{V(i\omega) x_0 e^{i\omega t}\} \\
&= (x_0 \sin \omega t)(\text{Re}\{V(i\omega)\}x_0 \sin \omega t + \text{Im}\{V(i\omega)\}x_0 \cos \omega t) \\
&= x_0^2 \, \text{Re}\{V(i\omega)\} \sin^2 \omega t + x_0^2 \, \text{Im}\{V(i\omega)\} \sin \omega t \cos \omega t.
\end{aligned} \tag{3.54}$$

The mean power flow, when averaged over a full cycle, is given by

$$\langle \Pi(t) \rangle = \frac{1}{T} \int_0^T \Pi(t) \, dt \tag{3.55}$$

where $T = 2\pi/\omega$. On substituting for $\Pi(t)$ from (3.54) and evaluating the integral we find that

$$\langle \Pi(t) \rangle = \tfrac{1}{2} x_0^2 \, \text{Re}\{V(i\omega)\} \tag{3.56}$$

since

$$\frac{\omega}{2\pi} \int_0^{2\pi/\omega} \sin^2 \omega t \, dt = \frac{1}{2} \tag{3.57}$$

and

$$\frac{\omega}{2\pi} \int_0^{2\pi/\omega} \sin \omega t \cos \omega t \, dt = 0. \tag{3.58}$$

Consider this calculation for a lightly damped linear system when the excitation frequency ω is close to a natural frequency, for example ω_j. Then one mode dominates the response and we assume, from (2.57), that the receptance is given by

$$H(i\omega) \simeq \frac{\beta_j(i\omega) + \alpha_j}{(i\omega)^2 + 2\zeta_j\omega_j(i\omega) + \omega_j^2}. \tag{3.59}$$

The corresponding mobility is, from (2.9),

$$V(i\omega) = i\omega H(i\omega) \simeq \frac{\beta_j(i\omega)^2 + \alpha_j(i\omega)}{(i\omega)^2 + 2\zeta_j\omega_j(i\omega) + \omega_j^2}. \tag{3.60}$$

For small damping we have seen that ζ_j and β_j are small and so, near resonance,

$$V(i\omega) \underset{\omega=\omega_j}{\simeq} \frac{\alpha_j(i\omega_j)}{2\zeta_j\omega_j(i\omega_j)} = \frac{\alpha_j}{2\zeta_j\omega_j}. \tag{3.61}$$

Then, on substituting this result into (3.56), the average power flow into the mode is

$$\langle \Pi(t) \rangle \simeq \frac{x_0^2 \alpha_j}{4\zeta_j\omega_j} \tag{3.62}$$

where x_0 is the amplitude of the excitation (units of force), α_j is a real coefficient (units of mass^{-1}), ω_j is the natural frequency (units of time^{-1}) and ζ_j is the modal damping ratio (dimensionless). The modal damping ratio for a lightly damped mode of a linear system can be calculated from (3.62) if the average power flow into the system at resonance can be measured.

Modal energy

Continuing with a lightly-damped linear system whose direct receptance is given by (3.59) and whose corresponding direct mobility is given by (3.60), where ζ_j and β_j are assumed small and for which $\omega \simeq \omega_j$, the modal mass is $1/\alpha_j$ and the modal stiffness ω_j^2/α_j. This can be seen from the receptance equation (3.59), because the units of receptance are (displacement/force) = mass$^{-1} \times$ time^2 and for $\omega \gg \omega_j$, the modal response

$$H(i\omega) \underset{\omega\gg\omega_j}{\simeq} \frac{\alpha_j}{(i\omega)^2} \tag{3.63}$$

is the response of a mass of magnitude $1/\alpha_j$. Similarly for $\omega \ll \omega_j$, the modal response is

$$H(i\omega) \underset{\omega \ll \omega_j}{\simeq} \frac{\alpha_j}{\omega_j^2} \tag{3.64}$$

which is the response of a spring of stiffness ω_j^2/α_j.

The kinetic energy of a lightly-damped mode at resonance ω_j (when this mode alone dominates the response) will be defined as $T_j(t) \equiv T_j$ where

$$T_j(t) = \tfrac{1}{2}v^2(t)/\alpha_j \tag{3.65}$$

and its potential energy will be defined as $U_j(t) \equiv U_j$ where

$$U_j(t) = \tfrac{1}{2}y^2(t)\omega_j^2/\alpha_j. \tag{3.66}$$

From (3.53) and (3.60), for $\omega = \omega_j$ and recalling that we are using 'the imaginary part' definition for frequency-response functions,

$$T_j \simeq \frac{\alpha_j x_0^2}{8\zeta_j^2 \omega_j^2} \sin^2 \omega_j t. \tag{3.67}$$

From (3.59), subject to the same conditions,

$$U_j \simeq \frac{\alpha_j x_0^2}{8\zeta_j^2 \omega_j^2} \cos^2 \omega_j t \tag{3.68}$$

and hence the total modal energy at resonance is

$$T_j + U_j \simeq \frac{\alpha_j x_0^2}{8\zeta_j^2 \omega_j^2}. \tag{3.69}$$

We repeat that this result (3.69) is for small damping so that one mode dominates the response and, in the receptance (3.59), ζ_j and β_j are both small.

Proportional energy loss per cycle

For a lightly damped linear system which is excited harmonically at a frequency close to one of its resonant frequencies, we can now calculate the proportional energy loss per cycle. From (3.62), the energy supplied by the excitation during one period $T = 2\pi/\omega_j$ is

$$\langle \Pi(t) \rangle \frac{2\pi}{\omega_j} \simeq \frac{\pi x_0^2 \alpha_j}{2\zeta_j \omega_j^2}. \tag{3.70}$$

For steady-state vibration, this must equal the energy dissipated by damping per cycle, D_j. Hence

$$D_j \simeq \frac{\pi x_0^2 \alpha_j}{2\zeta_j \omega_j^2} \tag{3.71}$$

and the ratio

$$\frac{\text{energy dissipated per cycle by mode } j}{\text{total energy of vibration in mode } j} = \frac{D_j}{T_j + U_j} \simeq 4\pi\zeta_j \tag{3.72}$$

after substituting from (3.69) and (3.71). The proportional energy loss per cycle at resonance is therefore given by 4π times the damping ratio. For steady forced vibration, the energy lost is replaced by the energy received from the excitation. For free vibration (3.72) is still approximately true, subject to the same assumption that one lightly damped resonant mode dominates the response. Provided that $\zeta_j \ll 1$, the change in amplitude per cycle is small and so (3.69) and (3.71) remain approximately true.

The damping *loss factor*, η_j, is defined in terms of the proportional energy dissipation per cycle by

$$\eta_j = \frac{1}{2\pi} \frac{D_j}{T_j + U_j} \tag{3.73}$$

so that, from (3.72) for a linear system at resonance,

$$\eta_j \simeq 2\zeta_j \tag{3.74}$$

and the loss factor for mode j is twice the modal damping ratio.

Loss angle of a resilient element

Another measure of damping that is used widely is the angle of phase lag or *loss angle*, ψ, of an element which provides damping. Usually this is an element with both stiffness and damping properties, for example an elastomeric resilient material in the form of a block or slab. Each such element is considered separately. Suppose that a unidirectional resilient element provides stiffness and damping, and consider the receptance of the element for force excitation and displacement response when clamped at one end, as shown in Fig. 3.5(a). If, for an applied force

$$x(t) = e^{i\omega t} \tag{3.75}$$

the response is

$$y(t) = H(i\omega) e^{i\omega t} \tag{3.76}$$

where $H(i\omega)$ is the receptance, then the element's loss angle is defined by the equation

$$\tan \psi = -\frac{\text{Im}\{H(i\omega)\}}{\text{Re}\{H(i\omega)\}}. \tag{3.77}$$

The value of $\tan \psi$ is sometimes called the *structural damping factor*.

If the resilient element can be modelled by a linear spring and dashpot in parallel (see Fig. 3.5(b)) the equation of motion is

$$c \frac{dy}{dt} + ky = x \tag{3.78}$$

and the receptance $H(i\omega)$ is given by

$$H(i\omega) = \frac{1}{c(i\omega) + k} \tag{3.79}$$

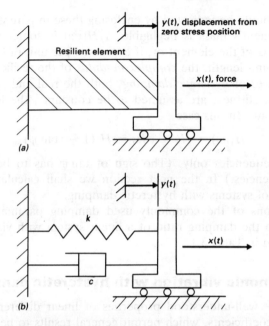

Fig. 3.5 (*a*) Resilient element with force input and displacement output, (*b*) simplified model of the resilient element

so that, in this case,

$$\tan \psi = \frac{c\omega}{k}. \tag{3.80}$$

When the spring and dashpot are part of a single-degree-of-freedom oscillator such as that shown in Fig. 1.1, then, from (1.24) and (1.25), an alternative version of (3.80) is

$$\tan \psi = \frac{c}{m} \frac{m}{k} \omega = 2\zeta \frac{\omega}{\omega_N} \tag{3.81}$$

where ω_N is the natural frequency of the oscillator and ζ is its damping ratio.

In many practical cases, the behaviour of resilient elements cannot be described by linear differential equations with constant coefficients. However, under harmonic force excitation with constant amplitude and frequency, the corresponding displacement response is often very nearly harmonic at the same frequency so that (3.76) is still satisfied to a close approximation. But, in general, the receptance now depends, not only on frequency, but also on the amplitude of the excitation, on the magnitude of the static load which may be superimposed on the dynamically fluctuating excitation, and on the temperature and age of the resilient element. For convenience we shall still write $H(i\omega)$ for the receptance of such an element although, strictly, the receptance's dependence on parameters other than ω should be indicated by enclosing these in parentheses with $i\omega$. When the element's mass is negligible, $1/H(i\omega)$ is sometimes called the *complex stiffness* of the element or, if expressed per unit of loaded area for an element of unit length, the *complex modulus* of the resilient element.

In special cases of *hysteretic damping*, both the real and imaginary parts of the complex stiffness are assumed to be constants; the loss angle ψ is then also constant. In this case

$$H(i\omega) = H_r + i\,H_i = H_r(1 - i\tan\psi) \tag{3.82}$$

for positive frequencies only. (The sign of $\tan\psi$ has to be reversed for negative frequencies.) In the next section we shall calculate the steady-state response of systems with hysteretic damping.

The definitions of the commonly used damping parameters and their relationships to the damping ratio of a linear system with viscous damping are summarized in Table 3.1.

Forced harmonic vibration with hysteretic damping

Because of the well-understood properties of linear differential equations with constant coefficients, which permit general results to be obtained, the theory of multiple-degree-of-freedom vibrating systems is based on the analysis of equations of this special form. All the damping forces are assumed to be proportional to velocity.

In many practical problems of mechanical and structural vibration, the linear viscous damping assumption is unlikely to be accurate. When damping arises from internal friction in resilient materials, frictional forces are often found to be independent or nearly independent of velocity. Then the hysteretic damping model (3.82) gives a better description of the harmonic behaviour of individual damping elements than can be obtained by using a linear viscous model.

This behaviour can be represented for an N-degree-of-freedom system by replacing each modal stiffness by a corresponding complex stiffness according to (3.82). Then the general modal expansion formula (3.1) has its natural frequency term ω_k^2 replaced by $\omega_k^2(1 + i\tan\psi_k)$, where ψ_k is the loss angle of the kth mode, and (3.1) becomes

$$H(i\omega) = \sum_{k=1}^{N} \frac{\alpha_k}{(i\omega)^2 + \omega_k^2(1 + i\tan\psi_k)}. \tag{3.83}$$

This formula may be compared with the general expansion (2.57) for a linear system with viscous damping.

For a single degree of freedom, (3.83) gives

$$H(i\omega) = \frac{\dfrac{\alpha}{\omega_N^2}}{\left(1 - \dfrac{\omega^2}{\omega_N^2}\right) + i\tan\psi} \tag{3.84}$$

where ω_N is the natural frequency and $\tan\psi$ is the structural damping factor. Hence the magnitude of the receptance, $|H(\mathrm{i}\omega)|$, is given by

$$|H(\mathrm{i}\omega)| = \frac{\dfrac{\alpha}{\omega_N^2}}{\left[\left(1 - \dfrac{\omega^2}{\omega_N^2}\right)^2 + \tan^2\psi\right]^{1/2}} \tag{3.85}$$

and the angle θ by which the receptance (displacement) output lags its (force) input is given by

$$\tan\theta = \frac{\tan\psi}{\left(1 - \dfrac{\omega^2}{\omega_N^2}\right)}. \tag{3.86}$$

The equations (3.85) and (3.86) correspond to (1.27) and (1.28) for a linear, single-degree-of-freedom system with viscous damping. In Fig. 3.6(a), $|H(\mathrm{i}\omega)|$ is plotted against ω/ω_N and, in Fig. 3.6(b), the phase angle θ is plotted against ω/ω_N, with separate curves shown for $\tan\psi = 0.1, 0.2, 0.4, 1, 2$ and 10 in each case. These graphs correspond to Figs 1.2(a) and (b) for the linear, viscous case. For hysteretic damping we see from Fig. 3.6(a) that the maximum amplitude of the receptance occurs exactly at $\omega = \omega_N$ rather than at a frequency slightly less than ω_N as for the viscous damping case. Also, from Fig. 3.6(b), the phase lag is not zero for zero frequency when there is hysteretic damping, but for both hysteretic and viscous damping the phase lag is 90 degrees at $\omega = \omega_N$ and approaches 180 degrees as $\omega \to \infty$.

The receptance (3.84) can be thought of as the response of a system whose displacement output $y(t)$ is related to its harmonic force input $x(t) = x_0 \mathrm{e}^{\mathrm{i}\omega t}$ by the equation

$$m\ddot{y} + \frac{k\tan\psi}{\omega}\,\dot{y} + ky = x_0 \mathrm{e}^{\mathrm{i}\omega t}, \quad \omega > 0; \tag{3.87}$$

the equivalent viscous damping coefficient c_{eq} is given by

$$c_{eq} = \frac{k\tan\psi}{\omega} \tag{3.88}$$

and is a function of frequency. Therefore, for hysteretic damping, $H(\mathrm{i}\omega)$ is the solution for steady-state harmonic vibration of a system for which the magnitude of its equivalent viscous damping coefficient depends on the excitation frequency. When this frequency changes, the magnitude of the equivalent damping coefficient changes. Therefore Figs 3.6(a) and (b) do not represent the response of a system described by a single differential equation with constant coefficients. Instead, they give the loci of the responses of a continuous series of linear systems, with the damping parameter changing with frequency. At each different frequency, the corresponding system is represented by a different linear differential equation with constant coefficients.

Table 3.1 Comparison of alternative measures of damping

Parameter	Definition	Relation to the damping ratio of a linear mode with viscous damping	Comments
Damping ratio	$\zeta_j = \dfrac{c_j}{c_{j\text{crit}}}$	ζ_j	Applies for mode j of a linear system with viscous damping. When $\zeta_j = 1$, the decay of mode j is just non-oscillatory.
Logarithmic decrement	$\delta_j = \log_e\left[\dfrac{y_j(t)}{y_j(t+\tau_j)}\right]$ (3.30) Also $\delta_j \simeq \dfrac{\Delta y_j}{y_j}$ (3.37) and $\delta_j \simeq 2\pi\dfrac{-\mathrm{Re}(\lambda_j)}{|\mathrm{Im}(\lambda_j)|}$ (3.39)	$\delta_j \simeq 2\pi\zeta_j$ (3.33) ($\zeta_j \ll 1$)	Applies for decaying free vibration, see Fig. 3.4(a). Only mode j is assumed to be excited. Its period of decaying oscillation is τ_j; $\Delta y_j/y_j$ is the proportional loss of amplitude per cycle; λ_j is either of the mode's eigenvalues.
Proportional bandwidth of resonance	$\dfrac{\Delta\omega_j}{\omega_j}$	$\dfrac{\Delta\omega_j}{\omega_j} \simeq 2\zeta_j$ (3.49) ($\zeta_j \ll 1$)	Applies for steady-state forced vibration of mode j, see Fig. 3.4(b). $\Delta\omega_j$ is the bandwidth of the resonance of ω_j measured at $1/\sqrt{2}$ of its peak.
Quality factor	$Q_j = \dfrac{\omega_j}{\Delta\omega_j}$	$Q_j \simeq \dfrac{1}{2\zeta_j}$ (3.50) ($\zeta_j \ll 1$)	Also applies for steady-state forced vibration; defined as the inverse of the proportional bandwidth of resonance.

Table 3.1 (cont.)

Parameter	Definition	Relation to the damping ratio of a linear mode with viscous damping	Comments
Proportional energy loss per cycle at resonance	$\dfrac{D_j}{T_j + U_j}$	$\dfrac{D_j}{T_j + U_j} \simeq 4\pi \zeta_j$ $\ (\zeta_j \ll 1)$ (3.72)	For mode j, D_j = energy dissipated by damping per cycle, T_j = modal kinetic energy, U_j = modal potential energy. Steady-state forced vibration at the resonant frequency ω_j is assumed.
Loss factor	$\eta_j = \dfrac{1}{2\pi}\left(\dfrac{D_j}{T_j + U_j}\right)$ (3.73)	At resonance, $\omega = \omega_j$, $\eta_j \simeq 2\zeta_j$ $\ (\zeta_j \ll 1)$ (3.74)	Defined as the energy loss per radian divided by the total vibrational energy.
Loss angle	ψ	$\tan\psi = 2\zeta\,\dfrac{\omega}{\omega_N}$ (3.81)	Applies for the steady-state forced vibration of a resilient element (see, for example, Fig. 3.5). The loss angle ψ is the angle by which the displacement of the resilient element lags behind the harmonic force applied to the element.
Structural damping factor	$\tan\psi = -\dfrac{\mathrm{Im}\{H(i\omega)\}}{\mathrm{Re}\{H(i\omega)\}}$		

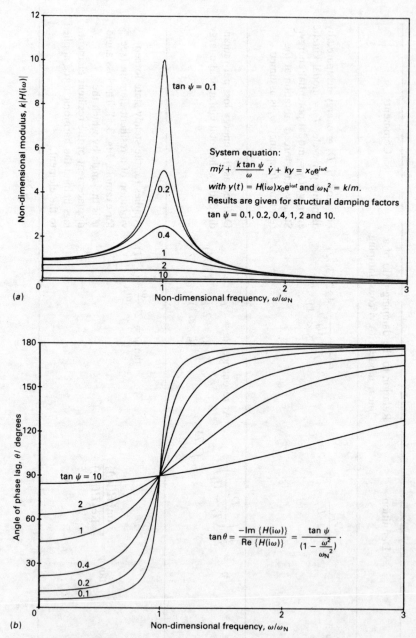

System equation:

$$m\ddot{y} + \frac{k\tan\psi}{\omega}\,\dot{y} + ky = x_0 e^{i\omega t}$$

with $y(t) = H(i\omega)x_0 e^{i\omega t}$ and $\omega_N{}^2 = k/m$.
Results are given for structural damping factors
$\tan\psi = 0.1, 0.2, 0.4, 1, 2$ and 10.

$$\tan\theta = \frac{-\mathrm{Im}\,\{H(i\omega)\}}{\mathrm{Re}\,\{H(i\omega)\}} = \frac{\tan\psi}{(1 - \frac{\omega^2}{\omega_N{}^2})}.$$

Fig. 3.6 (*a*) Magnitude of the receptance of a single-degree-of-freedom system with hysteretic damping. (*b*) Angle of phase lag of the same receptance

In the section on damping in Chapter 11 we shall explore the properties of hysteretic damping in greater detail.

Numerical example

Consider a six-degree-of-freedom system with hysteretic damping. If the receptance of this system is defined by (3.83) where the six natural frequencies ω_k, $k = 1$ to 6, are

$$\omega_1 = 2 \text{ rad/s}, \qquad \omega_2 = 5 \text{ rad/s}, \qquad \omega_3 = 10 \text{ rad/s}$$

$$\omega_4 = 20 \text{ rad/s}, \qquad \omega_5 = 40 \text{ rad/s}, \qquad \omega_6 = 60 \text{ rad/s}$$

(3.89)

the structural damping factors $\tan \psi_k$, $k = 1$ to 6, are all the same so that

$$\tan \psi_k = 0.05 \text{ for all } k \tag{3.90}$$

and the coefficients of the partial fractions α_k, $k = 1$ to 6, are all the same so that

$$\alpha_k = 1 \text{ for all } k \tag{3.91}$$

then

$$H(i\omega) = \frac{1}{(4 - \omega^2) + i\,0.2} + \frac{1}{(25 - \omega^2) + i\,1.25} + \frac{1}{(100 - \omega^2) + i\,5} +$$

$$+ \frac{1}{(400 - \omega^2) + i\,20} + \frac{1}{(1600 - \omega^2) + i\,80} +$$

$$+ \frac{1}{(3600 - \omega^2) + i\,180}. \tag{3.92}$$

For this choice of the α_k's and for no damping, there will be five zero frequencies, spaced between the six natural frequencies. This is typical of the direct receptance of a system of masses and springs (rather than of a cross-receptance when there will be less than five zero frequencies; see, for example, equations (ix) and (x) of the example on p. 61).

In Fig. 3.7(a), the magnitude of $H(i\omega)$ calculated from (3.92) is plotted against ω for a frequency range 1 to 100 rad/s. In order to make the graph non-dimensional, $H(i\omega)$ is divided by

$$\sum_{k=1}^{6} \alpha_k / \omega_k^2$$

before it is plotted. The case for zero damping is plotted also, together with the skeletal backbone (whose position is located as described earlier in this chapter). In Fig. 3.7(b) the magnitude of the corresponding mobility,

$$|i\omega H(i\omega)| / \left(\sum_{k=1}^{6} \alpha_k / \omega_k^2 \right)$$

is plotted to the same scales, again with the case of zero damping and the graph's skeleton shown for comparison. The dynamic range of the mobility graph covers about 51 dB (-20 to 31 dB), whereas the corresponding range of the receptance graph covers about 77 dB (− 53 to 24 dB), which is one reason why mobility is often a more suitable experimental parameter than is receptance.

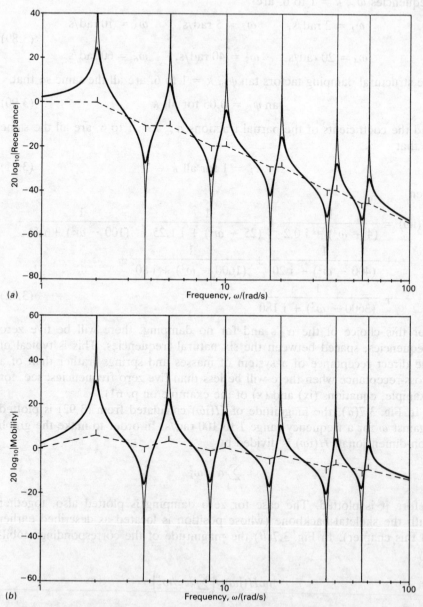

Fig. 3.7 (*a*) Magnitude of the direct receptance of a typical six-degree-of-freedom system with hysteretic damping with tan $\psi = 0.05$ for all modes. The asymptotes for zero damping, and the graph's 'skeleton', are shown for comparison. (*b*) Magnitude of the direct mobility for the same system as in Fig. 3.7(*a*)

Figure 3.8 is a polar graph of the same mobility as in Fig. 3.7(*b*). At $\omega = 0$, the graph starts at the origin of coordinates and then travels in a sequence of nearly circular paths, negotiating a full circle for each resonant peak. Only the frequency range 0 to 25 rad/s is covered in this figure so that there are only four circles for the first four resonant peaks at $\omega = 2$, 5, 10 and 20 rad/s. The positions of these four frequencies are marked on the graph and it can be seen that each falls very close to the real axis. For a single-mode system, the natural frequency falls exactly on the real axis (Problem 3.1); for a multi-mode system, the contributions to the response by adjacent modes make the mobility's phase angle at resonance slightly different from zero.

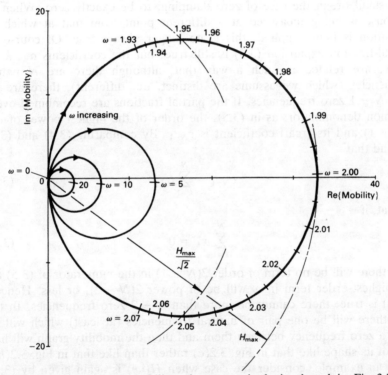

Fig. 3.8 Polar graph of the mobility whose magnitude is plotted in Fig. 3.7(*b*), drawn for the frequency range 0 to 25 rad/s only (to include the first four natural frequencies). A construction is shown to estimate the damping of the first mode by using the method of Fig. 3.4(*b*)

The damping of each mode can be extracted from the appropriate circle by measuring its bandwidth at the 'half-power' points, as defined in Fig. 3.4(*b*). This is illustrated on Fig. 3.8 for the lowest-frequency mode. With the origin of the graph as centre, a circular arc is drawn to just touch the polar graph. The radius of this circle is H_{max}, where H now stands for mobility. Two circular arcs of radius $H_{max}/\sqrt{2}$ are then drawn to intersect the polar graph and the frequencies of the intersection points are read off. In Fig. 3.8 they are $\omega = 1.95$ and 2.05 rad/s, approximately. Hence the bandwidth $\Delta\omega$ (see Fig. 3.4(b)) is 0.1 rad/s and so, from (3.49), $2\zeta_1 = 0.1/2$, giving an equivalent modal damping ratio of 0.025. From (3.81), at resonance $\tan\psi = 2\zeta$, giving $\tan\psi_1 = 0.05$, as we know it to be.

The behaviour characterized by Figs 3.7 and 3.8 is typical of the direct receptance and mobility of a multiple-degree-of-freedom system. When the displacement (or velocity) response is measured at the point at which the force excitation is applied, there are zero frequencies between every pair of adjacent natural frequencies. These are the frequencies at which the system acts as a perfect vibration absorber and forces the response to be very small or, in the case of zero damping, to be exactly zero. When the response is being measured at a different point from that at which the excitation is being applied, this is no longer always true. Of course the partial-fraction expansion (3.3) is still true, but the coefficients α_k, $k = 1$ to N, are related in such a way that, although there are N natural frequencies (which we assume are distinct, i.e. different), there are less than $N - 1$ zero frequencies. If the partial fractions are recombined over a common denominator, as in (3.5), the order of the highest power of ω is $2(N - 1)$ and its (real) coefficient is c_{N-1}. By comparing (3.4) and (3.5), we find that

$$c_{N-1} = \sum_{k=1}^{N} \alpha_k \tag{3.93}$$

so that, if

$$\sum_{k=1}^{N} \alpha_k = 0 \tag{3.94}$$

then there will be no term of order $2(N - 1)$ in the numerator of (3.5) and the highest-order term in ω will be of power $2(N - 2)$, or less. Hence if (3.94) is true, there cannot be more than $N - 2$ zero frequencies. In that case there will be one pair of natural frequencies (at least) which will not have a zero frequency between them and then the mobility graph will have part of its shape like that in Fig. 3.2(c) rather than like that in Fig. 3.2(b).

As an example, consider the case when $H(i\omega)$ is again given by (3.83) with $N = 6$, and with the natural frequencies ω_k specified by (3.89) and the damping angles ψ_k specified by (3.90). However, instead of choosing the coefficients α_k according to (3.91), we put instead

$$\alpha_1 = \alpha_2 = 2$$
$$\alpha_3 = \alpha_4 = \alpha_5 = \alpha_6 = -1. \tag{3.95}$$

In this case (3.94) is satisfied so that there will not be more than four zero frequencies. Instead of (3.92), we now have

$$H(i\omega) = \frac{2}{(4 - \omega^2) + i\,0.2} + \frac{2}{(25 - \omega^2) + i\,1.25} - \frac{1}{(100 - \omega^2) + i\,5} -$$

$$- \frac{1}{(400 - \omega^2) + i\,20} - \frac{1}{(1600 - \omega^2) + i\,80} -$$

$$- \frac{1}{(3600 - \omega^2) + i\,180}. \tag{3.96}$$

This represents a typical cross-receptance of a lightly damped mechanical system with six degrees of freedom. The magnitude of the corresponding cross-mobility is $|i\omega H(i\omega)|$ and, after normalizing by dividing by

$$\sum_{k=1}^{6} \alpha_k / \omega_k^2,$$

this mobility function is plotted against ω in Fig. 3.9 which may be compared with Fig. 3.7(b). Because there is no zero frequency between the second and third natural frequencies, the skeleton does not receive a change of slope of $+40$ dB/decade here. As a result, all the segments of the skeleton for frequencies above 10 rad/s have a slope that is -40 dB/decade steeper than in Fig. 3.7(a). Because one zero frequency has been omitted, the graph's asymptote for large ω has a slope of

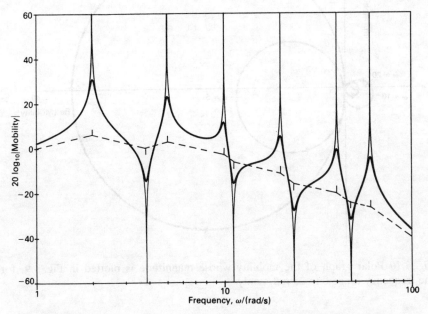

Fig. 3.9 Magnitude of a typical cross-mobility for a six-degree-of-freedom system with hysteretic damping with $\tan\psi = 0.05$ for all modes. The asymptotes for zero damping and the graph's 'skeleton' are shown for comparison

88   *General response properties*

−60 dB/decade (18 dB/octave) instead of −20 dB/decade (6 dB/octave) in Fig. 3.7(*b*). If *n* zero frequencies had been omitted, the final slope would have been −(20 + 40*n*) dB/decade which is −(6 + 12*n*) dB/decade (approx.).

In Fig. 3.10, the same cross-mobility,

$$i\omega H(i\omega)\bigg/\bigg(\sum_{k=1}^{6}\alpha_k/\omega_k^2\bigg)$$

where $H(i\omega)$ is given by (3.96), is plotted in polar form for comparison with Fig. 3.8. The frequency range is again limited to between 0 and 25 rad/s so as to include the first four resonant peaks only. The circles for resonances at $\omega = 2$ and $\omega = 5$ rad/s are positioned as before; they are of different radius because of the different α_k and the different scaling factor

$$\sum_{k=1}^{6}\alpha_k/\omega_k^2.$$

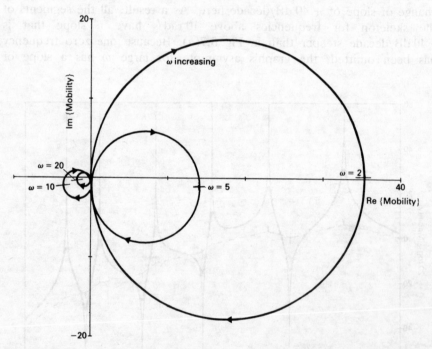

Fig. 3.10 Polar graph of the mobility whose magnitude is plotted in Fig. 3.9, for the frequency range 0 to 25 rad/s only

The circles for the resonances at $\omega = 10$ and $\omega = 20$ rad/s are located on the opposite side of the imaginary axis because of the minus signs in $\alpha_3 = -1$ and $\alpha_4 = -1$ in (3.96). As the circle for the second resonance is completed when ω increases from 5 to 10 rad/s, the graph does not return close to its origin, but reverses in direction to follow the circle for the third resonance. On close examination of Fig. 3.10, it will be seen that this is a significant difference in the shape of the graph when compared with the shape of its transitions from one circle to the next between the other resonances. This different behaviour is the consequence of there being no zero frequency between the natural frequencies $\omega_2 = 5$ rad/s and $\omega_3 = 10$ rad/s (see Fig. 3.9). Further consideration of the properties of cross-receptance and cross-mobility functions is the subject of Problem 3.2.

Time for resonant oscillations to build up

It is often interesting to know how rapidly a resonant oscillation can build up. Consider the excitation of a single mode represented by

$$m\ddot{y} + c\dot{y} + ky = x \tag{3.97}$$

or, in terms of its undamped natural frequency ω_N and damping ratio ζ, by

$$\ddot{y} + 2\zeta\omega_N\dot{y} + \omega_N^2 y = \frac{x}{m}. \tag{3.98}$$

Let the excitation be

$$x \equiv x(t) = x_0 \cos \omega_N t, \ t \geqslant 0 \tag{3.99}$$

and the initial conditions be

$$y = \dot{y} = 0 \text{ at } t = 0. \tag{3.100}$$

The excitation can be thought of as being switched on to an initially dormant mode at $t = 0$. How rapidly does the oscillation build up?

The solution to (3.98) subject to excitation (3.99) and initial conditions (3.100) can be obtained from the general result (1.4) after first working out $\phi_1(t)$ and $\phi_2(t)$ from (1.5) and (1.6). However, the algebra is quite lengthy (Problem 3.3) and a quicker solution can be obtained as follows. From the theory of linear differential equations, the general solution of (3.98) consists of two parts: any particular solution and the complementary solution, which is the solution (with two arbitrary constants) of the homogeneous equation

$$\ddot{y} + 2\zeta\omega_N\dot{y} + \omega_N^2 y = 0. \tag{3.101}$$

We know that eventually there will be a steady resonant oscillation at the frequency of excitation, which in this case is ω_N. By substituting the trial solution

$$y_1(t) = Y \sin \omega_N t \tag{3.102}$$

it is easy to see that this must be

$$y_1(t) = \frac{1}{2\zeta\omega_N^2}\left(\frac{x_0}{m}\right)\sin\omega_N t. \tag{3.103}$$

The complete solution must become asymptotic to this particular solution when $t \to \infty$. The complementary solution is

$$y_2(t) = C_1 e^{\lambda_1 t} + C_2 e^{\lambda_2 t} \tag{3.104}$$

where λ_1 and λ_2 are the eigenvalues of (3.101), which are

$$\lambda_1, \lambda_2 = -\zeta\omega_N \pm i\omega_N\sqrt{1-\zeta^2} \tag{3.105}$$

and so

$$y_2(t) = e^{-\zeta\omega_N t}\left(C_1 e^{i\omega_N\sqrt{(1-\zeta^2)}t} + C_2 e^{-i\omega_N\sqrt{(1-\zeta^2)}t}\right) \tag{3.106}$$

or, since $y_2(t)$ must be real,

$$y_2(t) = e^{-\zeta\omega_N t}\left[A\cos\omega_N\sqrt{1-\zeta^2}t + B\sin\omega_N\sqrt{1-\zeta^2}t\right] \tag{3.107}$$

where

$$A = C_1 + C_2 \text{ and } B = i(C_1 - C_2). \tag{3.108}$$

The complete solution of (3.98) with (3.99) is therefore

$$y(t) = y_1(t) + y_2(t) = \frac{1}{2\zeta\omega_N^2}\left(\frac{x_0}{m}\right)\sin\omega_N t +$$

$$+ e^{-\zeta\omega_N t}[A\cos\omega_N\sqrt{1-\zeta^2}\,t + B\sin\omega_N\sqrt{1-\zeta^2}t]. \tag{3.109}$$

To satisfy the initial conditions (3.100), we find that

$$A = 0 \text{ and } B = -\frac{1}{2\zeta\omega_N^2\sqrt{1-\zeta^2}}\left(\frac{x_0}{m}\right). \tag{3.110}$$

Defining y_0 as the static deflection that would be caused by force x_0, so that

$$y_0 = \frac{x_0}{k} = \frac{x_0}{m}\left(\frac{1}{\omega_N^2}\right) \tag{3.111}$$

we can write the complete solution in the final form

$$\frac{y(t)}{y_0} = \frac{1}{2\zeta}\left[\sin\omega_N t - \frac{e^{-\zeta\omega_N t}}{\sqrt{1-\zeta^2}}\sin\omega_N\sqrt{1-\zeta^2}t\right]. \tag{3.112}$$

This solution describes how the resonant oscillation builds up after harmonic excitation $x_0\cos\omega_N t$ is applied at $t = 0$ to an initially dormant system. The reference deflection y_0 is defined in terms of x_0 by equation (3.111).

Figure 3.11 shows a typical response for $\zeta = 0.1$, plotted below its excitation. The response has reached nearly its full amplitude in only about five cycles.

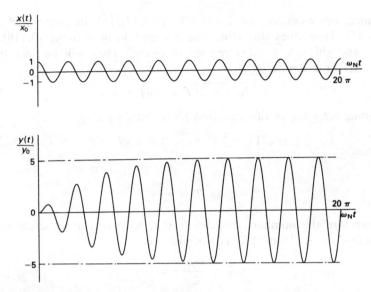

Fig. 3.11 Build-up of the oscillations $y(t)$ of a mode whose damping ratio is $\zeta = 0.1$ when excitation $x(t)$ at its resonant frequency is switched on at $t = 0$

We can investigate how this result depends on damping by considering equation (3.112). Since only a few cycles elapse before the term in $\sin \omega_N \sqrt{1 - \zeta^2} t$ has disappeared, $\sin \omega_N t$ and $\sin \omega_N \sqrt{1 - \zeta^2} t$ can be considered to remain approximately in phase over the time-span of interest. Because they subtract in equation (3.112), the response will have built up to 95% of its final amplitude when

$$\frac{e^{-\zeta_N t}}{\sqrt{1 - \zeta^2}} = 0.05 \qquad (3.113)$$

which is when

$$\omega_N t = \frac{1}{\zeta} \ln\left[\frac{20}{\sqrt{1 - \zeta^2}}\right]. \qquad (3.114)$$

The number of cycles completed is

$$n = \frac{\omega_N t}{2\pi} \qquad (3.115)$$

so that, from (3.114),

$$n = \frac{1}{2\pi\zeta} \ln\left[\frac{20}{\sqrt{1 - \zeta^2}}\right]. \qquad (3.116)$$

This expression is plotted in Fig. 3.12.

When the damping is small, $\zeta < 0.01$, a large number of cycles are passed through before the amplitude reaches 95% of its maximum at resonance. For example, for $\zeta = 0.001$, from (3.116) the number of cycles is $n = 477$. How does this affect the assumption in deriving (3.116), that $\sin \omega_N t$ and $\sin \omega_N \sqrt{1 - \zeta^2} t$ remain in phase? They will be 180° out of phase after time T where

$$\omega_N \sqrt{1 - \zeta^2} T = \omega_N T - \pi. \tag{3.117}$$

Expanding the l.h.s. of this equation gives, for ζ small,

$$\omega_N T (1 - \tfrac{1}{2} \zeta^2 + \ldots) = \omega_N T - \pi \tag{3.118}$$

so that

$$\omega_N T = \frac{2\pi}{\zeta^2} \tag{3.119}$$

and therefore the number of cycles N that have to elapse before $\sin \omega_N t$ and $\sin \omega_N \sqrt{1 - \zeta^2} t$ are 180° out of phase is

$$N = \frac{\omega_N T}{2\pi} = \frac{1}{\zeta^2}. \tag{3.120}$$

For $\zeta = 0.001$, this is $N = 10^6$. Our assumption that $\sin \omega_N t$ and $\sin \omega_N \sqrt{1 - \zeta^2} t$ remain in phase until the decaying exponential function in (3.112) has made the amplitude of the term in $\sin \omega_N \sqrt{1 - \zeta^2} t$ only 5% of the amplitude of the term in $\sin \omega_N t$ requires the two harmonic functions to remain in phase for $n = 477$ cycles. Since $477 \ll 10^6$, this remains a reasonable assumption.

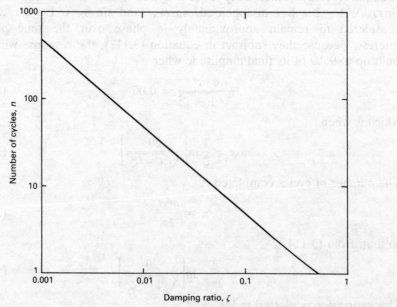

Fig. 3.12 Number of cycles to reach 95% of final resonant amplitude for an initially dormant mode with damping ratio ζ (calculated from equation (3.116))

In the limit when $\zeta = 0$, n becomes infinite. On taking the limit of equation (3.112) when $\zeta \to 0$ (Problem 3.4), we find that, for no damping,

$$\frac{y(t)}{y_0} = \frac{\omega_N t}{2} \sin \omega_N t \tag{3.121}$$

so that the oscillation then continues to grow indefinitely, with its amplitude increasing linearly with time.

Acceleration through resonance

There are many practical cases where the frequency of excitation changes, for example as a machine runs up to speed, and the excitation frequency passes through resonance but does not remain there. This raises the question: what proportion of the full resonant amplitude is reached when the frequency of excitation passes through resonance?

Consider the response of equation (3.98), assumed to be initially dormant at $t = 0$ so that the initial conditions are as in (3.100), when, instead of (3.99), the excitation is

$$x \equiv x(t) = x_0 \cos(\tfrac{1}{2}\,\alpha t^2), \; t \geqslant 0. \tag{3.122}$$

This will be the case if there is constant angular acceleration α because the angular velocity after time t will be

$$\omega = \alpha t \tag{3.123}$$

and the total angular rotation will be

$$\theta = \tfrac{1}{2}\omega t = \tfrac{1}{2}\alpha t^2. \tag{3.124}$$

The equation of motion is then

$$\ddot{y} + 2\zeta\omega_N\dot{y} + \omega_N^2 y = \frac{x_0}{m} \cos(\tfrac{1}{2}\,\alpha t^2), \; t \geqslant 0 \tag{3.125}$$

subject to

$$y = \dot{y} = 0 \text{ at } t = 0. \tag{3.126}$$

From Chapter 1, the general solution is given from (1.13), (1.5), (1.6) and (1.37) by

$$y(t) = \frac{1}{(\lambda_1 - \lambda_2)} [\phi_1(t) - \phi_1(0)] \, e^{\lambda_1 t}$$

$$+ \frac{1}{(\lambda_2 - \lambda_1)} [\phi_2(t) - \phi_2(0)] \, e^{\lambda_2 t} \tag{3.127}$$

where

$$\lambda_1, \lambda_2 = -\zeta\omega_N \pm i\,\omega_N\sqrt{1 - \zeta^2} \tag{3.128}$$

and

$$\phi_1(t) = \int e^{-\lambda_1 t} \frac{x_0}{m} \cos(\tfrac{1}{2} \alpha t^2) \, dt \qquad (3.129)$$

$$\phi_2(t) = \int e^{-\lambda_2 t} \frac{x_0}{m} \cos(\tfrac{1}{2} \alpha t^2) \, dt.$$

On substituting for $\phi_1(t)$ and $\phi_2(t)$ from (3.129) into (3.127)

$$\underset{t>0}{y(t)} = \frac{x_0}{m} \frac{1}{(\lambda_1 - \lambda_2)} e^{\lambda_1 t} \int_0^t e^{-\lambda_1 \tau} \cos(\tfrac{1}{2} \alpha \tau^2) \, d\tau +$$

$$+ \frac{x_0}{m} \frac{1}{(\lambda_2 - \lambda_1)} e^{\lambda_2 t} \int_0^t e^{-\lambda_2 \tau} \cos(\tfrac{1}{2} \alpha \tau^2) \, d\tau. \qquad (3.130)$$

After substituting the complex eigenvalues from (3.128), (3.130) contains four integrals of the type

$$\int_0^t e^{-\zeta \omega_N \tau} \cos[\omega_N \sqrt{1 - \zeta^2} \tau] \cos(\tfrac{1}{2} \alpha \tau^2) \, d\tau \qquad (3.131)$$

which can only be integrated numerically. A general analytical solution is not possible. Instead, it is necessary to resort to approximate methods and this was first done successfully by F. M. Lewis in 1932 [54]. At that time it was not possible to integrate numerically with sufficient accuracy to obtain the solution of (3.130) directly, but this can now be done quite easily. The numerical techniques will be described in Chapter 10 and we shall go into the details there, but the result of a typical calculation is shown in Fig. 3.13. Figure 3.13(*b*) shows the response of (3.125) when accelerated through resonance for the case when the damping ratio $\zeta = 0.05$. The excitation is shown in Fig. 3.13(*a*). To shorten the computation, the calculation begins at $t = 100/\omega_N$, when the excitation is assumed to be suddenly switched on to an initially dormant system. Therefore, the initial conditions are taken to be

$$y = \dot{y} = 0 \text{ at } t = 100/\omega_N \qquad (3.132)$$

instead of at $t = 0$. The acceleration is chosen to be $\alpha = 0.005 \, \omega_N^2$, so that

$$\omega = \alpha t = 0.5 \omega_N \text{ at } t = 100/\omega_N \qquad (3.133)$$

and

$$\omega = 1.5 \omega_N \text{ at } t = 300/\omega_N. \qquad (3.134)$$

The instantaneous frequency αt begins at half the resonant frequency ω_N at the left-hand edge of the graph and accelerates through resonance to 1.5 times the resonant frequency at the right-hand edge.

In Fig. 3.14, the response of Fig. 3.13 is compared with the envelope of amplitude versus frequency for steady-state harmonic vibration. The upper envelope (the upper broken line) is the curve in Fig. 1.2(*a*) for $\zeta = 0.05$. The lower envelope is the reflection of this curve about the horizontal axis. The frequency scale is obtained from equation (3.123) with $\alpha = 0.005 \, \omega_N^2$.

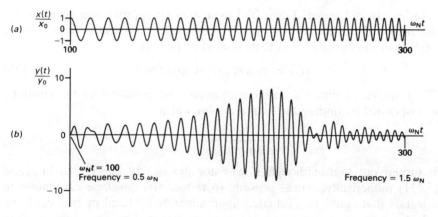

Fig. 3.13 Acceleration through resonance of a mode with damping ratio $\zeta = 0.05$. The excitation $x_0 \cos(\frac{1}{2}\alpha t^2)$ is plotted above the response and has $\alpha = 0.005\omega_N{}^2$. The initial conditions are $y = \dot{y} = 0$ at $\omega_N t = 100$

It can be seen from Fig. 3.14 that the response reaches its maximum amplitude after $\omega = \alpha t$ has passed through $\omega = \omega_N$ and that the maximum amplitude is less than that for steady-state constant-frequency vibration. This is a general result. The greater the acceleration, the more the peak amplitude is reduced and the more it is displaced to a frequency higher than ω_N. If this situation is reversed and the frequency of excitation is decelerated through resonance, the peak amplitude is still reduced, but the frequency at which maximum amplitude occurs is now displaced downwards so that it occurs at a frequency lower than ω_N.

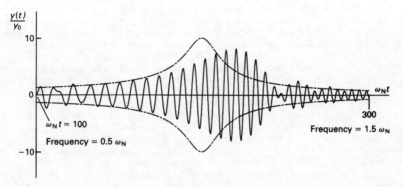

Fig. 3.14 Comparison between the response of a mode whose frequency of excitation is accelerating through resonance (from Fig. 3.13) and the envelope of amplitude versus frequency for steady-state harmonic vibration (from Fig. 1.2(a)). The damping ratio is $\zeta = 0.05$ and the angular acceleration is $\alpha = 0.005\omega_N{}^2$

In his original paper, Lewis [54] calculated an approximate envelope for the peaks of the transient response. His method was to include a phase angle ϕ in the excitation, so that, instead of (3.122),

$$x(t) = x_0 \cos(\tfrac{1}{2}\alpha t^2 + \phi), \quad t \geq 0. \tag{3.135}$$

The response at time t then includes ϕ and the equation for the envelope was obtained by finding the extremum for which

$$\frac{\partial x(t)}{\partial \phi}\bigg|_{t=\text{constant}} = 0. \tag{3.136}$$

It turned out that, although it was not practicable in 1932 to integrate (3.131) numerically, it was possible to reduce the envelope calculation to integrals that could be evaluated approximately by hand or that could be calculated by using approximate series expansions. Lewis used this method to draw approximate envelopes for the transient response for several different rates of acceleration and deceleration for the cases when $\zeta = 0.025, 0.05, 0.1$ and 0.2. In the accelerating case, the initial conditions were zero displacement and velocity at $t = 0$; in the decelerating case they were zero motion at $t = \infty$. For the deceleration calculation, the excitation has an initially infinite frequency which decreases as t increases. The magnitude of the instantaneous frequency at which the peak response occurs is displaced from ω_N by almost the same amounts, upwards when accelerating and downwards when decelerating. The peak response, which is always less than the steady-state harmonic response at resonance, is slightly greater when decelerating than when accelerating at the same rate.

These results can all be verified by computing specific cases using the numerical integration methods described in Chapter 10.

Chapter 4

Matrix analysis

First-order formulation of the equation of motion

In this chapter we return to the general response equation (2.1). So far we have considered only the steady-state harmonic solution of (2.1) for the case of positive damping. Now we shall investigate this equation's general solution using a matrix approach which lends itself to numerical calculations.

We begin by defining a general forcing function $f(t) \equiv f$ by

$$f(t) = b_m \frac{\mathrm{d}^m x}{\mathrm{d}t^m} + b_{m-1} \frac{\mathrm{d}^{m-1} x}{\mathrm{d}t^{m-1}} + \ldots + b_1 \frac{\mathrm{d}x}{\mathrm{d}t} + b_0 x \qquad (4.1)$$

with which the equation of motion (2.1) becomes

$$a_n \frac{\mathrm{d}^n y}{\mathrm{d}t^n} + a_{n-1} \frac{\mathrm{d}^{n-1} y}{\mathrm{d}t^{n-1}} + \ldots + a_1 \frac{\mathrm{d}y}{\mathrm{d}t} + a_0 y = f. \qquad (4.2)$$

Next, we break down this nth-order equation in y into n separate first-order equations by the following method. If we define $n - 1$ new variables $y_1, y_2, \ldots, y_{n-1}$ by the equations

$$y_1 \quad = \frac{\mathrm{d}}{\mathrm{d}t}(y)$$

$$y_2 \quad = \frac{\mathrm{d}}{\mathrm{d}t}(y_1) \quad = \frac{\mathrm{d}^2}{\mathrm{d}t^2}(y) \qquad (4.3)$$

$$\vdots \qquad \vdots \qquad \vdots$$

$$y_{n-1} = \frac{\mathrm{d}}{\mathrm{d}t}(y_{n-2}) \quad = \frac{\mathrm{d}^{n-1}}{\mathrm{d}t^{n-1}}(y)$$

then (4.2) can be expressed as

$$a_n \frac{\mathrm{d}}{\mathrm{d}t}(y_{n-1}) + a_{n-1} y_{n-1} + \ldots + a_1 y_1 + a_0 y = f \qquad (4.4)$$

which is a first-order equation in the n variables $y, y_1, y_2, \ldots, y_{n-1}$. Together with the $n - 1$ first-order equations which are the definitions (4.3), we then have a set of n first-order equations in n variables. These can be written in the form

$$\frac{dy}{dt} = y_1$$

$$\frac{dy_1}{dt} = y_2$$

$$\vdots \qquad \vdots$$

$$\frac{dy_{n-2}}{dt} = y_{n-1}$$

$$\frac{dy_{n-1}}{dt} = -\frac{a_{n-1}}{a_n} y_{n-1} - \frac{a_{n-2}}{a_n} y_{n-2} - \cdots$$

$$\cdots - \frac{a_1}{a_n} y_1 - \frac{a_0}{a_n} y + \frac{1}{a_n} f$$

$$(4.5)$$

or, in matrix notation,

$$\frac{d}{dt}\begin{bmatrix} y \\ y_1 \\ y_2 \\ \vdots \\ y_{n-2} \\ y_{n-1} \end{bmatrix} = \begin{bmatrix} 0 & 1 & 0 & 0 & \cdots & 0 & 0 \\ 0 & 0 & 1 & 0 & \cdots & 0 & 0 \\ 0 & 0 & 0 & 1 & \cdots & 0 & 0 \\ \vdots & \vdots & \vdots & \vdots & \cdots & \vdots & \vdots \\ 0 & 0 & 0 & 0 & \cdots & 0 & 1 \\ \frac{-a_0}{a_n} & \frac{-a_1}{a_n} & \frac{-a_2}{a_n} & \frac{-a_3}{a_n} & \cdots & \frac{-a_{n-2}}{a_n} & \frac{-a_{n-1}}{a_n} \end{bmatrix}\begin{bmatrix} y \\ y_1 \\ y_2 \\ \vdots \\ y_{n-2} \\ y_{n-1} \end{bmatrix} + \begin{bmatrix} 0 \\ 0 \\ 0 \\ \vdots \\ 0 \\ \frac{f}{a_n} \end{bmatrix}.$$

$$(4.6)$$

In the shorthand of matrix analysis, the n equations (4.5) can therefore be written as the single matrix equation

$$\frac{d}{dt} y = Ay + F \qquad (4.7)$$

where the orders of the matrices $y \equiv y(t)$ and $F \equiv F(t)$ are $n \times 1$ and the order of the square matrix A is $n \times n$. In control terminology, this is called the state equation for the system represented by (2.1) and y is the state vector giving the instantaneous values of the response $y(t)$ and its first $n - 1$ derivatives.

We shall now consider how (4.7) can be used to obtain a general solution for $y(t)$ when $f(t)$ is any general function of time, t.

Eigenvalues of the characteristic equation

First, consider the solution of (4.7) for no excitation. Then the free motion has the general form

$$y(t) = e^{\lambda t} Y \tag{4.8}$$

where Y is an $n \times 1$ column matrix whose elements are independent of t. On substituting for y from (4.8) into (4.7) with $F = 0$, we find that

$$\lambda Y = AY \tag{4.9}$$

or, on rearrangement,

$$[A - \lambda I] Y = O \tag{4.10}$$

which is a set of n simultaneous algebraic equations with the unknown parameter λ. From the theory of simultaneous equations, the solution of the set (4.10) will be just

$$Y = O \tag{4.11}$$

unless the determinant of their coefficients is zero, i.e. unless

$$\det[A - \lambda I] = 0. \tag{4.12}$$

Because this is a determinant of a matrix of order $n \times n$, there will be n solutions of λ which satisfy (4.12) and these are the n eigenvalues of the system or, in mathematical terms, the *n eigenvalues of the matrix A*.

Example 4.1 Finding the A-matrix and its eigenvalues

Find the A matrix for the single-degree-of-freedom system defined by (1.1) and shown in Fig. 1.1, and use (4.12) to find an equation for its eigenvalues.

On putting $y_1 = dy/dt$ into (1.1), we find that

$$m \frac{dy_1}{dt} + cy_1 + ky = x.$$

Hence

$$\frac{d}{dt} \begin{bmatrix} y \\ y_1 \end{bmatrix} = \begin{bmatrix} 0 & 1 \\ -k/m & -c/m \end{bmatrix} \begin{bmatrix} y \\ y_1 \end{bmatrix} + \begin{bmatrix} 0 \\ x/m \end{bmatrix}$$

so that

$$A = \begin{bmatrix} 0 & 1 \\ -k/m & -c/m \end{bmatrix}.$$

Then

$$\det[A - \lambda I] = \det \begin{bmatrix} -\lambda & 1 \\ -k/m & -c/m - \lambda \end{bmatrix}$$

$$= (-\lambda)\left(-\frac{c}{m} - \lambda\right) - (1)\left(-\frac{k}{m}\right)$$

and so (4.12) gives

$$\lambda^2 + \frac{c}{m}\lambda + \frac{k}{m} = 0$$

in agreement with (1.3).

On substituting the free-vibration solution (4.8) into the original nth-order equation of motion (4.2) with no excitation, we see that the n eigenvalues λ_j, $j = 1$ to n, are the n roots of the *characteristic equation*

$$a_n\lambda^n + a_{n-1}\lambda^{n-1} + \ldots + a_1\lambda + a_0 = 0. \tag{4.13}$$

The same equation for λ is of course obtained by substituting for A from (4.6) into (4.12) and then evaluating the determinant (Problem 4.1). If the system is described by an nth-order differential equation in the response parameter $y(t)$, then it will have n eigenvalues which can be calculated by solving (4.12) or its equivalent (4.13).

The calculation of eigenvalues in a practical case when $n > 2$ almost always requires the application of a computer library program. There are a number of different eigenvalue programs which are widely available. These programs require the elements of the A matrix to be entered and then calculate sequentially the values of λ which satisfy (4.12). The availability of such programs is an important advantage of the first-order formulation of linear system response described above. Many of the worked examples and many of the problems in this book have been solved by using a computer program which calculates the eigenvalues of an arbitrary A matrix with real elements. In order to check the answers to these examples and problems, the reader will need to use a similar program. The method of doing this is described in Chapter 5 and the detailed logic of such a calculation in Chapter 7.

Example 4.2 Calculating eigenvalues

Calculate the eigenvalues of the system whose free vibration is described by the differential equation

$$\frac{d^6y}{dt^6} + 15\frac{d^5y}{dt^5} + 200\frac{d^4y}{dt^4} + 1500\frac{d^3y}{dt^3} = 0.$$

From (4.13), the eigenvalues λ_j, $j = 1$ to 6, are the solutions of the sixth-order equation

$$\lambda^6 + 15\lambda^5 + 200\lambda^4 + 1500\lambda^3 = 0.$$

Alternatively, from (4.6) and (4.12), λ_j are the roots of

$$\det \begin{bmatrix} -\lambda & 1 & 0 & 0 & 0 & 0 \\ 0 & -\lambda & 1 & 0 & 0 & 0 \\ 0 & 0 & -\lambda & 1 & 0 & 0 \\ 0 & 0 & 0 & -\lambda & 1 & 0 \\ 0 & 0 & 0 & 0 & -\lambda & 1 \\ 0 & 0 & 0 & -1500 & -200 & -15-\lambda \end{bmatrix} = 0.$$

By using a computer program, or, in this simple case by hand calculation, the six eigenvalues are:

$$\lambda_1 = \lambda_2 = \lambda_3 = 0$$

$$\lambda_4 = -10$$

$$\lambda_5, \lambda_6 = -2.5 \pm i\, 2.5\sqrt{23}.$$

We shall be concerned only with systems described by a differential equation of the form (4.2) with real coefficients. Then the coefficients of the characteristic polynomial (4.13) are all real and, as we saw in Chapter 2, the eigenvalues are always real or, if they are complex, occur only in complex-conjugate pairs.

Eigenvectors

Each of the n eigenvalues λ_j, $j = 1$ to n, of the $n \times n$ A matrix allows a solution to be found for equation (4.9). If Y_j is the solution vector corresponding to λ_j, then Y_j is defined, from (4.9), by

$$\lambda_j Y_j = A Y_j. \tag{4.14}$$

The elements† of the $n \times 1$ column matrix Y_j are the (generally complex) amplitudes of y and its $n - 1$ derivatives when the system is in free motion with time dependence $e^{\lambda_j t}$. If all the eigenvalues are distinct, so that there are n different eigenvalues, there will be n different *eigenvectors* Y_j, $j = 1$ to n. The n different equations like (4.14) can then be combined into a single equation. If we define a new $n \times n$ matrix U whose columns are the n eigenvectors Y_j, this consolidated form of (4.14) is

$$U[\text{diag } \lambda_j] = AU \tag{4.15}$$

where $[\text{diag } \lambda_j]$ is a diagonal matrix whose diagonal elements are the n eigenvalues, written in the same order as the corresponding eigenvectors in the columns of U.

---

† Terminology: Some books refer to the components of a vector rather than to the elements of a vector, but we shall generally prefer the term element for both vectors and matrices.

The elements of the column vector y in (4.8) are, from (4.6) and (4.7), the response parameter y followed by its first $n - 1$ derivatives, in order. Hence the elements of the eigenvector Y_j in (4.14) are the amplitudes of y and its derivatives, so that

$$Y_j = Y_j \begin{bmatrix} 1 \\ \lambda_j \\ \lambda_j^2 \\ \vdots \\ \lambda_j^{n-2} \\ \lambda_j^{n-1} \end{bmatrix}. \tag{4.16}$$

Equation (4.14) is true whatever the value of Y_j in (4.16) and, if we arbitrarily normalize the eigenvectors by putting $Y_j = 1$, $j = 1$ to n, the eigenvector matrix U has the form

$$U = \begin{bmatrix} 1 & 1 & \cdots & 1 \\ \lambda_1 & \lambda_2 & \cdots & \lambda_n \\ \lambda_1^2 & \lambda_2^2 & \cdots & \lambda_n^2 \\ \vdots & \vdots & \cdots & \vdots \\ \lambda_1^{n-2} & \lambda_2^{n-2} & \cdots & \lambda_n^{n-2} \\ \lambda_1^{n-1} & \lambda_2^{n-1} & \cdots & \lambda_n^{n-1} \end{bmatrix} \tag{4.17}$$

Provided that all the λ_j, $j = 1$ to n, are different then all the eigenvectors will be independent, in which case U has an inverse, and we can pre-multiply (4.15) by U^{-1} to obtain

$$[\text{diag } \lambda_j] = U^{-1}AU. \tag{4.18}$$

Normal coordinates

The last equation is important because it allows a coordinate transformation to be made which uncouples the n first-order equations (4.7). If we define a new $n \times 1$ column vector q by the transformation

$$q = U^{-1}y \tag{4.19}$$

where U is the eigenvector matrix, then on substituting from (4.19) into the general first-order equation (4.7), we obtain

$$U \frac{\mathrm{d}}{\mathrm{d}t} q = AUq + F. \tag{4.20}$$

On pre-multiplying by U^{-1}, this becomes

$$\frac{\mathrm{d}}{\mathrm{d}t} q = U^{-1} AUq + U^{-1}F \tag{4.21}$$

and, with (4.18),

$$\frac{d}{dt}q = [\text{diag } \lambda_j]q + U^{-1}F. \tag{4.22}$$

Example 4.3 Uncoupling the equations of motion

Write out equation (4.22) in full for the single-degree-of-freedom system defined by (1.1) and Fig. 1.1.

If the two eigenvalues are λ_1, λ_2 (assumed different) then

$$[\text{diag } \lambda_j] = \begin{bmatrix} \lambda_1 & 0 \\ 0 & \lambda_2 \end{bmatrix}$$

and, from (4.17),

$$U = \begin{bmatrix} 1 & 1 \\ \lambda_1 & \lambda_2 \end{bmatrix}.$$

For this simple example, we can find U^{-1} algebraically because, if

$$U^{-1} = \begin{bmatrix} a & b \\ c & d \end{bmatrix},$$

then we must have

$$UU^{-1} = \begin{bmatrix} 1 & 1 \\ \lambda_1 & \lambda_2 \end{bmatrix}\begin{bmatrix} a & b \\ c & d \end{bmatrix} = \begin{bmatrix} 1 & 0 \\ 0 & 1 \end{bmatrix}$$

and multiplying out the two matrices we find that

$$a + c = 1$$
$$b + d = 0$$
$$\lambda_1 a + \lambda_2 c = 0$$
$$\lambda_1 b + \lambda_2 d = 1$$

giving

$$U^{-1} = \begin{bmatrix} \dfrac{\lambda_2}{\lambda_2 - \lambda_1} & \dfrac{1}{\lambda_1 - \lambda_2} \\[3mm] \dfrac{\lambda_1}{\lambda_1 - \lambda_2} & \dfrac{1}{\lambda_2 - \lambda_1} \end{bmatrix}.$$

Also, by comparing (4.6) and (4.7),

$$F = \begin{bmatrix} 0 \\ \dfrac{x(t)}{m} \end{bmatrix}$$

so that, in full,

$$
\frac{d}{dt}\begin{bmatrix} q_1 \\ q_2 \end{bmatrix} = \begin{bmatrix} \lambda_1 & 0 \\ 0 & \lambda_2 \end{bmatrix}\begin{bmatrix} q_1 \\ q_2 \end{bmatrix} + \begin{bmatrix} \dfrac{\lambda_2}{\lambda_2 - \lambda_1} & \dfrac{1}{\lambda_1 - \lambda_2} \\[2ex] \dfrac{\lambda_1}{\lambda_1 - \lambda_2} & \dfrac{1}{\lambda_2 - \lambda_1} \end{bmatrix}\begin{bmatrix} 0 \\ \dfrac{x(t)}{m} \end{bmatrix}.
$$

The two separate (uncoupled) equations for q_1, q_2 are therefore

$$
\frac{dq_1}{dt} = \lambda_1 q_1 + \frac{1}{(\lambda_1 - \lambda_2)}\frac{x(t)}{m}
$$

and

$$
\frac{dq_2}{dt} = \lambda_2 q_2 + \frac{1}{\lambda_2 - \lambda_1}\frac{x(t)}{m}.
$$

By defining q in terms of the inverse of the eigenvector matrix according to (4.19), it is always possible to uncouple the first-order equations (4.7), provided that all the eigenvalues λ_j, $j = 1$ to n, are distinct. The n elements q are called the *normal coordinates* of the system.

General solution for arbitrary excitation

For a passive system whose response dies away if the excitation is removed for a sufficiently long period of time, equation (4.22) can be used to derive a general solution for $y(t)$ if the forcing function $f(t)$ defined by (4.1) is specified. Each of the normal coordinates q_j, $j = 1$ to n, occurs in one row only of the matrix equation (4.22). Consider the jth row of (4.22) which is

$$
\frac{d}{dt}q_j = \lambda_j q_j + \phi_j \tag{4.23}
$$

where ϕ_j denotes the jth row of $U^{-1}F$. This is a first-order linear differential equation for $q_j(t)$ with λ_j constant and with $\phi_j \equiv \phi_j(t)$ a function of t. It has a general solution which may be found by multiplying (4.23) by the integrating factor $e^{-\lambda_j t}$ and rearranging terms to give

$$
\frac{d}{dt}\{e^{-\lambda_j t}q_j(t)\} = e^{-\lambda_j t}\phi_j(t). \tag{4.24}
$$

On integrating this equation, we obtain

$$
e^{-\lambda_j t}q_j(t) = \int e^{-\lambda_j t}\phi_j(t)\,dt + C_j \tag{4.25}
$$

where C_j is an arbitrary constant of integration, and multiplying through by $e^{\lambda_j t}$, the solution for the normal coordinate $q_j(t)$ is

$$
q_j(t) = e^{\lambda_j t}\int e^{-\lambda_j t}\phi_j(t)\,dt + e^{\lambda_j t}C_j. \tag{4.26}
$$

There is a similar result for each of the other n rows of (4.22).

The n separate equations for $q_j(t)$, $j = 1$ to n, can be combined into a single matrix equation. If C is an $n \times 1$ column vector of the constants of integration C_j, $j = 1$ to n, this single equation is

$$q(t) = [\text{diag } e^{\lambda_j t}] \left[\int [\text{diag } e^{-\lambda_j t}] \, U^{-1}F \, dt + C \right]. \tag{4.27}$$

To check that (4.27) is true, note that elements in the jth row of the matrix product AB are the result of multiplying the elements in the jth row of A with the elements in each of the columns of B. Since the jth row of $[\text{diag } e^{-\lambda_j t}]$ has only one element and $U^{-1}F$ has only one column, the jth row of the product $[\text{diag } e^{-\lambda_j t}] \, [U^{-1}F]$ is just $e^{-\lambda_j t} \, \phi_j(t)$, where $\phi_j(t)$ is the jth row of $[U^{-1}F]$.

The solution in the original coordinates $y \equiv y(t)$ can be recovered from $q \equiv q(t)$ by using the transformation (4.19) and so obtaining

$$y(t) = U[\text{diag } e^{\lambda_j t}] \left[\int [\text{diag } e^{-\lambda_j t}] \, U^{-1}F(t) \, dt + C \right]. \tag{4.28}$$

This is a general solution for the $n \times 1$ vector $y(t)$ whose elements are the response parameter and its first $n - 1$ derivatives, according to (4.5), U is the $n \times n$ eigenvector matrix defined by (4.17), and $F(t)$ is the $n \times 1$ excitation vector defined by (4.6) with (4.7). C is an $n \times 1$ vector of constants of integration whose values have to be determined from the initial conditions.

Equation (4.28) provides a complete general solution for the response of the linear system given by (2.1) starting from the equivalent pair of equations (4.1) and (4.2). Its derivation depends on being able to find an eigenvector matrix U that allows the A matrix to be diagonalized according to (4.18). This will always be possible when there are no repeated eigenvalues, in which case all the columns of U are independent and therefore the inverse matrix U^{-1} exists. In Chapter 6 we shall consider how the solution is altered when there are repeated eigenvalues (as there were in Example 4.2 above).

Application to a single-degree-of-freedom system

We are now in a position to prove the general results stated in (1.4) for the response of a single-degree-of-freedom system. Using the results of Example 4.3 for U, U^{-1} and F we have, for one degree of freedom,

$$[U^{-1}F] = \frac{x(t)}{m} \begin{bmatrix} \dfrac{1}{(\lambda_1 - \lambda_2)} \\[2ex] \dfrac{1}{(\lambda_2 - \lambda_1)} \end{bmatrix} \tag{4.29}$$

and

$$[\text{diag } e^{-\lambda_i t}] \, [U^{-1}F] = \frac{x(t)}{m} \begin{bmatrix} e^{-\lambda_1 t} \dfrac{1}{(\lambda_1 - \lambda_2)} \\ e^{-\lambda_2 t} \dfrac{1}{(\lambda_2 - \lambda_1)} \end{bmatrix}. \tag{4.30}$$

Hence we find that

$$[\text{diag } e^{\lambda_i t}] \left[\int [\text{diag } e^{-\lambda_i t}] \, U^{-1}F \, dt + C \right]$$

$$= \begin{bmatrix} e^{\lambda_1 t} \left\{ \dfrac{1}{(\lambda_1 - \lambda_2)} \int e^{-\lambda_1 t} \dfrac{x(t)}{m} \, dt + C_1 \right\} \\ e^{\lambda_2 t} \left\{ \dfrac{1}{(\lambda_2 - \lambda_1)} \int e^{-\lambda_2 t} \dfrac{x(t)}{m} \, dt + C_2 \right\} \end{bmatrix}$$

$$= \begin{bmatrix} e^{\lambda_1 t} \left\{ \dfrac{1}{(\lambda_1 - \lambda_2)} \, \phi_1(t) + C_1 \right\} \\ e^{\lambda_2 t} \left\{ \dfrac{1}{(\lambda_2 - \lambda_1)} \, \phi_2(t) + C_2 \right\} \end{bmatrix} \tag{4.31}$$

where the functions $\phi_1(t)$ and $\phi_2(t)$ are defined by (1.5) and (1.6). Therefore, from (4.28),

$$\begin{bmatrix} y(t) \\ \dfrac{d}{dt} y(t) \end{bmatrix} = \begin{bmatrix} 1 & 1 \\ \lambda_1 & \lambda_2 \end{bmatrix} \begin{bmatrix} e^{\lambda_1 t} \left\{ \dfrac{1}{(\lambda_1 - \lambda_2)} \, \phi_1(t) + C_1 \right\} \\ e^{\lambda_2 t} \left\{ \dfrac{1}{(\lambda_2 - \lambda_1)} \, \phi_2(t) + C_2 \right\} \end{bmatrix}$$

$$= \begin{bmatrix} e^{\lambda_1 t} \left\{ \dfrac{1}{(\lambda_1 - \lambda_2)} \, \phi_1(t) + C_1 \right\} + e^{\lambda_2 t} \left\{ \dfrac{1}{(\lambda_2 - \lambda_1)} \, \phi_2(t) + C_2 \right\} \\ \lambda_1 e^{\lambda_1 t} \left\{ \dfrac{1}{(\lambda_1 - \lambda_2)} \, \phi_1(t) + C_1 \right\} + \lambda_2 e^{\lambda_2 t} \left\{ \dfrac{1}{(\lambda_2 - \lambda_1)} \, \phi_2(t) + C_2 \right\} \end{bmatrix}. \tag{4.32}$$

Equation (4.32) confirms the results given in Chapter 1 as (1.4) and (1.7).

Solution for the harmonic response

We return now to the general case and the solution of the general linear-response equation

$$a_n \frac{d^n y}{dt^n} + a_{n-1} \frac{d^{n-1}y}{dt^{n-1}} + \ldots + a_1 \frac{dy}{dt} + a_0 y$$

$$= b_m \frac{d^m x}{dt^m} + b_{m-1} \frac{d^{m-1}x}{dt^{m-1}} + \ldots + b_1 \frac{dx}{dt} + b_0 x. \quad (2.1)$$

Equation (4.28) gives the response vector $y(t)$ for $y(t)$ and its $n-1$ derivatives for any arbitrary excitation $x(t)$, from which the forcing-function vector $F(t)$ in (4.28) can be calculated from (4.1) and (4.6) with (4.7). We shall consider now the application of (4.28) to the special case of harmonic excitation when

$$x(t) = e^{i\omega t}. \quad (4.33)$$

On substituting for $x(t)$ from (4.33) into (4.1), we obtain

$$f(t) = \{b_m(i\omega)^m + b_{m-1}(i\omega)^{m-1} + \ldots + b_1(i\omega) + b_0\}\, e^{i\omega t} \quad (4.34)$$

which, with the definition of $B(i\omega)$ in (2.4), can be written

$$f(t) = B(i\omega)\, e^{i\omega t}. \quad (4.35)$$

Then, from the definition of the forcing vector F given by (4.6), we have

$$F(t) = \begin{bmatrix} 0 \\ 0 \\ 0 \\ \vdots \\ 0 \\ B(i\omega)/a_n \end{bmatrix} e^{i\omega t}. \quad (4.36)$$

The eigenvector matrix U, which appears in the general solution (4.28), is given by (4.17), where $\lambda_1, \lambda_2, \ldots, \lambda_n$ are the n eigenvalues of the characteristic equation (4.13). We can therefore now work out the matrix products in the general solution, beginning with $U^{-1}F(t)$.

Since all the elements in $F(t)$ are zero except for the last element, we need to evaluate only the elements in the last column of U^{-1} because only these elements of U^{-1} multiply the last element of $F(t)$. This calculation is left for the reader in Problem 4.2, where it can be seen that the element in the jth row of the nth column of U^{-1} is

$$\frac{1}{(\lambda_j - \lambda_1)(\lambda_j - \lambda_2) \ldots (\lambda_j - \lambda_n)} \quad (4.37)$$

with the factor which would be zero omitted. The $n \times 1$ column matrix $U^{-1}F(t)$ can then be pre-multiplied by the $n \times n$ matrix $[\mathrm{diag}\ e^{-\lambda_j t}]$ to give

$$[\text{diag } e^{-\lambda_j t}] \, U^{-1}F(t) = \begin{bmatrix} \dfrac{B(i\omega)}{a_n(\lambda_1 - \lambda_2)(\lambda_1 - \lambda_3) \ldots (\lambda_1 - \lambda_n)} \, e^{(i\omega - \lambda_1)t} \\[2em] \dfrac{B(i\omega)}{a_n(\lambda_2 - \lambda_1)(\lambda_2 - \lambda_3) \ldots (\lambda_2 - \lambda_n)} \, e^{(i\omega - \lambda_2)t} \\[1em] \vdots \\[1em] \dfrac{B(i\omega)}{a_n(\lambda_n - \lambda_1)(\lambda_n - \lambda_2) \ldots (\lambda_n - \lambda_{n-1})} \, e^{(i\omega - \lambda_n)t} \end{bmatrix}.$$

$$(4.38)$$

Following the general solution (4.28), we now integrate (4.38) with respect to time, t, and the jth element of the new $n \times 1$ matrix

$$\int [\text{diag } e^{-\lambda_j t}] \, U^{-1}F(t) \, dt \qquad (4.39)$$

can be seen to be

$$\frac{B(i\omega)}{a_n(\lambda_j - \lambda_1)(\lambda_j - \lambda_2) \ldots (\lambda_j - \lambda_{j-1})(i\omega - \lambda_j)(\lambda_j - \lambda_{j+1}) \ldots (\lambda_j - \lambda_n)} \, e^{(i\omega - \lambda_j)t}.$$

$$(4.40)$$

Next we have to pre-multiply by $[\text{diag } e^{\lambda_j t}]$, and the jth element of the resulting $n \times 1$ matrix is

$$\frac{B(i\omega)}{a_n(\lambda_j - \lambda_1)(\lambda_j - \lambda_2) \ldots (\lambda_j - \lambda_{j-1})(i\omega - \lambda_j)(\lambda_j - \lambda_{j+1}) \ldots (\lambda_j - \lambda_n)} \, e^{i\omega t} \quad (4.41)$$

which, if we use the symbol Π to denote the repeated product of factors, may be written as

$$\frac{B(i\omega)}{a_n(i\omega - \lambda_j) \displaystyle\prod_{\substack{k=1 \\ k \neq j}}^{n} (\lambda_j - \lambda_k)} \, e^{i\omega t} \qquad (4.42)$$

In evaluating (4.28), we have also to work out the product $[\text{diag } e^{\lambda_j t}]C$ where C is the $n \times 1$ column matrix of arbitrary constants of integration. In this special case, the result is zero. The reason is that we are looking for a steady-state response condition, after all the starting transients have died away. For the transients to die away, there must be positive damping so that the real parts of the system's eigenvalues λ_j, $j = 1$ to n, must all be negative. If the real parts of the λ_j are all negative, the terms in $[\text{diag } e^{\lambda_j t}]$ all decay exponentially with time. Therefore, the contributions to the response vector $y(t)$ from the terms stemming from $U[\text{diag } e^{\lambda_j t}]C$ in (4.28) will all approach zero when $t \to \infty$. We conclude that the steady-state response to harmonic excitation is given by the remaining terms in (4.28), and the contributions from $U[\text{diag } e^{\lambda_j t}]C$ can be neglected.

Hence, with the eigenvector matrix U defined by (4.17), and with the integrated matrix product (4.39) consisting of terms like (4.40), we can complete the matrix multiplication in (4.28). The result is an $n \times 1$ column matrix whose elements are $y(t)$, followed by its first $n-1$ derivatives, in order. The first element is

$$y(t) = \sum_{j=1}^{n} \frac{B(i\omega)}{a_n(i\omega - \lambda_j) \prod_{\substack{k=1 \\ k \neq j}}^{n} (\lambda_j - \lambda_k)} e^{i\omega t} \tag{4.43}$$

or, if in the usual notation,

$$y(t) = H(i\omega)\, e^{i\omega t} \tag{4.44}$$

the complex frequency-response function $H(i\omega)$ is given by

$$H(i\omega) = B(i\omega) \sum_{j=1}^{n} \frac{1}{a_n(i\omega - \lambda_j) \prod_{\substack{k=1 \\ k \neq j}}^{n} (\lambda_j - \lambda_k)}. \tag{4.45}$$

Comparison with the general expansion in partial fractions

In Chapter 2 we showed how the frequency-response function

$$H(i\omega) = \frac{B(i\omega)}{A(i\omega)} \tag{2.2}$$

can always be expanded as a series of partial fractions so that

$$H(i\omega) = \sum_{j=1}^{n} \frac{p_j}{i\omega - \lambda_j} \tag{2.42}$$

where

$$p_j = \frac{B(\lambda_j)}{a_n \prod_{\substack{k=1 \\ k \neq j}}^{n} (\lambda_j - \lambda_k)}. \tag{2.45}$$

The conditions on which this expansion depends are that (i) the eigenvalues are distinct, and (ii) the order in $i\omega$ of $B(i\omega)$ is less than the corresponding order of $A(i\omega)$, which means that the coefficient m in (2.4) is less than n in (2.3). The first condition applies also to the general analysis based on equation (4.28), but in this chapter we have placed no restrictions on $B(i\omega)$.

On comparing the general expansion (4.45) that we have just obtained with the previous result (2.42), we see that these two expansions are not quite the same. The new result (4.45) can be written as

$$H(i\omega) = B(i\omega) \sum_{j=1}^{n} \frac{q_j}{i\omega - \lambda_j} \tag{4.46}$$

where

$$q_j = \frac{1}{a_n \prod\limits_{\substack{k=1 \\ k \neq j}} (\lambda_j - \lambda_k)} \tag{4.47}$$

for comparison with (2.42) and (2.45). Since we know that

$$A(i\omega) = a_n \prod_{k=1}^{n} (i\omega - \lambda_k) \tag{2.38}$$

the reader can check that the partial-fraction expansion in (4.46) is the expansion of $1/A(i\omega)$, which is

$$\frac{1}{A(i\omega)} = \sum_{j=1}^{n} \frac{q_j}{i\omega - \lambda_j} \tag{4.48}$$

where q_j is given by (4.47). This is true whatever the form of $B(i\omega)$ and so, in this chapter, no restriction has had to be placed on the order of $B(i\omega)$.

The result (2.42) from Chapter 2 is a partial-fraction expansion of $H(i\omega)$. It is an important general result and depends on the order of the numerator of $H(i\omega)$ being less than the order of its denominator. In this chapter, we have derived a general solution (4.28) for the response of the linear system (2.1) to arbitrary excitation. As a special case, we calculated from (4.28) the steady-state response to harmonic excitation and thus found an alternative expression (4.45) for the frequency-response function $H(i\omega)$. The latter expression involves a partial-fraction expansion of $1/A(i\omega)$ according to (4.48), whereas in (2.42) the whole of $H(i\omega)$ is expressed as the summation of its partial fractions.

Case of coupled second-order equations

In mechanical and structural engineering there are many cases when the equations for small-amplitude vibration consist of a set of coupled, linear differential equations of second order. For example, the three-degree-of-freedom system shown in Fig. 2.7 is described by the three coupled second-order equations (2.58), (2.59) and (2.60). We shall now consider the response of a general system with M degrees of freedom whose M second-order equations of motion can be represented in the matrix form

$$m\ddot{y} + c\dot{y} + ky = x. \tag{4.49}$$

The mass, damping and stiffness matrices m, c and k are each of order $M \times M$ and all their elements are assumed to be real. The $M \times 1$ excitation vector x has M elements, each of which may be a different function of time. The $M \times 1$ response vector y defines the instantaneous values of the M coordinates of the system and $\dot{y}$ and $\ddot{y}$ are the corresponding $M \times 1$ vectors defining the derivatives of y. In many practical cases, x

will be a vector of forces and y will be a vector of displacements, but x could equally be a vector of torques, or a mixture of forces and torques, and y could be a vector of angular displacements, or a mixture of angular and linear displacements.

Starting from the M coupled second-order differential equations (4.49), it is always possible in theory to obtain a set of M independent differential equations each of the form of (2.1). If we write (4.49) in the form

$$\left[m \frac{d^2}{dt^2} + c \frac{d}{dt} + k \right] y = x \tag{4.50}$$

then the solution for the response vector y is

$$y = \left[m \frac{d^2}{dt^2} + c \frac{d}{dt} + k \right]^{-1} x \tag{4.51}$$

which is a set of M uncoupled equations for the M elements of y. Each of these uncoupled equations has the form of (2.1).

Example 4.4 Transforming to nth-order form

The equations of motion for the three-degree-of-freedom system shown in Fig. 2.7 can be written, corresponding to (4.49), in the form

$$\begin{bmatrix} m & 0 & 0 \\ 0 & m & 0 \\ 0 & 0 & m \end{bmatrix} \begin{bmatrix} \ddot{y}_1 \\ \ddot{y}_2 \\ \ddot{y}_3 \end{bmatrix} + \begin{bmatrix} 0 & 0 & 0 \\ 0 & c & 0 \\ 0 & 0 & 0 \end{bmatrix} \begin{bmatrix} \dot{y}_1 \\ \dot{y}_2 \\ \dot{y}_3 \end{bmatrix} + $$
$$+ \begin{bmatrix} 2k & -k & 0 \\ -k & 2k & -k \\ 0 & -k & 2k \end{bmatrix} \begin{bmatrix} y_1 \\ y_2 \\ y_3 \end{bmatrix} = \begin{bmatrix} x \\ 0 \\ 0 \end{bmatrix} \tag{4.52}$$

or, corresponding to (4.51), as

$$\begin{bmatrix} y_1 \\ y_2 \\ y_3 \end{bmatrix} = $$

$$\begin{bmatrix} \left(m \dfrac{d^2}{dt^2} + 2k \right) & -k & 0 \\ -k & \left(m \dfrac{d^2}{dt^2} + c \dfrac{d}{dt} + 2k \right) & -k \\ 0 & -k & \left(m \dfrac{d^2}{dt^2} + 2k \right) \end{bmatrix}^{-1} \begin{bmatrix} x \\ 0 \\ 0 \end{bmatrix}. \tag{4.53}$$

The inverse matrix in (4.53) can be calculated from the general result that

$$a^{-1} = \frac{\text{adj } a}{\det a} \tag{4.54}$$

where, in this example, for a defined by (4.53),

adj $a =$

$$
\begin{bmatrix}
\left(m^2\dfrac{d^4}{dt^4} + mc\dfrac{d^3}{dt^3} + \right. & \left(mk\dfrac{d^2}{dt^2} + 3k^2\right) & k^2 \\[4pt]
\left. +4mk\dfrac{d^2}{dt^2} + 2ck\dfrac{d}{dt} + 3k^2\right) & & \\[12pt]
\left(mk\dfrac{d^2}{dt^2} + 2k^2\right) & \left(m^2\dfrac{d^4}{dt^4} + 4mk\dfrac{d^2}{dt^2} + 4k^2\right) & \left(mk\dfrac{d^2}{dt^2} + 2k^2\right) \\[12pt]
k^2 & \left(mk\dfrac{d^2}{dt^2} + 2k^2\right) & \left(m^2\dfrac{d^4}{dt^4} + mc\dfrac{d^3}{dt^3} + \right. \\[4pt]
& & \left. +4mk\dfrac{d^2}{dt^2} + 2ck\dfrac{d}{dt} + 3k^2\right)
\end{bmatrix}
$$

$$\tag{4.55}$$

and

$$
\det a = m^3\frac{d^6}{dt^6} + m^2c\frac{d^5}{dt^5} + 6m^2k\frac{d^4}{dt^4} + 4mck\frac{d^3}{dt^3}
$$

$$
+ 10mk^2\frac{d^2}{dt^2} + 4ck^2\frac{d}{dt} + 4k^3 \tag{4.56}
$$

(see Problem 4.4). The differential equation relating the response variable $y_1(t)$ to the excitation $x(t)$ is given by the first row of (4.53) which, using the above results, gives

$$
m^3\frac{d^6y_1}{dt^6} + m^2c\frac{d^5y_1}{dt^5} + 6m^2k\frac{d^4y_1}{dt^4} + 4mck\frac{d^3y_1}{dt^3} +
$$

$$
+ 10mk^2\frac{d^2y_1}{dt^2} + 4ck^2\frac{dy_1}{dt} + 4k^3y_1
$$

$$
= m^2\frac{d^4x}{dt^4} + mc\frac{d^3x}{dt^3} + 4mk\frac{d^2x}{dt^2} + 2ck\frac{dx}{dt} + 3k^2x. \tag{4.57}
$$

The second and third rows of (4.53) give corresponding equations relating $y_2(t)$ and $y_3(t)$ to $x(t)$.

By comparing (4.57) with the expression (2.63) for the frequency-response function $H_1(i\omega)$, it can be seen that the two results are in agreement.

Once the describing equations have been manipulated into the general form of (2.1), for example as in (4.57) above, the method described earlier in this chapter for reducing them to a set of first-order equations can be followed. However, it is not necessary to uncouple the equations by solving (4.51) before making the reduction to first-order form. It is quicker and simpler to go directly from the second-order set (4.49) to a corresponding set of first-order equations, as follows.

Reduction of *M* second-order equations to 2*M* first-order equations

The M coupled second-order equations (4.49) are written in terms of the Mth-order vector of (generalized) displacements y. If we define a new Mth-order vector w as the derivative of y so that

$$w = \dot{y} \tag{4.58}$$

and

$$\dot{w} = \ddot{y} \tag{4.59}$$

then (4.49) may be rewritten as

$$m\dot{w} + cw + ky = x \tag{4.60}$$

which gives

$$\dot{w} = -m^{-1}cw - m^{-1}ky + m^{-1}x. \tag{4.61}$$

If next we define a new vector z of order $2M$ so that

$$z = \begin{bmatrix} y \\ w \end{bmatrix} \tag{4.62}$$

then we can combine (4.58) and (4.61) into the single matrix equation

$$\dot{z} = \begin{bmatrix} \dot{y} \\ \dot{w} \end{bmatrix} = \begin{bmatrix} O & I \\ -m^{-1}k & -m^{-1}c \end{bmatrix} \begin{bmatrix} y \\ w \end{bmatrix} + \begin{bmatrix} O \\ m^{-1}x \end{bmatrix}. \tag{4.63}$$

By defining a new A matrix of order $2M \times 2M$ so that

$$A = \begin{bmatrix} O & I \\ -m^{-1}k & -m^{-1}c \end{bmatrix} \tag{4.64}$$

and a new $2M \times 1$ excitation vector F so that

$$F = \begin{bmatrix} O \\ m^{-1}x \end{bmatrix}, \tag{4.65}$$

we can write (4.63) in the simple form

$$\dot{z} = Az + F \tag{4.66}$$

which is the standard state equation defining $2M$ coupled first-order linear differential equations in the state variables.

It is important to note the differences between the pair of equations (4.6) and (4.7) derived previously and the alternative pair of equations (4.63) and (4.66) that we have now obtained. The $n \times 1$ vector y in the first pair (4.6) and (4.7) consists of the response variable $y(t)$ and its first $n - 1$ derivatives. It applies for the case when $y(t)$ is a single response variable which is related to its excitation by a differential equation of the form (2.1) with derivatives of order up to

$$\frac{d^n y}{dt^n}.$$

In contrast, the $2M \times 1$ state vector z in the second pair of equations (4.63) and (4.66) consists of the instantaneous values of M different response parameters, $y_1, y_2, \ldots, y_M$, for each of the M degrees of freedom, followed by the M instantaneous values of their first derivatives (in the same order).

Both equations (4.7) and (4.66) may describe the same M-degree-of-freedom system. Then the order of the A-matrix must be the same in the two cases, so that

$$n = 2M. \tag{4.67}$$

The first equation (4.7) relates one of the output variables and the derivatives of this variable to order $(2M - 1)$ to one of the inputs. There are $2M$ coupled first-order equations. The second equation (4.66) relates the M output variables and their first derivatives to all the inputs. There are again $2M$ coupled first-order equations, but these are a different set of equations involving different response variables and so having a different A-matrix and a different excitation vector, F.

As we have explained already, the equations for an M-degree-of-freedom system in the standard form (4.49) can be transformed either via (4.51) to the first-order form (4.7) or directly to the alternative first-order form (4.66). In (4.7), the state of the system is defined by the value of the chosen output $y(t)$ together with the values of the first $(2M - 1)$ derivatives of $y(t)$†. In (4.66), the state of the system is defined by the values of the M different outputs together with the values of the M first derivatives of these outputs. Since both equations define the same system, these must be equivalent definitions and either can, in theory, be derived from the other.

General solution of *M* coupled second-order equations

We can now follow the procedure used earlier when solving (4.7) to obtain a general solution of (4.66) and hence of the set of M coupled second-

---

† Note: In (4.7) the rth derivative of $y(t)$ is denoted by $y_r(t)$ according to the definitions (4.5). In the second-order formulation, (4.49), derivatives are denoted by differentiation dots, and the subscripts identify the number of the output.

order equations (4.49). Corresponding to (4.8), we define

$$z(t) = e^{\lambda t}Z \tag{4.68}$$

where Z is the $2M \times 1$ eigencolumn vector for eigenvalue λ, and a new $2M \times 2M$ eigencolumn matrix U each of whose columns is one of the eigenvectors. The $2M$ eigenvalues are, as in (4.12), the solutions of

$$\det[A - \lambda I] = 0 \tag{4.69}$$

and, as in (4.18),

$$[\text{diag } \lambda_j] = U^{-1}AU. \tag{4.70}$$

Then, defining normal coordinates by the $2M \times 1$ vector q where, as in (4.19),

$$q = U^{-1}z \tag{4.71}$$

we conclude, as in (4.22), that

$$\frac{\text{d}}{\text{d}t} q = [\text{diag } \lambda_j]q + U^{-1}F. \tag{4.72}$$

The general solution of (4.72) is given by (4.27) and then the inverse transformation to (4.71) gives, by comparison with (4.28),

$$z(t) = U[\text{diag } e^{\lambda_j t}]\left[\int [\text{diag } e^{-\lambda_j t}]U^{-1}F(t) \, \text{d}t + C\right]. \tag{4.73}$$

This is the general solution for the set of M second-order equations (4.49). It depends on there being $2M$ distinct eigenvalues λ_j, $j = 1$ to $2M$, so that the columns of U are independent and U^{-1} exists. The $2M \times 1$ response vector $z(t)$ consists of the M elements of the displacement vector $y(t)$ in (4.49) followed, in the same order, by the elements of the velocity vector $\dot{y}(t)$. The elements of jth column of U are the corresponding elements of $y(t)$ and $\dot{y}(t)$ for free motion with time dependence for all the coordinates $e^{\lambda_j t}$, $j = 1$ to $2M$. The $2M \times 1$ excitation vector $F(t)$ is defined by (4.65), where $x \equiv x(t)$ in (4.65) is the $M \times 1$ vector of forces on the r.h.s. of (4.49). The $2M \times 1$ vector C on the right of (4.73) is a vector of arbitrary constants of integration.

Example 4.5 General response calculation

Find the response of the non-conservative two-degree-of-freedom system† defined by (4.49), where

$$m = \begin{bmatrix} 1 & 1 \\ 0 & 1 \end{bmatrix}, \quad c = \begin{bmatrix} -3 & -4 \\ 3 & 8 \end{bmatrix}, \quad k = \begin{bmatrix} -5 & -6 \\ -4 & 0 \end{bmatrix} \tag{4.74}$$

---

† This example is taken from Fawzy and Bishop [27]. The solution given here is based on that in Newland [74].

and

$$x = \begin{bmatrix} 0 \\ 0 \end{bmatrix}, \text{ for } t \leq 0$$

$$= \begin{bmatrix} 18t \\ 0 \end{bmatrix}, \text{ for } t > 0. \qquad (4.75)$$

When discussing harmonic-response characteristics in Chapters 2 and 3, we have assumed that the system being studied is conservative or, in other words, that the motion is positively damped. In that case, the initial transient motions decay away and steady harmonic conditions become established when sufficient time has elapsed since the excitation was 'switched on'. The solution (4.45) derived in this chapter for steady harmonic response depends on the same assumption that there is positive damping so that all the system's eigenvalues have negative real parts. However, the general response equations (4.28) and (4.73) are not subject to any such assumption about the form of the eigenvalues, and both apply for any linear system with constant coefficients. To illustrate this point, the system defined by equations (4.74) and (4.75) above is non-conservative and we shall see that all its eigenvalues do not have negative real parts.

Since the equations are given as a set of two second-order linear differential equations with constant coefficients we can use the general solution (4.73). As a first step, we have to find the A-matrix defined by (4.64). The inverse-mass matrix m^{-1}, which can be found either by applying the general formula (4.54) or by a simple *ad hoc* calculation, is

$$m^{-1} = \begin{bmatrix} 1 & -1 \\ 0 & 1 \end{bmatrix}.$$

Hence

$$m^{-1}k = \begin{bmatrix} -1 & -6 \\ -4 & 0 \end{bmatrix} \text{ and } m^{-1}c = \begin{bmatrix} -6 & -12 \\ 3 & 8 \end{bmatrix}$$

and so, from (4.64),

$$A = \begin{bmatrix} 0 & 0 & 1 & 0 \\ 0 & 0 & 0 & 1 \\ 1 & 6 & 6 & 12 \\ 4 & 0 & -3 & -8 \end{bmatrix}$$

and, from (4.65),

$$F = \begin{bmatrix} 0 \\ 0 \\ 0 \\ 0 \end{bmatrix} \text{ for } t \leq 0$$

$$= \begin{bmatrix} 0 \\ 0 \\ 18t \\ 0 \end{bmatrix} \text{ for } t > 0.$$

The system's eigenvalues can be calculated from the A-matrix by using a computer program or they can be found by hand calculation. From (4.69), the eigenvalues are the solutions of

$$\det \begin{bmatrix} -\lambda & 0 & 1 & 0 \\ 0 & -\lambda & 0 & 1 \\ 1 & 6 & (6-\lambda) & 12 \\ -4 & 0 & -3 & (-8-\lambda) \end{bmatrix} = 0$$

which gives

$$-\lambda\,[-\lambda\{(6-\lambda)(-8-\lambda) - (-3)(12)\} + (1)\{(6)(-3)\}] +$$

$$+ (1)\,[(1)\,\{-(4)(6)\} + (-\lambda)\{(12)\,(4) - (1)(-8-\lambda)\}]$$

$$= \lambda^4 + 2\lambda^3 - 13\lambda^2 - 38\lambda - 24$$

$$= (\lambda + 1)\,(\lambda + 2)\,(\lambda + 3)\,(\lambda - 4) = 0$$

so that

$$\lambda_1 = -1,\ \lambda_2 = -2,\ \lambda_3 = -3,\ \lambda_4 = 4.$$

From (4.14), the jth column of the eigenvector matrix U is the column vector Y_j which is the solution of

$$\lambda_j Y_j = A Y_j. \tag{4.76}$$

Beginning with $j = 1$, this gives, for the first column of U,

$$\lambda_1 \begin{bmatrix} Y_{11} \\ Y_{21} \\ Y_{31} \\ Y_{41} \end{bmatrix} = A \begin{bmatrix} Y_{11} \\ Y_{21} \\ Y_{31} \\ Y_{41} \end{bmatrix}$$

so that

$$(-1) \begin{bmatrix} Y_{11} \\ Y_{21} \\ Y_{31} \\ Y_{41} \end{bmatrix} = \begin{bmatrix} 0 & 0 & 1 & 0 \\ 0 & 0 & 0 & 1 \\ 1 & 6 & 6 & 12 \\ 4 & 0 & -3 & -8 \end{bmatrix} \begin{bmatrix} Y_{11} \\ Y_{21} \\ Y_{31} \\ Y_{41} \end{bmatrix}.$$

Hence

$$-Y_{11} = Y_{31}$$
$$-Y_{21} = Y_{41}$$

(4.77)

and

$$-Y_{31} = Y_{11} + 6Y_{21} + 6Y_{31} + 12Y_{41}$$
$$-Y_{41} = 4Y_{11} - 3Y_{31} - 8Y_{41}. \tag{4.78}$$

On substituting for Y_{31} and Y_{41} from (4.77) into (4.78), we find that both of (4.78) give the same result that

$$Y_{21} = -Y_{11}$$

and the first eigenvector is

$$Y_1 = Y_{11} \begin{bmatrix} 1 \\ -1 \\ -1 \\ 1 \end{bmatrix}$$

where Y_{11} is arbitrary. It does not matter how we choose Y_{11}, and we shall arbitrarily scale all the eigenvectors so that their first element is unity in each case. Therefore the first eigenvector, which is the first column of U is

$$Y_1 = \begin{bmatrix} 1 \\ -1 \\ -1 \\ 1 \end{bmatrix}.$$

On substituting the three other eigenvalues into (4.76) and solving for the elements of their corresponding eigenvectors, we find that, after normalization,

$$Y_2 = \begin{bmatrix} 1 \\ -5/6 \\ -2 \\ 5/3 \end{bmatrix}, \quad Y_3 = \begin{bmatrix} 1 \\ -13/15 \\ -3 \\ 13/5 \end{bmatrix}, \quad Y_4 = \begin{bmatrix} 1 \\ -1/6 \\ 4 \\ -2/3 \end{bmatrix}.$$

and therefore the eigenvector matrix in this example is

$$U = \begin{bmatrix} 1 & 1 & 1 & 1 \\ -1 & -5/6 & -13/15 & -1/6 \\ -1 & -2 & -3 & 4 \\ 1 & 5/3 & 13/5 & -2/3 \end{bmatrix}. \tag{4.79}$$

Calculation of all the eigenvectors of an A-matrix of order $n \times n$ involves the solution of n different sets of n simultaneous linear algebraic equations, one set for each different eigenvalue. Libraries of scientific computer programs include appropriate programs using one of a number of suitable algorithms, and in practical problems it is most likely that one such program will be needed. A simple eigenvector calculation procedure is explained in Chapter 7 and a corresponding logical flow diagram is included in Appendix 5.

Returning to the implementation of (4.73), we need the inverse of

U. This can be calculated from *U* either by computer or by hand from (4.54), and is

$$U^{-1} = \begin{bmatrix} -31/10 & -21/5 & 7/10 & 3/5 \\ 7 & 6 & -2 & -3 \\ -45/14 & -15/7 & 15/14 & 15/7 \\ 11/35 & 12/35 & 8/35 & 9/35 \end{bmatrix}. \quad (4.80)$$

The two remaining matrices in (4.73) that we need are

$$[\text{diag } e^{-\lambda_j t}] = \begin{bmatrix} e^t & 0 & 0 & 0 \\ 0 & e^{2t} & 0 & 0 \\ 0 & 0 & e^{3t} & 0 \\ 0 & 0 & 0 & e^{-4t} \end{bmatrix} \quad (4.81)$$

and

$$[\text{diag } e^{\lambda_j t}] = \begin{bmatrix} e^{-t} & 0 & 0 & 0 \\ 0 & e^{-2t} & 0 & 0 \\ 0 & 0 & e^{-3t} & 0 \\ 0 & 0 & 0 & e^{4t} \end{bmatrix}. \quad (4.82)$$

With these we can then complete the matrix products in (4.73) to find

$$U^{-1}F = 18t \begin{bmatrix} 7/10 \\ -2 \\ 15/14 \\ 8/35 \end{bmatrix}, \quad t > 0$$

and

$$[\text{diag } e^{-\lambda_j t}] \, U^{-1}F = 18t \begin{bmatrix} 7/10 \, e^t \\ -2 \, e^{2t} \\ 15/14 \, e^{3t} \\ 8/35 \, e^{-4t} \end{bmatrix}, \quad t > 0.$$

Next we can evaluate the integrals to find

$$\int [\text{diag } e^{-\lambda_j t}] \, U^{-1}F \, dt = \begin{bmatrix} 63/5 \, e^t(t - 1) \\ -9 \, e^{2t}(2t - 1) \\ 15/7 \, e^{3t}(3t - 1) \\ -9/35 \, e^{-4t}(4t + 1) \end{bmatrix}, \quad t > 0. \quad (4.83)$$

The response vector $z(t)$, $t > 0$, can then be calculated from (4.73). First, we note from (4.62) and (4.58) that

$$z(t) = \begin{bmatrix} y_1(t) \\ y_2(t) \\ \dot{y}_1(t) \\ \dot{y}_2(t) \end{bmatrix} \quad (4.84)$$

where y_1 and y_2 are the displacement coordinates for the (two-degree-of-freedom) system. Combining (4.84) with (4.83) in the general response equation (4.73) gives, for $t > 0$,

$$z = \begin{bmatrix} y_1 \\ y_2 \\ \dot{y}_1 \\ \dot{y}_2 \end{bmatrix} = U[\text{diag } e^{\lambda_j t}] \begin{bmatrix} 63/5 \ e^t(t-1) + C_1 \\ -9 \ e^{2t}(2t-1) + C_2 \\ 15/7 \ e^{3t}(3t-1) + C_3 \\ -9/35 \ e^{-4t}(4t+1) + C_4 \end{bmatrix}$$

which, using (4.82) to substitute for $[\text{diag } e^{\lambda_j t}]$, becomes

$$\begin{bmatrix} y_1 \\ y_2 \\ \dot{y}_1 \\ \dot{y}_2 \end{bmatrix} = U \begin{bmatrix} 63/5 \ (t-1) + C_1 \ e^{-t} \\ -9 \ (2t-1) + C_2 \ e^{-2t} \\ 15/7 \ (3t-1) + C_3 \ e^{-3t} \\ -9/35 \ (4t+1) + C_4 \ e^{4t} \end{bmatrix}$$

and, using (4.79) to substitute for U, gives

$$\begin{bmatrix} y_1 \\ y_2 \\ \dot{y}_1 \\ \dot{y}_2 \end{bmatrix} =$$

$$= \begin{bmatrix} -6 + C_1 \ e^{-t} + C_2 \ e^{-2t} + C_3 \ e^{-3t} + C_4 \ e^{4t} \\ 7 - 3t - C_1 \ e^{-t} - 5/6 \ C_2 \ e^{-2t} - 13/15 \ C_3 \ e^{-3t} - 1/6 \ C_4 \ e^{4t} \\ -C_1 \ e^{-t} - 2C_2 \ e^{-2t} - 3C_3 \ e^{-3t} + 4C_4 \ e^{4t} \\ -3 + C_1 \ e^{-t} + 5/3 \ C_2 \ e^{-2t} + 13/5 \ C_3 \ e^{-3t} - 2/3 \ C_4 \ e^{4t} \end{bmatrix},$$

for $t > 0$. $\hspace{2cm}$ (4.85)

The values of the four arbitrary constants depend on the initial conditions. For example, if we specify

$$y_1 = y_2 = \dot{y}_1 = \dot{y}_2 = 0$$

at $t = 0$, then we can solve (4.85) for C_1, C_2, C_3 and C_4 to find

$$C_1 = -63, \ C_2 = 369, \ C_3 = -1875/7, \ C_4 = -225/7$$

and in this case the complete solution for y_1 and y_2 for $t > 0$ is

$$y_1 = -6 - 63 \ e^{-t} + 369 \ e^{-2t} - (1875/7) \ e^{-3t} - (225/7) \ e^{4t}$$

and $\hspace{6cm}$ (4.86)

$$y_2 = 7 - 3t + 63 \ e^{-t} - (615/2) \ e^{-2t} + (1625/7) \ e^{-3t} + (75/14) \ e^{4t}.$$

The corresponding expressions for $\dot{y}_1$ and $\dot{y}_2$ can be found either from the lower two rows of (4.85) or by differentiating (4.86). The solutions for $t \leq 0$ can be obtained by noting that, for no excitation, the integrals in (4.83) are zero, so that the solution is the same as (4.85) except that the terms which are not multiplied by a C disappear from the right-hand side. If, at some time $t < 0$, the instantaneous values of y_1, y_2, $\dot{y}_1$ and $\dot{y}_2$ are specified, the four arbitrary constants C can be determined and then the motion is prescribed completely for all $t < 0$.

We have now covered all the matrix algebra for the analysis of linear vibration problems and in the next chapters we shall apply this to a variety of vibration-response calculations.

Chapter 5

Natural frequencies and mode shapes

Introduction

In this chapter we shall consider how to calculate the natural frequencies and mode shapes of multiple-degree-of-freedom linear systems.

First, we limit the analysis to conservative systems. The term 'conservative' means that energy is conserved, and free vibration then persists for ever. These are the simplest systems to understand and their eigenvectors are entirely real so that the motions of the different coordinates are either in phase or 180° out of phase (in anti-phase) with each other.

Later, the analysis will be applied to the general non-conservative case. Then the eigenvectors have complex components and free vibration decays (or grows, if the system is unstable) with different coordinates having different relative phases.

All except the very simplest problems require computer calculations of eigenvalues and eigenvectors, and part of this chapter is concerned with explaining how this may be done. The emphasis here is on how to apply suitable computer programs to make practical calculations. We shall not at first consider how the programs work: that is a separate subject which is discussed in Chapter 7. To illustrate the computer procedures, specimen calculations will be made using the programs for which logical flow diagrams are given in the appendices, but the reader can use alternative computer library programs instead if these are available. The basic strategy is in three parts:

(i) Organize the equations of motion so that the eigenvalue problem may be represented in the basic form

$$Az = \lambda z. \tag{5.1}$$

(ii) Use a computer program to find the eigenvalues λ of the A-matrix.
(iii) Use the same or another computer program to calculate the corresponding eigenvectors.†

---

† In some algorithms the eigenvectors are generated simultaneously with the eigenvalues, but in the general-purpose QR program described in Chapter 7 the eigenvalues only are computed. A separate program is then necessary to compute the eigenvectors.

We now pursue this strategy, beginning with the conservative case.

Conservative systems

We shall assume that the equations of motion are known and that we start with these in the standard form of (4.49) for M degrees of freedom, which for free vibration with no damping is

$$m\ddot{y} + ky = O \tag{5.2}$$

where m and k are of order $M \times M$ and have only real elements. For initial conditions such that only one mode is excited, the free vibration solution is known to be

$$y(t) = e^{i\omega t}Y \tag{5.3}$$

where ω is the natural frequency of free vibration and Y defines the relative amplitudes of the different coordinates. On substituting (5.3) into (5.2), we get

$$-\omega^2 mY + kY = O. \tag{5.4}$$

After pre-multiplying by m^{-1}, this can be written in the form

$$m^{-1}kY = \omega^2 Y \tag{5.5}$$

which is the same as (5.1) if

$$A = m^{-1}k, \tag{5.6}$$

$$z = Y \tag{5.7}$$

and

$$\lambda = \omega^2. \tag{5.8}$$

In order to determine the natural frequencies and mode shapes of the undamped M-degree-of-freedom system defined by (5.2), we have to form the A matrix according to (5.6) and then compute its eigenvalues

$$\lambda_j = \omega_j^2, j = 1 \text{ to } M \tag{5.9}$$

using a program to calculate the eigenvalues of a real matrix A, and then its eigenvectors

$$Y_j, j = 1 \text{ to } M \tag{5.10}$$

using a corresponding program to calculate eigenvectors. A logical flow diagram for this calculation is given in Fig. 5.1.

It will be shown in Chapter 11 that, for the small-amplitude vibration of most structural and many mechanical systems, the equations of motion can be arranged so that the mass and stiffness matrices m and k are symmetric matrices. The inverse mass matrix m^{-1} is then also symmetric, but in general the product $m^{-1}k$ is not symmetric and so the A matrix defined by

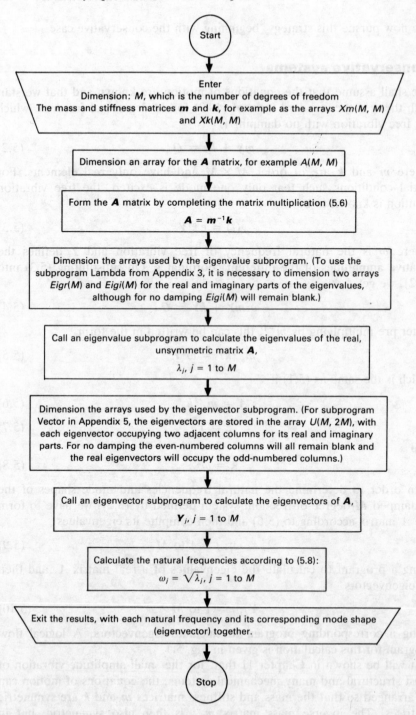

Fig. 5.1 Logical flow diagram for calculating the natural frequencies and mode shapes of an undamped linear system with M degrees of freedom

(5.6) is not a symmetric matrix. For large problems this is a disadvantage because more efficient algorithms may be used to extract the eigenvalues of a symmetric matrix than can be applied to a general non-symmetric matrix. Therefore some computer library programs take advantage of the symmetry of *m* and *k* to transform *A* to a symmetric matrix before extracting its eigenvalues. The details of this so-called similarity transformation are given in Chapter 11 but such refinement is not necessary for the examples in this chapter and we shall proceed with the calculation procedure in Fig. 5.1. This calls a general eigenvalue program for a real, unsymmetric matrix such as the QR program in Chapter 7 and the appendices.

The reader who is using a library program will probably find that the procedure in Fig. 5.1 is included in the library program and then it is only necessary to enter the elements of the $M \times M$ mass and stiffness matrices *m* and *k*.

Example calculations for undamped free vibration

Example 5.1 Systems with three degrees of freedom

First consider the three-degree-of-freedom systems in Fig. 5.2. Their behaviour is discussed in detail in Den Hartog ([18], Ch. 4) and they all have the same equations which the reader can check are given by:

$$\begin{bmatrix} m & 0 & 0 \\ 0 & m & 0 \\ 0 & 0 & m \end{bmatrix} \begin{bmatrix} \ddot{y}_1 \\ \ddot{y}_2 \\ \ddot{y}_3 \end{bmatrix} + \begin{bmatrix} 0 & 0 & 0 \\ 0 & c & 0 \\ 0 & 0 & 0 \end{bmatrix} \begin{bmatrix} \dot{y}_1 \\ \dot{y}_2 \\ \dot{y}_3 \end{bmatrix}$$

$$+ \begin{bmatrix} 2k & -k & 0 \\ -k & 2k & -k \\ 0 & -k & 2k \end{bmatrix} \begin{bmatrix} y_1 \\ y_2 \\ y_3 \end{bmatrix} = O \qquad (5.11)$$

where *m* represents mass in cases (*a*) and (*b*) and inertia in case (*c*), *c* represents the linear viscous damping coefficient in cases (*a*) and (*b*) and torsional viscous damping coefficient in case (*c*), *k* represents the linear spring stiffness in case (*a*), the transverse stiffness T/l in case (*b*) and the torsional stiffness in case (*c*). The first of these three systems was used to illustrate the analysis in Chapter 2 and is shown, in an equivalent horizontal form, in Fig. 2.7.

We shall return to the damped motion later, but for the present take $c = 0$, when (5.11) has the standard form (5.2). To make a typical calculation, we set

$$m = 1.0$$

$$k = 1.0$$

with the units being, for example, kg and N/m in cases (*a*) and (*b*), and $kg\,m^2$ and Nm/rad in case (*c*). Then we have

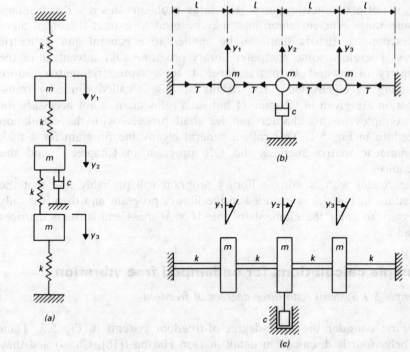

Fig. 5.2 Three vibrating systems which have the same equations of motion (5.11). In each case, displacements are measured from the static equilibrium position. In case (*b*), the effect of gravity is excluded. (*a*) Longitudinal vibration of masses and springs. (*b*) Transverse vibration of masses attached to a stretched string. (*c*) Torsional vibration of wheels on an elastic shaft

$$
m = \begin{bmatrix} 1 & 0 & 0 \\ 0 & 1 & 0 \\ 0 & 0 & 1 \end{bmatrix} \quad \text{and} \quad k = \begin{bmatrix} 2 & -1 & 0 \\ -1 & 2 & -1 \\ 0 & -1 & 2 \end{bmatrix}
$$

and, since $m^{-1} = m$, the corresponding A matrix is, from (5.6)

$$
A = \begin{bmatrix} 2 & -1 & 0 \\ -1 & 2 & -1 \\ 0 & -1 & 2 \end{bmatrix}.
$$

On carrying out the calculation in Fig. 5.1, we then find that the three eigenvalues are

$$\lambda_1 = 0.5858$$

$$\lambda_2 = 2.0000$$

$$\lambda_3 = 3.4142$$

with the units being in $(\text{rad/s})^2$. From (5.8), the corresponding natural frequencies are

$$\omega_1 = 0.7654$$

$$\omega_2 = 1.4142$$

$$\omega_3 = 1.8478$$

in rad/s. The eigenvectors come out to be

$$Y_1 = \begin{bmatrix} 1.0000 \\ 1.4142 \\ 1.0000 \end{bmatrix}, \; Y_2 = \begin{bmatrix} 1.0000 \\ 0.0000 \\ -1.0000 \end{bmatrix}, \; Y_3 = \begin{bmatrix} 1.0000 \\ -1.4142 \\ 1.0000 \end{bmatrix}.$$

The first element of each of these is given as unity but this normalization is arbitrary. Only the ratios between elements are defined and alternative eigenvector programs may normalize differently. One common method is to normalize so that the sum of the squares of the elements is equal to unity; another method is to set the element with the largest modulus equal to unity. In order to visualize mode shapes, it is helpful to set one of the elements to unity and in this book we shall set the first element to unity (unless this element is zero or very close to zero). Notice that there is a zero element in the second eigenvector Y_2 in the present example. This is because there is a node at the middle coordinate in the second mode. To the accuracy of the eigenvectors listed, which is five significant figures, this element is entered as zero, but the computer returns a very small number which is its approximation for zero. The small difference from zero is due to round-off error in the computer as a result of the finite word size (number of significant figures) at which the computer operates.

In the lowest-frequency mode, for which $\omega_1 = 0.7654$ rad/s, the three masses move in phase, with the centre mass having an amplitude 1.4142 times the amplitude of the two outer masses. The middle-frequency mode, for which $\omega_2 = 1.4142$ rad/s, has the centre mass stationary while the two outer masses move in anti-phase through equal amplitudes. The highest-frequency mode, for which $\omega_3 = 1.8478$ rad/s, has the centre mass moving in anti-phase to the two outer masses and having 1.4142 times the amplitude of the outer masses. In Problem 5.1 the reader can confirm that the exact answers for these results are

$$\lambda_1 = 2 - \sqrt{2}$$

$$\lambda_2 = 2$$

$$\lambda_3 = 2 + \sqrt{2}$$

with corresponding eigenvectors (in matrix form)

$$U = \begin{bmatrix} 1 & 1 & 1 \\ \sqrt{2} & 0 & -\sqrt{2} \\ 1 & -1 & 1 \end{bmatrix}$$

thus confirming the results in Table 2.1 of Chapter 2.

The amplitude and phase relationships for the three modes can be illustrated clearly by considering the vibration of the string in case (*b*) of Fig. 5.2. The deflection of the string, at its position of maximum amplitude, is shown in Fig. 5.3 for vibration at the natural frequencies. In mode 1 all points on the string have some amplitude of vibration (except of course the two ends); in mode 2 there is a nodal point at the middle of the string; in mode 3 there are two nodes, each located between an outer mass and the middle mass. This is characteristic of the undamped free vibration of one-dimensional systems like those in Fig. 5.2. Each higher mode has one node more than the last.

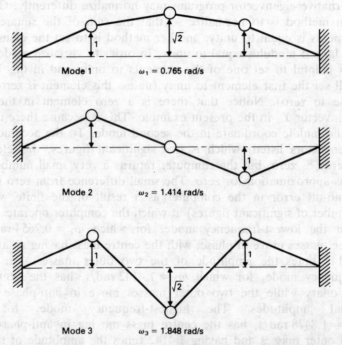

Fig. 5.3 Mode shapes for the three natural modes of each of the undamped systems shown in Fig. 5.2 when *m* = 1 kg, *k* = 1 N/m (or other consistent units)

Example 5.2 Bending vibrations of a tall chimney

Next we consider a practical problem: the vibration of a tall, free-standing industrial chimney. Because of their inherent low damping, free-standing welded-steel chimneys are prone to oscillate in the wind. There is a tendency for a steady wind to generate vortices which are shed regularly from opposite sides of the chimney. As successive vortices form and break away, they develop an alternating sideways force on the chimney, and the frequency at which this happens depends on the wind speed. When the vortex-shedding frequency is close to one of the chimney's natural frequencies for swaying oscillations, then vibrations will build up to an amplitude which, if continued long enough, will cause the chimney to fail by metal fatigue.

Whether self-excitation occurs or not has been found to depend on the overall damping in the chimney's swaying modes of vibration [89]. If there is enough damping, oscillations will not build up even though the vortex shedding frequency and a natural frequency of the chimney are the same. One method of artificially increasing the damping in the chimney is to mount the chimney on a resilient foundation incorporating bearing pads made of a high-damping material. When the chimney flexes, the resilient foundation deforms and its high damping increases the total rate of energy dissipation of the chimney.

This example involves calculating the natural frequencies and mode shapes of a seven-degree-of-freedom model of a chimney with no damping.

Later in the chapter, we shall investigate how the addition of a resilient foundation alters these results and how the damping of the lowest-frequency mode, which is the mode most likely to suffer from wind excitation, may be increased by the action of a resilient foundation incorporating a high-damping material.

Figure 5.4 shows a lumped-parameter model of a chimney in which the chimney is modelled by seven rigid, massless bars hinged together. The flexural rigidity of the chimney is represented by rotational springs, k, at each joint; the mass of the chimney is represented by point masses, m, located at the centre of each rod. The seven coordinates, y_1 to y_7, give the lateral movement of the ends of the rods, as shown in the figure. The equations of motion may be found in various ways. One method is to consider rotational equilibrium about successive hinge joints, starting from the top of the chimney. This process is helped by employing d'Alembert's principle, which allows the problem to be reduced to one of statical analysis by assuming that static forces (equal to mass times acceleration) act at each point mass, with their directions being opposite to those of the assumed accelerations of each mass.

For the top bar, rotational equilibrium about its hinge requires that

$$mg \frac{(y_7 - y_6)}{2} - \frac{m}{2}(\ddot{y}_7 + \ddot{y}_6)\frac{l}{2} = k\left(\frac{y_7 - y_6}{l} - \frac{y_6 - y_5}{l}\right). \quad (5.12)$$

For rotational equilibrium of the top two bars taken together about the second joint from the top,

$$mg\left(\frac{y_7 + y_6}{2} - y_5\right) + mg\frac{(y_6 - y_5)}{2} - \frac{m}{2}(\ddot{y}_7 + \ddot{y}_6)\left(\frac{3l}{2}\right) -$$

$$- \frac{m}{2}(\ddot{y}_6 + \ddot{y}_5)\frac{l}{2} = k\left(\frac{y_6 - y_5}{l} - \frac{y_5 - y_4}{l}\right) \quad (5.13)$$

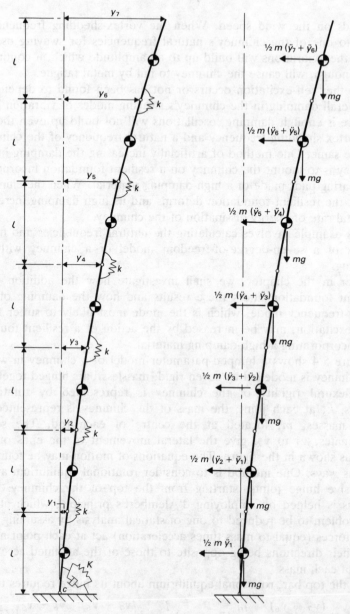

Fig. 5.4 Idealized model of a flexible chimney on a resilient foundation with damping

and, for the top three bars taken together about the third joint from the top

$$mg\left(\frac{y_7 + y_6}{2} - y_4\right) + mg\left(\frac{y_6 + y_5}{2} - y_4\right) + mg\left(\frac{y_5 - y_4}{2}\right) -$$

$$- \frac{m}{2}(\ddot{y}_7 + \ddot{y}_6)\frac{5l}{2} - \frac{m}{2}(\ddot{y}_6 + \ddot{y}_5)\frac{3l}{2} - \frac{m}{2}(\ddot{y}_5 + \ddot{y}_4)\frac{l}{2}$$

$$= k\left(\frac{y_5 - y_4}{l} - \frac{y_4 - y_3}{l}\right) \qquad (5.14)$$

and so on, until the bottom joint has been reached. No damping is assumed except at the bottom joint, where the rotational damping coefficient is the viscous element c. Initially, we shall take this to be zero, but we retain it in the equations for later use.

All these equations fall into the standard form

$$m\ddot{y} + c\dot{y} + ky = O \qquad (5.15)$$

where we have

$$m = \frac{ml}{4}\begin{bmatrix} 0 & 0 & 0 & 0 & 0 & 1 & 1 \\ 0 & 0 & 0 & 0 & 1 & 4 & 3 \\ 0 & 0 & 0 & 1 & 4 & 8 & 5 \\ 0 & 0 & 1 & 4 & 8 & 12 & 7 \\ 0 & 1 & 4 & 8 & 12 & 16 & 9 \\ 1 & 4 & 8 & 12 & 16 & 20 & 11 \\ 4 & 8 & 12 & 16 & 20 & 24 & 13 \end{bmatrix}$$

$$(5.16)$$

and

$$k = \frac{mg}{2} \times$$

$$\begin{bmatrix} 0 & 0 & 0 & 0 & \frac{2k}{mgl} & \left(-\frac{4k}{mgl}+1\right) & \left(\frac{2k}{mgl}-1\right) \\ 0 & 0 & 0 & \frac{2k}{mgl} & \left(-\frac{4k}{mgl}+3\right) & \left(\frac{2k}{mgl}-2\right) & -1 \\ 0 & 0 & \frac{2k}{mgl} & \left(-\frac{4k}{mgl}+5\right) & \left(\frac{2k}{mgl}-2\right) & -2 & -1 \\ 0 & \frac{2k}{mgl} & \left(-\frac{4k}{mgl}+7\right) & \left(\frac{2k}{mgl}-2\right) & -2 & -2 & -1 \\ \frac{2k}{mgl} & \left(-\frac{4k}{mgl}+9\right) & \left(\frac{2k}{mgl}-2\right) & -2 & -2 & -2 & -1 \\ \left(-\frac{4k}{mgl}+11\right) & \left(\frac{2k}{mgl}-2\right) & -2 & -2 & -2 & -2 & -1 \\ \left(\frac{2K}{mgl}-2\right) & -2 & -2 & -2 & -2 & -2 & -1 \end{bmatrix}$$

$$(5.17)$$

The damping matrix c has all its elements zero except for $c_{7,1} = c/l$.

If derived in other ways, the mass, damping and stiffness matrices may look quite different from those obtained above, but that is only because the equations are organized in different forms. For example, any two rows of all the matrices may be added together without altering the equations of motion (see Problem 5.2). The physical dimensions of the elements in the m, c and k matrices also look peculiar at first sight until it is recognized that they relate to the equations of moment equilibrium where, in (5.15), the coordinates y have the dimensions of length. Hence if M, L, T denote the dimensions of mass, length and time, the dimensions of the elements of m are ML, the dimensions of the elements of c are MLT^{-1} and those of k are MLT^{-2}.

As a numerical example, we now take the case of a typical steel chimney which is 42 m high, 2.25 m diameter, has a wall thickness of 6.8 mm, and a total weight of 21 tonnes. Then the length of each link in the model of Fig. 5.4 is $l = 6$ m and the mass per link is $m = 3\,000$ kg. In order to find the rotational stiffness between adjacent links, k, we need to find the bending stiffness of a 6 m length of the chimney, Fig. 5.5. From Euler beam theory, we have

$$\phi = \frac{Ml}{EI} \tag{5.18}$$

where ϕ is the angle of rotational deflection of the two ends of a beam of length l subjected to a bending moment M. EI is the bending stiffness of the beam, where E is Young's modulus and I is the second moment of area of the beam's cross-section which is given by

$$I = \frac{\pi}{64} [D^4 - (D - 2t)^4] \simeq \frac{\pi}{8} D^3 t \tag{5.19}$$

when the wall thickness t is much less than the diameter D. Substituting (5.19) into (5.18), gives

$$k = \frac{M}{\phi} = \frac{EI}{l} = \frac{\pi}{8} \frac{ED^3 t}{l} \tag{5.20}$$

and for

$$E = 2.1 \times 10^{11} \text{ N/m}^2$$

$$D = 2.25 \text{ m}$$

$$t = 6.8 \text{ mm}$$

$$l = 6 \text{ m}$$

we find that $k = 1 \times 10^9$ N m/rad approximately.

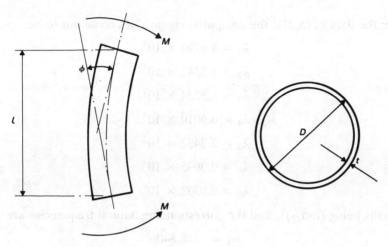

Fig. 5.5 Bending deflection of a straight beam of length *l* under a bending moment *M*. The beam's cross-section is shown in the right-hand view

The rotational stiffness K at the bottom of the chimney is determined by two factors: the flexibility of the lower half of the bottom link shown in Fig. 5.4, and the flexibility of the foundation. Assuming, initially, that the foundation is completely rigid, we shall put $K = 2k = 2 \times 10^9$ N m/rad. The full set of parameter values for the chimney model in Fig. 5.4 is then

length of link	$l = 6$ m
mass per link	$m = 3 \times 10^3$ kg
rotational stiffness between links	$k = 10^9$ N m/rad
rotational stiffness at ground level	$K = 2 \times 10^9$ N m/rad
rotational damping at ground level	$c = 0$
acceleration due to gravity	$g = 9.81$ m/s^2.

(5.21)

We are now ready to make the eigenvalue and eigenvector calculations for the undamped case, following the same calculation procedure as before, Fig. 5.1. In this example, the dimensions of the mass and stiffness matrices are 7×7, so that the A matrix calculated from (5.6) also has dimensions 7×7. There are seven natural frequencies, which have to be calculated from the seven eigenvalues by (5.8), and there are seven corresponding mode shapes which are defined by the eigenvectors. For each mode, the ratios between the amplitudes of vibration in successive coordinates are given by the elements of the corresponding eigenvector.

For the data in (5.21), the computed eigenvalues come out to be

$$\lambda_1 = 4.6793 \times 10^1$$

$$\lambda_2 = 1.8542 \times 10^3$$

$$\lambda_3 = 1.5234 \times 10^4$$

$$\lambda_4 = 6.6010 \times 10^5$$

$$\lambda_5 = 2.3452 \times 10^5$$

$$\lambda_6 = 9.3095 \times 10^5$$

$$\lambda_7 = 9.9352 \times 10^6$$

the units being $(rad/s)^2$, and the corresponding natural frequencies are

$$\omega_1 = \quad 6.8406$$

$$\omega_2 = \quad 43.060$$

$$\omega_3 = \quad 123.43$$

$$\omega_4 = \quad 256.92$$

$$\omega_5 = \quad 484.27$$

$$\omega_6 = \quad 964.86$$

$$\omega_7 = 3152.0$$

with the units in rad/s.

The eigenvectors which correspond to these eigenvalues are listed, with the eigenvalues and natural frequencies, in Table 5.1.

Table 5.1 Eigenvectors of the seven-degree-of-freedom chimney in Fig. 5.4 when $l = 6$ m, $m = 3 \times 10^3$ kg, $k = 10^9$ N m/rad, $K = 2 \times 10^9$ N m/rad and $c = 0$. These mode shapes are illustrated in Fig. 5.6

Eigenvector no. 1 corresponding to eigenvalue:		Eigenvector no. 2 corresponding to eigenvalue:	
Real part	Imag. part	Real part	Imag. part
+4.679 E+01	+0.000 E+00	+1.854 E+03	+0.000 E+00
for which the natural frequency is:		for which the natural frequency is:	
+6.841 E+00 rad/s		+4.306 E+01 rad/s	
is as follows:		is as follows:	
+1.000 E+00	+0.000 E+00	+1.000 E+00	+0.000 E+00
+3.605 E+00	+0.000 E+00	+2.569 E+00	+0.000 E+00
+7.426 E+00	+0.000 E+00	+3.503 E+00	+0.000 E+00
+1.209 E+01	+0.000 E+00	+3.084 E+00	+0.000 E+00
+1.727 E+01	+0.000 E+00	+1.226 E+00	+0.000 E+00
+2.270 E+01	+0.000 E+00	−1.609 E+00	+0.000 E+00
+2.819 E+01	+0.000 E+00	−4.763 E+00	+0.000 E+00

Eigenvector no. 3 corresponding to eigenvalue:	
Real part	Imag. part
+1.523 E+04	+0.000 E+00
for which the natural frequency is: +1.234 E+02 rad/s	
is as follows:	
+1.000 E+00	+0.000 E+00
+1.535 E+00	+0.000 E+00
+5.936 E−01	+0.000 E+00
−9.150 E−01	+0.000 E+00
−1.339 E+00	+0.000 E+00
−8.664 E−02	+0.000 E+00
+1.920 E+00	+0.000 E+00

Eigenvector no. 4 corresponding to eigenvalue:	
Real part	Imag. part
+6.601 E+04	+0.000 E+00
for which the natural frequency is: +2.569 E+02 rad/s	
is as follows:	
+1.000 E+00	+0.000 E+00
+4.379 E−01	+0.000 E+00
−9.016 E−01	+0.000 E+00
−4.972 E−01	+0.000 E+00
+8.517 E−01	+0.000 E+00
+4.837 E−01	+0.000 E+00
−1.250 E+00	+0.000 E+00

Eigenvector no. 5 corresponding to eigenvalue:	
Real part	Imag. part
+2.345 E+05	+0.000 E+00
for which the natural frequency is: +4.843 E+02 rad/s	
is as follows:	
+1.000 E+00	+0.000 E+00
−5.985 E−01	+0.000 E+00
−5.167 E−01	+0.000 E+00
+1.003 E+00	+0.000 E+00
−2.630 E−01	+0.000 E+00
−7.716 E−01	+0.000 E+00
+1.156 E+00	+0.000 E+00

Eigenvector no. 6 corresponding to eigenvalue:	
Real part	Imag. part
+9.310 E+05	+0.000 E+00
for which the natural frequency is: +9.649 E+02 rad/s	
is as follows:	
+1.000 E+00	+0.000 E+00
−1.445 E+00	+0.000 E+00
+1.184 E+00	+0.000 E+00
−3.424 E−01	+0.000 E+00
−6.667 E−01	+0.000 E+00
+1.343 E+00	+0.000 E+00
+1.538 E+00	+0.000 E+00

Eigenvector no. 7 corresponding to eigenvalue:	
Real part	Imag. part
+9.935 E+06	+0.000 E+00
for which the natural frequency is: +3.152 E+03 rad/s	
is as follows:	
+1.000 E+00	+0.000 E+00
−1.935 E+00	+0.000 E+00
+2.758 E+00	+0.000 E+00
−3.421 E+00	+0.000 E+00
+3.885 E+00	+0.000 E+00
−4.125 E+00	+0.000 E+00
+4.186 E+00	+0.000 E+00

The eigenvector matrix has order 7×7 and each eigenvector is one of its columns, as follows

$$U = \begin{bmatrix} 1 & 1 & 1 & 1 & 1 & 1 & 1 \\ 3.6 & 2.6 & 1.5 & 0.4 & -0.6 & -1.4 & -1.9 \\ 7.4 & 3.5 & 0.6 & -0.9 & -0.5 & 1.2 & 2.8 \\ 12.1 & 3.1 & -0.9 & -0.5 & 1.0 & -0.3 & -3.4 \\ 17.3 & 1.2 & -1.3 & 0.9 & -0.3 & -0.7 & 3.9 \\ 22.7 & -1.6 & -0.1 & 0.5 & -0.8 & 1.3 & -4.1 \\ 28.2 & -4.8 & 1.9 & -1.2 & 1.2 & -1.5 & 4.2 \end{bmatrix}$$

with the elements given to one decimal place.

This data has been used to draw Fig. 5.6, which shows the chimney's mode shapes plotted in the order of their ascending natural frequencies. We see that the first mode does not have a nodal point, the second mode has one node, the third mode has two nodes, and so on. This leads to a description of each mode by the number of nodes it possesses. For example, the lowest-frequency mode is called the zero-node mode, and the highest-frequency mode (for this model) is called the six-node mode.

Example 5.3 Torsional vibrations of a diesel-electric generator system

The next calculation is for a six-cylinder diesel engine and flywheel driving an electric generator, Fig. 5.7. The problem is one of torsional vibration. The harmonics of the engine's torque may cause serious torsional vibrations if the speed of rotation is such that an excitation frequency is close to one of the natural frequencies of the system (see, for example, Den Hartog [18], Ch. 5). It is important to know the natural frequencies so that the system can be designed to avoid unintended resonances.

The particular system chosen for this example was discussed in a paper published in 1957 about an improvement to the approximate Holzer method for calculating torsional natural frequencies by hand (Crandall and Strang [17]). At the time there was great interest in such approximate methods, but now these have been superseded by eigenvalue computer methods and we are able to find natural frequencies and mode shapes in seconds using standard computer library programs.

The system in Fig. 5.7 has eight degrees of freedom corresponding to the eight coordinates needed to specify the angular positions of the eight wheels. Let the angles ϕ_1 to ϕ_8 shown in Fig. 5.7 define the

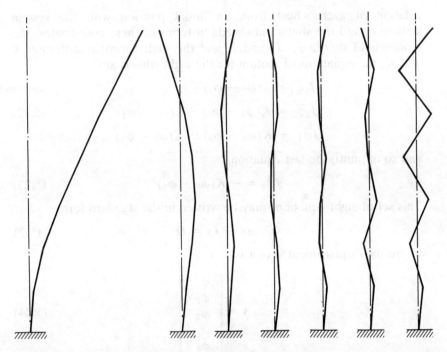

Fig. 5.6 Eigenvectors for the undamped chimney in Fig. 5.4 when $l = 6$ m, $m = 3000$ kg, $k = 10^9$ N m/rad, $K = 2 \times 10^9$ N m/rad, $c = 0$

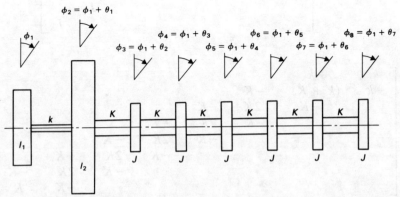

Fig. 5.7 Torsional vibration system representing a six-cylinder diesel engine with flywheel (wheel I_2) driving an electric generator (wheel I_1). The wheels are assumed to be rigid and the elastic shafts to be massless

rotation of each wheel from an initial position with the system stationary and the shafts untwisted. In terms of these coordinates, the moments of inertia I_1, I_2 and J, and the shaft torsional stiffnesses k and K, the equations of motion for the eight wheels are

$$I_1\ddot{\phi}_1 = k(\phi_2 - \phi_1)$$
$$I_2\ddot{\phi}_2 = K(\phi_3 - \phi_2) - k(\phi_2 - \phi_1) \qquad (5.22)$$
$$J\ddot{\phi}_3 = K(\phi_4 - \phi_3) - K(\phi_3 - \phi_2)$$

and so on, until the last equation

$$J\ddot{\phi}_8 = - K(\phi_8 - \phi_7). \qquad (5.23)$$

This set of eight equations may be written in the standard form

$$m\ddot{y} + ky = O \qquad (5.2)$$

where the displacement vector is

$$y = \begin{bmatrix} \phi_1 \\ \phi_2 \\ \phi_3 \\ \vdots \\ \phi_8 \end{bmatrix} \qquad (5.24)$$

and the mass and stiffness matrices are

$$m = \begin{bmatrix} I_1 & & & & & & & \\ & I_2 & & & & & & \\ & & J & & & & & \\ & & & J & & & & \\ & & & & J & & & \\ & & & & & J & & \\ & & & & & & J & \\ & & & & & & & J \end{bmatrix} \qquad (5.25)$$

and

$$k = \begin{bmatrix} k & -k & & & & & & \\ -k & (k+K) & -K & & & & & \\ & -K & 2K & -K & & & & \\ & & -K & 2K & -K & & & \\ & & & -K & 2K & -K & & \\ & & & & -K & 2K & -K & \\ & & & & & -K & 2K & -K \\ & & & & & & -K & K \end{bmatrix}$$

$$(5.26)$$

All elements not shown in these square matrices are zero elements. Since m is a diagonal matrix, its inverse can be written down immediately as

$$m^{-1} = \begin{bmatrix} I_1^{-1} & & & & & & & \\ & I_2^{-1} & & & & & & \\ & & J^{-1} & & & & & \\ & & & J^{-1} & & & & \\ & & & & J^{-1} & & & \\ & & & & & J^{-1} & & \\ & & & & & & J^{-1} & \\ & & & & & & & J^{-1} \end{bmatrix}$$

$$(5.27)$$

and so, in this problem, the A matrix is

$$A = m^{-1}k =$$

$$\begin{bmatrix} -k/I_1 & k/I_1 & & & & & & \\ k/I_2 & -\dfrac{(k+K)}{I_2} & K/I_2 & & & & & \\ & K/J & -2K/J & K/J & & & & \\ & & K/J & -2K/J & K/J & & & \\ & & & K/J & -2K/J & K/J & & \\ & & & & K/J & -2K/J & K/J & \\ & & & & & K/J & -2K/J & K/J \\ & & & & & & K/J & -K/J \end{bmatrix}.$$

$$(5.28)$$

We are now able to proceed with the calculation of this system's eigenvalues and vectors, following the procedure in Fig. 5.1. The following numerical data will be assumed, which is the same data as used by Crandall and Strang [17].

Moments of inertia

$$I_1 = 24000 \text{ lb inch s}^2 = 2715.0 \text{ kg m}^2$$

$$I_2 = 75000 \text{ lb inch s}^2 = 8484.4 \text{ kg m}^2$$

$$J = 2560 \text{ lb inch s}^2 = 289.6 \text{ kg m}^2$$

Shaft stiffnesses

$$k = 13.5 \times 10^6 \text{ lb inch/rad} = 1.527 \times 10^6 \text{ N m/rad}$$

$$K = 6.75 \times 10^8 \text{ lb inch/rad} = 7.636 \times 10^7 \text{ N m/rad}.$$

$$(5.29)$$

The results are as follows:

Eigenvalues	Corresponding frequency (rad/s)	(Hz)
-3.292×10^{-6}	—	—
7.107×10^{2}	26.66	4.243
1.800×10^{4}	134.2	21.35
1.351×10^{5}	367.5	58.49
3.423×10^{5}	585.0	93.11
5.921×10^{5}	769.5	122.5
8.275×10^{5}	909.7	144.8
9.944×10^{5}	997.2	158.7

The first of these eigenvalues is the computer's error for zero. By considering the mechanics of the system of wheels and shafts in Fig. 5.7, we know that one solution for its free motion is just rigid-body rotation of the whole system. Provided that the system is not restrained by any connection to a fixed support, which it is not, then steady rotation can continue at any arbitrary angular speed. Since the direction of this rotation never reverses, its frequency of reversal is zero, and we have a zero-frequency rigid-body mode. The eigenvalue for this solution is $\lambda_1 = 0$, and the corresponding eigenvector is

$$Y_1 = \begin{bmatrix} \phi_1 \\ \phi_2 \\ \phi_3 \\ \vdots \\ \phi_8 \end{bmatrix} = \begin{bmatrix} 1 \\ 1 \\ 1 \\ \vdots \\ 1 \end{bmatrix}. \tag{5.30}$$

We can easily check that this solution satisfies (5.1) by substituting for A from (5.28) and $z = Y_1$ from (5.30). Working out the matrix multiplication Az, we see the each element in the resulting column vector is the sum of the elements in the corresponding row of the A matrix. Since the elements in each row of A add up to zero, it follows that the left-hand side of (5.1) is zero and equals the right-hand side which is zero because the eigenvalue λ_1 is zero.

Although the eigenvalue subprogram Lambda (Appendix 3) and the eigenvector subprogram Vector (Appendix 5) will work when there is a zero eigenvalue, the calculation loses accuracy because of the (theoretically infinite) difference in the order of magnitude of the largest and smallest eigenvalues (see Problem 5.3). More accurate results can be obtained by reframing the problem so that the zero eigenvalue is avoided.

This can be done by selecting new coordinates $\theta_1, \theta_2, \ldots, \theta_7$, chosen to represent the angle of twist of the shafts. Instead of measuring the angular movement of the wheels from a fixed datum, we now measure the relative angular movement of adjacent wheels, so that

$$\phi_2 = \phi_1 + \theta_1, \; \phi_3 = \phi_1 + \theta_2, \; \text{etc.} \qquad (5.31)$$

as shown in Fig. 5.7. Now writing the equations of motion of the separate wheels in terms of $\theta_1, \theta_2, \ldots, \theta_7$, we obtain

$$I_1 \ddot{\phi}_1 = k\theta_1$$

$$I_2(\ddot{\phi}_1 + \ddot{\theta}_1) = K(\theta_2 - \theta_1) - k\theta_1 \qquad (5.32)$$

$$J(\ddot{\phi}_1 + \ddot{\theta}_2) = K(\theta_3 - \theta_2) - K(\theta_2 - \theta_1)$$

and so on, until

$$J(\ddot{\phi}_1 + \ddot{\theta}_7) = - K(\theta_7 - \theta_6). \qquad (5.33)$$

By using the first of (5.32), we can eliminate $\ddot{\phi}_1$ and we are then left with the following seven equations of motion for the system

$$I_2 \ddot{\theta}_1 = - k \frac{I_2}{I_1} \theta_1 + K(\theta_2 - \theta_1) - k\theta_1$$

$$J\ddot{\theta}_2 = - k \frac{J}{I_1} \theta_1 + K(\theta_3 - \theta_2) - K(\theta_2 - \theta_1)$$

$$\vdots \qquad \vdots \qquad \vdots \qquad \qquad (5.34)$$

$$J\ddot{\theta}_7 = - k \frac{J}{I_1} \theta_1 - K(\theta_7 - \theta_6).$$

When written in the standard form (5.2), we have

$$y = \begin{bmatrix} \theta_1 \\ \theta_2 \\ \vdots \\ \theta_7 \end{bmatrix}, \qquad (5.35)$$

$$m = \begin{bmatrix} I_2 & & & & & & \\ & J & & & & & \\ & & J & & & & \\ & & & J & & & \\ & & & & J & & \\ & & & & & J & \\ & & & & & & J \end{bmatrix}, \qquad (5.36)$$

and

$$k = \begin{bmatrix} k + K + k\dfrac{I_2}{I_1} & -K \\ -K + k\dfrac{J}{I_1} & 2K & -K \\ k\dfrac{J}{I_1} & & -K & 2K & -K \\ k\dfrac{J}{I_1} & & & -K & 2K & -K \\ k\dfrac{J}{I_1} & & & & -K & 2K & -K \\ k\dfrac{J}{I_1} & & & & & -K & 2K & -K \\ k\dfrac{J}{I_1} & & & & & & -K & K \end{bmatrix}.$$

(5.37)

Using the same numerical parameter values as before, and following the standard procedure in Fig. 5.1, we then obtain a set of eigenvalues which is identical with that obtained before except that the zero eigenvalue is eliminated from the list.

In Table 5.2, the eigenvector for the lowest-frequency twisting mode is listed, (a) when calculated from the eight-degree-of-freedom model, and (b) when calculated from the seven-degree-of-freedom model. The eigenvectors look completely different. This is because they describe different coordinates. In case (a), the elements of the eigenvector give the absolute angles of rotation of the eight wheels. In case (b), the elements of the eigenvector give the angles of rotation of wheels 2 to 8 measured relative to the angle of rotation of the first wheel (wheel I_1). The fact that both eigenvectors represent the same deflection pattern can be seen by calculating the relative angles from the absolute angles. These are

$$\phi_2 - \phi_1 = -0.2637 - 1.0000 = -1.2637 = \theta_1$$

$$\phi_3 - \phi_2 = -0.2681 + 0.2637 = -0.0044 = \theta_2 - \theta_1$$

$$\phi_4 - \phi_3 = -0.2719 + 0.2681 = -0.0038 = \theta_3 - \theta_2$$

$$\phi_5 - \phi_4 = -0.2749 + 0.2719 = -0.0030 = \theta_4 - \theta_3 \quad (5.38)$$

$$\phi_6 - \phi_5 = -0.2771 + 0.2749 = -0.0022 = \theta_5 - \theta_4$$

$$\phi_7 - \phi_6 = -0.2786 + 0.2771 = -0.0015 = \theta_6 - \theta_5$$

$$\phi_8 - \phi_7 = -0.2794 + 0.2786 = -0.0008 = \theta_7 - \theta_6.$$

Normalizing the relative angles so that $\theta_1 = \phi_2 - \phi_1 = 1$, we then obtain

Table 5.2 Results for the lowest (non-zero) frequency eigenvector of the torsional system in Fig. 5.7. The coordinates in case (*a*) are angles ϕ_1 to ϕ_8, listed in order; in case (*b*) they are angles θ_1 to θ_7

(a) 8 degrees of freedom   (b) 7 degrees of freedom

Eigenvector no. 2 corresponding to eigenvalue:		Eigenvector no 1. corresponding to eigenvalue:	
Real part	Imag. part	Real part	Imag. part
+7.1073 E+02	+0.0000 E+00	+7.1073 E+02	+0.0000 E+00
is as follows:		is as follows:	
+1.0000 E+00	+0.0000 E+00	+1.0000 E+00	+0.0000 E+00
−2.6368 E−01	+0.0000 E+00	+1.0035 E+00	+0.0000 E+00
−2.6813 E−01	+0.0000 E+00	+1.0065 E+00	+0.0000 E+00
−2.7185 E−01	+0.0000 E+00	+1.0088 E+00	+0.0000 E+00
−2.7485 E−01	+0.0000 E+00	+1.0106 E+00	+0.0000 E+00
−2.7710 E−01	+0.0000 E+00	+1.0118 E+00	+0.0000 E+00
−2.7860 E−01	+0.0000 E+00	+1.0124 E+00	+0.0000 E+00
−2.7935 E−01	+0.0000 E+00		

$$\theta_1 = 1$$

$$\theta_2 = 1 + \frac{0.0044}{1.2637} = 1.0035$$

$$\theta_3 = \theta_2 + \frac{0.0038}{1.2637} = 1.0065$$

$$\theta_4 = \theta_3 + \frac{0.0030}{1.2637} = 1.0089 \tag{5.39}$$

$$\theta_5 = \theta_4 + \frac{0.0022}{1.2637} = 1.0106$$

$$\theta_6 = \theta_5 + \frac{0.0015}{1.2637} = 1.0118$$

$$\theta_7 = \theta_6 + \frac{0.0008}{1.2637} = 1.0124$$

which agree with the results listed in Table 5.2(*b*).

This lowest-frequency twisting mode is one in which the engine, represented by the six wheels J and its flywheel I_2, swings almost as a rigid unit against the electric generator, represented by the wheel I_1. The mode shape is illustrated in Fig. 5.8, which is drawn from the data in Table 5.2. For that mode only, the equations of motion reduce approximately to

$$I_1 \ddot{\phi}_1 = k\theta_1 \tag{5.40}$$

and

$$(I_2 + 6J)(\ddot{\phi}_1 + \ddot{\theta}_1) = -k\theta_1. \tag{5.41}$$

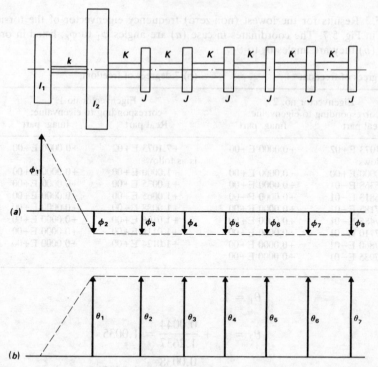

Fig. 5.8 Lowest (non-zero) frequency mode shape for the system shown above when the parameter values are as specified in equations (5.29). (*a*) Eight-degree-of-freedom model: data from Table 5.2(*a*). Seven-degree-of-freedom model: data from Table 5.2(*b*)

Eliminating $\ddot{\phi}_1$ we have

$$(I_2 + 6J)\ddot{\phi}_1 + \left(\frac{I_2 + 6J}{I_1} k + k\right)\theta_1 = 0 \qquad (5.42)$$

and the natural frequency is given by

$$f = \frac{\omega}{2\pi} = \frac{1}{2\pi}\left[\frac{\dfrac{I_2 + 6J}{I_1} k + k}{I_2 + 6J}\right]^{1/2} \qquad (5.43)$$

which, with the parameter values listed above, gives

$$f = \frac{\omega}{2\pi} = 4.246 \text{ Hz}$$

which is very close to the exact value of 4.243 Hz.

Finally, before leaving this problem, we note that reducing the number of degrees of freedom from eight to seven has eliminated one of the coordinates of the system. This was done by substituting for $\ddot{\phi}_1$ from the first of equations (5.32) into the other equations (5.32). Notice that the equations must be written in such a manner that one coordinate can be removed by elimination without destroying the standard form of the equations required for the eigenvalue calculation. With the equations of motion in their original form (5.22, 5.23), that would not have been possible.

This procedure for eliminating one degree of freedom is sometimes called *static condensation* of the equations because the equations are condensed in their order before the dynamic calculation begins. The same approach can be used when one of the masses in a system is zero. In that case the inverse mass matrix m^{-1} does not exist and the method we have described will not work unless the degree of freedom associated with the zero mass is condensed out before the calculation begins.

As an example, consider the system shown in Fig. 5.7 for the case when the flywheel inertia I_2 is zero. In that case equations (5.22) become

$$I_1\ddot{\phi}_1 = k(\phi_2 - \phi_1)$$

$$0 = K(\phi_3 - \phi_2) - k(\phi_2 - \phi_1) \tag{5.44}$$

$$J\ddot{\phi}_3 = K(\phi_4 - \phi_3) - K(\phi_3 - \phi_2)$$

and so on. The equation with zero inertia may be condensed out quite simply by solving for ϕ_2 in terms of ϕ_1 and ϕ_3 from the second equation, and then substituting this result into all the other equations (5.44) to eliminate the coordinate ϕ_2 and so reduce the number of degrees of freedom by one.

Non-conservative systems

For the general (linear) case, the equations of motion are assumed to have the standard form (4.49). For free vibration there is no excitation, so that $x = 0$, and

$$m\ddot{y} + c\dot{y} + ky = 0 \tag{5.45}$$

where m, c and k are each real matrices which have order $M \times M$ if there are M degrees of freedom. The solution of (5.45) is of the form

$$y(t) = e^{\lambda t}Y \tag{5.46}$$

where

$$\lambda^2 mY + \lambda cY + kY = 0. \tag{5.47}$$

This is not convenient for calculating the eigenvalues because it is not in the standard first-order form (5.1). However, following the same general approach as in Chapter 4, we define a new $M \times 1$ vector W by

$$W = \lambda Y \tag{5.48}$$

so that (5.47) may be rewritten in the form

$$\lambda m W + c W + k Y = O. \tag{5.49}$$

On rearranging the order of (5.48) and (5.49), we then obtain the pair of matrix equations

$$\lambda Y = W$$

and $$\tag{5.50}$$

$$\lambda W = -m^{-1}kY - m^{-1}cW.$$

As in Chapter 4, these may be combined into the single matrix equation

$$\lambda \begin{bmatrix} Y \\ W \end{bmatrix} = \begin{bmatrix} O & I \\ -m^{-1}k & -m^{-1}c \end{bmatrix} \begin{bmatrix} Y \\ W \end{bmatrix}. \tag{5.51}$$

By defining

$$Z = \begin{bmatrix} Y \\ W \end{bmatrix} \tag{5.52}$$

and

$$A = \begin{bmatrix} O & I \\ -m^{-1}k & -m^{-1}c \end{bmatrix} \tag{5.53}$$

this can then be written in the standard first-order form

$$AZ = \lambda Z \tag{5.54}$$

from which the eigenvalues and eigenvectors can be calculated following the same strategy as before, but with the logical flow diagram of Fig. 5.1 now replaced by that in Fig. 5.9.

To implement this strategy, it is convenient to prepare a suitable subprogram to form the A matrix from the m, c and k matrices. In general, the A matrix cannot be transformed to symmetric form, and the eigenvalue program used to extract the eigenvalues of A must be a program suitable for a real, unsymmetric matrix, such as the QR program described in Chapter 7 and in the appendices.

For M degrees of freedom, the A matrix will be of order $2M \times 2M$, and there will be $2M$ eigenvalues which will either be real or will occur in complex-conjugate pairs. This is necessary because if $\lambda = \alpha + i\omega$ satisfies the determinant (4.12), the real and imaginary parts of (4.12) must be separately zero, and so $\lambda^* = \alpha - i\omega$ will also satisfy (4.12). Each complex eigenvalue will be accompanied by a complex eigenvector. Together these satisfy equation (5.47), whose real and imaginary parts must be separately zero. It follows that complex eigenvectors also occur in complex conjugate pairs because, if (5.47) is satisfied by λ and Y, then it will also be satisfied by λ^* and Y^*.

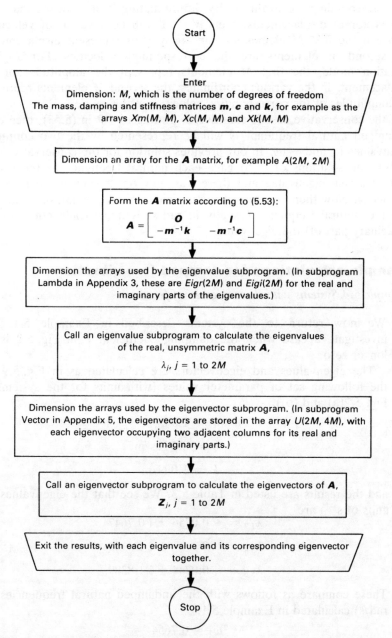

Fig. 5.9 Logical flow diagram for calculating the natural frequencies and mode shapes of a damped linear system with M degrees of freedom

The eigenvectors now have $2M$ elements, the first M of which are the elements of Y in (5.46), and the second M of which are the elements of W which, from (5.48), are the same as Y except that they are multiplied by the corresponding eigenvalue λ. By differentiating (5.46), we see that, if Y is a vector of displacements, then $W = \lambda Y$ will be a vector of velocities. Hence if the first M elements of an eigenvector represent displacements, the second M elements are the corresponding velocities. For a given vibration mode, the first M elements represent the amplitudes of the displacements in the various coordinates; the second M elements represent the amplitudes of the corresponding velocities in this mode.

If the conservative case is considered, putting $c = O$ in (5.53), then each undamped natural frequency ω will be represented by the two conjugate eigenvalues $i\omega$ and $-i\omega$. In our previous solution for the conservative case (only), the solutions of (5.5) gave each natural frequency as the square root of a real eigenvalue and there was only one eigenvalue per natural frequency. Now there are two imaginary eigenvalues per natural frequency and the natural frequency (usually in rad/s) is numerically equal to the (imaginary part of) the eigenvalue.

Example calculations for damped free vibration

Example 5.4 Systems with three degrees of freedom

We now return to the systems described in Example 5.1, and investigate a case when the damping coefficient c in Fig. 5.2 is no longer zero.

The eigenvalues and eigenvectors are calculated as in Fig. 5.9 for the following set of parameter values (with units for the systems in Fig. 5.2(a) and (b)).

$$m = 1.0 \text{ kg}$$

$$c = 0.3 \text{ N s/m}$$

$$k = 1.0 \text{ N/m}$$

and the results are listed in Table 5.3. We see that the eigenvalues (in units of s^{-1}) are

$$\lambda_{1,2} = -0.0756 \pm i\, 0.7647$$

$$\lambda_{3,4} = 0 \qquad \pm i\, 1.4142 \qquad (5.55)$$

$$\lambda_{5,6} = -0.0744 \pm i\, 1.8389.$$

These compare as follows with the undamped natural frequencies (in rad/s) calculated in Example 5.1.

$$\omega_1 = 0.7654$$

$$\omega_2 = 1.4142$$

$$\omega_3 = 1.8478$$

The addition of damping has made no difference to the middle natural frequency but has slightly reduced the two other natural frequencies. The middle-frequency mode is not affected because there is a node at the middle mass (see Fig. 5.3) and so the addition of damping here has no effect on this mode. The effect of damping on the other two modes is, however, typical: each eigenvalue now has a negative real part, and its imaginary part (representing the natural frequency) is slightly reduced.

Table 5.3 Eigenvalues and eigenvectors for the three-degree-of-freedom systems in Fig. 5.2, for $m = 1.0$ kg, $c = 0.3$ N s/m and $k = 1.0$ N/m

Eigenvector no. 1 corresponding to eigenvalue:		Eigenvector no. 2 corresponding to eigenvalue:	
Real part	Imag. part	Real part	Imag. part
-7.560 E-02	$+7.647$ E-01	-7.560 E-02	-7.647 E-01
is as follows:		is as follows:	
$+1.000$ E$+00$	$+0.000$ E$+00$	$+1.000$ E$+00$	$+0.000$ E$+00$
$+1.421$ E$+00$	-1.156 E-01	$+1.421$ E$+00$	$+1.156$ E-01
$+1.000$ E$+00$	-7.142 E-12	$+1.000$ E$+00$	$+7.142$ E-12
-7.560 E-02	$+7.647$ E-01	-7.560 E-02	-7.647 E-01
-1.901 E-02	$+1.095$ E$+00$	-1.901 E-02	-1.095 E$+00$
-7.560 E-02	$+7.647$ E-01	-7.560 E-02	-7.647 E-01

Eigenvector no. 3 corresponding to eigenvalue:		Eigenvector no. 4 corresponding to eigenvalue:	
Real part	Imag. part	Real part	Imag. part
-1.150 E-11	$+1.414$ E$+00$	-1.150 E-11	-1.414 E$+00$
is as follows:		is as follows:	
$+1.000$ E$+00$	$+0.000$ E$+00$	$+1.000$ E$+00$	$+0.000$ E$+00$
$+2.500$ E-10	$+3.253$ E-11	$+2.500$ E-10	-3.253 E-11
-1.000 E$+00$	$+1.061$ E-10	-1.000 E$+00$	-1.061 E-10
$+3.450$ E-11	$+1.414$ E$+00$	$+3.450$ E-11	-1.414 E$+00$
-4.600 E-11	$+3.536$ E-10	-4.600 E-11	-3.536 E-10
-1.385 E-10	-1.414 E$+00$	-1.385 E-10	$+1.414$ E$+00$

Eigenvector no. 5 corresponding to eigenvalue:		Eigenvector no. 6 corresponding to eigenvalue:	
Real part	Imag. part	Real part	Imag. part
-7.440 E-02	$+1.839$ E$+00$	-7.440 E-02	-1.839 E$+00$
is as follows:		is as follows:	
$+1.000$ E$+00$	$+0.000$ E$+00$	$+1.000$ E$+00$	$+0.000$ E$+00$
-1.376 E$+00$	-2.736 E-01	-1.376 E$+00$	$+2.736$ E-01
$+1.000$ E$+00$	-6.756 E-11	$+1.000$ E$+00$	$+6.756$ E-11
-7.440 E-02	$+1.839$ E$+00$	-7.440 E-02	-1.839 E$+00$
$+6.055$ E-01	-2.510 E$+00$	$+6.055$ E-01	$+2.510$ E$+00$
-7.440 E-02	$+1.839$ E$+00$	-7.440 E-02	-1.839 E$+00$

The eigenvector matrix, which was a 3×3 matrix for the analysis in Example 5.1, is now a 6×6 matrix, each of whose elements may be complex. To three decimal places where appropriate, the first two columns are

$$
U_1 = \begin{bmatrix} 1 & + \mathrm{i}\, 0 \\ 1.421 & - \mathrm{i}\, 0.116 \\ 1 & + \mathrm{i}\, 0 \\ -0.076 & + \mathrm{i}\, 0.765 \\ -0.019 & + \mathrm{i}\, 1.095 \\ -0.076 & + \mathrm{i}\, 0.765 \end{bmatrix}, \quad U_2 = \begin{bmatrix} 1 & - \mathrm{i}\, 0 \\ 1.421 & + \mathrm{i}\, 0.116 \\ 1 & - \mathrm{i}\, 0 \\ -0.076 & - \mathrm{i}\, 0.765 \\ -0.019 & - \mathrm{i}\, 1.095 \\ -0.076 & - \mathrm{i}\, 0.765 \end{bmatrix} \tag{5.56}
$$

and the first three elements of these compare with the first column of U for the undamped case which, from Example 5.1, is

$$
U_1 = \begin{bmatrix} 1 \\ \sqrt{2} \\ 1 \end{bmatrix}.
$$

In the first mode of the damped case, the outer masses continue to move exactly in phase through the same amplitude but the middle mass is now slightly out of phase with the outer masses and is moving through a slightly larger relative amplitude that in the undamped case. The second three elements of the columns of the 6×6 matrix give the relative velocities of the three masses. These are no longer at exactly $90°$ phase difference from their corresponding displacements. We shall discuss the physical interpretation of these results shortly, but consider first how the third and fourth columns of the damped U compare with the middle column of the undamped case. From Table 5.3

$$
U_3 = \begin{bmatrix} 1 & + \mathrm{i}\, 0 \\ 0 & - \mathrm{i}\, 0 \\ -1 & + \mathrm{i}\, 0 \\ 0 & + \mathrm{i}\, 1.414 \\ 0 & + \mathrm{i}\, 0 \\ 0 & - \mathrm{i}\, 1.414 \end{bmatrix}, \quad U_4 = \begin{bmatrix} 1 & - \mathrm{i}\, 0 \\ 0 & + \mathrm{i}\, 0 \\ -1 & - \mathrm{i}\, 0 \\ 0 & - \mathrm{i}\, 1.414 \\ 0 & - \mathrm{i}\, 0 \\ 0 & + \mathrm{i}\, 0.414 \end{bmatrix} \tag{5.57}
$$

while the middle column in the undamped case is

$$
U_2 = \begin{bmatrix} 1 \\ 0 \\ -1 \end{bmatrix}.
$$

The fifth and sixth columns of the damped U are

$$
U_5 = \begin{bmatrix} 1 & + \mathrm{i}\, 0 \\ -1.376 & - \mathrm{i}\, 0.274 \\ 1 & + \mathrm{i}\, 0 \\ -0.074 & + \mathrm{i}\, 1.839 \\ 0.606 & - \mathrm{i}\, 2.510 \\ -0.074 & + \mathrm{i}\, 1.839 \end{bmatrix}, \quad U_6 = \begin{bmatrix} 1 & - \mathrm{i}\, 0 \\ -1.376 & + \mathrm{i}\, 0.274 \\ 1 & - \mathrm{i}\, 0 \\ -0.074 & - \mathrm{i}\, 1.839 \\ 0.606 & + \mathrm{i}\, 2.510 \\ -0.074 & - \mathrm{i}\, 1.839 \end{bmatrix} \tag{5.58}
$$

while the third column in the undamped case is

$$U_3 = \begin{bmatrix} 1 \\ -\sqrt{2} \\ 1 \end{bmatrix}.$$

For the third and fourth columns, defined in the damped case by U_3 and U_4, it is easy to see that the second three elements of each are the result of multiplying the first three elements by $\lambda_3 = \text{i}\ 1.414$ for U_3 and by $\lambda_4 = -\text{i}\ 1.414$ for U_4. Similarly, the second three elements of each of U_1, U_2, U_5 and U_6 are the result of multiplying the first three elements of each by

$$\lambda_1 = -0.0756 + \text{i}\ 0.7647, \quad \lambda_2 = -0.0756 - \text{i}\ 0.7647,$$

$$\lambda_5 = -0.0744 + \text{i}\ 1.8389, \text{ and } \lambda_6 = -0.0744 - \text{i}\ 1.8389,$$

respectively. The first element in each column is normalized to have unity for its real part and zero for its imaginary part, but this is optional and alternative eigenvector programs may have different methods of normalizing the elements.

The physical dimensions of the elements of the eigenvectors are the dimensions of y for elements 1 to 3 and the dimensions of $\dot{y}$ for elements 4 to 6. Therefore for the data used in this example, elements 1 to 3 will have units of displacement and elements 4 to 6 will have units of velocity. As explained already, the absolute magnitude of the elements is arbitrary, so that the units may be m (for elements 1 to 3) and m/s (for elements 4 to 6), or, equally, they could be mm and mm/s or ft and ft/s. In some problems the dimensions of y may be mixed, for example linear displacement for some elements and rotational displacement for other elements. In such circumstances the physical dimensions of the eigenvectors will be mixed in the same way.

Intepretation of complex eigenvalues and eigenvectors

Suppose that λ_j is a real eigenvalue and that its corresponding eigenvector is

$$U_j \equiv Z_j = \begin{bmatrix} Y_j \\ W_j \end{bmatrix} \tag{5.59}$$

Here, U_j, which is the jth column of U, is identical with Z_j defined by (5.52); Y_j is the vector of displacements, and $W_j = \lambda_j Y_j$ is the corresponding vector of velocities. Then the time history of the vector of displacements is given by (5.46), where the elements of Y_j are all real. All the displacements therefore decay or grow together (depending whether λ_j is negative or positive) with the initial conditions being such that the elements of $y(t)$ start in the relative proportions of Y_j. Similarly, the velocity components also all decay or all grow together, thus keeping the relative proportions of W_j.

Now consider the case when the eigenvalues and eigenvectors are complex. We have seen that, if this is so, they occur only in complex-conjugate pairs. Let the complex eigenvalues be λ_k and $\lambda_{k+1} = \lambda_k^*$, with a corresponding pair of complex-conjugate eigenvectors U_k and $U_{k+1} = U_k^*$. From (5.59), the vectors of displacements are Y_k and Y_k^*. Hence the displacement response for free vibration in this mode is given by, from (5.46),

$$y(t) = c_k\, \mathrm{e}^{\lambda_k t}\, Y_k + c_{k+1}\, \mathrm{e}^{\lambda_k^* t}\, Y_k^* \tag{5.60}$$

where c_k and c_{k+1} are arbitrary constants. The elements of $y(t)$ must all be real because we are dealing with a physical problem for which an imaginary time history would not have meaning. If c_{k+1} is the complex conjugate of c_k, then the second group of terms on the right-hand side of (5.60) will be the conjugate of the first group of terms. (This is true because, if $D = ABC$, then $D^* = A^*B^*C^*$, Problem 5.3.) Then the r.h.s. of (5.60) will be real because the imaginary parts of the two groups of terms will cancel.

We can select any arbitrary value for the constant c_k, and if we put $c_k = c_k^* = 1$, then (5.60) gives

$$y(t) = \mathrm{e}^{\lambda_k t}\, Y_k + \mathrm{e}^{\lambda_k^* t}\, Y_k^*. \tag{5.61}$$

The displacement response in a mode with complex eigenvalues is therefore obtained by combining the separate responses in the two eigenvectors which describe this mode to give the free-vibration response equation (5.61).

Now let

$$\lambda_k = -\alpha + i\omega$$
$$\lambda_{k+1} = \lambda_k^* = -\alpha - i\omega \tag{5.62}$$

and substitute into (5.61) to obtain

$$y(t) = \mathrm{e}^{-\alpha t}\, (\mathrm{e}^{i\omega t}\, Y_k + \mathrm{e}^{-i\omega t}\, Y_k^*). \tag{5.63}$$

This response can be visualized graphically on an Argand diagram, when each element of $y(t)$ is represented by two counter-rotating decaying vectors. In the complex plane of Fig. 5.10, a typical pair of elements Y_k and Y_k^* are shown in view (a); the complex exponentials $\mathrm{e}^{i\omega t}$ and $\mathrm{e}^{-i\omega t}$ are shown in view (b); and the combinations $Y_k\,\mathrm{e}^{i\omega t}$ and $Y_k^*\,\mathrm{e}^{-i\omega t}$ are shown in view (c). The response $y(t)$ for the appropriate element of $y(t)$ is the addition of these two complex quantities, which rotate in opposite directions about the origin of the diagram at angular rate ω, multiplied by the decaying exponential $\mathrm{e}^{-\alpha t}$. The term *phasor* is sometimes used to describe such rotating complex quantities. The addition of the two phasors is twice the projection onto the real axis of either of them, and hence we get the result that

$$y(t) = 2\,e^{-\alpha t}\,|Y_k|\cos(\omega t + \phi_k) \tag{5.64}$$

where the phase angle ϕ_k is given by

$$\tan\phi_k = \operatorname{Im}\{Y_k\}/\operatorname{Re}\{Y_k\}. \tag{5.65}$$

All the elements of $y(t)$ are represented by phasors which counter-rotate at the same speed ω, and which decay exponentially with time constant $1/\alpha$. The phase angles of the different elements are different because ϕ_k, which is given in (5.65), is generally different for each different element Y_k of the eigenvector Y_k.

If the arbitrary constants c_k and $c_{k+1} = c_k^*$ are chosen not to be unity, an additional phase angle is introduced into the result (5.64), but this is the same for every element of the response vector $y(t)$ and does not alter the relative phasing between individual elements (Problem 5.4).

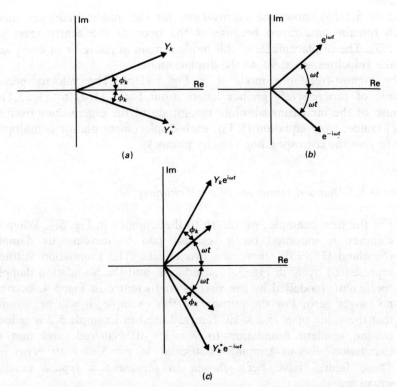

Fig. 5.10 Argand diagram for a typical coordinate of an oscillatory mode: (*a*) complex-conjugate pair of elements of an eigenvector; (*b*) counter-rotating phasors of unit length; and (*c*) the result of multiplying the complex quantities in (*a*) and (*b*)

In order to represent a damped natural mode, it is no longer possible to draw a single mode-shape diagram like Figs 5.3, 5.6 and 5.8. Generally, the individual coordinates no longer move in phase or in anti-phase so that they no longer reach their extremes of motion together. Instead, it is helpful to draw a phasor diagram for the elements of each eigenvector. This shows the relative phases as well as the relative amplitudes of the separate coordinates. This has been done in Fig. 5.11 for the three-degree-of-freedom system considered in the previous section.

Each oscillatory mode is represented by a pair of eigenvalues and a pair of eigenvectors. For the lowest-frequency mode, the eigenvectors are shown in Fig. 5.11(*a*). To keep the diagram clear, each eigenvector is shown separately, although the pair of eigenvectors have to be combined as in Fig. 5.10 in order to obtain the coordinate responses according to equation (5.63). The direction of rotation of the phasors is determined by the corresponding eigenvalue, λ. If $\lambda = -\alpha + i\omega$, then the phasors rotate in a counter-clockwise direction; if $\lambda = -\alpha - i\omega$, then the phasors rotate clockwise.

Figure 5.11(*b*) shows the eigenvectors for the middle-frequency mode, which remains undamped because of the node at the centre mass (see Fig. 5.3). The displacements of this mode remain in phase or in anti-phase, and the velocities are at 90° to the displacements.

The highest-frequency mode is in Fig. 5.11(*c*). The velocity phasors become of progressively greater length from Fig. 5.11(*a*) to Fig. 5.11(*c*) because of the increasing absolute magnitude of the eigenvalues from (*a*) to (*c*) (since, from equation (5.48), each displacement phasor is multiplied by λ to give the corresponding velocity phasor).

Example 5.5 Damped vibrations of a tall chimney

> For the next example, we return to the chimney in Fig. 5.4. When the chimney is mounted on a resilient pad to increase its damping (Newland [71, 73]), there are two effects. The foundation stiffness, represented by K in Fig. 5.4, is reduced, and the foundation damping coefficient, modelled by the viscous coefficient c in Fig. 5.4, becomes no longer zero. For the purpose of this example, it will be assumed that the value of $K = 2 \times 10^9$ N m/rad used in Example 5.2 is reduced by the resilient foundation to $K = 1 \times 10^9$ N m/rad, and that the foundation viscous-damping coefficient is $c = 5.85 \times 10^7$ N m s/rad. These figures have been chosen to represent a typical practical situation.
>
> Using the mass matrix in (5.16), the stiffness matrix in (5.17) and a damping matrix which is a 7×7 null matrix except for $c_{7,1} = c/l$ where the length l is defined on Fig. 5.4, we now follow through the eigenvalue and eigenvector calculation of Fig. 5.9.

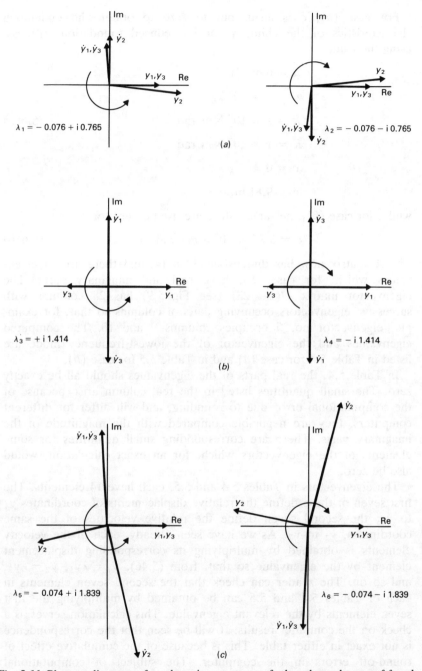

Fig. 5.11 Phasor diagrams for the eigenvectors of the three-degree-of-freedom systems in Fig. 5.2 when $m = 1.0$ kg, $c = 0.3$ N s/m, $k = 1.0$ N/m (or other consistent units): (*a*) lowest-frequency mode; (*b*) middle-frequency mode; and (*c*) highest-frequency mode

For case (a), c is again put to zero to obtain the undamped characteristics of the chimney for its reduced foundation stiffness, using the values

$$l = 6 \text{ m}$$

$$m = 3 \times 10^3 \text{ kg}$$

$$k = 1 \times 10^9 \text{ N m/rad} \tag{5.66a}$$

$$K = 1 \times 10^9 \text{ N m/rad}$$

$$c = 0$$

$$g = 9.81 \text{ m/s}^2$$

while, for case (b), the same values are used except for

$$c = 5.85 \times 10^7 \text{ N m s/rad.} \tag{5.66b}$$

The A matrix now has dimensions 14×14, and there are 14 eigenvalues which, for case (b), have real and imaginary parts. The eigenvector matrix $U(14, 28)$ (see Fig. 5.9) has 28 columns with successive eigenvectors occupying pairs of columns so that, for example, eigenvector no. 5 occupies columns 9 and 10. The computed eigenvalues and the eigenvector of the lowest-frequency mode are listed in Table 5.4 for case (a) and in Table 5.5 for case (b).

In Table 5.4, the real parts of the eigenvalues should all be exactly zero. The small quantities listed in the real column arise because of the computational error due to rounding, and will differ for different computers; they are negligible compared with the magnitude of the imaginary parts. There are corresponding small quantities for some elements of the eigenvectors which, for an exact calculation, would also be zero.

The eigenvectors in Tables 5.4 and 5.5. each have 14 elements. The first seven of these define the relative displacements of coordinates y_1 to y_7; the second seven define the relative velocities of the same coordinates, $\dot{y}_1$ to $\dot{y}_7$. As we have seen already, each of the velocity elements is obtained by multiplying its corresponding displacement element by the eigenvalue so that, from (5.46), $\dot{y}_1 = \lambda y_1$, $\dot{y}_2 = \lambda y_2$, and so on. The reader can check that the second seven elements in each of Tables 5.4 and 5.5 can be obtained by multiplying the first seven elements by the relevant eigenvalue. This calculation serves as a check on the computer results. It will be seen that the correspondence is not exact in either table. This is because of the cumulative effect of round-off errors in the computer. The subject of computational accuracy is discussed in the last section of this chapter.

From Table 5.4, the undamped natural frequencies for case (a) can be compared with those calculated in Example 5.2 for the same chimney except that $K = 2 \times 10^9$ instead of 1×10^9 N m/rad. The

Table 5.4 The eigenvalues and first eigenvector of the seven-degree-of-freedom chimney in Fig. 5.4, for the undamped case when $l = 6\,\mathrm{m}$, $m = 3 \times 10^3\,\mathrm{kg}$, $k = K = 1 \times 10^9\,\mathrm{N\,m/rad}$ and $c = 0$. For comparison with the results for the damped case in Table 5.5, these results have been calculated by following the procedure in Fig. 5.9. The data in Table 5.1 (for $K = 2 \times 10^9\,\mathrm{N\,m/rad}$) was calculated by the procedure in Fig. 5.1

No.	The calculated eigenvalues are: Real part	Imag. part
1	+1.542 E−10	+6.031 E+00
2	+1.542 E−10	−6.031 E+00
3	−1.670 E−10	+3.920 E+01
4	−1.670 E−10	−3.920 E+01
5	+1.137 E−11	+1.156 E+02
6	+1.137 E−11	−1.156 E+02
7	+1.371 E−12	+2.472 E+02
8	+1.371 E−12	−2.472 E+02
9	+8.740 E−14	+4.757 E+02
10	+8.740 E−14	−4.757 E+02
11	+1.000 E−14	+9.594 E+02
12	+1.000 E−14	−9.594 E+02
13	−1.500 E−14	+3.150 E+03
14	−1.500 E−14	−3.150 E+03

Eigenvector no. 1 corresponding to eigenvalue: Real part	Imag. part
+1.542 E−10	+6.031 E+00
+1.000 E+00	+0.000 E+00
+2.799 E+00	−5.271 E−11
+5.200 E+00	−1.635 E−10
+8.017 E+00	−3.149 E−10
+1.109 E+01	−4.910 E−10
+1.428 E+01	−6.790 E−10
+1.750 E+01	−8.701 E−10
−1.458 E−07	+6.032 E+00
+7.495 E−10	+1.688 E+01
+1.788 E−09	+3.136 E+01
+3.136 E−09	+4.836 E+01
+4.671 E−09	+6.687 E+01
+6.297 E−09	+8.611 E+01
+7.946 E−09	+1.055 E+02

is as follows:

Table 5.5 The eigenvalues and first eigenvector of the seven-degree-of-freedom chimney in Fig. 5.4, for the damped case when $l = 6$ m, $m = 3 \times 10^3$ kg, $k = K = 1 \times 10^9$ N m/rad and $c = 5.85 \times 10^7$ N m/rad

No.	The calculated eigenvalues are: Real part	Imag. part
1	-4.724 E-01	$+6.109$ E$+00$
2	-4.724 E-01	-6.109 E$+00$
3	-4.335 E$+01$	$+0.000$ E$+00$
4	-8.511 E$+00$	$+4.689$ E$+01$
5	-8.511 E$+00$	-4.689 E$+01$
6	-1.836 E$+01$	$+1.563$ E$+02$
7	-1.836 E$+01$	-1.563 E$+02$
8	-3.341 E$+01$	$+3.594$ E$+02$
9	-3.341 E$+01$	-3.594 E$+02$
10	-7.571 E$+01$	$+8.038$ E$+02$
11	-7.571 E$+01$	-8.038 E$+02$
12	-1.344 E$+03$	$+0.000$ E$+00$
13	-2.532 E$+02$	$+2.996$ E$+03$
14	-2.532 E$+02$	-2.996 E$+03$

Eigenvector no. 1 corresponding to eigenvalue: Real part	Imag. part
-4.724 E-01	$+6.109$ E$+00$
$+1.000$ E$+00$	$+0.000$ E$+00$
$+2.776$ E$+00$	$+2.875$ E-01
$+5.138$ E$+00$	$+7.934$ E-01
$+7.903$ E$+00$	$+1.452$ E$+00$
$+1.091$ E$+01$	$+2.203$ E$+00$
$+1.404$ E$+01$	$+2.998$ E$+00$
$+1.719$ E$+01$	$+3.806$ E$+00$
-4.719 E-01	$+6.108$ E$+00$
-3.068 E$+00$	$+1.683$ E$+01$
-7.274 E$+00$	$+3.101$ E$+01$
-1.260 E$+01$	$+4.760$ E$+01$
-1.861 E$+01$	$+6.563$ E$+01$
-2.495 E$+01$	$+8.435$ E$+01$
-3.137 E$+01$	$+1.033$ E$+02$

is as follows:

figures compare as listed in Table 5.6. All the natural frequencies have been reduced by the reduction in stiffness, although the proportional reduction is less for the high-frequency modes whose natural frequencies depend more on the stiffnesses between the seven sections, k, rather than on the base stiffness, K.

Table 5.6 Undamped natural frequencies in rad/s for the chimney model in Fig. 5.4 for the same parameter values, except for the foundation stiffness, K (see equations (5.21) and (5.66))

$K = 2 \times 10^9$ N m/rad	$K = 1 \times 10^9$ N m/rad
6.841	6.031
43.06	39.20
123.4	115.6
256.9	247.2
484.3	475.7
964.9	959.4
3152	3150

For the damped chimney, case (*b*), all the eigenvalues have negative real parts, and it can be seen in Table 5.5 that there are now only six pairs of oscillatory eigenvalues. One pair of complex-conjugate eigenvalues has been replaced by two (different) real eigenvalues. The addition of damping has extinguished one oscillatory mode of vibration.

At first sight, it is not clear which pair of eigenvalues in the undamped case, Table 5.4, has disappeared to create two real eigenvalues in the damped case, Table 5.5. To find out, we need to increment the damping in small steps and follow how the eigenvalues change as a result. When this is done for the parameter values in (5.66), it turns out that the two eigenvalues $\pm$ i 247.2 in Table 5.4 are the ones that experience increasing negative real parts until, when $c = 3.51 \times 10^7$ N m s/rad (approximately), they merge to give two real eigenvalues. The progressive change in these eigenvalues as damping is increased is shown in the root locus diagram in Fig. 5.12. This may be compared with the corresponding diagram in Chapter 1 for a single-mode system, Fig. 1.8. Traditionally, the term 'root locus' rather than 'eigenvalue locus' is used for this diagram; the eigenvalues are the roots of the system's characteristic equation (see equation (4.13)).

We can now see the effect of adding a damped resilient seating to a typical chimney. Its lowest natural frequency has been reduced from

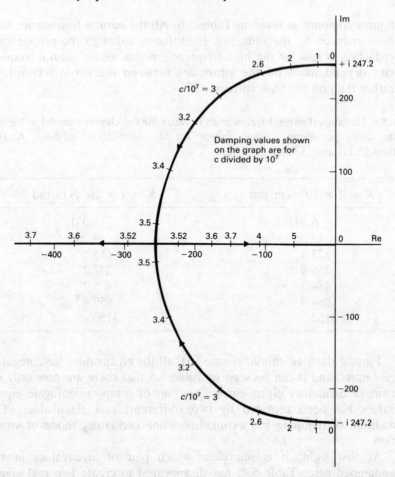

Fig. 5.12 Root locus diagram showing the migration of a pair of complex-conjugate roots of the chimney in Fig. 5.4 as the damping coefficient c is increased from zero to $5 \times 10^7 \, \text{N m s/rad}$

$6.841 \, \text{rad/s} = 1.09 \, \text{Hz}$ (from Table 5.1) to $6.109 \, \text{rad/s} = 0.97 \, \text{Hz}$ (Table 5.5) and the damping of this mode has been increased from zero (in theory) to that represented by the eigenvalues

$$- 0.472 \pm i \, 6.109.$$

From Chapter 3, the corresponding logarithmic decrement, δ_1, is, from (3.39)

$$\delta_1 = 2\pi \frac{-\text{Re}\{\lambda_1\}}{|\text{Im}\{\lambda_1\}|} \qquad (5.67)$$

$$= 2\pi \left(\frac{0.472}{6.109}\right) = 0.49$$

and, from (3.33), the modal damping ratio is given by

$$\zeta_1 \simeq \delta_1/2\pi = 0.077. \tag{5.68}$$

The susceptibility of a chimney to wind excitation is much reduced if the damping of its lowest-frequency mode exceeds a certain critical level (see, for example, Scruton and Flint [89], Walshe and Wootton [109]). For example, a typical 30 m high self-supporting chimney with a diameter of 1 m and a mass per unit length of 250 kg/m requires a damping ratio $\zeta_1 > 0.06$ approximately if significant self-excitation is to be prevented (Newland [73]). Therefore if the damping of a chimney can be increased by the amount given in equation (5.68), that is extremely important for its successful design.

When the damped chimney is in free vibration in one of its modes, the amplitudes of all its coordinates decay exponentially according to $e^{-\alpha t}$ where α is the magnitude of the real part of the corresponding eigenvalue. However, we have seen that the coordinates no longer vibrate in phase or in anti-phase and, generally, all the coordinates will have different phase angles. For the lowest-frequency mode, the phase angles are illustrated in Fig. 5.13 where the first eigenvector is drawn to scale on an Argand diagram. Because this eigenvector corresponds to the eigenvalue

$$- 0.472 + i\, 6.109$$

with the imaginary part having a + sign, the phasors rotate counter-clockwise about the diagram's origin (see Fig. 5.10). We can see that, for this lowest mode, the phase differences are small and the deflected shape of the chimney as it vibrates in its lowest mode will be barely distinguishable from the undamped deflection shape.

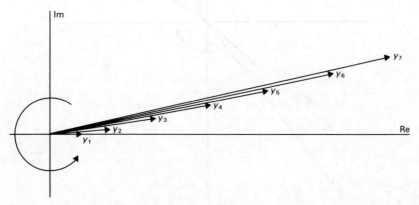

Fig. 5.13 Phasor diagram for the first eigenvector of the seven-degree-of-freedom chimney in Fig. 5.4 drawn from the data in Table 5.5. The corresponding eigenvalue is $-0.472 + i\, 6.109$, the units being seconds^{-1}

However, for the second mode, the effect is more obvious. Figure 5.14 is a phasor diagram for the second mode, drawn from the data in Table 5.7. It corresponds to the eigenvalue

$$-8.511 + i\,46.89$$

which gives a logarithmic decrement of 1.14 and a modal damping ratio of 0.18, approximately. By considering the projections of the phasors onto the real axis as they rotate in 45° increments, the positions of the chimney at time intervals of $T/8$, where $T = 2\pi/46.89$ is the period, have been calculated. To allow for the exponential decay $e^{-\alpha t}$, where $\alpha = 8.511$, which is occurring equally for all the phasors, the lengths of the phasors have to be reduced at each step of the calculation. The results are plotted in Fig. 5.15. This diagram shows successive stages in the free vibration of the chimney in its second mode.

The phase differences between coordinates can now be seen to be having a significant effect in distorting the chimney from its undamped mode shape (compare the second of Fig. 5.6). It is no longer possible to speak of the second mode as the 'one-node mode' because, for part of each period, there are now two nodes, with the positions of the nodes moving up and down the chimney as vibration takes place.

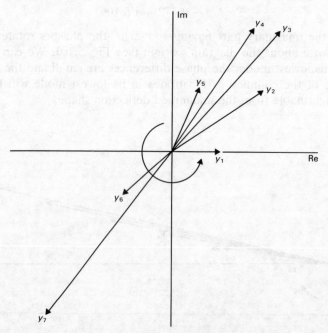

Fig. 5.14 Phasor diagram for the fourth eigenvector of the chimney in Fig. 5.4, drawn from the data in Table 5.7. The corresponding eigenvalue is $-8.511 + i\,46.89$ which, from the list of eigenvalues in Table 5.5, describes the oscillatory mode with the second-lowest natural frequency

Table 5.7 Fourth eigenvector of the damped seven-degree-of-freedom chimney in Fig. 5.4 for $l = 6$ m, $m = 3 \times 10^3$ kg, $k = K = 1 \times 10^9$ N m/rad and $c = 5.85 \times 10^7$ N m s/rad

| | Eigenvector no. 4 corresponding to eigenvalue: | |
	Real part	Imag. part
	-8.511 E+00	$+4.689$ E+01
is as follows:		
	$+1.000$ E+00	$+0.000$ E+00
	$+1.859$ E+00	$+1.241$ E+00
	$+2.127$ E+00	$+2.373$ E+00
	$+1.647$ E+00	$+2.473$ E+00
	$+5.206$ E−01	$+1.273$ E+00
	-9.901 E−01	-8.745 E−01
	-2.617 E+00	-3.342 E+00
	-8.508 E+00	$+4.689$ E+01
	-7.400 E+01	$+7.660$ E+01
	-1.294 E+02	$+7.956$ E+01
	-1.300 E+02	$+5.617$ E+01
	-6.413 E+01	$+1.358$ E+01
	$+4.944$ E+01	-3.899 E+01
	$+1.790$ E+02	-9.429 E+01

Example 5.6 Stability of a railway bogie

This example is about the running stability of a two-axle railway bogie (or, in US terminology, a two-axle truck).

The purpose of the bogie is to provide guidance and to steer the train along its track. The steering action depends on the shape of the wheels. These are cone-shaped when new with, typically, a 1 in 20 cone semi-angle. The wheels are secured to a rigid axle to form a wheelset. When this deviates from the centre of the track, one wheel has a larger rolling radius than the other wheel. Therefore the centre of one wheel travels faster than the centre of the other wheel and the wheelset steers itself back towards its central position. If a single wheelset of negligible mass is allowed to move without restraint, its self-steering property gives rise to an undamped oscillation (called hunting) which, for small amplitudes, has a frequency (Problem 5.6)

$$\omega = V \sqrt{\frac{\alpha}{rb}} \quad \text{(rad/s)} \tag{5.69}$$

and wavelength (along the track)

$$\lambda = 2\pi \sqrt{\frac{br}{\alpha}} \quad \text{(m)} \tag{5.70}$$

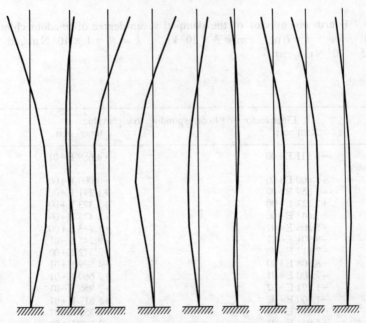

Fig. 5.15 Successive positions of the chimney in Fig. 5.4 when in free vibration in its second damped natural mode, drawn at time intervals of $T/8$ where T is the period, corresponding to 45° rotations of the phasors in Fig. 5.14. The phasors decay exponentially according to $e^{-\alpha t}$ where, from Table 5.7, $\alpha = 8.511$; $T = 2\pi/\alpha$, where $\alpha = 46.89$

where

V = velocity of the bogie (m/s)

r = mean rolling radius of the wheels (m)

b = half the distance between the two points of wheel-to-rail contact (m)

α = cone semi-angle of the wheels (assumed small).

Because motion is governed entirely by the geometry of the wheels, which roll without slipping, the frequency given by (5.69) is called the kinematic frequency, and the wavelength given by (5.70) is called the kinematic wavelength of the wheelset.

A similar hunting motion occurs when a massless two-axle bogie with a rigid frame moves along the track without restraint. In this case, pure rolling motion is no longer possible because one wheelset pulls against the other and some slip or creep of the wheels over the rails occurs. However, subject to various simplifying assumptions about the nature of creep, the bogie's motion is still determined only by the geometry of the bogie and there is again an undamped oscillation of frequency (Problem 5.6)

$$f_N = V \sqrt{\frac{\alpha}{rb(1 + l^2/b^2)}} \quad \text{(cycles/s)} \quad (5.71)$$

and wavelength (the so-called 'long wavelength')

$$\lambda = 2\pi \sqrt{\frac{br}{\alpha} (1 + l^2/b^2)} \quad \text{(m)} \quad (5.72)$$

where

l = half the distance between the axles (m).

The fundamental problem of rail vehicle guidance is to make use of the self-steering action of conical wheels while avoiding the occurrence of a self-excited oscillation or 'bogie hunting' phenomenon. Whether the effect of the vehicle, suspension and bogie frame on the wheelsets acts to stabilize or to destabilize the neutrally-damped wheelset kinematic motion determines whether the vehicle will run smoothly or not. If the effect is destabilizing, oscillatory motion of the wheelsets builds up until motion is limited only by contact between the wheel flanges and the rails, when an uncomfortable ride results with heavy wheel wear. Furthermore, it is not only necessary for the system to be marginally stable so that hunting is avoided on straight track. The rate of return of the wheelsets to their central positions after an initial displacement must be fast enough to prevent flange–rail contact when negotiating curves.

In this example, the dynamic stability of a simplified two-axle bogie is examined. To keep the problem manageable as an example, the study is confined to the so-called 'secondary hunting' regime in which the car body is assumed to act as an inertial mass and be uninfluenced by the motion of the bogie. This is generally the most severe hunting motion, and the most difficult to cure. Primary hunting, which involves appreciable movement of the car body, occurs at lower speeds and can usually be controlled by adjusting the viscous damping in the suspension system. For secondary hunting, motion is independent of the rest of the train and it is only necessary to describe and analyse a single bogie.

It will be assumed that the bogie is travelling at constant speed, V, on straight track. The linearized equations for small deviations from a straight-line path will be derived and it will be seen that these can be expressed in the standard form

$$m\ddot{y} + c\dot{y} + ky = 0. \quad (5.73)$$

The numerical problem is then to solve for the system's eigenvalues

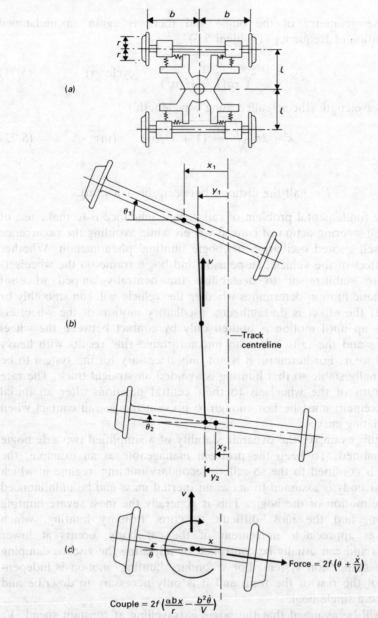

Couple = $2f\left(\dfrac{\alpha bx}{r} - \dfrac{b^2\dot\theta}{V}\right)$

Force = $2f\left(\theta + \dfrac{\dot x}{V}\right)$

Fig. 5.16 (*a*) Plan view of a simplified bogie with lateral and longitudinal wheelset flexibility relative to the bogie's central frame; (*b*) definition of coordinates; (*c*) resultant creep force and couple acting on a wheelset (after Newland [69], *courtesy of the American Society of Mechnical Engineers*)

and eigenvectors to determine how they depend on the bogie's design parameters. There must be no eigenvalues with positive real parts denoting an exponentially increasing or unstable solution, and the negative real parts must be sufficiently large that every mode is satisfactorily damped and sufficiently stable.

A plan view of the simplified bogie to be analysed is shown in Fig. 5.16(a), and the specification of the six coordinates to define its position are given in Fig. 5.16(b). There are three separate components to be considered: the two wheelsets and the frame. For each we have to write down two equations of dynamic equilibrium: (i) for forces laterally, and (ii) for moments about the yaw axis. Together there will be six coupled second-order equations so that the *m, c* and *k* matrices will have order 6×6 and the *A* matrix derived according to the procedure in Fig. 5.9 will have order 12×12.

The forces that act on the wheels as a result of their contact with the rails are called creep forces. They are derived on the assumption that linear creep theory applies (see, for example, Johnson [50]). According to this theory

$$\text{creep force} = \frac{f}{V} \text{ (creep velocity)} \tag{5.74}$$

where f is a constant coefficient, V is the velocity of the bogie, and the creep velocity is defined as the difference between the actual velocity of a wheel's centre and the velocity that this centre would have if the wheel were rolling without slip at the same angular velocity. In terms of the lateral displacement, x, of the wheelset, and its yaw angle, θ (both defined in Fig. 5.16(b)), it is shown in Problem 5.6 that the creep forces acting on a wheelset may be represented as a single resultant lateral force at the wheelset's centre

$$2f\left(\theta + \frac{\dot{x}}{V}\right) \tag{5.75}$$

and a single resultant yaw–angle couple

$$2f\left(\frac{\alpha b}{r} x - \frac{b^2\dot{\theta}}{V}\right) \tag{5.76}$$

acting in the directions shown in Fig. 5.16(c). The creep coefficient, f, has the dimensions of force. In deriving (5.75) and (5.76), the lateral and longitudinal creep coefficients are assumed to be the same, the effect of spin creep is ignored, and the amplitudes of movement are assumed to be small (see Problem 5.6).

With this information, and defining the following additional terms

m = wheelset mass

I = wheelset moment of inertia about its centre

M = mass of frame

J = moment of inertia of frame about its centre

k = lateral stiffness between the frame and each wheelset

c = yaw angle stiffness between the frame and each wheelset

K = lateral stiffness between the centre of the frame and the vehicle (which in this example is assumed to be ground)

the equations of motion can be written as follows:

Lateral equilibrium of front wheelset

$$m\ddot{x}_1 + \frac{2f}{V}\dot{x}_1 + kx_1 + 2f\theta_1 - ky_1 = 0. \qquad (5.77)$$

Yaw-angle equilibrium of front wheelset

$$I\ddot{\theta}_1 + \frac{2fb^2}{V}\dot{\theta}_1 - 2f\frac{\alpha b}{r}x_1 + c\theta_1 + \frac{c}{2l}y_1 - \frac{c}{2l}y_2 = 0. \qquad (5.78)$$

Lateral equilibrium of trailing wheelset

$$m\ddot{x}_2 + \frac{2f}{V}\dot{x}_2 + kx_2 + 2f\theta_2 - ky_2 = 0. \qquad (5.79)$$

Yaw-angle equilibrium of trailing wheelset

$$I\ddot{\theta}_2 + \frac{2fb^2}{V}\dot{\theta}_2 - 2f\frac{\alpha b}{r}x_2 + c\theta_2 + \frac{c}{2l}y_1 - \frac{c}{2l}y_2 = 0. \qquad (5.80)$$

Lateral equilibrium of frame

$$\frac{M}{2}\ddot{y}_1 + \frac{M}{2}\ddot{y}_2 - kx_1 - kx_2 + (K/2 + k)y_1 + (K/2 + k)y_2 = 0. \qquad (5.81)$$

Yaw equilibrium of frame

$$-\frac{J}{2l}\ddot{y}_1 + \frac{J}{2l}\ddot{y}_2 + klx_1 - c\theta_1 - klx_2 - c\theta_2 - \left(kl + \frac{c}{l}\right)y_1$$
$$+ \left(kl + \frac{c}{l}\right)y_2 = 0. \qquad (5.82)$$

These equations assume that the bogie can rotate about its centre-pivot without friction or other restraint. Also, for simplicity, the lateral forces arising from changes in direction of the normal wheel–rail reaction forces are omitted. When a wheelset is displaced laterally, the planes of wheel–rail contact change, and therefore the normal force vectors change their direction. They thus contribute to the lateral forces acting on the wheelset. However, for small deflections, these gravitational terms do not normally affect the trend of the results significantly (Problem 5.6).

If the response vector y in (5.73) is defined as

$$y' = [x_1, \theta_1, x_2, \theta_2, y_1, y_2]$$ (5.83)

then the mass, damping and stiffness matrices for the standard form of the equations (5.73) are:

$$m = \begin{bmatrix} m & & & & & \\ & I & & & & \\ & & m & & & \\ & & & I & & \\ & & & & M/2 & M/2 \\ & & & & -J/2l & J/2l \end{bmatrix},$$ (5.84)

and

$$c = \begin{bmatrix} 2f/V & & & & & \\ & 2fb^2/V & & & & \\ & & 2f/V & & & \\ & & & 2fb^2/V & & \\ & & & & 0 & \\ & & & & & 0 \end{bmatrix}$$ (5.85)

and

$$k = \begin{bmatrix} k & 2f & 0 & 0 & -k & 0 \\ -2f\alpha b/r & c & 0 & 0 & c/2l & -c/2l \\ 0 & 0 & k & 2f & 0 & -k \\ 0 & 0 & -2f\alpha b/r & c & c/2l & -c/2l \\ -k & 0 & -k & 0 & K/2 + k & K/2 + k \\ kl & -c & -kl & -c & -kl -c/l & kl + c/l \end{bmatrix}.$$ (5.86)

The following parameter values, which are typical of a passenger car's bogie, will be used for numerical calculations:

$$\begin{aligned} r &= 0.4 \text{ m} \\ b &= 0.76 \text{ m} \\ l &= 0.8 \text{ m} \\ \alpha &= 0.05 \\ m &= 1500 \text{ kg} \\ I &= 600 \text{ kg m}^2 \\ M &= 2500 \text{ kg} \\ J &= 1500 \text{ kg m}^2 \\ K &= 10^6 \text{ N/m} \end{aligned}$$ (5.87)

$c = 5 \times 10^6 \, \mathrm{N\,m/rad}$ except variable for Fig. 5.19

$k = 40c \, \mathrm{N/m}$

$f = 10^7 \, \mathrm{N}$

V = variable for Fig. 5.17
    50 m/s for Figs 5.18 and 5.19.

The eigenvalues and eigenvectors can now be computed following the strategy in Fig. 5.9.

Two typical sets of results are listed in Table 5.8. These are for the data above with $c = 5 \times 10^6 \, \mathrm{N\,m/rad}$. There are 12 eigenvalues and they are listed for two different velocities. One set of results is for $V = 50 \, \mathrm{m/s}$ and the other set for $V = 80 \, \mathrm{m/s}$.

At 50 m/s, all the eigenvalues have negative real parts so that the system has positive damping in all its modes. However, for $V = 80 \, \mathrm{m/s}$, the first pair of eigenvalues has a positive real part, which describes an unstable response with a diverging solution. At some intermediate speed between 50 and 80 m/s there is a critical velocity at which the real part of the first pair of eigenvalues is zero, and this critical velocity marks the theoretical boundary between a stable and an unstable bogie response.

In Fig. 5.17, the information given by the first pair of eigenvalues is plotted against velocity, for the range $V = 0$ to $V = 100 \, \mathrm{m/s}$. In Fig. 5.17(a), the frequency of the mode, which is the magnitude of the imaginary part of the eigenvalue, is plotted and, in Fig. 5.17(b), the damping ratio of the mode, calculated from (5.67) and (5.68) as the modulus of the ratio of the real part of the eigenvalue to its imaginary part, is plotted. The modal frequency lies between the kinematic frequency of a single wheelset and the kinematic frequency of a rigid two-axle bogie, and the critical speed is about 75 m/s. In Table 5.9, the eigenvector for this mode is listed for $V = 50 \, \mathrm{m/s}$.

The eigenvector has 12 elements, the first six describing the displacements and the second six describing the velocities of the coordinates $x_1, \theta_1, x_2, \theta_2, y_1, y_2$ which define the position of the three components of the bogie, Fig. 5.16(b). The six displacements are drawn to scale on the Argand diagram in Fig. 5.18 with the angular displacements θ_1, θ_2 multiplied by the half-wheelspacing $b = 0.76 \, \mathrm{m}$ so that they may be compared with the translational displacements x_1, x_2, y_1 and y_2. There is very little relative lateral displacement between the wheelsets and the bogie's frame because, to a close approximation, $y_1 = x_1$ and $y_2 = x_2$. The displacement of the front wheelset leads the displacement of the rear wheelset by about 23° and the yaw-angle displacements of the wheelsets lag by almost (but not exactly) 90° behind their corresponding lateral displacements.

Table 5.8 Eigenvalues for the flexible two-axle bogie in Fig. 5.16, for the parameter values given as equations (5.87). The units are seconds^{-1}

No.	Velocity, $V = 50$ m/s	Velocity $V = 80$ m/s
1,2	$-2.00 \pm$ i 18.51	$+0.51 \pm$ i 28.25
3,4	$-28.92 \pm$ i 20.47	$-34.69 \pm$ i 46.38
5	-157.6	
6	-144.8	$-107.4 \pm$ i 18.99
7,8	$-361.2 \pm$ i 0.58	$-194.5 \pm$ i 6.46
9,10	$-55.90 \pm$ i 522.6	$-36.70 \pm$ i 534.1
11,12	$-52.50 \pm$ i 536.6	$-34.55 \pm$ i 547.6

Table 5.9 Eigenvector for the hunting mode of the flexible bogie in Fig. 5.16, for the parameter values in equations (5.87) and at $V = 50$ m/s

Coordinate	
x_1	1
θ_1	$0.044 -$ i 0.321
x_2	$0.885 -$ i 0.378
θ_2	$-0.064 -$ i 0.381
y_1	$0.998 +$ i 0.004
y_2	$0.886 -$ i 0.381
$\dot{x}_1$	$-2.00 +$ i 18.5
$\dot{\theta}_1$	$5.86 +$ i 1.46
$\dot{x}_2$	$5.23 +$ i 17.1
$\dot{\theta}_2$	$7.18 -$ i 0.43
$\dot{y}_1$	$-2.07 +$ i 18.5
$\dot{y}_2$	$5.29 +$ i 17.2

The real part of the eigenvalue under these conditions is -2.0 s^{-1}, approximately, so that at 50 m/s the free response in this mode decays with an exponential time constant of approximately 0.5 s. As the bogie moves along the track, its motion has the form shown in Fig. 5.18. Since the frequency is approximately 18.5 rad/s, the period of the mode is $T = 2\pi/18.5 = 0.34$ s, and the wavelength of the path that the bogie traces out along the track is $VT = (50)\,(0.34) = 17$ m (approximately).

There are five other modes for the freely rolling motion of the bogie that are described by the eigenvalues in Table 5.8. At 80 m/s these are all oscillatory modes, but at 50 m/s one oscillatory mode is extinguished and its complex-conjugate pair of eigenvalues have been replaced by two real eigenvalues.

Two of the modes, numbers 9, 10 and 11, 12, describe vibrations which are predominantly those of the bogie's frame on its flexible mounting to the wheelsets, with very little relative creep of the wheels

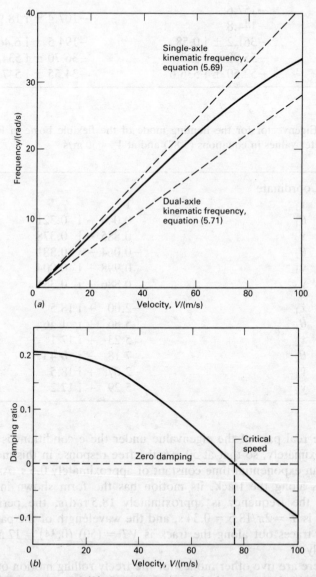

Fig. 5.17 (*a*) Frequency and (*b*) damping ratio of the hunting mode of the two-axle flexible bogie in Fig. 5.16, plotted as a function of velocity. The parameter values are listed as equations (5.87)

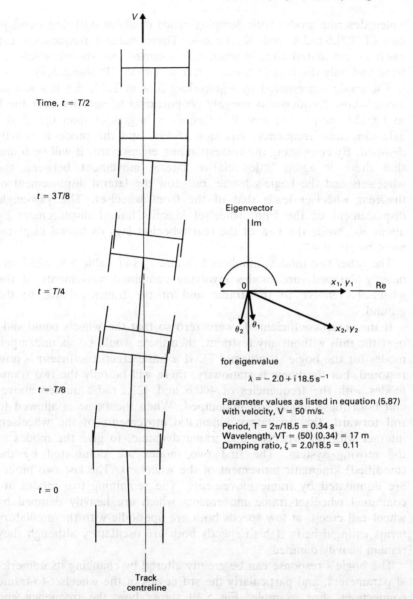

Time, $t = T/2$

$t = 3T/8$

Eigenvector

Im

$t = T/4$

0 x_1, y_1 Re

θ_2 θ_1

x_2, y_2

for eigenvalue

$t = T/8$

$\lambda = -2.0 + \mathrm{i}\,18.5\,\mathrm{s}^{-1}$

Parameter values as listed in equation (5.87)
with velocity, $V = 50$ m/s.

Period, $T = 2\pi/18.5 = 0.34$ s
Wavelength, $VT = (50)\,(0.34) = 17$ m
Damping ratio, $\zeta = 2.0/18.5 = 0.11$

$t = 0$

Track
centreline

Fig. 5.18 One of the pair of complex-conjugate eigenvectors for the hunting mode of the bogie in Fig. 5.16, with successive positions of the bogie during one half-period of its motion in this mode.

on the rails. This is best seen by computing the eigenvalues when the velocity is very small, say 1 m/s. The corresponding eigenvalues are then

$$-5.0 \pm \mathrm{i}\,400.6$$
$$-4.8 \pm \mathrm{i}\,421.2$$

which describe modes with damping ratios of about 0.01 and frequencies of 400.6 rad/s and 421.1 rad/s. These natural frequencies can easily be calculated directly when it is assumed that the wheelsets are fixed and only the bogie's frame is free to vibrate (Problem 5.7).

The mode represented by eigenvalues 3, 4 in Table 5.8 is a second mode whose frequency is roughly proportional to velocity over the 0 to 100 m/s range, but now this frequency is greater than the single-axle kinematic frequency, equation (5.69), and the mode is heavily damped. By computing the corresponding eigenvector, it will be found that there is again little relative lateral movement between the wheelsets and the bogie's frame, but now the lateral displacement of the rear wheelset leads that of the front wheelset. The yaw-angle displacement of the front wheelset lags its lateral displacement by about 30°, while the yaw of the rear wheelset lags its lateral displacement by about 44°.

The other two modes, numbers 5, 6 and 7, 8 in Table 5.8, which are heavily damped, are modes involving combined movements of the wheelsets relative to the frame and of the frame relative to the ground.

If the creep coefficient, f, were zero so that the wheels could slide over the rails without any restraint, then there would be six undamped modes for the bogie (Problem 5.7). If a finite creep coefficient is now restored, but the bogie is stationary, there will be only the two frame modes with the frequencies of 400.6 and 421.2 rad/s quoted above, and both these modes are undamped. When the bogie is allowed to roll forward, the oscillatory kinematic movements of the wheelsets interact with the wheelset and frame dynamics to give the modes of the moving system. The first two modes are dominated by the (modified) kinematic movement of the wheelsets. The last two modes are dominated by frame movements. The remaining two modes are combined wheelset–frame movements which are heavily damped by wheel–rail creep: at low speeds both are aperiodic with the oscillatory terms extinguished; at high speeds both are oscillatory although they remain heavily damped.

The bogie's response can be greatly altered by changing its numerical parameters, and particularly the stiffnesses of the wheelset-to-frame connections. For example, Fig. 5.19 shows how the frequency and damping of the hunting mode of the bogie (i.e. the least-damped mode of the bogie) depends on the wheelset yaw stiffness, c. Since a typical construction may involve rubber bush connections between wheelset and frame, increasing yaw stiffness may then be accompanied by increasing lateral stiffness, k, and the results in Fig. 5.19 assume that k is increased in proportion to c.

It can be seen that there is an optimum choice of wheelset-to-frame stiffness to achieve maximum damping of the hunting mode. However, this may not be the preferred choice of the bogie's stiffness parameters

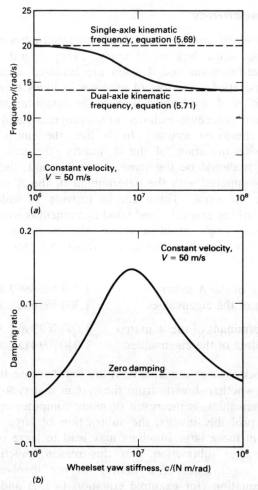

Fig. 5.19 (*a*) Frequency and (*b*) damping ratio of the hunting mode of the bogie in Fig. 5.16 at velocity $V = 50$ m/s, plotted as a function of the wheelset-to-frame yaw stiffness, c. The wheelset-to-frame lateral stiffness, k, is kept in proportion to the yaw stiffness so that $k/c = 40$ m^{-2}. Other parameter values are listed as equations (5.87)

because, in addition to bogie stability, it is also necessary to consider how the bogie responds to curved track. A good bogie must be able to follow changing track directions without allowing its wheel flanges to come into contact with the rails. For that a certain flexibility is essential so that the wheelsets can align themselves with the local normals to the track, rather than remaining exactly parallel (see, for example, Newland [69]). In practice, a compromise has to be struck between having adequate frame stiffness to ensure stability and having sufficient flexibility to permit satisfactory steering in curves.

Checks on accuracy

Because of round-off errors, eigenvalues computed numerically will inevitably suffer from some lack of accuracy. Many operations of addition, subtraction, multiplication and division are involved in their calculation, and at every operation some loss of precision is likely to occur because of the limited number of significant figures of the computer concerned.

The calculation procedure included in subprogram Lambda in Appendix 3 includes two checks on accuracy. In the first, the sum of the eigenvalues is compared with the trace of the A matrix (the sum of its diagonal elements), which should be the same. In the second, the product of the eigenvalues is compared with the determinant of the A matrix, and these should also be the same. These checks provide an indication that the programs are working properly, and good agreement is usually obtained.

For the railway bogie problem above, the checks gave the following results for the eigenvalues listed in Table 5.8 for the case when $V = 50$ m/s:

trace of the A matrix:	$-1.303\,466\,666\,7 \times 10^3$
sum of the eigenvalues:	$-1.303\,466\,666\,7 \times 10^3$
determinant of the A matrix:	$1.040\,769\,396\,1 \times 10^{26}$
product of the eigenvalues:	$1.040\,769\,415\,1 \times 10^{26}.$

The second check is more sensitive than the first because the calculation of a determinant, whether directly from the system matrix, or by multiplying together its eigenvalues, is the result of many computer operations, which at some stage probably involve the subtraction of large numbers. Small relative errors in these large numbers may lead to large relative errors in their residuals after subtraction. For this reason, practical methods of computing the eigenvalues of a matrix do not involve calculating its characteristic equation (for example equation (4.13)) and then searching for the solutions of λ which satisfy this equation. That is likely to be inaccurate because the characteristic equation probably becomes zero on account of large quantities cancelling each other, leading to large relative inaccuracies in the result. Also, it is not practicable to check the accuracy of an eigenvalue by computing $\det(A - \lambda I)$ to verify that this determinant is correctly zero. The numerical value of λ which makes the determinant zero may be significantly less accurate than the value computed by a computer library program, for example subprogram Lambda in Appendix 3.

Programs like Lambda work by performing a series of similarity transformations to bring the A matrix to a special form from which its eigenvalues can be obtained directly without evaluating any determinants. The procedure for doing this will be explained in Chapter 7 and need not concern us here except for one detail. This is that the eigenvalue extraction algorithm works by looking for zeros in the transformed version of the A

matrix. Because of round-off errors in the computer, the program has to know when to disregard a small element on the assumption that it is really only a computational error for zero. There are various methods of identifying when an element is negligible, and the considerations involved are discussed in Chapter 7. The method used in the computer programs in the appendices is to specify at the outset the magnitude of the quantity that will be taken to be effectively zero throughout the calculation.

In subprogram Lambda (which is described in Appendix 3) this quantity is set at 10^{-12} times the norm of the A matrix, which is the square root of the sum of the squares of all the elements of A. For the railway bogie problem above with the data listed in equations (5.87) and for $V = 50$ m/s and $c = 5 \times 10^6$ N m/rad, this is

$$\text{Quantity taken to be effectively zero: } 4.29 \times 10^{-7}$$

As seen above, the trace and sum of the eigenvalues then agree to the eleventh significant figure, and the determinant and the product of the eigenvalues agree to the seventh significant figure. Obviously, these numbers depend on the accuracy of the computer being used: the above results were obtained using a computer operating to 12 significant decimal figures. There is no point in setting the magnitude of 'zero' smaller than the accuracy that the computer can achieve, for reasons that are the subject of Problems 7.2 and 7.3.

In a few special cases, when there are repeated eigenvalues, or eigenvalues very close to each other, the accuracy of the eigenvalues may be less that suggested by the precision of the numerical checks described above (see Problem 7.5), and it may then be helpful to make small changes in the elements of the original A matrix and find out how sensitive the computed eigenvalues are to these changes.

The eigenvector subprogram Vector in Appendix 5 also incorporates its own check. For an A matrix of order $N \times N$, there will be N simultaneous equations for the N elements of each eigenvector. However, one element is arbitrary and, in program Vector, the first element is normalized to unity. That leaves N equations for $N - 1$ unknowns, and so the extra equation can be used as a check. It will be explained in Chapter 7 that, if a is the first row of the A matrix, and if eigenvector $Y_j = x + iy$ corresponds to eigenvalue $\lambda_j = \alpha + i\omega$, then ax should be the same as α and ay should be the same as ω. The output of subprogram Vector includes the results of these checks for each eigenvector. For the railway bogie problem above, results of the check calculations on the eigenvector listed in Table 5.9 are

Eigenvalue calculated from the eigenvector

$$- 1.997\,984\,737\,1 + i\ 18.513\,340\,144$$

compared with its initially computed value

$$- 1.997\,985\,017\,0 + i\ 18.513\,340\,054.$$

These agree to the sixth significant figure for the real part and to the eighth significant figure for the imaginary part. For the other eigenvectors, the computed accuracy varies, as listed in Table 5.10.

The poor agreement on the imaginary part of the check on the eigenvectors corresponding to the eigenvalues $-361.2 \pm i\,0.58$ (see Table 5.10) is small in absolute terms when it is seen that the imaginary component of the eigenvalues is of order 10^{-3} relative to the corresponding real parts.

Table 5.10 Accuracy check on the eigenvectors of the railway bogie model for the data given in equations (5.87) with $V = 50\,\text{m/s}$, when computed to 12-figure accuracy

| | Accuracy of eigenvector | |
	Real part	Imaginary part
Eigenvalue $\alpha \pm i\omega$	Number of significant digits to which ax and α agree	Number of significant digits to which ay and ω agree
$-2.00 \pm i\ 18.51$	7	9
$-28.92 \pm i\ 20.47$	8	8
-157.6	6	—
-144.8	8	—
$-361.2 \pm i\ 0.58$	6	2
$-55.90 \pm i\ 522.6$	7	8
$-52.50 \pm i\ 536.6$	7	7

The eigenvector subprogram Vector in Appendix 5 automatically scales the first element of each eigenvector to $1 + i\,0$. This arbitrary scaling fails if there happens to be a node at the first coordinate. In that case the subprogram will show an error message which will say that one or more elements of the eigenvector are either indefinite or infinite. If the former, one or more elements of the eigenvector (which are identified in the error message) will be returned as zero. If the latter, all elements of the eigenvector will be returned as zero. To obtain the eigenvector for such a mode, the coordinates should be reordered so that a different coordinate is listed first.

Chapter 6

Singular and defective matrices

Singular mass matrix

In order to find the natural frequencies and mode shapes of a conservative system

$$m\ddot{y} + ky = 0 \qquad (6.1)$$

we have to find the eigenvalues and eigenvectors of

$$A = m^{-1}k. \qquad (6.2)$$

For a non-conservative system represented by

$$m\ddot{y} + c\dot{y} + ky = 0 \qquad (6.3)$$

we need the eigenvalues and eigenvectors of

$$A = \begin{bmatrix} 0 & I \\ -m^{-1}k & -m^{-1}c \end{bmatrix}. \qquad (6.4)$$

Obviously the A matrices will not exist if m^{-1} does not exist, which will be the case if

$$\det m = 0. \qquad (6.5)$$

Then the procedures for calculating the eigensystems set out in the logical flow diagrams in Figs 5.1 and 5.9 cannot be used without modification.

The problem is that one (at least) of the eigenvalues becomes infinite when $\det m = 0$. This may be seen by going back to first principles to search for the solutions

$$y(t) = e^{\lambda t}y \qquad (6.6)$$

of (6.3). On substituting for $y(t)$ in (6.3) from (6.6), we have

$$[\lambda^2 m + \lambda c + k]y = 0. \qquad (6.7)$$

This has a non-trivial solution for y only if

$$\det[\lambda^2 m + \lambda c + k] = 0. \qquad (6.8)$$

For M degrees of freedom, the order of each of the m, c and k matrices is

$M \times M$ and then (6.8) leads to the characteristic equation

$$a_{2M}\lambda^{2M} + a_{2M-1}\lambda^{2M-1} + \ldots + a_1\lambda + a_0 = 0 \qquad (6.9)$$

from which there will normally be $2M$ solutions for λ, which are the $2M$ eigenvalues. However, the coefficient a_{2M} is given by (Problem 6.1)

$$a_{2M} = \det m \qquad (6.10)$$

so that, if $\det m = 0$, the characteristic equation (6.9) will be of order $2M - 1$ (provided that a_{2M-1} is not also zero) and there will then be only $2M - 1$ eigenvalues.

What has happened to the missing eigenvalue may be found by rewriting (6.9) in the form

$$a_{2M}(\lambda - \lambda_{2M})(\lambda - \lambda_{2M-1}) \ldots (\lambda - \lambda_2)(\lambda - \lambda_1) = 0 \qquad (6.11)$$

where $\lambda_1, \lambda_2, \ldots, \lambda_{2M}$ are the $2M$ eigenvalues. Multiplying out (6.11) and then comparing the constant term with the corresponding constant term in (6.9), which must be the same, gives

$$a_{2M}\lambda_{2M}\lambda_{2M-1} \ldots \lambda_2\lambda_1 = a_0. \qquad (6.12)$$

Provided that $a_0 \neq 0$, we see from (6.12) that, if $a_{2M} = 0$, then one (at least) of the eigenvalues must be infinite to prevent the left-hand side of (6.12) becoming zero. Even if $a_0 = 0$ so that one of the eigenvalues is zero, there will still be an infinite eigenvalue if $a_1 \neq 0$ or if at least one of the other a's remains non-zero (Problem 6.1).

The conclusion is that, if $\det m = 0$, at least one of the $2M$ eigenvalues does not exist. In mechanical problems this will generally be because one of the physical coordinates involves the movement of an element with zero mass. A mode with an eigenvalue of infinite modulus then occurs and, in mathematical terms, this mode's eigenvalue no longer exists.

Three-degree-of-freedom system with a singular mass matrix

Consider a system whose equations have the form

$$\begin{bmatrix} m_{11} & 0 & m_{13} \\ 0 & 0 & 0 \\ m_{31} & 0 & m_{33} \end{bmatrix} \begin{bmatrix} \ddot{y}_1 \\ \ddot{y}_2 \\ \ddot{y}_3 \end{bmatrix} + \begin{bmatrix} c_{11} & 0 & c_{13} \\ c_{21} & c_{22} & c_{23} \\ c_{31} & 0 & c_{33} \end{bmatrix} \begin{bmatrix} \dot{y}_1 \\ \dot{y}_2 \\ \dot{y}_3 \end{bmatrix} +$$

$$+ \begin{bmatrix} k_{11} & k_{12} & k_{13} \\ k_{21} & k_{22} & k_{23} \\ k_{31} & k_{32} & k_{33} \end{bmatrix} \begin{bmatrix} y_1 \\ y_2 \\ y_3 \end{bmatrix} = O \qquad (6.13)$$

in which the coordinate y_2 has no mass terms associated with it, so that $m_{12} = m_{22} = m_{32} = 0$. We shall demonstrate in Chapter 11 that for many problems the mass matrix m is symmetrical. Subject to this assumption, $m_{21} = m_{12} = 0$ and $m_{23} = m_{32} = 0$. The second of equations (6.13) then has no $\ddot{y}$ terms and can, if necessary, be subtracted from the equations above and below to make $c_{12} = c_{32} = 0$ if they are not already zero. Then, after defining

$$m_1 = \begin{bmatrix} m_{11} & m_{13} \\ m_{13} & m_{33} \end{bmatrix}$$

$$c_1 = \begin{bmatrix} c_{11} & c_{13} \\ c_{31} & c_{33} \end{bmatrix}$$

and

$$k_1 = \begin{bmatrix} k_{11} & k_{12} & k_{13} \\ k_{31} & k_{32} & k_{33} \end{bmatrix}, \tag{6.14}$$

by excluding the second equation of (6.13), the remaining two equations can be written

$$m_1 \begin{bmatrix} \ddot{y}_1 \\ \ddot{y}_3 \end{bmatrix} + c_1 \begin{bmatrix} \dot{y}_1 \\ \dot{y}_3 \end{bmatrix} + k_1 \begin{bmatrix} y_1 \\ y_2 \\ y_3 \end{bmatrix} = \mathbf{0}. \tag{6.15}$$

If we also define two new variables

$$\begin{bmatrix} w_1 \\ w_3 \end{bmatrix} = \begin{bmatrix} \dot{y}_1 \\ \dot{y}_3 \end{bmatrix} \tag{6.16}$$

then (6.15) gives

$$\begin{bmatrix} \dot{w}_1 \\ \dot{w}_3 \end{bmatrix} = -m_1^{-1} c_1 \begin{bmatrix} w_1 \\ w_3 \end{bmatrix} - m_1^{-1} k_1 \begin{bmatrix} y_1 \\ y_2 \\ y_3 \end{bmatrix} \tag{6.17}$$

and the excluded second equation can be written

$$\dot{y}_2 = -\frac{k_{21}}{c_{22}} y_1 - \frac{k_{22}}{c_{22}} y_2 - \frac{k_{23}}{c_{22}} y_3 - \frac{c_{21}}{c_{22}} w_1 - \frac{c_{23}}{c_{22}} w_3. \tag{6.18}$$

Combining (6.17) and (6.18), we can put the equations in the standard form

$$\dot{z} = Az \tag{6.19}$$

where

$$z = [y_1, y_2, y_3, w_1, w_3]^{\mathrm{T}} \tag{6.20}$$

and

$$A = \begin{bmatrix} 0 & 0 & 0 & \vdots & 1 & 0 \\ -\dfrac{k_{21}}{c_{22}} & -\dfrac{k_{22}}{c_{22}} & -\dfrac{k_{23}}{c_{22}} & \vdots & -\dfrac{c_{21}}{c_{22}} & -\dfrac{c_{23}}{c_{22}} \\ 0 & 0 & 0 & \vdots & 0 & 1 \\ \hline & -m_1^{-1} k_1 & & \vdots & & -m_1^{-1} c_1 \end{bmatrix}. \tag{6.21}$$

Therefore, subject to the mass matrix being singular because it has the form in (6.13), the computational procedure in Fig. 5.9 can still be used to calculate the natural frequencies and mode shapes of a system for which m^{-1} does not exist, provided that the A matrix is calculated from (6.21) or its equivalent, instead of from (5.53). If the order of the A matrix in (6.19) is $N \times N$, then N replaces $2M$, and $2N$ replaces $4M$ in Fig. 5.9.

Example 6.1 System with a zero mass coordinate

As a specific example, consider the three systems in Fig. 5.2 with the middle mass reduced to zero. Then

$$m_1 = \begin{bmatrix} m & 0 \\ 0 & m \end{bmatrix}$$

$$c_1 = O \qquad (6.22)$$

and

$$k_1 = \begin{bmatrix} 2k & -k & 0 \\ 0 & -k & 2k \end{bmatrix}$$

and, from (6.21), the A matrix is

$$A = \begin{bmatrix} 0 & 0 & 0 & 1 & 0 \\ k/c & -2k/c & k/c & 0 & 0 \\ 0 & 0 & 0 & 0 & 1 \\ -2k/m & k/m & 0 & 0 & 0 \\ 0 & k/m & -2k/m & 0 & 0 \end{bmatrix}. \qquad (6.23)$$

The eigensystem for this matrix has been computed for the parameter values used in Example 5.4, which are

$$m = 1.0 \text{ kg}$$

$$c = 0.3 \text{ N s/m} \qquad (6.24)$$

$$k = 1.0 \text{ N/m}$$

and the results are listed in Table 6.1. Each eigenvector has five elements which, from (6.20) with (6.16), are the three displacements y_1, y_2, y_3 in order, followed by the velocities $\dot{y}_1$ and $\dot{y}_3$. If we want $\dot{y}_2$, this has to be calculated from the usual result that $\dot{y}_2 = \lambda y_2$.

There are now only two oscillatory modes. Their natural frequencies are close to the undamped natural frequencies of 1 rad/s and $\sqrt{2}$ rad/s (see Problem 6.1). The first mode (eigenvalues 1 and 2) has a damping ratio of about 0.075 with a mode shape that is similar to mode 1 in Fig. 5.3, except that the displacement of the central point (the point of zero mass) is almost the same as that of the two outer masses. The mid-point is slightly out of phase with the motion of the two outer masses. Mode 2 (eigenvalues 3 and 4) is identical with the second mode on Fig. 5.3 because this involves no motion of the central point. Mode 3 in Fig. 5.3 has now become a single aperiodic mode with, from Table 6.1, a decaying time constant of $1/6.517 = 0.15$ s, approximately. This decaying mode has a shape with a large central deflection which is some 44 times greater than the displacements of the two outer masses.

Table 6.1 Eigenvalues and eigenvectors for the three-degree-of-freedom systems in Fig. 5.2 after modification to remove the central mass in each case. The two outer masses remain $m = 1.0$ kg, and $c = 0.3$ N s/m, $k = 1.0$ N/m, as before. These results compare with those in Table 5.3, where the middle mass is not zero

Eigenvector no. 1 corresponding to eigenvalue:		Eigenvector no. 2 corresponding to eigenvalue:	
Real part	Imag. part	Real part	Imag. part
−7.496 E−02	+1.009 E+00	−7.496 E−02	−1.009 E+00
is as follows:		is as follows:	
+1.000 E+00	+0.000 E+00	+1.000 E+00	+0.000 E+00
+9.882 E−01	−1.512 E−01	+9.882 E−01	+1.512 E−01
+1.000 E+00	+5.937 E−11	−1.000 E+00	−5.937 E−11
−7.496 E−02	+1.009 E+00	−7.496 E−02	−1.009 E+00
−7.496 E−02	+1.009 E+00	−7.496 E−02	−1.009 E+00

Eigenvector no. 3 corresponding to eigenvalue:		Eigenvector no. 4 corresponding to eigenvalue:	
Real part	Imag. part	Real part	Imag. part
+3.100 E−12	+1.414 E+00	+3.100 E−12	−1.414 E+00
is as follows:		is as follows:	
−1.000 E+00	+0.000 E+00	+1.000 E+00	+0.000 E+00
+1.614 E−10	−9.158 E−12	+1.614 E−10	+9.158 E−12
−1.000 E+00	+5.016 E−11	−1.000 E+00	−5.016 E−11
−9.576 E−12	+1.414 E+00	−9.576 E−12	−1.414 E+00
−7.431 E−11	−1.414 E+00	−7.431 E−11	+1.414 E+00

Eigenvector no. 5 corresponding to eigenvalue:	
Real part	Imag. part
−6.517 E+00	+0.000 E+00
is as follows:	
+1.000 E+00	+0.000 E+00
+4.447 E+01	+0.000 E+00
+1.000 E+00	+0.000 E+00
−6.517 E+00	+0.000 E+00
−6.517 E+00	+0.000 E+00

General case when one degree of freedom has zero mass

The method used in the previous example can be extended to the general case of M degrees of freedom, as follows. Assuming that the rth equation has no second-order terms, row r of the mass matrix $\boldsymbol{m}$ will have only zero elements. Also assuming, as before, that the mass matrix $\boldsymbol{m}$ is symmetrical (Chapter 11), so that $m_{rj} = m_{jr}$, then column r also has only zero elements. Let $\boldsymbol{m}_1$ be the $(M - 1) \times (M - 1)$ matrix obtained by deleting the rth row and rth column of $\boldsymbol{m}$.

The damping matrix will generally be a full matrix, but its rth column can have all its elements c_{jr} above and below c_{rr} set to zero by subtracting multiples of row r from all the other rows. Since multiples of the rth equation must be subtracted from the other $M - 1$ equations, the damping and stiffness matrices are modified, but the mass matrix is unaltered because we have assumed that there are no mass terms in the rth equation. Let $\boldsymbol{c}$ and $\boldsymbol{k}$ be the damping and stiffness matrices after this operation has been carried out, so that $c_{jr} = 0$, except for $j = r$.

Let $\boldsymbol{c}_1$ be the $(M - 1) \times (M - 1)$ matrix obtained by deleting the rth row and rth column of $\boldsymbol{c}$ and let $\boldsymbol{c}^{(r)}$ denote the deleted rth row with element c_{rr} removed. Also let $\boldsymbol{k}_1$ be the $(M - 1) \times M$ matrix obtained by deleting the rth row of $\boldsymbol{k}$ and let $\boldsymbol{k}^{(r)}$ be the row that has been deleted. Then, by following the same reasoning as for the three-degree-of-freedom case considered previously, the $M - 1$ second-order equations and one first-order equation may be combined into the standard first-order form

$$\dot{z} = Az \tag{6.25}$$

by defining a $2M - 1$ vector z for the M displacements $y_1, y_2, \ldots, y_M$ and $M - 1$ velocities $\dot{y}_1, \dot{y}_2, \ldots, \dot{y}_{r-1}, \dot{y}_{r+1}, \ldots, \dot{y}_m$, so that

$$z = [y_1, y_2, \ldots, y_M, \dot{y}_1, \dot{y}_2, \ldots, \dot{y}_{r-1}, \dot{y}_{r+1}, \ldots, \dot{y}_M]^T \tag{6.26}$$

with the velocity term $\dot{y}_r$ omitted. The A matrix now has order $(2M - 1) \times (2M - 1)$, and is given by

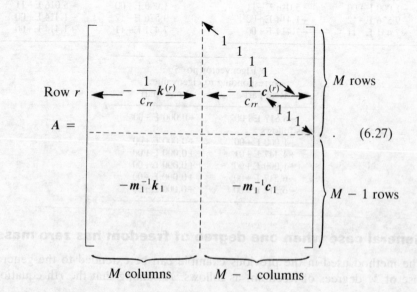

$$A = \qquad (6.27)$$

The upper M rows of A are zero except for the rth row and for the diagonal lines of 1's such that

$$a_{j, M+j} = 1, \qquad 1 \leq j \leq r - 1$$

and

$$a_{j, M-1+j} = 1, \qquad r + 1 \leq j \leq M.$$

(6.28)

Multiple eigenvalues

When the state matrix A of a problem has been found, its eigenvalues can be computed as explained in Chapter 5. Usually, all the eigenvalues will be different, or, in mathematical terms, they will be distinct. But sometimes the same eigenvalue is repeated, and then the A matrix is said to have *multiple eigenvalues*. This provides no difficulty for computer programs for eigenvalue extraction, but it does complicate the eigenvector calculation.

If there is a repeated eigenvalue, there may be a corresponding number of different, independent eigenvectors. But it is more likely that there will not be an independent eigenvector for each repeated eigenvalue. Then the system of eigenvectors is said to be *defective* and it is no longer possible to find an eigenvector matrix U for which

$$U^{-1}AU = [\text{diag } \lambda_j].$$

(6.29)

First consider the case when it *is* possible to satisfy (6.29). Let there be two eigenvalues λ_1 for which the columns of U are two independent vectors z_1 and z_2. Then we know that

$$Az_1 = \lambda_1 z_1$$

(6.30)

and

$$Az_2 = \lambda_1 z_2$$

(6.31)

if the state equation (6.25) is to be satisfied. If a new vector z_3 is defined by

$$z_3 = \alpha z_1 + \beta z_2$$

(6.32)

where α and β are arbitrary multipliers, then it is clear from (6.30) and (6.31) that

$$Az_3 = \lambda_1 z_3$$

(6.33)

so that z_3 is also an eigenvector of A. Hence if z_1 and z_2 are independent eigenvectors of A for the same eigenvalue λ_1, than any linear combination of z_1 and z_2 is also an eigenvector. Therefore U is no longer unique when the eigenvalues are repeated, unlike the case when the eigenvalues are distinct (except, of course, for the individual scaling of columns, which is arbitrary).

However, in developing the general theory of modal response, it does not matter whether U is unique, and provided that any U can be found for which (6.29) is true, then the general analysis applies just as if the eigenvalues were distinct.

In some problems for which there are repeated eigenvalues it will not be possible to find an independent set of eigenvectors, and then an eigenvector matrix U to satisfy (6.29) cannot be found. It is not possible to find a similarity transformation which will reduce A to diagonal form. Instead, the best that can be done is to find a matrix W for which, instead of (6.29), we have

$$W^{-1}AW = J \tag{6.34}$$

where J is the so-called *Jordan matrix* which is a nearly diagonal matrix with the eigenvalues along its principal diagonal and with a number of unit elements in its super-diagonal line or, alternatively, in its sub-diagonal line. We shall consider transformations to the first of these forms, the upper Jordan form, in the analysis that follows, but it is equally possible, with appropriate adjustments, to use the lower Jordan form.

Suppose that one eigenvalue λ_1 occurs twice and that two independent eigenvectors for λ_1 cannot be found. Then it is always possible to find a matrix W for which

$$W^{-1}AW = J = \begin{bmatrix} \lambda_1 & 1 & & & & \\ 0 & \lambda_1 & & & & \\ & & \lambda_3 & & & \\ & & & \lambda_4 & & \\ & & & & \ddots & \\ & & & & & \lambda_N \end{bmatrix} \tag{6.35}$$

where the order of A and W is assumed to be $N \times N$. The other eigenvalues $\lambda_3, \lambda_4, \ldots, \lambda_N$ are assumed to be distinct and columns 3 to N of W are the usual independent eigenvectors, scaled in whatever way is desired. Also, the first column of W is the independent eigenvector corresponding to λ_1. However, column 2 of W is not an independent eigenvector. It may be found as follows.

Pre-multiplying (6.35) by W gives

$$AW = W \begin{bmatrix} \lambda_1 & 1 & & & & \\ 0 & \lambda_1 & & & & \\ & & \lambda_3 & & & \\ & & & \lambda_4 & & \\ & & & & \ddots & \\ & & & & & \lambda_N \end{bmatrix}. \tag{6.36}$$

Then, if the columns of W are called $w^{(1)}, w^{(2)}, \ldots, w^{(N)}$, the first columns on both sides of (6.36) give

$$Aw^{(1)} = \lambda_1 w^{(1)} \tag{6.37}$$

confirming that $w^{(1)}$ is the usual eigenvector of A. The second columns on both sides of (6.36) give

$$Aw^{(2)} = w^{(1)} + \lambda_1 w^{(2)} \tag{6.38}$$

from which it is evident that $w^{(2)}$ is not an eigenvector because it does not satisfy an equation like (6.37). Instead, $w^{(2)}$ is called a *principal vector* of A and it can be obtained from (6.38) provided that $w^{(1)}$ is known first.

The general theory of eigenvalue analysis (see, for example, Gantmacher [33, 34]) shows that the principal vectors of a matrix are independent, although they are not unique. Their lack of uniqueness is clear when it is seen that, if $w^{(2)}$ is a solution for (6.38), then, because of (6.37), so is $w^{(2)} + \alpha w^{(1)}$ a solution, where α is an arbitrary multiplier.

If the eigenvalue λ_1 occurs three times there may be three separate λ_1s on the diagonal of the Jordan matrix, or there may be one separate λ_1 and a 2×2 Jordan sub-matrix

$$C_2(\lambda_1) = \begin{bmatrix} \lambda_1 & 1 \\ 0 & \lambda_1 \end{bmatrix} \tag{6.39}$$

or there may be no separate λ_1s and a 3×3 Jordan sub-matrix

$$C_3(\lambda_1) = \begin{bmatrix} \lambda_1 & 1 & 0 \\ 0 & \lambda_1 & 1 \\ 0 & 0 & \lambda_1 \end{bmatrix}. \tag{6.40}$$

If we define

$$C_1(\lambda_1) = \lambda_1 \tag{6.41}$$

and call this a Jordan sub-matrix of order one, then a full Jordan matrix can always be written in terms of a series of Jordan sub-matrices disposed along its principal diagonal. For example, if A has order 6×6 and has only two distinct eigenvalues, λ_1, which occurs four times, and λ_2, which occurs twice, the Jordan matrix J may be

$$J = \begin{bmatrix} C_1(\lambda_1) & & & & & \\ & C_1(\lambda_1) & & & & \\ & & C_1(\lambda_1) & & & \\ & & & C_1(\lambda_1) & & \\ & & & & C_1(\lambda_2) & \\ & & & & & C_1(\lambda_2) \end{bmatrix} \tag{6.42}$$

or it could be

$$J = \begin{bmatrix} C_4(\lambda_1) & \\ & C_2(\lambda_2) \end{bmatrix} \tag{6.43}$$

or any other sequence of Jordan submatrices for which the combined order of the λ_1 submatrices is four and of the λ_2 submatrices is two.

For a given A matrix, the form of the Jordan matrix is unique except for the ordering of the sub-matrices along the diagonal. The number of independent eigenvectors associated with a repeated eigenvalue is equal to the number of Jordan sub-matrices of this eigenvalue in the Jordan canonical form. To determine the number of independent eigenvectors, each case has to be considered individually.

We can think of an eigenvector as being a special case of a principal vector, and so we shall refer to W as the *principal-vector matrix* for any problem with repeated eigenvalues.

Example 6.2 Calculating the Jordan matrix and principal vectors

The following example, which is based on Example 3 of Newland [74], is to find the eigenvalues, the Jordan matrix J and the principal-vector matrix W for a system which satisfies

$$m\ddot{y} + c\dot{y} + ky = 0 \tag{6.44}$$

where

$$m = \begin{bmatrix} 1 & 0 \\ 0 & 0 \end{bmatrix}, c = \begin{bmatrix} 2 & 1 \\ 0 & 1 \end{bmatrix} \text{ and } k = \begin{bmatrix} 1 & 2 \\ 0 & 1 \end{bmatrix}. \tag{6.45}$$

Since the m matrix is singular, we have to form the A matrix by using (6.27), where

$$r = 2, \quad m_1 = 1, \quad c_1 = 2, \quad k_1 = [1 \ 1], \tag{6.46}$$
$$c^{(2)} = 0 \quad \text{and} \quad k^{(2)} = [0 \ 1]$$

and

$$A = \begin{bmatrix} 0 & 0 & 1 \\ 0 & -1 & 0 \\ -1 & -1 & -2 \end{bmatrix}. \tag{6.47}$$

Note that k_1 is the upper row of k after the lower row has been subtracted to make $c_{12} = 0$. The eigenvalues of A are the solutions of

$$\det[A - \lambda I] = 0$$

which with A from (6.47) gives

$$(\lambda + 1)^3 = 0$$

so that

$$\lambda_1 = \lambda_2 = \lambda_3 = -1. \tag{6.48}$$

If the first column of the principal-vector matrix is $w^{(1)}$, where

$$w^{(1)} = \begin{bmatrix} w_{11} \\ w_{21} \\ w_{31} \end{bmatrix}$$

then, from (6.37),

$$\begin{bmatrix} 0 & 0 & 1 \\ 0 & -1 & 0 \\ -1 & -1 & -2 \end{bmatrix} \begin{bmatrix} w_{11} \\ w_{21} \\ w_{31} \end{bmatrix} = - \begin{bmatrix} w_{11} \\ w_{21} \\ w_{31} \end{bmatrix}$$

giving

$$w_{31} = - w_{11}$$

$$- w_{21} = - w_{21} \qquad (6.49)$$

$$- w_{11} - w_{21} - 2w_{31} = - w_{31}.$$

On substituting from the first of these equations into the third, we find that

$$w_{21} = 0$$

and so the eigenvector is

$$w^{(1)} = \begin{bmatrix} 1 \\ 0 \\ -1 \end{bmatrix} \qquad (6.50)$$

when the first element is normalized to unity. Also, (6.49) have no other solution and so there is only one independent eigenvector. It follows from the previous theory that the Jordan sub-matrix will, in this example, be the full Jordan matrix, and hence

$$J = \begin{bmatrix} -1 & 1 & 0 \\ 0 & -1 & 1 \\ 0 & 0 & -1 \end{bmatrix}. \qquad (6.51)$$

We then have to find the remaining two columns of the principal-vector matrix W for which

$$AW = WJ. \qquad (6.52)$$

The second column $w^{(2)}$ must be the solution of (6.38) with $w^{(1)}$ given by (6.50) with $\lambda_1 = -1$, and, from (6.52), the third column $w^{(3)}$ will be the solution of

$$Aw^{(3)} = w^{(2)} - w^{(3)}. \qquad (6.53)$$

From (6.38)

$$\begin{bmatrix} 0 & 0 & 1 \\ 0 & -1 & 0 \\ -1 & -1 & -2 \end{bmatrix} \begin{bmatrix} w_{12} \\ w_{22} \\ w_{32} \end{bmatrix} = \begin{bmatrix} 1 \\ 0 \\ -1 \end{bmatrix} - \begin{bmatrix} w_{12} \\ w_{22} \\ w_{32} \end{bmatrix} \qquad (6.54)$$

which gives

$$w_{32} = 1 - w_{12}$$

$$-w_{22} = -w_{22} \tag{6.55}$$

$$-w_{12} - w_{22} - 2w_{32} = -1 - w_{32}.$$

There are only two independent equations for three unknowns, so if we arbitrarily put $w_{12} = \delta$, then the solution gives

$$w^{(2)} = \begin{bmatrix} \delta \\ 0 \\ 1 - \delta \end{bmatrix}. \tag{6.56}$$

Lastly, solving for the third column $w^{(3)}$ from (6.53) with $w^{(2)}$ given by (6.56), we get

$$\begin{bmatrix} 0 & 0 & 1 \\ 0 & -1 & 0 \\ -1 & -1 & -2 \end{bmatrix} \begin{bmatrix} w_{13} \\ w_{23} \\ w_{33} \end{bmatrix} = \begin{bmatrix} \delta \\ 0 \\ 1 - \delta \end{bmatrix} - \begin{bmatrix} w_{13} \\ w_{23} \\ w_{33} \end{bmatrix} \tag{6.57}$$

which gives

$$w_{33} = \delta - w_{13}$$

$$-w_{23} = -w_{23} \tag{6.58}$$

$$-w_{13} - w_{23} - 2w_{33} = 1 - \delta - w_{33}.$$

There are again only two independent equations for three unknowns, so that putting $w_{13} = \varepsilon$ we find

$$w^{(3)} = \begin{bmatrix} \varepsilon \\ -1 \\ \delta - \varepsilon \end{bmatrix} \tag{6.59}$$

where ε is a second arbitrary quantity. If we put $\delta = \varepsilon = 1$, so that the first elements of all the columns of W are normalized to unity, the result is that the principal-vector matrix is

$$W = \begin{bmatrix} 1 & 1 & -1 \\ 0 & 0 & -1 \\ -1 & 0 & 0 \end{bmatrix}. \tag{6.60}$$

The eigenvector sub-program Vector in Appendix 5 produces only one eigenvector for the case of repeated eigenvalues and, in a numerical study, it will be necessary to check whether there are any other independent eigenvectors and then to use a separate calculation to find the principal vectors from the eigenvector (or eigenvectors if more than one).

When there are multiple eigenvalues, and the system matrix A cannot be transformed to a diagonal matrix, the general result (4.28) for the response to arbitrary excitation does not apply without modification. For many problems, a repeated eigenvalue is a curiosity for a particular set of parameter values, and response calculations for a nearby set of values when the eigenvalues are sufficiently distinct may be adequate. Then equation (4.28) for distinct eigenvalues is all that is needed. But in a few situations, the presence of one or more repeated eigenvalues is a feature of the problem, and then the response calculations require special treatment. We shall consider the necessary modifications to the general response equation (4.28) in Chapter 8. An example of a problem which has multiple eigenvalues and which requires such special treatment is the following problem of torsional vibration.

Example of a torsional system with multiple eigenvalues

The practical problem on which this example is based is the torsional vibration of a marine propulsion system having a fluid drive. A diesel engine is sometimes connected to reduction gears and the ship's propeller by a fluid coupling or 'fluid flywheel' (see Bishop *et al.* [8]). A primitive model of such a system consists of three inertias I_1, I_2, I_3 with the first two connected by a shaft of torsional stiffness k and the second two connected by a viscous coupling of torsional viscous coefficient c, Fig. 6.1. Wheel I_1 represents the ship's propeller, wheel I_2 the reduction gears, and wheel I_3 the engine. Shaft k is the propeller shaft and viscous connection c models the fluid coupling.

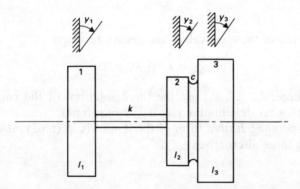

Fig. 6.1 Simplified torsional model of a marine propulsion system with a diesel engine (wheel I_3) driving through a fluid coupling to reduction gears (represented by wheel I_2) and the ship's propeller (wheel I_1). (After Fig. 9 of Ref. [8]. *Courtesy of the Institute of Marine Engineers*)

The equations of free torsional vibration of this system can be written in the standard second-order form (6.3) where the reader can check that

$$m = \begin{bmatrix} I_1 & 0 & 0 \\ 0 & I_2 & 0 \\ 0 & 0 & I_3 \end{bmatrix},$$

$$c = \begin{bmatrix} 0 & 0 & 0 \\ 0 & c & -c \\ 0 & -c & c \end{bmatrix}, \tag{6.61}$$

$$k = \begin{bmatrix} k & -k & 0 \\ -k & k & 0 \\ 0 & 0 & 0 \end{bmatrix},$$

and then, from (6.4),

$$A = \begin{bmatrix} 0 & 0 & 0 & 1 & 0 & 0 \\ 0 & 0 & 0 & 0 & 1 & 0 \\ 0 & 0 & 0 & 0 & 0 & 1 \\ -k/I_1 & k/I_1 & 0 & 0 & 0 & 0 \\ k/I_2 & -k/I_2 & 0 & 0 & -c/I_2 & c/I_2 \\ 0 & 0 & 0 & 0 & c/I_3 & -c/I_3 \end{bmatrix}. \tag{6.62}$$

The eigenvalues of A are the solutions of

$$\det(A - \lambda I) = 0 \tag{6.63}$$

which gives

$$\lambda^3 \left[\lambda^3 + c\left(\frac{1}{I_2} + \frac{1}{I_3}\right)\lambda^2 + k\left(\frac{1}{I_1} + \frac{1}{I_2}\right)\lambda + kc\left(\frac{1}{I_1 I_2} + \frac{1}{I_2 I_3} + \frac{1}{I_3 I_1}\right) \right] = 0. \tag{6.64}$$

Therefore three of the eigenvalues are always zero and

$$\lambda_1 = \lambda_2 = \lambda_3 = 0. \tag{6.65}$$

The other three, λ_4, λ_5, λ_6, are the three solutions of the cubic equation which remains after deleting the factor λ^3 from (6.64).

The corresponding Jordan form of the A matrix in (6.62) must be one of the following three alternatives

(i)

$$J = \begin{bmatrix} 0 & & & & & \\ & 0 & & & & \\ & & 0 & & & \\ & & & \lambda_4 & & \\ & & & & \lambda_5 & \\ & & & & & \lambda_6 \end{bmatrix} \tag{6.66}$$

(ii) either

$$J = \begin{bmatrix} 0 & & & & & \\ & 0 & 1 & & & \\ & & 0 & & & \\ & & & \lambda_4 & & \\ & & & & \lambda_5 & \\ & & & & & \lambda_6 \end{bmatrix}$$

or

$$J = \begin{bmatrix} 0 & 1 & & & & \\ & 0 & & & & \\ & & 0 & & & \\ & & & \lambda_4 & & \\ & & & & \lambda_5 & \\ & & & & & \lambda_6 \end{bmatrix} \tag{6.67}$$

depending how the eigenvectors are ordered, and

(iii)

$$J = \begin{bmatrix} 0 & 1 & & & & \\ & 0 & 1 & & & \\ & & 0 & & & \\ & & & \lambda_4 & & \\ & & & & \lambda_5 & \\ & & & & & \lambda_6 \end{bmatrix} \tag{6.68}$$

with all the elements not shown being zero elements. In order to decide which of these is the correct form we need to find how many independent eigenvectors are associated with the three repeated eigenvalues $\lambda = 0$.

When the system is stationary, angles y_1, y_2, y_3 (see Fig. 6.1) may have any values provided that $y_1 = y_2$. Hence a possible eigenvector for $\lambda = 0$ is

$$w = [1, 1, \alpha, 0, 0, 0]^{\text{T}} \tag{6.69}$$

where α is an arbitrary real constant. There are infinitely many possible eigenvectors corresponding to $\lambda = 0$, on account of the infinite range possible for α. But only two of these are independent eigenvectors because, for example, if one is

$$w^{(1)} = [1, 1, -1, 0, 0, 0]^{\text{T}} \tag{6.70}$$

and the other is

$$w^{(2)} = [1, 1, 1, 0, 0, 0]^{\text{T}} \tag{6.71}$$

then the rest can all be obtained by combining $w^{(1)}$ and $w^{(2)}$ in appropriate proportions.

Since there are two independent eigenvectors for $\lambda = 0$, (6.67) gives the correct form for the Jordan matrix, and there is one principal vector for $\lambda = 0$ which is not also an eigenvector. Let the first two columns of J be the eigenvectors and the third column be the principal vector, so that J is the first of the two alternatives in (6.67). Then from (6.34), we have

$$AW = W \begin{bmatrix} 0 & & & & & \\ & 0 & 1 & & & \\ & & 0 & & & \\ & & & \lambda_4 & & \\ & & & & \lambda_5 & \\ & & & & & \lambda_6 \end{bmatrix} \tag{6.72}$$

and equating the third columns of both sides,

$$Aw^{(3)} = w^{(2)}. \tag{6.73}$$

Leaving $w^{(2)}$ in the general form of (6.69), with α arbitrary, we then have

$$\begin{bmatrix} 0 & 0 & 0 & 1 & 0 & 0 \\ 0 & 0 & 0 & 0 & 1 & 0 \\ 0 & 0 & 0 & 0 & 0 & 1 \\ -k/I_1 & k/I_1 & 0 & 0 & 0 & 0 \\ k/I_2 & -k/I_2 & 0 & 0 & -c/I_2 & -c/I_2 \\ 0 & 0 & 0 & 0 & c/I_3 & -c/I_3 \end{bmatrix} \begin{bmatrix} w_{13} \\ w_{23} \\ w_{33} \\ w_{43} \\ w_{53} \\ w_{63} \end{bmatrix} = \begin{bmatrix} 1 \\ 1 \\ \alpha \\ 0 \\ 0 \\ 0 \end{bmatrix} \tag{6.74}$$

which gives

$$w_{43} = 1$$

$$w_{53} = 1$$

$$w_{63} = \alpha \tag{6.75}$$

$$-w_{13} + w_{23} = 0$$

$$k(w_{13} - w_{23}) + c(-w_{53} + w_{63}) = 0$$

$$w_{53} - w_{63} = 0.$$

According to the last of these, $w_{53} = w_{63}$, and therefore the arbitrary parameter α can only be 1. We conclude that the eigenvectors must be ordered so that $w^{(1)}$ is given by (6.70) and $w^{(2)}$ by (6.71), rather than the reverse, because otherwise α cannot be unity. If the first element w_{13} in (6.75) is called β (arbitrary) and the third element w_{33}, which does not appear in (6.75), is γ (also arbitrary), then the principal vector $w^{(3)}$ is

$$w^{(3)} = [\beta \; \beta \; \gamma \; 1 \; 1 \; 1]^{\mathrm{T}} \tag{6.76}$$

where β and γ are arbitrary. We shall put $\beta = \gamma = 1$ and take

$$w^{(3)} = [1 \; 1 \; 1 \; 1 \; 1 \; 1]^{\mathrm{T}}. \tag{6.77}$$

To complete this calculation, we need the remaining three eigenvalues,

λ_4, λ_5, λ_6, and their corresponding eigenvectors. For the following parameter values

$$I_1 = 3 \text{ kg m}^2, \ I_2 = 1.5 \text{ kg m}^2, \ I_3 = 4.5 \text{ kg m}^2$$

$$k = 200 \text{ N m/rad}, \ c = 135/8 \text{ N m s/rad},$$

(6.78)

which do not represent a practical case, but which have been used in
previous discussions of this problem (Newland [74]), the eigenvalues and
eigenvectors have been calculated in the usual way. The full set of
eigenvalues is

$$\lambda_1 = 0$$

$$\lambda_2 = 0$$

$$\lambda_3 = 0$$

(6.79)

$$\lambda_4 = -10$$

$$\lambda_5 = (5/2)(-1 + i\sqrt{23}) = -2.5 + i\,11.99$$

$$\lambda_6 = (5.2)(-1 - i\sqrt{23}) = -2.5 - i\,11.99$$

and the corresponding eigenvectors for λ_4, λ_5 and λ_6 are

$$w^{(4)} = [1, \ 5/2, \ -3/2, \ -10, \ -25, \ 15]^{\mathrm{T}},$$

(6.80)

$$w^{(5)} = \begin{bmatrix} 1 \\ (-17 - i\,3\,\sqrt{23})/16 \\ (-5 + i\,\sqrt{23})/16 \\ (-5 + i\,5\,\sqrt{23})/2 \\ (215 - i\,35\sqrt{23})/16 \\ (-45 - i\,15\sqrt{23})/16 \end{bmatrix} = \begin{bmatrix} 1 \\ -1.0625 - i\,0.8992 \\ -0.3125 + i\,0.2997 \\ -2.5 + i\,11.9896 \\ 13.4375 - i\,10.4909 \\ -2.8125 - i\,4.4961 \end{bmatrix}, \text{(6.81)}$$

$$w^{(6)} = w^{(5)*}.$$

(6.82)

For these parameter values, the Jordan matrix is therefore, from (6.72)

$$J = \begin{bmatrix} 0 \\ & 0 & 1 \\ & 0 & 0 \\ & & & -10 \\ & & & & -2.5 + i\,11.99 \\ & & & & & -2.5 - i\,11.99 \end{bmatrix}.$$

(6.83)

and the corresponding principal-vector matrix is

$$W = \begin{bmatrix} 1 & 1 & 1 & 1 & 1 & 1 \\ 1 & 1 & 1 & 2.5 & -1.0625 - i\,0.8992 & -1.0625 + i\,0.8992 \\ -1 & 1 & 1 & -1.5 & -0.3125 + i\,0.2997 & -0.3125 - i\,0.2997 \\ 0 & 0 & 1 & -10 & -2.5 + i\,11.9896 & -2.5 - i\,11.9896 \\ 0 & 0 & 1 & -25 & 13.4375 - i\,10.4909 & 13.4375 + i\,10.4909 \\ 0 & 0 & 1 & 15 & -2.8125 - i\,4.4961 & -2.8125 + i\,4.4961 \end{bmatrix}.$$

(6.84)

These results (6.83) and (6.84) will be used in a further discussion of this problem in Chapter 8.

Interpretation of principal vectors

For a system with multiple eigenvalues defined by

$$\dot{z} = Az \tag{6.85}$$

it is always possible to define a new response vector q by

$$q = W^{-1}z \tag{6.86}$$

where W is the principal-vector matrix. On substituting for z from (6.86) into (6.85)

$$W\dot{q} = AWq \tag{6.87}$$

so that

$$\dot{q} = W^{-1}AWq \tag{6.88}$$

which, from (6.34), gives

$$\dot{q} = Jq. \tag{6.89}$$

The vector q can still be called the normal coordinate vector, but not all its elements are independent of the other elements because J is no longer a diagonal matrix.

For example, suppose that A is of order 6×6 and has a multiple eigenvalue which occurs three times with two independent eigenvectors so that, as in the torsional vibration problem in the previous section,

$$J = \begin{bmatrix} \lambda_1 & & & & & \\ & \lambda_1 & 1 & & & \\ & & \lambda_1 & & & \\ & & & \lambda_4 & & \\ & & & & \lambda_5 & \\ & & & & & \lambda_6 \end{bmatrix}. \tag{6.90}$$

Then, if

$$q = [q_1, q_2, q_3, q_4, q_5, q_6]^T \tag{6.91}$$

from (6.89)

$$\begin{aligned} \dot{q}_1 &= \lambda_1 q_1 \\ \dot{q}_2 &= \lambda_1 q_2 + q_3 \\ \dot{q}_3 &= \lambda_1 q_3 \\ \dot{q}_4 &= \lambda_4 q_4 \\ \dot{q}_5 &= \lambda_5 q_5 \\ \dot{q}_6 &= \lambda_6 q_6. \end{aligned} \tag{6.92}$$

The solutions for q_1, q_3, q_4, q_5 and q_6 are of the form

$$q_r(t) = C_r \, e^{\lambda_r t}, \quad r = 1, 3, 4, 5 \text{ or } 6 \qquad (6.93)$$

and they are each independent of the other q_rs. The second normal coordinate q_2 is the exception, and this satisfies the second of (6.92) which, with q_3 from (6.93), gives

$$\dot{q}_2 - \lambda_1 q_2 = C_3 \, e^{\lambda_1 t}. \qquad (6.94)$$

Multiplying by the integrating factor $e^{-\lambda_1 t}$, we then find that

$$\frac{d}{dt}(q_2 \, e^{-\lambda_1 t}) = C_3 \qquad (6.95)$$

so that

$$q_2 \, e^{-\lambda_1 t} = C_2 + C_3 t \qquad (6.96)$$

or

$$q_2 = (C_2 + C_3 t) \, e^{\lambda_1 t}. \qquad (6.97)$$

On returning to the physical variables represented by the vector

$$z = [y_1, y_2, y_3, \dot{y}_1, \dot{y}_2, \dot{y}_3]^T \qquad (6.98)$$

then, from (6.86), if $w^{(r)}$ denotes the rth column of W,

$$z = [w^{(1)} \ w^{(2)} \ w^{(3)} \ w^{(4)} \ w^{(5)} \ w^{(6)}] \begin{bmatrix} q_1 \\ q_2 \\ q_3 \\ q_4 \\ q_5 \\ q_6 \end{bmatrix} \qquad (6.99)$$

and the transient solution for the free vibration of the system represented by (6.85) is

$$z = C_1 \, e^{\lambda_1 t} w^{(1)} + (C_2 + C_3 t) \, e^{\lambda_1 t} w^{(2)} + C_3 \, e^{\lambda_1 t} w^{(3)} + $$
$$+ C_4 \, e^{\lambda_4 t} w^{(4)} + C_5 \, e^{\lambda_5 t} w^{(5)} + C_6 \, e^{\lambda_6 t} w^{(6)}. \qquad (6.100)$$

Here $w^{(1)}$ and $w^{(2)}$ are the two (independent) eigenvectors for λ_1 and so free vibration in modes 1 and 2 is given by

$$\text{mode 1:} \qquad z_1(t) = C_1 \, e^{\lambda_1 t} w^{(1)}$$
$$\text{mode 2:} \qquad z_2(t) = C_2 \, e^{\lambda_1 t} w^{(2)}. \qquad (6.101)$$

For the case when all the C's are zero except for C_3, motion in mode 3 is given by

$$\text{mode 3:} \qquad z_3(t) = C_3 \, e^{\lambda_1 t}(t w^{(2)} + w^{(3)}) \qquad (6.102)$$

and depends on the eigenvector $w^{(2)}$ and its corresponding principal vector $w^{(3)}$.

The other modes are

$$\text{mode 4:} \qquad z_4(t) = C_4\, e^{\lambda_4 y}\, w^{(4)}$$

$$\text{mode 5:} \qquad z_5(t) = C_5\, e^{\lambda_5 t}\, w^{(5)} \qquad \qquad (6.103)$$

$$\text{mode 6:} \qquad z_6(t) = C_6\, e^{\lambda_6 t}\, w^{(6)}$$

where $w^{(4)}$, $w^{(5)}$ and $w^{(6)}$ are the three remaining (independent) eigenvectors.

For the torsional system in Fig. 6.1 for which $\lambda_1 = 0$, the first three modes are, from (6.84),

$$\text{mode 1: } z_1(t) = \begin{bmatrix} y_1(t) \\ y_2(t) \\ y_3(t) \\ \dot{y}_1(t) \\ \dot{y}_2(t) \\ \dot{y}_3(t) \end{bmatrix} = C_1 \begin{bmatrix} 1 \\ 1 \\ -1 \\ 0 \\ 0 \\ 0 \end{bmatrix} \qquad (6.104)$$

$$\text{mode 2: } z_2(t) = \begin{bmatrix} y_1(t) \\ y_2(t) \\ y_3(t) \\ \dot{y}_1(t) \\ \dot{y}_2(t) \\ \dot{y}_3(t) \end{bmatrix} = C_2 \begin{bmatrix} 1 \\ 1 \\ 1 \\ 0 \\ 0 \\ 0 \end{bmatrix} \qquad (6.105)$$

$$\text{mode 3: } z_3(t) = \begin{bmatrix} y_1(t) \\ y_2(t) \\ y_3(t) \\ \dot{y}_1(t) \\ \dot{y}_2(t) \\ \dot{y}_3(t) \end{bmatrix} = C_3 \begin{bmatrix} t+1 \\ t+1 \\ t+1 \\ 1 \\ 1 \\ 1 \end{bmatrix}. \qquad (6.106)$$

We can now describe these modes as follows. In mode 1, the system is at rest with wheels I_1 and I_2 having been rotated together in one direction and wheel I_3 rotated in the opposite direction. The angular rotation of I_1 and I_2 has been chosen arbitrarily to be the same as the angular rotation of I_3 in the opposite direction. In mode 2, the system is also at rest with all the wheels having been rotated in the same direction through the same angle. In mode 3, the wheels have an arbitrary constant angular velocity with all the wheels moving together at the same velocity. In (6.106), the first three elements of $z(t)$ are $C_3(t+1)$. It will be recalled from the previous section that the 1's which arise here were arbitrarily chosen values of β and γ in equation (6.76). These are now seen to represent the starting displacements of the three wheels at time $t = 0$ and obviously alternative starting positions would be equally valid.

The interpretation of a principal vector may be generalized as follows. Let eigenvalue λ_r occur twice and only have one independent eigenvector

$w^{(r)}$ so that there is a Jordan submatrix

$$\begin{bmatrix} \lambda_r & 1 \\ 0 & \lambda_r \end{bmatrix}. \tag{6.107}$$

One mode of free vibration is described in the usual way by

$$z_r(t) = C_r e^{\lambda_r t} w^{(r)} \tag{6.108}$$

and, from (6.102), there is a second mode given by

$$z_{r+1}(t) = C_{r+1} e^{\lambda_r t} (t w^{(r)} + w^{(r+1)}) \tag{6.109}$$

where $w^{(r)}$ is the rth column of W which is an eigenvector and $w^{(r+1)}$ is the $(r+1)$th column of W which is the corresponding principal vector.

The mode defined by (6.108) is a 'normal mode' with the properties described in Chapter 5. All the coordinates represented by the element of $z_r(t)$ have the same exponential time dependence, and their relative amplitudes are given by the elements $w^{(r)}$. Both λ_r and $w^{(r)}$ may be complex, in which case $z_r(t)$ is accompanied by its complex conjugate, for example $z_{r+2}(t)$.

The mode defined by (6.109) has a more complicated time dependence, with the eigenvector $w^{(r)}$ now multiplied by time t, and with the addition of the principal vector $w^{(r+1)}$. The coordinates of $z(t)$ no longer all have the same time dependence because this now depends on the relative magnitudes of the elements of $w^{(r)}$ and $w^{(r+1)}$ which will be different for different coordinates. Therefore $z_{r+1}(t)$ is not a normal mode in the conventional sense but it is still a mode of free vibration. In this mode, motion is defined by two columns of the principal-vector matrix W rather than by just a single column of W. If λ_r is complex then, in general, so will $w^{(r)}$ and $w^{(r+1)}$ be complex and $z_{r+1}(t)$ will be accompanied by its complex conjugate, for example $z_{r+3}(t)$ (see Problem 6.4).

If the eigenvalue λ_r occurs three times and has only one eigenvector $w^{(r)}$ so that there is a Jordan submatrix

$$\begin{bmatrix} \lambda_r & 1 & \\ & \lambda_r & 1 \\ & & \lambda_r \end{bmatrix}$$

then, by following the same reasoning as above for the simpler case of (6.107), it can be shown (Problem 6.4) that the modes of vibration for eigenvalue λ_r are

$$z_r(t) = C_r e^{\lambda_r t} w^{(r)} \tag{6.110}$$

$$z_{r+1}(t) = C_{r+1} e^{\lambda_r t} (t w^{(r)} + w^{(r+1)}) \tag{6.111}$$

and

$$z_{r+2}(t) = C_{r+2} e^{\lambda_r t} (\tfrac{1}{2} t^2 w^{(r)} + t w^{(r+1)} + w^{(r+2)}) \tag{6.112}$$

where

$w^{(r)}$ is the eigenvector defined by the rth column of W;

$w^{(r+1)}$ is the principal vector defined by the $(r + 1)$th column of W; and

$w^{(r+2)}$ is the principal vector defined by the $(r + 2)$th column of W.

The first mode for λ_r is defined only by the eigenvector $w^{(r)}$; the second mode for λ_r is defined by the sum for $t w^{(r)}$ and the first principal vector $w^{(r+1)}$; the third mode for λ_r is defined by the sum of $\frac{1}{2} t^2 w^{(r)} + t w^{(r+1)}$ and the second principal vector $w^{(r+2)}$.

In any particular example, we know how many principal vectors there are which are not independent eigenvectors if we know the form of the Jordan matrix. It has been shown by Zhu and Shi [112] that the Jordan form can always be found by examining the rank of test matrices derived from the A matrix. (The rank of a matrix is the number of its linearly independent rows or columns. This method may be useful when the number of independent eigenvectors is not readily apparent otherwise.

Chapter 7

Numerical methods for modal analysis

Calculation of eigenvalues

If a general matrix A of order $N \times N$ has N distinct eigenvalues, λ_j, $j = 1$ to N, then it is always possible to find an $N \times N$ matrix U for which

$$U^{-1}AU = [\operatorname{diag}\lambda_j]. \tag{7.1}$$

The N columns of U are the N independent eigenvectors of A. They are written in the same order as their corresponding eigenvalues in $[\operatorname{diag}\lambda_j]$.† For the case when the eigenvalues are not distinct, we have seen in Chapter 6 that it may not be possible to find a similarity transformation that reduces A to diagonal form. The nearest to diagonal form that can be achieved is the Jordan matrix which has the N eigenvalues as its diagonal elements and one or more elements equal to unity in its super-diagonal line or, alternatively, in its sub-diagonal line. In that case, instead of (7.1), we have

$$W^{-1}AW = J \tag{7.2}$$

where W is the $N \times N$ matrix of principal vectors of A and J is the Jordan matrix. Each column of W is either an independent principal vector (i.e. an eigenvector) or a principal vector which depends on an adjacent principal vector and is calculated as explained in Chapter 6. Each repeated eigenvalue, say λ_k, always has at least one independent eigenvector. The number of unit elements appearing next to the λ_ks in the super-diagonal or sub-diagonal line of J is equal to the number of principal vectors which are not also eigenvectors.

In the diagonal matrix $[\operatorname{diag}\lambda_j]$ in (7.1) and in the Jordan matrix J in (7.2), the eigenvalues are the diagonal elements. Theoretically it is always possible to find a similarity transformation to reduce a general A matrix to its Jordan form J. However, in order to evaluate the eigenvalues of A, we shall see that it is not necessary to find the matrix W which reduces A to J. Instead, it is only necessary to find a similarity transformation which reduces A to triangular form and, according to the general theory of

† For formal proofs of these results see, for example, Wilkinson [110], Chapter 1.

matrix analysis, this can always be achieved. If A is any matrix of order $N \times N$ and T is a triangular matrix of order $N \times N$, we can always find an $N \times N$ matrix S for which

$$S^{-1}AS = T. \tag{7.3}$$

The triangular matrix may be upper-triangular or lower-triangular. We shall assume that T is an upper-triangular matrix, in which case all the elements below its diagonal are zero. Obviously, $[\text{diag}\,\lambda_j]$ in (7.1) and the Jordan matrix in (7.2) can be regarded as special cases of the general triangular matrix T in (7.3).

The reason that the transformation (7.3) allows the eigenvalues of A to be found is because the diagonal elements of T are the eigenvalues of A. This follows from the general results (a) that the eigenvalues of a matrix are invariant under a similarity transformation, so that the eigenvalues of A and T are the same, and (b) that the eigenvalues of a triangular matrix are its diagonal elements (Wilkinson, [110], Chapter 1, p. 7 and p. 24).

Example 7.1 Eigenvalues of a triangular matrix

Find the eigenvalues of the 3×3 upper triangular matrix

$$T = \begin{bmatrix} t_{11} & t_{12} & t_{13} \\ 0 & t_{22} & t_{23} \\ 0 & 0 & t_{33} \end{bmatrix}.$$

The eigenvalues λ_j, $j = 1$ to 3, are the three solutions of λ in

$$\det[T - \lambda I] = 0$$

which gives

$$\det \begin{bmatrix} (t_{11} - \lambda) & t_{12} & t_{13} \\ 0 & (t_{22} - \lambda) & t_{23} \\ 0 & 0 & (t_{33} - \lambda) \end{bmatrix}$$

and, on evaluating the determinant,

$$(t_{11} - \lambda)(t_{22} - \lambda)(t_{33} - \lambda) = 0$$

so that

$$\lambda_1 = t_{11}, \quad \lambda_2 = t_{22} \quad \text{and} \quad \lambda_3 = t_{33}.$$

Most numerical methods for finding the eigenvalues of a general matrix A involve finding a similarity transformation which reduces A to a triangular matrix, T. The diagonal elements of T are then the required eigenvalues.

It turns out that it is best to transform the A matrix to triangular form in two steps. Step (i) involves transforming it to a Hessenberg matrix, H; step (ii) involves transforming H to triangular form, T. An upper-Hessenberg matrix has zero for all its elements below the sub-diagonal line, so that, if a cross represents any generally non-zero element, a 6×6 upper-Hessenberg matrix has the form

$$H = \begin{bmatrix} \times & \times & \times & \times & \times & \times \\ \times & \times & \times & \times & \times & \times \\ 0 & \times & \times & \times & \times & \times \\ 0 & 0 & \times & \times & \times & \times \\ 0 & 0 & 0 & \times & \times & \times \\ 0 & 0 & 0 & 0 & \times & \times \end{bmatrix}. \qquad (7.4)$$

A lower-Hessenberg matrix has zeros for all its elements above the super-diagonal line. In the following explanation we shall consider only matrices in their upper-Hessenberg form and we shall always begin with a system matrix A which is real.

Step (i) Transformation to Hessenberg form

The basis of this calculation is to generate zeros below the sub-diagonal by subtracting rows from each other in such a way that a similarity transform is executed. Suppose that the original matrix A is of order 6×6 and two columns have been reduced to Hessenberg form, so that

$$A_2 = \begin{bmatrix} a_{11} & a_{12} & a_{13} & a_{14} & a_{15} & a_{16} \\ a_{21} & a_{22} & a_{23} & a_{24} & a_{25} & a_{26} \\ 0 & a_{32} & a_{33} & a_{34} & a_{35} & a_{36} \\ 0 & 0 & a_{43} & a_{44} & a_{45} & a_{46} \\ 0 & 0 & a_{53} & a_{54} & a_{55} & a_{56} \\ 0 & 0 & a_{63} & a_{64} & a_{65} & a_{66} \end{bmatrix}. \qquad (7.5)$$

We can put zeros in the places occupied by a_{53} and a_{63} if we subtract a_{53}/a_{43} times row 4 from row 5 and a_{63}/a_{43} times row 4 from row 6. This can be achieved by pre-multiplying A_2 by the matrix†

$$N_4 = \begin{bmatrix} 1 & 0 & 0 & 0 & 0 & 0 \\ 0 & 1 & 0 & 0 & 0 & 0 \\ 0 & 0 & 1 & 0 & 0 & 0 \\ 0 & 0 & 0 & 1 & 0 & 0 \\ 0 & 0 & 0 & -a_{53}/a_{43} & 1 & 0 \\ 0 & 0 & 0 & -a_{63}/a_{43} & 0 & 1 \end{bmatrix} \qquad (7.6)$$

to give

$$N_4 A_2 = \begin{bmatrix} a_{11} & a_{12} & a_{13} & a_{14} & a_{15} & a_{16} \\ a_{21} & a_{22} & a_{23} & a_{24} & a_{25} & a_{26} \\ 0 & a_{32} & a_{33} & a_{34} & a_{35} & a_{36} \\ 0 & 0 & a_{43} & a_{44} & a_{45} & a_{46} \\ 0 & 0 & 0 & a'_{54} & a'_{55} & a'_{56} \\ 0 & 0 & 0 & a'_{64} & a'_{65} & a'_{66} \end{bmatrix} \qquad (7.7)$$

† The so-called *elementary matrix* N_4 in (7.6) is usually given the letter N (see, for example, Wilkinson, [110], Ch. 1, Sect. 40) even though the order of this matrix is $N \times N$, defined by the same letter.

To effect a similarity transform we must also post-multiply N_4A_2 by N_4^{-1}. In this case

$$N_4^{-1} = \begin{bmatrix} 1 & 0 & 0 & 0 & 0 & 0 \\ 0 & 1 & 0 & 0 & 0 & 0 \\ 0 & 0 & 1 & 0 & 0 & 0 \\ 0 & 0 & 0 & 1 & 0 & 0 \\ 0 & 0 & 0 & a_{53}/a_{43} & 1 & 0 \\ 0 & 0 & 0 & a_{63}/a_{43} & 0 & 1 \end{bmatrix} \qquad (7.8)$$

as the reader can easily check, and therefore

$$N_4A_2N_4^{-1} = \begin{bmatrix} a_{11} & a_{12} & a_{13} & \left(a_{14} + \dfrac{a_{53}}{a_{43}}a_{15} + \dfrac{a_{63}}{a_{43}}a_{16}\right) & a_{15} & a_{16} \\ a_{21} & a_{22} & a_{23} & \left(a_{24} + \dfrac{a_{53}}{a_{43}}a_{25} + \dfrac{a_{63}}{a_{43}}a_{26}\right) & a_{25} & a_{26} \\ 0 & a_{32} & a_{33} & \left(a_{34} + \dfrac{a_{53}}{a_{43}}a_{35} + \dfrac{a_{63}}{a_{43}}a_{36}\right) & a_{35} & a_{36} \\ 0 & 0 & a_{43} & \left(a_{44} + \dfrac{a_{53}}{a_{43}}a_{45} + \dfrac{a_{63}}{a_{43}}a_{46}\right) & a_{45} & a_{46} \\ 0 & 0 & 0 & \left(a'_{54} + \dfrac{a_{53}}{a_{43}}a'_{55} + \dfrac{a_{63}}{a_{43}}a'_{56}\right) & a'_{55} & a'_{56} \\ 0 & 0 & 0 & \left(a'_{64} + \dfrac{a_{53}}{a_{43}}a'_{65} + \dfrac{a_{63}}{a_{43}}a'_{66}\right) & a'_{65} & a'_{66} \end{bmatrix}$$

$$(7.9)$$

Post-multiplying by N_4^{-1} to complete the similarity transformation does not change the two zeros that had been added to the third column by pre-multiplying by N_4.

Notice that this method of transforming a matrix to Hessenberg form cannot be extended to putting zeros in the sub-diagonal line and thereby transforming A directly to triangular form in one step. If, instead of pre-multiplying by N_4 we had pre-multiplied by

$$N_3 = \begin{bmatrix} 1 & 0 & 0 & 0 & 0 & 0 \\ 0 & 1 & 0 & 0 & 0 & 0 \\ 0 & 0 & 1 & 0 & 0 & 0 \\ 0 & 0 & -a_{43}/a_{33} & 1 & 0 & 0 \\ 0 & 0 & -a_{53}/a_{33} & 0 & 1 & 0 \\ 0 & 0 & -a_{63}/a_{33} & 0 & 0 & 1 \end{bmatrix} \qquad (7.10)$$

this would have put three zeros in the third column of N_3A_2 (instead of two zeros in (7.7)), but at the same time would have over-written the existing zeros in the second column. Post-multiplication by N_3^{-1} would further confuse the picture by over-writing the new zeros (see Problem 7.1).

To complete the transformation of the complete matrix A to Hessenberg form requires repeated application of this procedure to give

$$H = N_5N_4N_3N_2AN_2^{-1}N_3^{-1}N_4^{-1}N_5^{-1} \qquad (7.11)$$

where N_2 puts four zeros into column 1, N_3 puts three zeros into column

2, N_4 puts two zeros into column 3 and N_5 puts the last zero into column 4. There are no zeros in columns 5 and 6.

In order to ensure the numerical stability of the calculation, we want to keep the multipliers a_{53}/a_{43} and a_{63}/a_{43} in (7.6) as small as possible. This can be achieved by examining the three elements a_{43}, a_{53} and a_{63} in the third column of A_2 to determine which has the largest absolute magnitude and then reordering the last three rows of A_2 so that the row with the largest element precedes the other two rows. Then the pivotal element a_{43} will be as large in magnitude as the calculation allows.

Suppose that the fourth and sixth row of A_2 have to be interchanged. This can be achieved by pre-multiplying A_2 by the matrix

$$T_{46} = \begin{bmatrix} 1 & 0 & 0 & 0 & 0 & 0 \\ 0 & 1 & 0 & 0 & 0 & 0 \\ 0 & 0 & 1 & 0 & 0 & 0 \\ 0 & 0 & 0 & 0 & 0 & 1 \\ 0 & 0 & 0 & 0 & 1 & 0 \\ 0 & 0 & 0 & 1 & 0 & 0 \end{bmatrix} \tag{7.12}$$

where T_{46} is almost an identity matrix except that the elements of unity that would have been on the diagonal in rows 4 and 6 have been switched from column 4 to column 6 and vice versa. In order to preserve the similarity transformation, the result of this multiplication must also be post-multiplied by T_{46}^{-1} and the reader can easily check that

$$T_{46}^{-1} \equiv T_{46} \tag{7.13}$$

so that T_{46} is its own inverse. Postmultiplication by T_{46} involves interchanging columns 4 and 6. Hence, if row 4 has been swapped with row 6, then column 4 must be swapped with column 6. It does not matter whether the rows are swapped first, and then the columns, or vice versa, because the result is the same. Therefore, to ensure numerical stability, before zeros are put into (for example) column 3, if necessary the rows below row 3 must be reordered by swapping two rows so that row 4 has the largest absolute value in column 3 of all the rows below row 3. Also, where rows have been swapped, the corresponding columns must be swapped to preserve similarity. Swapping columns does not affect the operations on column 3, but it does affect later stages of the calculation.

Since the elements of the Hessenberg matrix H which is similar to A are obtained by a process involving the successive combination of the elements of A, it is evident that if, A is real, then so must H be a real matrix and for this calculation we do not need to enter the field of complex numbers.

A logical flow diagram to illustrate the procedure for transforming A to its upper Hessenberg form is shown in Appendix 1.

Step (ii) Transformation from Hessenberg to triangular form

As a result of step (i), the general real A matrix has been transformed to a similar real, upper-Hessenberg matrix. We shall now show how this may be used to find the eigenvalues of A. As already mentioned, if H can be reduced to triangular form T by a similarity transformation, the eigenvalues of A are the diagonal elements of the triangular matrix T.

Since we shall often have cases when the eigenvalues occur in complex-conjugate pairs, some of the diagonal elements of T will generally be complex. To avoid working with complex numbers, it is not necessary to reduce H (and therefore A) to completely diagonal form; instead it turns out that the reduction may be stopped when a nearly diagonal form has been reached with each pair of complex conjugate eigenvalues occupying a 2×2 sub-matrix on the diagonal line of the full matrix. For example, for a 6×6 matrix with two pairs of complex eigenvalues, the Hessenberg matrix H would be reduced to the nearly diagonal form T' where

$$T' = \begin{bmatrix} a_{11} & a_{12} & a_{13} & a_{14} & a_{15} & a_{16} \\ a_{21} & a_{22} & a_{23} & a_{24} & a_{25} & a_{26} \\ 0 & 0 & a_{33} & a_{34} & a_{35} & a_{36} \\ 0 & 0 & a_{43} & a_{44} & a_{45} & a_{46} \\ 0 & 0 & 0 & 0 & a_{55} & a_{56} \\ 0 & 0 & 0 & 0 & 0 & a_{66} \end{bmatrix} \qquad (7.14)$$

and where all the elements are real. It can be shown from the theory of matrix analysis (see, for example, Wilkinson [110], p. 486) that the two real eigenvalues of A are $\lambda_5 = a_{55}$ and $\lambda_6 = a_{66}$ and that λ_1, λ_2 are given by the solutions of

$$\det \begin{bmatrix} (a_{11} - \lambda) & a_{12} \\ a_{21} & (a_{22} - \lambda) \end{bmatrix} = 0 \qquad (7.15)$$

and λ_3, λ_4 by the solutions of

$$\det \begin{bmatrix} (a_{33} - \lambda) & a_{34} \\ a_{43} & (a_{44} - \lambda) \end{bmatrix} = 0. \qquad (7.16)$$

Furthermore, the calculation may be expedited by noting that, when one of the elements in the sub-diagonal line of the transformed matrix becomes zero, the $N \times N$ matrix may be partitioned into two smaller matrices as shown below (for the case when $N = 7$ and sub-diagonal element $(4, 3)$ is zero):

$$T' = \begin{bmatrix} \times & \times & \times & \times & \times & \times & \times \\ \times & \times & \times & \times & \times & \times & \times \\ 0 & \times & \times & \times & \times & \times & \times \\ 0 & 0 & 0 & \times & \times & \times & \times \\ 0 & 0 & 0 & \times & \times & \times & \times \\ 0 & 0 & 0 & 0 & \times & \times & \times \\ 0 & 0 & 0 & 0 & 0 & \times & \times \end{bmatrix}$$

$$= \begin{bmatrix} X & Z \\ O & Y \end{bmatrix} \qquad (7.17)$$

where X is the 3×3 sub-matrix upper left and Y is the 4×4 sub-matrix lower right. The eigenvalues of T' (and therefore of the original A-matrix) can then be shown to be the eigenvalues of the partitioned sub-matrices X and Y (see Problem 7.6 and, for the general theory, Gantmacher [33], Ch. 2, Sect. 5). The sub-matrix Z has no further role in the calculation.

Example 7.2. Eigenvalues of a nearly triangular matrix

Find the eigenvalues of the nearly triangular matrix

$$T' = \begin{bmatrix} t_{11} & t_{12} & t_{13} \\ t_{21} & t_{22} & t_{23} \\ 0 & 0 & t_{33} \end{bmatrix}.$$

The eigenvalues of T' are the solutions of

$$\det[T' - \lambda I] = 0$$

which becomes

$$\det \begin{bmatrix} (t_{11} - \lambda) & t_{12} & t_{13} \\ t_{21} & (t_{22} - \lambda) & t_{23} \\ 0 & 0 & (t_{33} - \lambda) \end{bmatrix} = 0.$$

Expanding the determinant in the elements of column 1 gives

$$(t_{11} - \lambda) \det \begin{bmatrix} (t_{22} - \lambda) & t_{23} \\ 0 & (t_{33} - \lambda) \end{bmatrix} - t_{21} \det \begin{bmatrix} t_{12} & t_{13} \\ 0 & (t_{33} - \lambda) \end{bmatrix} = 0$$

leading to

$$[(t_{11} - \lambda)(t_{22} - \lambda) - t_{12}t_{21}](t_{33} - \lambda) = 0.$$

The eigenvalues of T' are thus the diagonal element t_{33} and the eigenvalues of the upper 2×2 sub-matrix centred on the diagonal line. Notice that the two elements t_{13} and t_{23} do not affect the eigenvalues.

Step (ii) of the eigenvalue calculation includes monitoring the transformed matrix to look for zeros in its sub-diagonal line, first by checking the Hessenberg matrix and then by checking the further reduced matrix after each iteration of its reduction towards triangular form. Whenever a zero (or an element of sufficiently small magnitude compared with the other non-zero elements) is found in the sub-diagonal, the triangularization process continues for the partitioned matrices X and Y separately. If the lower matrix Y (see equations (7.17)) is of order unity, its eigenvalue is equal to the single element. If Y is of order 2×2, then its eigenvalues can be found by solving a quadratic equation like (7.15). If Y is of order 3×3 or higher, the process of reduction to triangular form must continue until another zero appears in its sub-diagonal line.

The reduction of a Hessenberg matrix into a matrix with a zero in its sub-diagonal line, so that partitioning can be made, has to involve a similarity transformation. The so-called QR algorithm, Francis [28], does this in the following way. It is an iterative process. Assume that the initial Hessenberg matrix, H_1, has been transformed $s - 1$ times into H_s (which is also a Hessenberg matrix). The next iteration, involves completing the similarity transformation represented by

$$H_{s+1} = P_{N-1} \ldots P_2 P_1 H_s P_1^T P_2^T \ldots P_{N-1}^T \qquad (7.18)$$

where P_j is an orthogonal matrix (i.e. a real matrix whose inverse is the same as its transpose). For each iteration the transformation matrices P_j, $j = 1$ to $N - 1$ are recalculated. P_1 depends on the elements in the first column of H_s (chosen according to formulae to be given shortly), P_2 depends on the elements in the first column of

$$P_1 H_s P_1^T$$

(chosen according to different formulae, also to be given shortly), P_3 depends on the elements in the second column of

$$P_2 P_1 H_s P_1^T P_2^T$$

(chosen according to the same formulae as for P_2), and so on.

It has been shown by a remarkable tour de force in numerical analysis (see the original papers by Francis [28] and the discussion in Wilkinson [110]) that, when the transformation matrices P_j are chosen correctly, after a sufficient number of iterations defined by (7.18), H_s approaches an upper triangular matrix except for single sub-diagonal elements associated with each complex-conjugate pair of eigenvalues. Each non-zero sub-diagonal element is associated with a 2×2 matrix centred on the diagonal and the eigenvalues of this sub-matrix converge to the conjugate pair of eigenvalues of the original A matrix.

Choice of the transformation matrices for the QR method

Suppose that the Hessenberg matrix H has elements h_{ij} and that we are beginning the first iteration defined by (7.18). We first calculate the three elements (Wilkinson [110] p. 530)

$$x = h_{11}^2 + h_{12}h_{21} - h_{11}(k_1 + k_2) + k_1k_2$$

$$y = h_{21}(h_{11} + h_{22} - k_1 - k_2) \qquad (7.19)$$

$$z = h_{32}h_{21}$$

where the parameters k_1 and k_2 are chosen to improve the rate of convergence according to a separate algorithm to be described shortly. The transformation's first step from H to $P_1HP_1^T$ is effected by an operation on the first three rows of H (for pre-multiplication by P_1) followed by a corresponding operation on the (new) first three columns of H (for post-multiplication by P_1^T). Alternatively, the row and column operations can be performed in the reverse order. If we define:

$$S = (\text{sign } x) \sqrt{x^2 + y^2 + x^2}$$

$$A = 1 + \frac{x}{S} \quad \text{unless } S = 0 \text{ when } A = 2 \qquad (7.20)$$

$$B = \frac{y}{x + S} \quad \text{unless } S = 0 \text{ when } B = 0$$

$$C = \frac{z}{x + S} \quad \text{unless } S = 0 \text{ when } C = 0$$

then the operations on the rows h_{1j}, j_{2j}, h_{3j}, $j = 1$ to N, are given by

$$h_{1j} \rightarrow h_{1j} - Ah_{1j} - ABh_{2j} - ACh_{3j}$$

$$h_{2j} \rightarrow h_{2j} - ABh_{1j} - AB^2h_{2j} - ABCh_{3j} \qquad (7.21)$$

$$h_{3j} \rightarrow h_{3j} - ACh_{1j} - ABCh_{2j} - AC^2h_{3j}$$

and the operations on the first three columns h_{j1}, h_{j2}, h_{j3}, $j = 1$ to N, are given by

$$h_{j1} \rightarrow h_{j1} - Ah_{j1} - ABh_{j2} - ACh_{j3}$$

$$h_{j2} \rightarrow h_{j2} - ABh_{j1} - AB^2h_{j2} - ABCh_{j3} \qquad (7.22)$$

$$h_{j3} \rightarrow h_{j3} - ACh_{j1} - ABCh_{j2} - AC^2h_{j3}.$$

The second step is then to calculate $P_2(P_1HP_1^T)P_2^T$ where now x, y, z have new values defined by

$$x = h_{21}$$

$$y = h_{31} \qquad (7.23)$$

$$z = h_{41}$$

where h_{21}, h_{31} and h_{41} are the new values calculated in the first step, and the transformation according to the scheme of (7.21) and (7.22) is repeated but for rows 2 to 4 and columns 2 to 4. After completing this second step, the transformed matrix looks like (for $N = 7$)

$$
\text{Rows 3 to 5} \quad
\begin{bmatrix}
\times & \times & \times & \times & \times & \times & \times \\
\times & \times & \times & \times & \times & \times & \times \\
0 & x & \times & \times & \times & \times & \times \\
0 & y & \times & \times & \times & \times & \times \\
0 & z & \times & \times & \times & \times & \times \\
0 & 0 & 0 & 0 & \times & \times & \times \\
0 & 0 & 0 & 0 & 0 & \times & \times
\end{bmatrix}
\tag{7.24}
$$

Columns 3 to 5   Sub-diagonal line.

Notice that there are zeros below the sub-diagonal in column 1. The reader can check that this is the case by replacing h_{1j}, h_{2j}, h_{3j} in (7.21) by h_{2j}, h_{3j}, h_{4j}, respectively, and then calculating the new values of h_{31} and h_{41} from these equations, using (7.20) and (7.23). It will be found that the elements h_{31} and h_{41} are identically zero. However, note that non-zero elements have been introduced below the sub-diagonal in columns 2 and 3 in (7.24).

The third stage $P_3(P_2P_1HP_1^TP_2^T)P_3^T$ involves rows 3 to 5 and columns 3 to 5 where x, y, z are the new values of h_{32}, h_{42}, h_{52}, as shown in (7.24). This returns the non-zero elements below the sub-diagonal in column 2 to zero but inserts new non-zero elements below the sub-diagonal in columns 3 and 4. The transformation is repeated a total of $(N - 2)$ times until the transformed matrix looks like (for $N = 7$)

$$
\begin{bmatrix}
\times & \times & \times & \times & \times & \times & \times \\
\times & \times & \times & \times & \times & \times & \times \\
0 & \times & \times & \times & \times & \times & \times \\
0 & 0 & \times & \times & \times & \times & \times \\
0 & 0 & 0 & \times & \times & \times & \times \\
0 & 0 & 0 & 0 & x & \times & \times \\
0 & 0 & 0 & 0 & y & \times & \times
\end{bmatrix}
\tag{7.25}
$$

Rows $N - 1$, N

Columns $N - 1$, N

where the new x and y elements appear as shown and z has disappeared from the matrix. The final step in this iteration is

$$
P_{N-1}(P_{N-2}\ldots P_1HP_1^T\ldots P_{N-2}^T)P_{N-1}^T
$$

where only the last two rows and columns are affected so that (7.21) becomes

$$
\begin{aligned}
h_{N-1,j} &\to h_{N-1,j} - Ah_{N-1,j} - ABh_{N,j} \\
h_{N,j} &\to h_{N,j} - ABh_{N-1,j} - AB^2h_{N,j}
\end{aligned}
\tag{7.26}
$$

and (22) becomes

$$h_{j,N-1} \rightarrow h_{j,N-1} - Ah_{j,N-1} - ABh_{j,N}$$

$$h_{j,N} \rightarrow h_{j,N} - ABh_{j,N-1} - AB^2h_{j,N}.$$

(7.27)

The transformation of a matrix using transformation matrices P_j defined in this way is called Householder's transformation (see, for example, Wilkinson [10], p. 294), and the Hessenberg form of the matrix is maintained as the transformation progressively orders the eigenvalues and feeds them, in order, to the bottom right-hand corner of the transformed matrix. The key to the whole method is the selection of x, y and z for the first step, which is due to Francis [28].

When x, y and z for the first step are chosen according to (7.19) (the whole of one iteration consisting of $N-1$ steps), Francis showed that, after sufficient iterations, the transformed matrix will always reach the required almost triangular form. In practice, the number of iterations required has been shown to be remarkably few, and as a result this method of calculating the eigenvalues of an unsymmetric matrix has been widely used. Francis called his algorithm the QR transformation, and a logical flow diagram for the QR algorithm is shown in Appendix 2.

The algorithm works to reduce the sub-matrix Y of equation (7.17) towards diagonal form. If two adjacent sub-diagonal elements of Y are small (but not effectively zero), it was shown by Francis [28] that it is not necessary to begin the QR reduction at the first row of Y; instead reduction can begin at a lower row. If the two small sub-diagonal elements are $h_{i,i-1}$ and $h_{i+1,i}$, reduction can begin at row i and column i. When reduction begins at a row of Y other than row 1, Francis shows that element $h_{i,i-1}$ has to have its sign changed before the above operations begin. It is also shown by Francis [28] that an appropriate test of whether any two adjacent sub-diagonal elements $h_{i,i-1}$ and $h_{i+1,i}$ are small enough is that

$$\left| \frac{(|y| + |z|)h_{i,i-1}}{x} \right|$$

must be effectively zero where x, y and z are defined by (7.19), but with i replacing 1, $i+1$ replacing 2, and $i+2$ replacing 3 (see also Wilkinson [110], p. 536).

Although this refinement is not essential, it does significantly improve the effectiveness of the algorithm when calculating the eigenvalues of certain classes of matrices (for example, symmetric banded matrices) when a large number of iterations may otherwise be needed to extract all the eigenvalues. Whereas usually the algorithm without this refinement would extract eigenvalues in order of their absolute magnitude, a disadvantage of the refined algorithm is that it is less likely that the eigenvalues will now be extracted in order.

Although the parameters k_1 and k_2 in (7.19) are arbitrary, the rate of convergence of the matrix to its final form is very much improved if k_1 and k_2 are chosen appropriately. There are no specific formulae for k_1 and k_2 and different choices are possible (see e.g. the discussions in Wilkinson [110] and Francis [28]). In Appendix 3, a logical flow diagram is shown for a calculation which chooses k_1 and k_2 according to a very simple strategy that appears to work well. For the first iteration k_1 and k_2 are both set to zero. On the conclusion of this iteration, the eigenvalues λ_1, λ_2 of the bottom 2×2 sub-matrix are calculated and k_1, k_2 are set equal to λ_1, λ_2, respectively. If at the end of the jth iteration the sub-matrix has eigenvalues $\lambda_1^{(j)}$ and $\lambda_2^{(j)}$, then for iteration $(j + 1)$ we take

$$k_1^{(j+1)} = \lambda_1^{(j)}$$
$$k_2^{(j+1)} = \lambda_2^{(j)}. \tag{7.28}$$

Since k_1 and k_2 do not appear alone in (7.19) but only as their sum and product, we are not involved with complex numbers. This is because, if they are complex, $\lambda_1^{(j)}$ and $\lambda_2^{(j)}$ occur only as a conjugate pair. Hence

$$k_1^{(j+1)} + k_2^{(j+1)} = 2 \operatorname{Re}\{\lambda_1^{(j)}\}$$

and

$$k_1^{(j+1)} k_2^{(j+1)} = \lambda_1^{(j)}\lambda_1^{(j)*}. \tag{7.29}$$

The rationale behind this choice of k_1 and k_2 is that the rate of convergence depends on the value of the eigenvalue being calculated. A small eigenvalue has been shown to converge faster than a large eigenvalue converges. Choosing k_1 and k_2 according to (7.28) can be interpreted as shifting the origins of the eigenvalues being calculated so that, instead of converging on λ_1 and λ_2, the algorithm converges on $(\lambda_1 - k_1)$ and $(\lambda_2 - k_2)$, which is faster (see, for example, the discussion in Wilkinson [110], Chapter 8, Sect. 19, p. 505).

Practical eigenvalue calculation procedure

The algorithm in Appendix 3, called *Lambda*, describes a practical procedure for determining the eigenvalues of a real $N \times N$ matrix, A. It calls the algorithms in Appendices 1 and 2, called *Hmat* and *Qrmat*.

First, A is transformed to its upper Hessenberg form by using Hmat and then the QR transform in Qrmat is used to reduce the Hessenberg matrix progressively towards almost triangular form. In Qrmat, before each iteration of the QR transform, the sub-diagonal elements of the matrix are checked for zeros. An element is taken to be zero when its absolute magnitude is less than the magnitude of a small quantity which depends, in the limit, on the number of significant digits for the computer involved. The magnitude of this small quantity is specified in Lambda and its value can be changed if desired (see Problem 7.3). When a zero is found, the matrix is partitioned and the calculation in Qrmat continues with the lower sub-matrix. This process is repeated until the lowest sub-matrix is of order 1×1, in which case the eigenvalue is equal to the single element, or is of order 2×2, in which case Lambda finds the eigenvalues by solving a quadratic equation. The calculation then returns to Qrmat for the remaining part or parts of the partitioned matrix and the process continues calling Qrmat for each new iteration until all the eigenvalues have been found.

After each iteration of the QR transform, Lambda recalculates the zero-shift parameters k_1 and k_2 according to (7.28) except that, when the calculation has completed the extraction of eigenvalues from the lowest sub-matrix and is returning to a new sub-matrix, k_1 and k_2 are returned to zero for the first iteration on the new sub-matrix.

The program Lambda in Appendix 3 prints as output the quantity which has been taken to be effectively zero when searching the sub-diagonal elements. As noted above, this quantity can be adjusted depending on the precision of the computer used and the overall accuracy required. Also Lambda includes a comparison between the numerical values of (*a*) the sum of the eigenvalues and the trace of the A-matrix (i.e. the sum of its diagonal elements), which should be the same, and (*b*) the product of the eigenvalues and the determinant of the Hessenberg matrix, which should also be the same. The procedure involved in calculating the determinant is explained in the next section. Since the A-matrix and its Hessenberg form are similar matrices, they have the same determinant, and it is more convenient to calculate the value of this determinant by starting from the Hessenberg form. Although these numerical comparisons demonstrate that the programs are working properly, good correspondence between the numerical values in each case cannot be taken as an absolute guarantee of the accuracy of the eigenvalues concerned. In Problem 7.4 an example is given of an ill-conditioned matrix where some of the eigenvalues have errors of order 10^{-4}, while the comparisons (*a*) and (*b*) both agree to order 10^{-12}. However, this difficulty arises only for a proportion of cases with repeated eigenvalues (Wilkinson [110], p. 540), and such cases are rare in practical vibration problems. If in doubt, a sensitivity check can always be carried out by making a small alteration in the elements of the A-matrix in order to determine how sensitive the eigenvalues are to changes in the system matrix.

The next example calculation shows the evolution of a typical A-matrix towards upper-triangular form by repeated application of the QR algorithm.

Example 7.3 Calculation to find the eigenvalues of a 5 × 5 matrix

The following calculation has been made by using the program Lambda whose logical flow diagram is shown in Appendix 3. Lambda calls Hmat from Appendix 1 to make the transformation to Hessenberg form and Qrmat from Appendix 2 for each iteration of the QR transform. The computer used for the calculation had accuracy to 12 significant figures, and the quantity taken to be effectively zero was 2.24×10^{-10}.

For a 5×5 matrix

$$
\begin{bmatrix}
0.30 & 0.28 & 0.24 & 0.30 & 0.40 \\
0.24 & 0.02 & 0.72 & 0.43 & 0.17 \\
0.57 & 0.78 & 0.13 & 0.37 & 0.85 \\
0.53 & 0.25 & 0.51 & 0.37 & 0.16 \\
0.17 & 0.73 & 0.46 & 0.56 & 0.32
\end{bmatrix}
$$

the Hessenberg matrix calculated by Hmat is, with the results shown to three significant figures,

$$
\begin{bmatrix}
+3.00\,E-01 & +7.56\,E-01 & +5.99\,E-01 & +4.97\,E-01 & +2.80\,E-01 \\
+5.70\,E-01 & +1.06\,E+00 & +1.39\,E+00 & +9.20\,E-01 & +7.80\,E-01 \\
+0.00\,E+00 & +1.07\,E+00 & +4.19\,E-01 & +8.00\,E-01 & +4.97\,E-01 \\
+0.00\,E+00 & +0.00\,E+00 & -9.66\,E-01 & -3.28\,E-01 & -4.87\,E-01 \\
+0.00\,E+00 & +0.00\,E+00 & +0.00\,E+00 & -2.62\,E-01 & -3.07\,E-01
\end{bmatrix}.
$$

After five iterations of the QR algorithm by Qrmat, this has been transformed to

$$
\begin{bmatrix}
+1.98\,E+00 & +3.39\,E-02 & +1.65\,E+00 & -9.70\,E-01 & +9.77\,E-01 \\
-1.96\,E-05 & -2.40\,E-01 & +4.29\,E-01 & +2.13\,E-01 & +2.10\,E-01 \\
-1.10\,E-17 & -5.03\,E-02 & -1.09\,E-01 & +6.74\,E-01 & -3.71\,E-01 \\
+3.26\,E-18 & +0.00\,E+00 & -1.02\,E-01 & -5.65\,E-01 & -1.64\,E-01 \\
-4.41\,E-13 & +0.00\,E+00 & +3.00\,E-18 & -7.03\,E-12 & +7.48\,E-02
\end{bmatrix}.
$$

Note that the elements below the sub-diagonal line are no longer exactly zero because of the round-off error that the computer introduces into the QR calculation. The magnitude of element $A(5, 4)$ is less than 2.24×10^{-10} so that one eigenvalue has been identified as element $(5, 5)$, giving

$$\lambda_1 = A(5, 5) = 0.0748.$$

The calculation now proceeds using the deflated 4×4 matrix obtained by deleting the fifth row and fifth column before entering the A-matrix for another QR iteration. After three further iterations, the result has become

$$
\begin{bmatrix}
+1.98\,E+00 & -1.43\,E+00 & +1.18\,E+00 & +4.75\,E-01 & +9.77\,E-01 \\
-3.19\,E-11 & -4.10\,E-01 & +2.07\,E-01 & +3.89\,E-01 & +2.10\,E-01 \\
+1.01\,E-22 & -2.36\,E-01 & -1.43\,E-01 & -7.19\,E-01 & -3.71\,E-01 \\
-1.21\,E-23 & +5.00\,E-13 & +9.16\,E-03 & -3.62\,E-01 & -1.64\,E-01 \\
-4.41\,E-13 & +0.00\,E+00 & +3.00\,E-18 & -7.03\,E-12 & +7.48\,E-02
\end{bmatrix}.
$$

It can be seen that row 5 and column 5 are unchanged. Now the magnitude of element $A(2, 1)$ is less than 2.24×10^{-10} so that another eigenvalue has been identified as

$$\lambda_5 = A(1, 1) = 1.98.$$

Then a further deflation occurs to delete row 1 and column 1 before the QR calculation continues with the remaining 3×3 matrix. After four more iterations with this matrix, the result is

$$\begin{bmatrix} +1.98\,\text{E}+00 & -1.43\,\text{E}+00 & +1.18\,\text{E}+00 & +4.75\,\text{E}-01 & +9.77\,\text{E}-01 \\ -3.19\,\text{E}-11 & -3.89\,\text{E}-01 & +2.02\,\text{E}-01 & +4.01\,\text{E}-01 & +2.10\,\text{E}-01 \\ +1.01\,\text{E}-22 & -2.76\,\text{E}-01 & -1.40\,\text{E}-01 & -6.99\,\text{E}-01 & -3.71\,\text{E}-01 \\ -1.21\,\text{E}-23 & +0.00\,\text{E}+00 & -2.43\,\text{E}-11 & -3.85\,\text{E}-01 & -1.64\,\text{E}-01 \\ -4.41\,\text{E}-13 & +0.00\,\text{E}+00 & +3.00\,\text{E}-18 & -7.03\,\text{E}-12 & +7.48\,\text{E}-02 \end{bmatrix}.$$

The magnitude of element $A(4, 3)$ is now less than 2.24×10^{-10} and so is effectively zero. This identifies

$$\lambda_2 = A(4, 4) = -0.385$$

and the remaining two eigenvalues λ_3, λ_4 are the eigenvalues of the 2×2 sub-matrix

$$\begin{bmatrix} -3.89\,\text{E}-01 & +2.02\,\text{E}-01 \\ -2.76\,\text{E}-01 & -1.40\,\text{E}-01 \end{bmatrix}.$$

These are the solutions of

$$\det \begin{bmatrix} (-0.389 - \lambda) & 0.202 \\ -0.276 & (-0.140 - \lambda) \end{bmatrix}$$

which subprogram Lambda calculates to be

$$\lambda_3, \lambda_4 = -0.265 \pm i\,0.201.$$

The results of the complete calculation with the checks that are part of program Lambda (Appendix 3) are therefore as listed below. The numbering system identifies eigenvalues in order across the diagonal, starting from the bottom right-hand corner. Eigenvalue 5 is not 'discovered' by Lambda until eigenvalue 4 has been found, and so the cumulative number of iterations to find eigenvalue 5 is listed as the same as for eigenvalue 4, which is 11.

The calculated eigenvalues are:

No.	Real part	Imaginary part	Cumulative number of iterations
1	+7.4829 E−02	+0.0000 E+00	4
2	−3.8512 E−01	+0.0000 E+00	11
3	−2.6479 E−01	+2.0057 E−01	11
4	−2.6479 E−01	−2.0057 E−01	11
5	+1.9799 E+00	+0.0000 E+00	11

Check on accuracy

The quantity taken to be effectively zero is 2.24 E$-$10.

The trace of the A-matrix is $+1.140\,000\,000\,0$ E$+$00.

The sum of the eigenvalues is $+1.140\,000\,000\,2$ E$+$00.

The determinant of the H-matrix is $-6.295\,794\,000\,0$ E$-$03.

The product of the eigenvalues is $-6.295\,794\,003\,2$ E$-$03.

Calculation of the determinant of a Hessenberg matrix

The determinant of a matrix A is usually defined by its so-called Laplace expansion in row j by the formula

$$\det A = \sum_{k=1}^{N}(-1)^{j+k}a_{jk}M_{jk} \tag{7.30}$$

where M_{jk} is the minor of the element a_{jk}, which is the determinant of the square array left by deleting the jth row and kth column of A. There is an equivalent alternative expansion in column k by the formula

$$\det A = \sum_{j=1}^{N}(-1)^{j+k}a_{jk}M_{jk}. \tag{7.31}$$

An algorithm to compute $\det A$ from these expansions would be inefficient because of the very large number of multiplications involved in evaluating (7.30) and (7.31). Instead, a better method is to begin by reducing A to triangular form, T. Then we can see that the determinant is just the product of the diagonal elements of T (see Example 7.1). For the calculation of a determinant, it is not necessary for T to be a matrix which is similar to A. According to the properties of determinants (see, for example, Pipes and Hovanessian [81]), the value of a determinant is not changed by subtracting a multiple of one row from another row or a multiple of one column from another column. It is therefore possible to reduce A to triangular form by Gaussian elimination between the rows without altering the matrix's determinant. Since a similarity transformation is not necessary (compare the previous case for reduction to Hessenberg form, when it is necessary), corresponding column operations are not needed.

In order to maintain the stability of the Gaussian elimination, it is necessary to interchange the rows so that when multiples of row j are to be subtracted the magnitude of the pivotal element a_{jj} is as large as possible. This is permissible on account of a further property of determinants that the result of interchanging any two rows of a matrix only changes the sign of its determinant. Because similarity is not required, corresponding columns do not have to be interchanged.

There are various ways of organizing this calculation to reduce the number of multiplications needed, but in our case the reduction of A to triangular form has been partly completed already when calculating the Hessenberg matirc H. Although extra operations have been included to keep A and H similar matrices, which are not necessary for a calculation of $\det A$ only, there is no point in going back to the beginning again. Since H is similar to A, it has the same determinant, and therefore to find $\det A$ we need only find $\det H$. It turns out that there is a very efficient algorithm for calculating the determinant of a Hessenberg matrix, using Hyman's method (see, for example, Wilkinson [110], p. 426). This depends on the property that multiples of the columns of a matrix can be added without altering the value of its determinant. The procedure is to add multiples of columns 1 to $N - 1$ to column N of the Hessenberg matrix so that all elements of column N become zero except for the first element, which we call k. The modified matrix then has the form

$$
\begin{bmatrix}
h_{11} & \times & \times & \times & \times & \times & k \\
h_{21} & \times & \times & \times & \times & \times & 0 \\
0 & h_{32} & \times & \times & \times & \times & 0 \\
0 & 0 & \times & \times & \times & \times & 0 \\
0 & 0 & 0 & \times & \times & \times & 0 \\
0 & 0 & 0 & 0 & \times & \times & 0 \\
0 & 0 & 0 & 0 & 0 & h_{N,N-1} & 0
\end{bmatrix}
\tag{7.32}
$$

where the crosses represent other generally non-zero elements h_{jk}. This array has the same determinant as H, and so expanding the determinant of (7.32) in its last column (using (7.31) with $k = N$), we find that

$$
\det A = \det H = \pm\, k h_{21} h_{32} \dots h_{N,\,N-1}
\tag{7.33}
$$

since with row 1 and column N deleted the minor is a triangular matrix whose determinant is the product of its diagonal elements. From (7.31), the sign of $\det H$ is positive if N is odd and negative if N is even. In order to find the determinant we have only to find k.

If, to generate (7.32), column 1 had to multiplied by x_1, column 2 by x_2 and so on, before these were added to column N, we have the set of simultaneous equations

$$
x_1 h_{11} + x_2 h_{12} + x_3 h_{13} + \dots + x_{N-1} h_{1,\,N-1} + h_{1,N} = k
$$

$$
x_1 h_{21} + x_2 h_{22} + x_3 h_{23} + \dots + x_{N-1} h_{2,\,N-1} + h_{2,N} = 0
$$

$$
\vdots \qquad\qquad \vdots \qquad\qquad \vdots
\tag{7.34}
$$

$$
x_{N-2} h_{N-1,N-2} + x_{N-1} h_{N-1,N-1} + h_{N-1,N} = 0
$$

$$
x_{N-1} h_{N,N-1} + h_{N,N} = 0.
$$

There are N equations. The lower $N - 1$ can be solved for x_1 to x_{N-1}, starting from the bottom and working upwards. The top equation then gives the Nth unknown k directly.

It can be shown (Wilkinson [110], p. 430) that provided the sub-diagonal elements are not zero, equations (7.34) provide a stable solution, even if some of these elements are very small. If any of the sub-diagonal elements are zero, the matrix H may be partitioned as shown in (7.17) and then det H is the product of the determinants of the two partitioned matrices X and Y (see Problem 7.6).

A logical flow diagram for the evaluation of a determinant by Hyman's method is shown in Appendix 4.

Calculation of eigenvectors

In order to calculate the column eigenvector X corresponding to eigenvalue λ, we have to solve the N simultaneous linear equations described by

$$AX = \lambda X. \tag{7.35}$$

As we have seen, one element of each eigenvector is arbitrary. We have chosen to make the first element real and of unit magnitude. In the exceptional case when the first element is zero, such a normalization cannot be made and then it is necessary to set the second (or first non-zero) element to be real and unity.

Consider the case when the first element is not zero. The calculation that follows uses real arithmetic only and proceeds as follows. Let the eigenvector

$$X = x + iy \tag{7.36}$$

correspond to the eigenvalue

$$\lambda = \alpha + i\omega \tag{7.37}$$

where x, y, α and ω are real. Then (7.35) becomes

$$A(x + iy) = (\alpha + i\omega)(x + iy) \tag{7.38}$$

and, on separating the real and imaginary parts, this gives two equations

$$Ax - \alpha x + \omega y = O \tag{7.39}$$

and

$$Ay - \alpha y - \omega x = O. \tag{7.40}$$

We now choose unity for the first element of x and zero for the first element of y so that

$$x = \begin{bmatrix} 1 \\ x' \end{bmatrix} \quad \text{and} \quad y = \begin{bmatrix} 0 \\ y' \end{bmatrix} \tag{7.41}$$

where x' and y' are column vectors of order $N - 1$. If we also define:

a = the first row of A with order $1 \times N$;
B = the $(N - 1) \times (N - 1)$ matrix obtained by deleting the first row and first column of A; and

c = the first column of A with its first element deleted so that the order of c is $(N - 1) \times 1$,

the A matrix can be partitioned as shown below:

$$
A = \begin{bmatrix} & a \quad (1 \times N) & \\ \hline c & & B \\ (N-1)\times 1 & & (N - 1) \times (N - 1) \end{bmatrix} . \tag{7.42}
$$

The first row of (7.39) can then be written as

$$ax = \alpha \tag{7.43}$$

and the first row of (7.40) as

$$ay = \omega. \tag{7.44}$$

The remaining $(N - 1)$ rows of (7.39) are described by

$$c + Bx' - \alpha x' + \omega y' = O \tag{7.45}$$

and the remaining rows of (7.40) by

$$By' - \alpha y' - \omega x' = O. \tag{7.46}$$

Hence, from (7.46),

$$x' = \frac{1}{\omega}[B - \alpha I]y' \tag{7.47}$$

which, on substituting for x' in (7.45), gives

$$[(B - \alpha I)^2 + \omega^2 I]y' = -\omega c \tag{7.48}$$

or

$$[B^2 - 2\alpha B + (\alpha^2 + \omega^2)I]y' = -\omega c. \tag{7.49}$$

This last equation allows the $(N - 1)$ elements of y' to be found by solving

$N - 1$ simultaneous linear equations by Gaussian elimination (with inter-changes to ensure stability), where $\boldsymbol{B}$ and $\boldsymbol{c}$ are defined by (7.42). The corresponding $(N - 1)$ elements of $\boldsymbol{x}'$ can then be found directly from (7.47).

For the case when $\omega = 0$, so that the eigenvalue is real, the eigenvector is then also real, so that $\boldsymbol{y} = 0$, and (7.45) gives

$$[\boldsymbol{B} - \alpha\boldsymbol{I}]\boldsymbol{x}' = -\boldsymbol{c} \tag{7.50}$$

from which the $(N - 1)$ vector $\boldsymbol{x}'$ can be calculated by Gaussian elimination.

We see that equations (7.43) and (7.44) do not enter into the calculation for the vectors $\boldsymbol{x}'$ and $\boldsymbol{y}'$. They merely confirm that $x_1 = 1$ and $y_1 = 0$. Therefore they serve only as a check on the accuracy of the elements calculated from (7.49) and (7.50).

After the matrix on the left-hand side of (7.49) has been reduced to triangular form, some of its diagonal elements may be zero. In that case, some of the elements of the vector $\boldsymbol{y}'$ may be infinite. Alternatively, if, when a diagonal element is zero, the corresponding term on the right-hand side of (7.49) is also zero, then this element of $\boldsymbol{y}'$ will be indefinite. When there is only one such indefinite element, it may be possible to determine this element from the extra equation (7.44). Similarly, in the case of real eigenvectors, after the matrix on the left-hand side of (7.50) has been reduced to triangular form, if some of its diagonal elements are zero, then some of the elements of the real vector $\boldsymbol{x}'$ will be infinite or indefinite; if there is only one indefinite real element, it may be possible to obtain this from (7.43).

For the case of eigenvectors which have infinite elements when calculated from the above algorithm, the first element of the eigenvector cannot be normalized to unity and must really be zero. It would be possible to amend the algorithm so that it normalizes on the second or some other element of the state vector, and an automatic scaling feature can be added if desired. However, a simpler approach for the few cases when it is not possible to normalize the first element of the eigenvector to unity is to reorder the equations of motion so that the elements come in a different order. A different physical coordinate then comes first and so a different coordinate is normalized to unity when the calculation is rerun. If necessary, the reordering process can be repeated until a first coordinate is found which does not have a node for the mode in question.

A logical flow diagram for the eigenvector calculation described above is shown in Appendix 5. If the elements of an eigenvector are infinite or indefinite, the program's output says so and enters zeros for all the elements of the eigenvectors affected.

Inversion of a complex matrix

In order to complete some of the response calculations based on modal analysis theory, it is necessary to invert a complex matrix, $U(N, N)$. In principle the method of doing this is the same as the method for inverting a real matrix except that either complex arithmetic is used or the matrix is partitioned into its real and imaginary parts, which are stored in separate arrays. For example, the real parts could be stored in $U_r(N, N)$ and the imaginary parts in $U_i(N, N)$. In this case, if complex element $U(J, K)$ has to be divided by complex element $a = x + iy$ then the new $U(J, K)$ is given by

$$U(J, K) = \frac{U_r(J, K) + iU_i(J, K)}{x + iy} \tag{7.51}$$

so that the new real and imaginary parts of $U(J, K)$ are

$$U_r(J, K) = \frac{xU_r(J, K) + yU_i(J, K)}{x^2 + y^2} \tag{7.52}$$

and

$$U_i(J, K) = \frac{xU_i(J, K) - yU_r(J, K)}{x^2 + y^2}. \tag{7.53}$$

The straightforward method of calculating the inverse of a matrix $U(N, N)$ is to calculate the N columns of U^{-1} in turn. For example, the elements of column j of the inverse matrix are the solutions X_j of the equation

$$UX_j = \begin{bmatrix} O \\ 1 \\ O \end{bmatrix} \tag{7.54}$$

where X_j is the jth column of U^{-1} and the r.h.s. of (7.54) is a column matrix of order $N \times 1$ with all its elements zero except for the jth element which is unity. The solution can be obtained by Gaussian elimination with interchanges, followed by back-substitution, as already described.

A compact (but less accurate) method of organizing this calculation for numerical implementation is as follows. It is sometimes called the augmented matrix method (see Pipes and Hovanessian [81]). Consider the N simultaneous equations defined by

$$UX = Y \tag{7.55}$$

where X and Y are $N \times 1$ column vectors. Let Y be specified arbitrarily and imagine solving in principle for X to get

$$X = U^{-1}Y. \tag{7.56}$$

We want to find U^{-1}. If (7.55) is rewritten in the alternative form

$$[U, I]\begin{bmatrix} X \\ -Y \end{bmatrix} = O \tag{7.57}$$

and (7.56) is rewritten in the corresponding form

$$[I, U^{-1}]\begin{bmatrix} X \\ -Y \end{bmatrix} = O \qquad (7.58)$$

where I is the $N \times N$ identity matrix (which is of course real) and $[U, I]$ and $[I, U^{-1}]$ are matrices of order $N \times 2N$, then if we can transform (7.57) into (7.58) the required inverse matrix has been found.

Suppose that we begin with the $N \times 2N$ matrix $[U, I]$, where U is the complex matrix that has to be inverted, and perform Gaussian elimination across the full width of the $1 \times 2N$ rows. Multiples of each row are subtracted from the rows below until the left-hand half of the matrix, formerly occupied by U, has become an upper-triangular matrix. As usual with this method, before row j is subtracted from the rows below, if

$$|a_{kj}| > |a_{jj}|, \ k > j, \qquad (7.59)$$

then row k is swapped with row j. In this way the magnitudes of the diagonal elements (the 'pivots') are kept large at the early stages of the calculation and the reduction to triangular form can be shown to be an efficient and usually highly accurate method of triangularization (Wilkinson [110], p. 244).

The resulting upper-triangular matrix can now be transformed to a diagonal matrix by continuing the process of subtracting rows. Multiples of each pivotal row (starting with the second) are subtracted from the rows above so as to put zeros into all the off-diagonal positions above the diagonal of the $N \times N$ array formerly occupied by U. Effectively, the process of Gaussian elimination is continued, without further row interchanges, until the $N \times N$ array formerly occupied by U becomes a diagonal matrix. To transform this diagonal matrix into an identity matrix it is only necessary to divide each row by the corresponding diagonal element and the end result is that the $N \times 2N$ matrix $[U, I]$ in (7.57) has been transformed into the matrix $[I, U^{-1}]$ in (7.58).

Instead of making the transformation in two parts: (i) a transformation of U to upper-triangular form, and (ii) a transformation from upper-triangular to diagonal form, it is convenient to make both transformations together. The process begins at the left-hand side of $[U, I]$ and works progressively across to the right-hand side of U, putting zeros into all the positions above and below the diagonal by subtracting multiples of the pivotal row from all the other rows, above and below the pivot. As before, row interchanges are made between the pivotal row and the rows below in order to ensure that the magnitude of the pivot is as large as possible. To make the diagonal elements unity, each row is divided by the value of the pivot element as the calculation proceeds. When the calculation has been completed, the elements of U^{-1} occupy the right-hand half of the $N \times 2N$ array where originally there was the $N \times N$ identity matrix.

The process of Gaussian elimination with interchanges to obtain upper-triangular form can continue even if a diagonal element is zero. This is because there must be zeros for all the elements in this column below the diagonal (otherwise a row interchange would have occurred) and so the calculation can proceed to the next column without dividing by the zero pivot. This is not the case when zeros have to be put in all positions, above as well as below the diagonal. However, if the upper triangular array produced by Gaussian elimination with interchanges has a zero for one of its diagonal elements, then the determinant of this array is zero (the determinant of a triangular array is the product of its diagonal elements). In that case the inverse matrix U^{-1} does not exist, and so the calculation fails. As the elimination process involved in transforming (7.57) to (7.58) proceeds, the diagonal elements (after interchanging between rows below the pivotal row if necessary) are monitored and, if one becomes zero, the input matrix U is identified as being singular and the calculation is stopped.

A logical flow diagram for the inversion of a complex matrix by this method, using real arithmetic only, is shown in Appendix 6. The real parts of $U(N, N)$ are held in the array $U_r(N, N)$ and the imaginary parts in $U_i(N, N)$.

Discussion

The explanations given in this chapter are intended to illustrate the computational procedures involved in the numerical calculation of eigenvalues and vectors. Programs based on the logical flow diagrams in the appendices provide an opportunity to test the principles, and they have been found to be satisfactory for all the problems in this book and for many other practical studies that the author has undertaken. However, for large problems it will probably be advantageous to use computer library programs chosen to be appropriate for the problem in hand. For example, symmetric band matrices arise quite frequently, and it is inefficient to treat these matrices with algorithms designed for a general, unsymmetric matrix. In any case, such problems usually involve matrices of high order, and storage limitations may prevent this. For a symmetric band matrix, algorithms exist which will search for the eigenvalues nearest to a specified value and which will calculate the number of eigenvalues greater in magnitude than any limiting value. For dense but symmetric real matrices there are other special-purpose algorithms which are more efficient than the general QR algorithm, and these will be identified in computer library manuals.

In order to maintain good accuracy for computed eigenvalues, it is desirable that the A matrix should not be badly unbalanced. This is the case if the magnitudes of the elements in corresponding rows and columns are very different. For example, the matrix A will be unbalanced if, for row j, the norm

$$\|a_{\text{row}j}\| = \left(\sum_{k=1}^{N} a_{jk}^2 \right)^{1/2} \tag{7.60}$$

is very different from, for the corresponding column j,

$$||a_{\text{col}j}|| = \left(\sum_{k=1}^{N} a_{kj}^2 \right)^{1/2}. \tag{7.61}$$

If it is, then accuracy can be improved by subjecting the A matrix to a similarity transformation which seeks to equalize $||a_{\text{row}j}||$ and $||a_{\text{col}j}||$. With the machine accuracy available on modern computers, unbalance is not likely to be a problem for most applications but, for very large matrices or when particular accuracy is required for the eigenvalues, a preliminary balancing may be desirable, and library programs for general matrices usually include such a procedure.

The method used by library programs for evaluating eigenvectors may also differ from the method of solving the equations

$$AX_j = \lambda_j X_j \tag{7.62}$$

by Gaussian elimination and back substitution which has been described above and which is the basis of the program in Appendix 5. The latter is simple in concept and straightforward to program, and has been found to work well for many problems. However, for large matrices it may not be the most economical method.

An alternative method is to calculate the eigenvectors Y_j of the almost triangular matrix T' computed in the QR transform and then to compute the required eigenvectors X_j from Y_j. Since T' is almost triangular, its eigenvectors can be calculated easily and the process of Gaussian elimination is not needed. Since T' and A are similar matrices, there is a relation of the form

$$Q^{-1}AQ = T' \tag{7.63}$$

and the eigenvectors of A and T' are related by

$$X_j = QY_j \tag{7.64}$$

so that if the transformation matrix Q is known the required eigenvectors can be obtained by a single matrix multiplication.

If A, and therefore Q and T', are of order $N \times N$, the matrix multiplication in (7.64) involves N^2 separate multiplications. This compares with a number of order N^3 when solving (7.62). However, the transformation matrix Q in (7.63) and (7.64) has to be built up as the product of all the transformation matrices used in the QR algorithm. The effort in terms of the number of additional multiplications depends on how many iterations are required to extract all the eigenvalues and on how partitioning proceeds during the QR calculation. Which method is more economical therefore depends on the nature of the problem, but for large matrices the method of finding X_i from Y_i, rather than of solving for X_i directly, is generally more efficient (Wilkinson and Reinsch [111], II/15).

When only a few eigenvectors are required and the eigenvalues are well separated, then the method of inverse iteration may be the best method of finding these eigenvectors (Problem 7.8). This is a completely different method in which an iterative scheme is used to obtain progressively closer approximations to a required eigenvector and which has been found to work well and to give greater accuracy than may be possible with other methods. It is particularly useful for the case of large banded matrices when only a few eigenvalues and their corresponding eigenvectors may be needed.

Chapter 8

Response functions

General response of *M* coupled second-order equations

In the last section of Chapter 4 we obtained a general expression for the response to arbitrary excitation of the M coupled second-order equations

$$m\ddot{y} + c\dot{y} + ky = x \qquad (8.1)$$

where $y(t)$ is the $M \times 1$ response vector, $x(t)$ is the $M \times 1$ excitation vector and m, c and k are the real $M \times M$ mass, damping and stiffness matrices. We shall assume where necessary that m is non-singular so that its inverse m^{-1} exists. If the $2M \times 2M$ A matrix is

$$A = \begin{bmatrix} O & I \\ -m^{-1}k & -m^{-1}c \end{bmatrix} \qquad (8.2)$$

and the $2M \times 1$ excitation vector $F(t)$ is

$$F = \begin{bmatrix} O \\ m^{-1}x \end{bmatrix} \qquad (8.3)$$

then there is a corresponding set of $2M$ first-order equations

$$\dot{z} = Az + F \qquad (8.4)$$

where z is the $2M \times 1$ response vector

$$z = \begin{bmatrix} y \\ \dot{y} \end{bmatrix}. \qquad (8.5)$$

We shall now assume that it is possible to find $2M$ independent eigenvectors, so that

$$U^{-1}AU = [\text{diag } \lambda_j] \qquad (8.6)$$

where U is the $2M \times 2M$ matrix of (column) eigenvectors of A and λ_j, $j = 1$ to $2M$, are the $2M$ eigenvalues. Then, according to (4.73), the general solution of (8.4) is given by

$$z(t) = U[\text{diag } e^{\lambda_j t}]\left[\int [\text{diag } e^{-\lambda_j t}]U^{-1}F(t)\,dt + C\right] \qquad (8.7)$$

where C is a $2M \times 1$ vector of arbitrary constants which are determined by the initial conditions.

Because the second M elements of the response vector z are the derivatives of the first M elements, the second M elements of each eigenvector are obtained by multiplying the first M elements by the corresponding eigenvalue, and so the eigenvector matrix U can be partitioned so that (Problem 8.1)

$$U = \begin{bmatrix} U_{\text{upper}} \\ U_{\text{lower}} \end{bmatrix} = \begin{bmatrix} U_{\text{upper}} \\ U_{\text{upper}} [\text{diag } \lambda_j] \end{bmatrix} \tag{8.8}$$

where U_{upper} is the upper half of U and has order $M \times 2M$ and U_{lower} is the lower half of U, also of order $M \times 2M$, Also, for convenience in the following development, we shall partition U^{-1} into right-hand and left-hand halves, each of order $2M \times M$, so that

$$U^{-1} = [U_{\text{left}}^{-1} \quad U_{\text{right}}^{-1}]. \tag{8.9}$$

By using (8.9), we find that

$$U^{-1}F = [U_{\text{left}}^{-1} \quad U_{\text{right}}^{-1}] \begin{bmatrix} O \\ m^{-1}x \end{bmatrix}$$

$$= U_{\text{right}}^{-1} m^{-1} x. \tag{8.10}$$

The upper half of z, which from (8.5) is the response vector y, can then be seen from (8.7) to be given by

$$y(t) = U_{\text{upper}}[\text{diag } e^{\lambda_j t}] \left[\int [\text{diag } e^{-\lambda_j t}] U_{\text{right}}^{-1} m^{-1} x(t) \, dt + C \right]. \tag{8.11}$$

This equation gives the $M \times 1$ vector of the displacement response of (8.1), $y(t)$, in terms of the eigenvalues and eigenvectors of the problem and the mass matrix m which is assumed not to be singular. The only other assumption is that (8.6) is true. As we saw in Chapter 6, this will always be the case if the $2M$ eigenvalues are distinct, and may be so if there are multiple eigenvalues. Subject to these limitations, equation (8.11) is completely general and gives the complete response $y(t)$ of the M-degree-of-freedom system defined by (8.1) for arbitrary excitation $x(t)$.

Much of this chapter is devoted to interpreting (8.11) and applying it to different situations.

Properties of the partitioned eigenvector matrix

The partitioned halves of U and of U^{-1} are related. On substituting from (8.8) and (8.9) into

$$UU^{-1} = I \tag{8.12}$$

we get

$$\begin{bmatrix} U_{\text{upper}} \\ U_{\text{upper}} [\text{diag } \lambda_j] \end{bmatrix} [U_{\text{left}}^{-1} \quad U_{\text{right}}^{-1}] = I \qquad (8.13)$$

which, on multiplying the matrices, gives

$$\begin{bmatrix} U_{\text{upper}} U_{\text{left}}^{-1} & U_{\text{upper}} U_{\text{right}}^{-1} \\ U_{\text{upper}} [\text{diag } \lambda_j] U_{\text{left}}^{-1} & U_{\text{upper}} [\text{diag } \lambda_j] U_{\text{right}}^{-1} \end{bmatrix} = I \qquad (8.14)$$

where each of the sub-matrices in the four quadrants is of order $M \times M$ and I is the identity matrix of order $2M \times 2M$. We are interested in U_{upper} and U_{right}^{-1}, and from (8.14) it is evident that

$$U_{\text{upper}} \qquad U_{\text{right}}^{-1} = O$$
$$(M \times 2M) \quad (2M \times M) \quad (M \times M) \qquad (8.15)$$

and

$$U_{\text{upper}} \qquad [\text{diag } \lambda_j] \qquad U_{\text{right}}^{-1} = I$$
$$(M \times 2M) \quad (2M \times 2M) \quad (2M \times M) \quad (M \times M) \qquad (8.16)$$

where the orders of the matrices are shown in brackets underneath each term of the equations.

We have seen already that, when the elements of m, c and k are all real, and therefore that the elements of A are all real, then the eigenvalues and eigenvectors of A are either real or occur in complex-conjugate pairs. For eigenvalues, this is because if λ_r is a complex eigenvalue for which

$$\det[A - \lambda_r I] = 0 \qquad (8.17)$$

then the real and imaginary parts of the determinant must be separately zero. Changing λ_r to λ_r^* only changes the sign of the imaginary part of the determinant, A being real, and so if (8.17) is true then so is

$$\det[A - \lambda_r^* I] = 0. \qquad (8.18)$$

From (8.6), we know that

$$AU = U[\text{diag } \lambda_j] \qquad (8.19)$$

and so

$$Au^{(r)} = \lambda_r u^{(r)} \qquad (8.20)$$

where $u^{(r)}$ is the rth column of U. On taking the complex conjugates of both sides of (8.20), we get

$$Au^{(r)*} = \lambda_r^* u^{(r)*} \qquad (8.21)$$

so that, if λ_r, λ_{r+1} is a complex-conjugate pair of eigenvalues then so is $u^{(r)}$, $u^{(r+1)}$ a complex-conjugate pair of eigenvectors.

Next, we shall show that a similar result holds for the inverse eigenvector matrix U^{-1} except that now it is row r which is the complex conjugate of row $r + 1$.

From (8.6) we have

$$U^{-1}A = [\text{diag } \lambda_j]U^{-1} \qquad (8.22)$$

and if $v^{(r)}$ denotes the rth row of U^{-1} then

$$v^{(r)}A = \lambda_r v^{(r)} \qquad (8.23)$$

and, by taking complex conjugates of both sides,

$$v^{(r)*}A = \lambda_r^* v^{(r)*}. \qquad (8.24)$$

Hence if $\lambda_{r+1} = \lambda_r^*$, row $(r + 1)$ of U^{-1} will be the complex conjugate of row r, and vice versa.

It follows from the definitions (8.8) and (8.9) that, if $\lambda_{r+1} = \lambda_r^*$, then columns r and $(r + 1)$ of U_{upper} and rows r and $(r + 1)$ of U_{right}^{-1} are respectively complex conjugates of each other.

Frequency-response function matrix

Next we consider the response of the system defined by (8.1) to steady-state harmonic excitation. Let the excitation vector $x(t)$ have only one non-zero element,

$$x_s(t) = \text{e}^{i\omega t} \qquad (8.25)$$

so that

$$x(t) = \text{e}^{i\omega t}[0, 0, 0, \ldots, 1, \ldots, 0]^{\text{T}}. \qquad (8.26)$$
$$\uparrow$$
$$\text{Element } s$$

The general response equation (8.11) can be applied and, for $x(t)$ given by (8.26), the integral with respect to time in its right-hand side is

$$\int \text{e}^{i\omega t}[\text{diag } \text{e}^{-\lambda_j t}] \, \text{d}t = \int [\text{diag } \text{e}^{(i\omega - \lambda_j)t}] \, \text{d}t$$
$$= \left[\text{diag } \frac{\text{e}^{(i\omega - \lambda_j)t}}{i\omega - \lambda_j}\right]$$
$$= \left[\text{diag } \frac{1}{i\omega - \lambda_j}\right][\text{diag } \text{e}^{(i\omega - \lambda_j)t}]. \qquad (8.27)$$

On substituting from (8.26) and (8.27) into (8.11), we find that the matrix $[\text{diag } \text{e}^{\lambda_j t}]$ may be multiplied through to give

$$y(t) = \text{e}^{i\omega t}U_{\text{upper}}\left[\text{diag } \frac{1}{i\omega - \lambda_j}\right]U_{\text{right}}^{-1}m^{-1}\begin{bmatrix} O \\ 1 \\ O \end{bmatrix} + U_{\text{upper}}[\text{diag } \text{e}^{\lambda_j t}]C. \quad (8.28)$$

If we now assume that the system is passive, then all the eigenvalues λ_j, $j = 1$ to $2M$, will have negative real parts and so, for $t \to \infty$, the second set of terms on the r.h.s. of (8.28) with the vector of constants C will disappear and we are now left with

$$y(t) = e^{i\omega t} U_{\text{upper}} \left[\text{diag} \frac{1}{i\omega - \lambda_j} \right] U_{\text{right}}^{-1} M^{-1} \begin{bmatrix} O \\ 1 \\ O \end{bmatrix}. \qquad (8.29)$$

All the elements of the response vector $y(t)$ have the same harmonic time dependence, and using the frequency-response function notation $H_{rs}(i\omega)$ for the response at coordinate y_r to harmonic excitation applied at coordinate x_s, then we have

$$y(t) = e^{i\omega t} \begin{bmatrix} H_{1s}(i\omega) \\ H_{2s}(i\omega) \\ \vdots \\ H_{Ms}(i\omega) \end{bmatrix} \qquad (8.30)$$

and (8.29) gives

$$\begin{bmatrix} H_{1s}(i\omega) \\ H_{2s}(i\omega) \\ \vdots \\ H_{Ms}(i\omega) \end{bmatrix} = U_{\text{upper}} \left[\text{diag} \frac{1}{i\omega - \lambda_j} \right] U_{\text{right}}^{-1} m^{-1} \begin{bmatrix} O \\ 1 \\ O \end{bmatrix}. \qquad (8.31)$$

$$s\text{th element}$$

Finally, if we form an $M \times M$ matrix $H(i\omega)$ whose elements are the M^2 frequency-response functions $H_{rs}(i\omega)$, $r, s = 1$ to M, then, by combining M equations of the form (8.31) introduces an $M \times M$ identity matrix at the right-hand side and leads to the result that

$$H(i\omega) = U_{\text{upper}} \left[\text{diag} \frac{1}{i\omega - \lambda_j} \right] U_{\text{right}}^{-1} m^{-1}. \qquad (8.32)$$

Equation (8.32) is an important and compact result for the $M \times M$ matrix of frequency-response functions (or receptances, see Ch. 2) for the M-degree-of-freedom system defined by (8.1) which is assumed to be a passive system. For easy reference, the definitions of the various terms are repeated below.

$H(i\omega)$ has order $M \times M$ and element $H_{rs}(i\omega)$ gives the steady-state frequency response at coordinate y_r for unit harmonic excitation applied at coordinate x_s; U_{upper} is the $M \times 2M$ upper half of the eigenvector matrix, U; U_{right}^{-1} is the $2M \times M$ right-hand half of the inverse eigenvector matrix, U^{-1}; m^{-1} is the $M \times M$ inverse-mass matrix for (8.1), which is assumed to exist; ω is the angular frequency of the harmonic excitation (and response); λ_j, $j = 1$ to $2M$, are the eigenvalues which all have negative real parts;

$$\left[\text{diag} \frac{1}{i\omega - \lambda_j} \right]$$

is a $2M \times 2M$ diagonal matrix for which the jth diagonal element is

$$\frac{1}{i\omega - \lambda_j}.$$

The $2M$ columns of U are assumed to be independent (for which a sufficient, but not necessary, condition is that the $2M$ eigenvalues are distinct) and they have the same order as the order of the eigenvalues in

$$\left[\text{diag} \frac{1}{i\omega - \lambda_j} \right].$$

Computation of frequency-response functions

If a particular frequency-response function is required, for example $H_{rs}(i\omega)$, this may be extracted from the general result (8.32) as follows.

First, let the elements of U_{upper} be

$$u_{rj}, \ r = 1 \text{ to } M, \ j = 1 \text{ to } 2M, \tag{8.33}$$

let the elements of U_{right}^{-1} be

$$v_{jk}, \ j = 1 \text{ to } 2M, \ k = 1 \text{ to } M, \tag{8.34}$$

and let the elements of m^{-1} be

$$a_{ks}, \ k, \ s = 1 \text{ to } M. \tag{8.35}$$

Notice that the definition of v_{jk} in (8.34) differs from that used previously when v were defined as the elements of the full inverse eigenvector matrix, U^{-1}.

The matrix product

$$U_{\text{upper}} \left[\text{diag} \frac{1}{i\omega - \lambda_j} \right]$$

results in all the elements in successive columns of U_{upper} being multiplied by

$$\frac{1}{i\omega - \lambda_j},$$

and so the element r, k of the triple matrix product

$$U_{\text{upper}} \left[\text{diag} \frac{1}{i\omega - \lambda_j} \right] U_{\text{right}}^{-1}$$

is then given by

$$\sum_{j=1}^{2M} u_{rj} \left(\frac{1}{i\omega - \lambda_j} \right) v_{jk} \tag{8.36}$$

and hence the r, s element of $H(i\omega)$ is given by a double summation over j and k so that

$$H_{rs}(i\omega) = \sum_{k=1}^{M} \sum_{j=1}^{2M} u_{rj} \left(\frac{1}{i\omega - \lambda_j} \right) v_{jk} a_{ks}. \tag{8.37}$$

This is an important practical result. The elements u_{rj} of the eigenvector matrix U_{upper} and v_{jk} of the inverse eigenvector matrix U_{right}^{-1} only have to be calculated once. The elements a_{ks} of the inverse mass matrix are known, so that the summations

$$s_{js} = \sum_{k=1}^{M} v_{jk}a_{ks}, \; j = 1 \text{ to } 2M, \, s = 1 \text{ to } M \tag{8.38}$$

can each be calculated once only. Each computation of $H_{rs}(i\omega)$ at a particular frequency therefore involves only one summation over j, so that

$$H_{rs}(i\omega) = \sum_{j=1}^{2M} u_{rj}\left(\frac{1}{i\omega - \lambda_j}\right)s_{js}. \tag{8.39}$$

Equation (8.39) is the general expansion of $H_{rs}(i\omega)$ in partial fractions of the factors $(i\omega - \lambda_j)$ and may be compared with equation (2.42). The difference is that we now have a practical method of computing the constants

$$\begin{array}{ccc} u_{rj}s_{js} & = & p_j \\ \text{in equation (8.38)} & & \text{in equation (2.42)} \end{array} \tag{8.40}$$

for a multi-degree-of-freedom passive system represented by a set of M coupled second-order equations. To apply the result of Chapter 2 in a practical case where there is a set of second-order equations instead of a single equation (2.1), we have to (i) calculate the eigenvalues and (ii) assemble the second-order equations into the standard form (2.1) in order that equation (2.45) may be applied. Step (ii) is no longer necessary because we have a general method of calculating the A-matrix by using (8.2) and a general procedure for finding the eigenvalues and eigenvectors of A using the methods in Chapter 7. This gives the elements u_{rj} of the eigenvector matrix U. The inverse eigenvector matrix U^{-1} can then be calculated, so that its elements v_{jk} are determined, and then the coefficients s_{js} can be calculated from (8.38).

Figure 8.1 is a logical flow diagram for implementing the calculation of $H_{rs}(i\omega)$ from equation (8.39). It involves computing only the sth column of $U_{\text{right}}^{-1}m^{-1}$. The result is stored in a $2M \times 1$ array $H(2M)$. The elements in $H(2M)$ are then multiplied by corresponding elements in the rth row of U_{upper} and the results are over-written in $H(2M)$. Finally, each new element of $H(2M)$ is multiplied in turn by $1/(i\omega - \lambda_j)$, $j = 1$ to $2M$, and the results are added to give $H_{rs}(i\omega)$. This procedure is useful whenever it is necessary to calculate a frequency-response function.

Example 8.1 Frequency-response functions of the torsional system in Fig. 8.2

As an example of the application of (8.39), we use again the three-degree-of-freedom torsional system in Fig. 6.1 and compute the

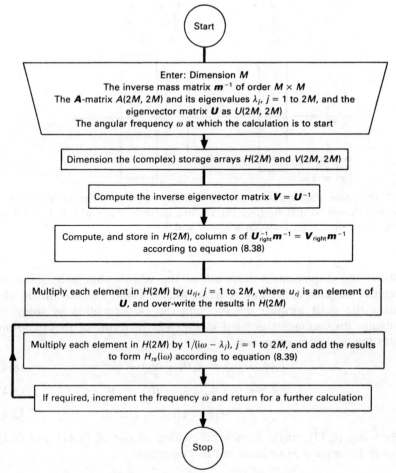

Fig. 8.1 Logical flow diagram for computing one of the frequency-response functions $H_{rs}(i\omega)$ for a system represented by a set of coupled second-order equations (with independent eigenvectors)

frequency-response function for the shaft torque (as output) when the input is torque excitation at wheel I_1. This represents in a highly simplified way the response at the propeller shaft to harmonic excitation at the propeller, which in practice would be caused by the cyclical changes in load on a propeller blade that occur every time a blade passes close to the ship's hull.

If the angular displacement of each wheel is measured from a fixed datum, as in Fig. 6.1, we saw in Chapter 6 that there are three zero eigenvalues and there are only five (not six) independent eigenvectors. Because (8.6) is not true, the general method described above breaks down and (8.39) does not apply. However, since we are not asked

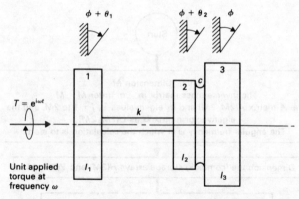

Fig. 8.2 The same torsional system as in Fig. 6.1 but with different displacement coordinates chosen so that θ_1 gives the relative angle between wheels 1 and 3 and θ_2 gives the relative angle between wheels 2 and 3

about the displacement response of the wheels, but only about the relative angular deflection between wheels 1 and 2 (since this is what gives the shaft torque) the problem can be simplified by using the angular displacements defined in Fig. 8.2. In terms of these coordinates the equations of motion are

$$I_1(\ddot{\phi} + \ddot{\theta}_1) = k(\theta_2 - \theta_1) + e^{i\omega t} \tag{8.41}$$

$$I_2(\ddot{\phi} + \ddot{\theta}_2) = k(\theta_1 - \theta_2) - c\dot{\theta}_2 \tag{8.42}$$

$$I_3\ddot{\phi} = c\dot{\theta}_2. \tag{8.43}$$

By using (8.43), angle ϕ may be condensed out of (8.41) and (8.42) (as in Example 5.3) to leave the two equations

$$I_1\ddot{\theta}_1 + \frac{I_1}{I_3}c\dot{\theta}_2 + k\theta_1 - k\theta_2 = e^{i\omega t} \tag{8.44}$$

$$I_2\ddot{\theta}_2 + \left(1 + \frac{I_2}{I_3}\right)c\dot{\theta}_2 - k\theta_1 + k\theta_2 = 0 \tag{8.45}$$

or, in the standard form (8.1), for $M = 2$,

$$m = \begin{bmatrix} I_1 & 0 \\ 0 & I_2 \end{bmatrix}, c = \begin{bmatrix} 0 & (I_1/I_3)c \\ 0 & (1 + I_2/I_3)c \end{bmatrix}, k = \begin{bmatrix} k & -k \\ -k & k \end{bmatrix}. \tag{8.46}$$

From (8.2), the A matrix is

$$A = \begin{bmatrix} 0 & 0 & 1 & 0 \\ 0 & 0 & 0 & 1 \\ -k/I_1 & k/I_1 & 0 & -c/I_3 \\ k/I_2 & -k/I_2 & 0 & -(1/I_2 + 1/I_3)c \end{bmatrix} \tag{8.47}$$

and, for the same parameter values that were used in Chapter 6, namely

$$I_1 = 3 \text{ kg m}^2, \ I_2 = 1.5 \text{ kg m}^2, \ I_3 = 4.5 \text{ kg m}^2,$$
$$k = 200 \text{ N m/rad}, \ c = 135/8 \text{ N m s/rad}, \tag{8.48}$$

the eigenvalues and eigenvectors can be computed in the usual way and are

$$\lambda_1 = 0$$
$$\lambda_2 = -10$$
$$\lambda_3 = -2.5 + i \ 11.99 \tag{8.49}$$
$$\lambda_4 = -2.5 - i \ 11.99$$

and the eigenvector matrix is

$$U = \begin{bmatrix} 1 & 1 & 1 & 1 \\ 1 & 1.6 & -0.345 - i \ 0.992 & -0.345 + i \ 0.992 \\ 0 & -10 & -2.5 + i \ 11.99 & -2.5 - i \ 11.99 \\ 0 & -16 & 12.76 - i \ 1.654 & 12.76 + i \ 1.654 \end{bmatrix}. \tag{8.50}$$

The corresponding inverse eigenvector matrix U^{-1} can be computed from (8.50), for example by using subprogram Cinv in Appendix 6, and gives

$$U^{-1} =$$

$$\begin{bmatrix} 0 & 1 & 0.0889 & 0.0444 \\ 0.417 & -0.417 & -0.0417 & -0.0521 \\ 0.292 - i \ 0.235 & -0.292 + i \ 0.235 & -0.0236 - i \ 0.0194 & 0.003\,82 + i \ 0.0209 \\ 0.292 + i \ 0.235 & -0.292 - i \ 0.235 & -0.0236 + i \ 0.0194 & 0.003\,82 - i \ 0.0209 \end{bmatrix}. \tag{8.51}$$

In order to find the frequency-response function for the shaft torque, we calculate first the frequency-response functions for the two angles of relative rotation θ_1 and θ_2. These we have called $H_{11}(i\omega)$ and $H_{21}(i\omega)$, the first subscript denoting the angle and the second subscript the position of the excitation, which is at wheel 1. Then, since

$$\theta_1(t) = H_{11}(i\omega) \, e^{i\omega t} \text{ and } \theta_2(t) = H_{21}(i\omega) \, e^{i\omega t}, \tag{8.52}$$

if we denote the shaft torque by

$$T(t) = k(\theta_1 - \theta_2) \tag{8.53}$$

and call the frequency-response function for the shaft torque $H_{T1}(i\omega)$, then

$$T(t) = H_{T1}(i\omega) \, e^{i\omega t} = k[H_{11}(i\omega) - H_{21}(i\omega)] e^{i\omega t} \tag{8.54}$$

so that the required shaft-torque frequency-response function is

$$H_{T1}(i\omega) = k[H_{11}(i\omega) - H_{21}(i\omega)].$$ (8.55)

To compute $H_{11}(i\omega)$ we have $r = s = 1$ in (8.39), and so

$$H_{11}(i\omega) = \sum_{j=1}^{4} u_{1j}\left(\frac{1}{i\omega - \lambda_j}\right)s_{j1}$$ (8.56)

where, from (8.38),

$$s_{j1} = \sum_{k=1}^{2} v_{jk}a_{k1}, \quad j = 1 \text{ to } 4.$$ (8.57)

For the diagonal mass matrix in (8.46), its inverse is

$$m^{-1} = \begin{bmatrix} 1/I_1 & 0 \\ 0 & 1/I_2 \end{bmatrix} = \begin{bmatrix} 1/3 & 0 \\ 0 & 2/3 \end{bmatrix}$$ (8.58)

for the values in (8.48). Hence the coefficients of m^{-1} are

$$a_{11} = 1/3, \; a_{12} = a_{21} = 0, \; a_{22} = 2/3.$$ (8.59)

Using these values in (8.57)

$$s_{11} = v_{11}/3, \; s_{21} = v_{21}/3, \; s_{31} = v_{31}/3, \; s_{41} = v_{41}/3$$ (8.60)

so that (8.56) gives

$$H_{11}(i\omega) = \frac{u_{11}v_{11}}{3}\left(\frac{1}{i\omega - \lambda_1}\right) + \frac{u_{12}v_{21}}{3}\left(\frac{1}{i\omega - \lambda_2}\right) +$$

$$+ \frac{u_{13}v_{31}}{3}\left(\frac{1}{i\omega - \lambda_3}\right) + \frac{u_{14}v_{41}}{3}\left(\frac{1}{i\omega - \lambda_4}\right)$$ (8.61)

where, from (8.50),

$$u_{11} = u_{12} = u_{13} = u_{14} = 1$$ (8.62)

and, from (8.51),

$$v_{11} = 0.0889$$

$$v_{21} = -0.0417$$ (8.63)

$$v_{31} = -0.0236 - i\,0.0194$$

$$v_{41} = -0.0236 + i\,0.0194$$

when it is remembered that v_{j1} are the elements in the first column of U_{right}^{-1}, which is column 3 of U^{-1} in this example.

In the same way, the corresponding expression for $H_{21}(i\omega)$ is, from (8.39),

$$H_{21}(i\omega) = \frac{u_{21}v_{11}}{3}\left(\frac{1}{i\omega - \lambda_1}\right) + \frac{u_{22}v_{21}}{3}\left(\frac{1}{i\omega - \lambda_2}\right) +$$

$$+ \frac{u_{23}v_{31}}{3}\left(\frac{1}{i\omega - \lambda_3}\right) + \frac{u_{24}v_{41}}{3}\left(\frac{1}{i\omega - \lambda_4}\right)$$ (8.64)

where

$$u_{21} = 1, \ u_{22} = 1.6, \ u_{23} = -0.345 - i\,0.992, \ u_{24} = -0.345 + i\,0.992.$$

$$(8.65)$$

For the data in (8.49), (8.62), (8.63) and (8.65), $|H_{11}(i\omega)|$ and $|H_{21}(i\omega)|$ are plotted against angular frequency ω (rad/s) in Fig. 8.3. At low frequencies, $|H_{11}(i\omega)|$ and $|H_{21}(i\omega)|$ increase towards infinity at $\omega = 0$. This is because $\lambda_1 = 0$, so that the first term in each of the expansions (8.61) and (8.64) has a factor $1/i\omega$.

The torque frequency-response function $H_{T1}(i\omega)$ can be calculated from (8.55), which gives

$$H_{T1}(i\omega)/k = \frac{(u_{12} - u_{22})v_{21}}{3}\left(\frac{1}{i\omega - \lambda_2}\right) + \frac{(u_{13} - u_{23})v_{31}}{3}\left(\frac{1}{i\omega - \lambda_3}\right) +$$

$$+ \frac{(u_{14} - u_{24})v_{41}}{3}\left(\frac{1}{i\omega - \lambda_4}\right) \tag{8.66}$$

since the first term in the expansions disappears because $u_{11} = u_{21}$ in this example. For the values listed above, this is

$$H_{T1}(i\omega)/k = \frac{0.008\,34}{i\omega + 10} - \frac{0.004\,17 + i\,0.0165}{i\omega + 2.5 - i\,11.99} - \frac{0.004\,17 - i0.0165}{i\omega + 2.5 + 11.99}$$

$$= \frac{0.008\,34}{i\omega + 10} - \frac{(i\,0.008\,34\omega - 0.3748)}{-\omega^2 + i\,5\omega + 150} \tag{8.67}$$

and $|H_{T1}(i\omega)|/k$ is also plotted in Fig. 8.3. Instead of plotting shaft torque directly, it is convenient to normalize this by dividing by the shaft stiffness k, as in (8.67), so that the modulus of the angle of shaft twisting is plotted.

The limit which the shaft twist approaches when $\omega \to 0$ can be checked by considering what happens when a steady unidirectional torque of unit magnitude is applied to wheel 1. All the wheels accelerate at the same rate

$$\ddot{\phi} = \frac{1}{I_1 + I_2 + I_3} \tag{8.68}$$

with a constant angular deflection being maintained between wheels 1 and 2 and a constant relative angular velocity being maintained between wheels 2 and 3. The torque to accelerate I_2 and I_3 must be transmitted through the shaft, and this carries a torque of magnitude

$$(I_2 + I_3)\ddot{\phi} = \frac{I_2 + I_3}{I_1 + I_2 + I_3} \tag{8.69}$$

which, for the values in (8.48), is equal to $2/3$. For an applied torque of $1\,\text{N\,m}$, the shaft torque is therefore $2/3\,\text{N\,m}$, and so the shaft angle of twist is $2/3k = 1/300$ rad, which is the asymptote in Fig. 8.3.

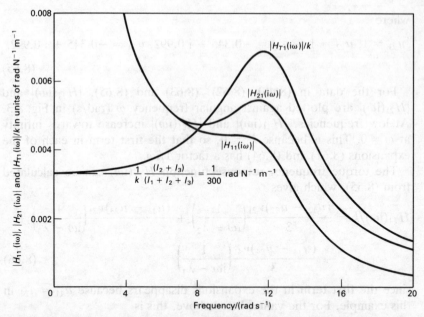

Fig. 8.3 Frequency response of the torsional system in Fig. 8.2. $H_{11}(i\omega)$ is the angular displacement response at wheel 1 for torque excitation at wheel 1; $H_{21}(i\omega)$ is the angular displacement response at wheel 2 for torque excitation at wheel 1; $H_{T1}(i\omega)$ is the shaft torque response for torque excitation at wheel 1. The numerical data is given in equations (8.48)

Because, for an input torque of zero frequency, there is a steady relative angular velocity between wheels 2 and 3, the relative deflections, θ_1 and θ_2, of wheels 1 and 2 are increasing steadily with time. This is why $H_{11}(i\omega)$ and $H_{21}(i\omega)$ have the factor $1/i\omega$ and become infinite when $\omega = 0$.

Frequency-response functions when the eigenvector matrix is defective

If it is not possible to find a matrix U of independent eigenvectors, then (8.6) is not true and it is no longer possible to use the general response equation (8.7) to calculate frequency-response functions. However, a general expression for $H(i\omega)$ can still be found in terms of the Jordan matrix J. From Chapter 6, if W is the principal-vector matrix for A, then

$$W^{-1}AW = J \tag{8.70}$$

where J has the almost diagonal structure of Jordan blocks described in Chapter 6. Then, in terms of the normal coordinate vector

$$q = W^{-1}z \tag{8.71}$$

the equations of motion (8.4) become

$$W\dot{q} = AWq + F \tag{8.72}$$

and, after pre-multiplying by W^{-1} and using (8.70),

$$\dot{q} = Jq + W^{-1}F. \tag{8.73}$$

If all the elements of the forcing function $x(t)$ have harmonic time dependence $e^{i\omega t}$, so that

$$x(t) = e^{i\omega t}x(i\omega) \tag{8.74}$$

the steady-state response of a passive system will also be harmonic so that

$$q(t) = e^{i\omega t}q(i\omega). \tag{8.75}$$

Then (8.73) gives

$$i\omega q(i\omega) = Jq(i\omega) + W^{-1}F(i\omega) \tag{8.76}$$

or

$$[i\omega I - J]q(i\omega) = W^{-1}F(i\omega). \tag{8.77}$$

The vector of physical responses is, from (8.71) and (8.77),

$$z(i\omega) = W[i\omega I - J]^{-1}W^{-1}F(i\omega). \tag{8.78}$$

As before for U in this chapter, we now partition the principal-vector matrix into

$$W = \begin{bmatrix} W_{\text{upper}} \\ W_{\text{lower}} \end{bmatrix} = \begin{bmatrix} W_{\text{upper}} \\ W_{\text{upper}}[\text{diag } \lambda_j] \end{bmatrix} \tag{8.79}$$

and

$$W^{-1} = [W_{\text{left}}^{-1} \quad W_{\text{right}}^{-1}] \tag{8.80}$$

with which definitions, and using (8.3) and (8.5), (8.78) gives

$$y(i\omega) = W_{\text{upper}}[i\omega I - J]^{-1}W_{\text{right}}^{-1}m^{-1}x(i\omega). \tag{8.81}$$

When

$$x(i\omega) = [1, 0, 0, 0, \ldots, 0]^{\text{T}} \tag{8.82}$$

then

$$y(i\omega) = [H_{11}(i\omega), H_{21}(i\omega), \ldots, H_{M1}(i\omega)]^{\text{T}}. \tag{8.83}$$

Similarly, if

$$x(i\omega) = [0, 1, 0, 0, \ldots, 0]^{\text{T}} \tag{8.84}$$

then

$$y(i\omega) = [H_{21}(i\omega), H_{22}(i\omega), \ldots, H_{M2}(i\omega)]^{\text{T}}, \tag{8.85}$$

and so on. By combining all these sets of equations, $x(i\omega)$ becomes an $M \times M$ identity matrix and $y(i\omega)$ becomes the $M \times M$ frequency-response function matrix $H(i\omega)$, so that

$$H(i\omega) = W_{\text{upper}}[i\omega I - J]^{-1}W_{\text{right}}^{-1}m^{-1} \qquad (8.86)$$

instead of the previous equation (8.32). Obviously, (8.86) correctly reduces to (8.32) when the J matrix is diagonal (i.e. when there are $2M$ independent eigenvectors). As before, (8.86) applies only to a passive system for which a steady-state harmonic response can become established and therefore all the eigenvalues λ_j, $j = 1$ to $2M$, must have negative real parts.

When J is not a diagonal matrix (and usually it will not be diagonal if there are multiple eigenvalues), the general simplified form (8.39) does not apply without correction. Because the form of J is not known initially, and differs from one problem to the next, each case has to be handled individually in order to work out an algorithm which avoids multiplying three (probably large) matrices W_{upper}, $[i\omega I - J]^{-1}$ and $[W_{\text{right}}^{-1}m^{-1}]$ every time that $H_{rs}(i\omega)$ is needed for a new value of ω. The method is illustrated in the following example calculation and in Problem 8.2.

Example 8.2 Frequency-response function of a system with repeated eigenvalues

For this calculation we return to the torsional system in Fig. 8.2 but will use the coordinates in Fig. 6.1. Then the A-matrix has order 6×6 and is given by equation (6.62) and there are six eigenvalues, three of which are zero. These are listed in equations (6.79). The Jordan matrix is given in (6.83), and the principal-vector matrix is (6.84). Suppose that we want to calculate $H_{11}(i\omega)$, when the input is unit harmonic torque at wheel 1 and the output is the angular displacement of wheel 1 from a fixed datum (i.e. the angle y_1 of Fig. 6.1, not the relative angle θ_1 of Fig. 8.2).

On calculating the inverse of the complex W matrix in (6.84), we find that

$$W_{\text{right}}^{-1} =$$

$$\begin{bmatrix} 0.0444 & 0.0222 & -0.0667 \\ -0.3333 & -0.1667 & -0.5 \\ 0.3333 & 0.1667 & 0.5 \\ -0.0167 & -0.0208 & 0.0375 \\ -0.0139 - i\,0.0180 & -0.0007 + i\,0.0158 & 0.0146 + i\,0.0022 \\ -0.0139 + i\,0.0180 & -0.0007 - i\,0.0158 & 0.0146 - i\,0.0022 \end{bmatrix}$$

$$(8.87)$$

The mass matrix (6.61) is diagonal and so

$$
\boldsymbol{m}^{-1} =
\begin{bmatrix}
1/I_1 & & \\
& 1/I_2 & \\
& & 1/I_3
\end{bmatrix}
=
\begin{bmatrix}
1/3 & & \\
& 2/3 & \\
& & 2/9
\end{bmatrix}
\tag{8.88}
$$

and from (6.83)

$$
[i\omega I - J] =
$$

$$
\begin{bmatrix}
i\omega & & & & & \\
& i\omega & -1 & & & \\
& 0 & i\omega & & & \\
& & & i\omega+10 & & \\
& & & & i\omega+2.5-i\,11.99 & \\
& & & & & i\omega+2.5+i\,11.99
\end{bmatrix}
\tag{8.89}
$$

This matrix has to be inverted in order to use it in (8.86). To invert a matrix of diagonal blocks, it is only necessary to invert each block separately (Problem 8.2) to give

$$
(i\omega I - J)^{-1} =
$$

$$
\begin{bmatrix}
1/i\omega & & & & & \\
& 1/i\omega & 1/(i\omega)^2 & & & \\
& 0 & 1/i\omega & & & \\
& & & 1/(i\omega+10) & & \\
& & & & 1/(i\omega+2.5-i\,11.99) & \\
& & & & & 1/(i\omega+2.5+i\,11.99)
\end{bmatrix}
\tag{8.90}
$$

Then the first column of $(i\omega I - J)^{-1}\boldsymbol{W}_{\text{right}}^{-1}\boldsymbol{m}^{-1}$ is

$$
\begin{bmatrix}
\dfrac{0.0444}{3}\left(\dfrac{1}{i\omega}\right) \\[2ex]
\dfrac{-0.3333}{3}\left(\dfrac{1}{i\omega}\right)+\dfrac{0.3333}{3}\left(\dfrac{1}{i\omega}\right)^2 \\[2ex]
\dfrac{0.3333}{3}\left(\dfrac{1}{i\omega}\right) \\[2ex]
\dfrac{-0.0167}{3}\left(\dfrac{1}{i\omega+10}\right) \\[2ex]
\dfrac{-0.0139-i\,0.0180}{3}\left(\dfrac{1}{i\omega+2.5-i\,11.99}\right) \\[2ex]
\dfrac{-0.0139+i\,0.0180}{3}\left(\dfrac{1}{i\omega+2.5+i\,11.99}\right)
\end{bmatrix}
\tag{8.91}
$$

and, since the first row of $\boldsymbol{W}_{\text{upper}}$ is a row of unit elements, $H_{11}(i\omega)$ is the sum of the elements in (8.91), so that

$$H_{11}(i\omega) = \frac{1}{3}\left[\frac{0.0444}{i\omega} + \frac{0.3333}{(i\omega)^2} - \frac{0.0167}{(i\omega + 10)} - \right.$$
$$\left. - \frac{(0.0139 + i\,0.0180)}{(i\omega + 2.5 - i\,11.99)} - \frac{(0.0139 - i\,0.0180)}{(i\omega + 1.5 + i\,11.99)}\right] \qquad (8.92)$$

or, when placed over a common denominator,

$$H_{11}(i\omega) = \frac{(1/3)(i\omega)^3 + 5(i\omega)^2 + (400/9)(i\omega) + 500/3}{(i\omega)^5 + 15(i\omega)^4 + 200(i\omega)^3 + 1500(i\omega)^2}. \qquad (8.93)$$

The term with a factor $1/(i\omega)^2$ in (8.92) arises because of the corresponding super-diagonal term in (8.90) which is itself a consequence of the fact that the third column of W is a principal vector and not an independent eigenvector. The general expansion (8.39) is modified by this additional term. If w_{rs} denotes an element of W_{upper} and s_{rs} denotes an element of $W_{right}^{-1}m^{-1}$, then (8.92) may be written as

$$H_{11}(i\omega) = \sum_{j=1}^{6} w_{1j}\frac{1}{(i\omega - \lambda_j)}s_{j1} + w_{12}\frac{1}{(i\omega)^2}s_{31}. \qquad (8.94)$$

The second subscript of w_{12} and the first subscript of s_{31} are determined by the row and column of J in which the super-diagonal unit occurs.

This result may be further generalized for the frequency-response function $H_{rs}(i\omega)$ for output $y_r(i\omega)$ with input $x_s(i\omega)$. If there is only one principal vector which is not also an independent eigenvector, so that there is only one super-diagonal element of unity in the Jordan matrix, and this occurs in row k and column $(k + 1)$ of J, then it is shown in Problem 8.2 that

$$H_{rs}(i\omega) = \sum_{j=1}^{2M} w_{rj}\frac{1}{(i\omega - \lambda_j)}s_{js} + w_{rk}\frac{1}{(i\omega - \lambda_k)^2}s_{k+1,s}. \qquad (8.95)$$

When there is more than one super-diagonal unit element in the Jordan matrix there are further additional terms in the expansion (8.95) and these can be found in the same way (Problem 8.2, part (vi)).

Alternative method of computing the frequency-response function matrix

The advantage of the modal-analysis method for calculating frequency-response functions is that this method allows efficient numerical computations. If all the eigenvectors are independent so that (8.6) is true, the algorithm illustrated in Fig. 8.1 can be followed. If (8.6) is not true, a similarly efficient algorithm can still be used after amending Fig. 8.1 to include the extra terms introduced by the Jordan matrix (Problem 8.2).

However, if computational efficiency is not important, an alternative approach is the *direct method* of harmonic response calculation. Starting from the M coupled second-order equations in the form (8.1), if

$$x(t) = e^{i\omega t}x(i\omega), \qquad (8.96)$$

then, assuming that the system is passive so that steady-state harmonic oscillations can become established,

$$y(t) = e^{i\omega t}y(i\omega). \qquad (8.97)$$

On substituting (8.96) and (8.97) into (8.1) and solving for $y(i\omega)$, we get

$$y(i\omega) = [(i\omega)^2 m + (i\omega)c + k]^{-1}x(i\omega). \qquad (8.98)$$

When

$$x(i\omega) = [0, 0, 0, \ldots, 1, \ldots, 0]^{\mathrm{T}} \qquad (8.99)$$
$$\uparrow$$
$$\text{Element } s$$

then, from the definition of the frequency-response functions,

$$y(i\omega) = [H_{1s}(i\omega), H_{2s}(i\omega), \ldots, H_{Ms}(i\omega)]^{\mathrm{T}}. \qquad (8.100)$$

Combining the M sets of equations obtained by putting the unit element in (8.99) into each of its M possible positions, we find that the matrix of frequency-response functions $H(i\omega)$ can be expressed in the alternative form

$$H(i\omega) = [(i\omega)^2 m + (i\omega)c + k]^{-1}. \qquad (8.101)$$

Equation (8.101) is true for any passive system. It is completely equivalent to the modal expansion (8.86) and to (8.32), which is a special case of (8.86). Because of the time required for matrix inversion, computing $H(i\omega)$ from (8.101) is generally a slower procedure than making the matrix multiplications needed to compute the right-hand side of (8.86). But the direct method does not involve finding eigenvalues and eigenvectors and, when results are needed for only a limited number of frequencies, the overall time of the complete calculation may be shorter.

A disadvantage of the direct method is that there is no way of computing only a few of the elements of $H(i\omega)$ without finding all of its elements. This is because numerical procedures for inverting a matrix, such as the subprogram Cinv of Appendix 6, compute progressively all the elements of the inverted matrix, and it is not possible to obtain one element without the others. As we have seen, the individual elements of $H(i\omega)$ can be computed separately from (8.32) and (8.86) and this is important when detailed results are needed for only a few of the M^2 response functions in $H(i\omega)$.

Impulse-response function matrix

In Chapter 1 we calculated the response of a single-degree-of-freedom system to a unit impulsive input defined by

$$x(t) = \delta(t) \tag{8.102}$$

where $\delta(t)$ is the Dirac delta function. This is zero everywhere except at $t = 0$ where it is infinite in such a way that

$$\int f(t)\delta(t)\,dt = 0, \text{ for } t < 0 \tag{8.103}$$
$$= f(t = 0), \text{ for } t > 0$$

provided that the function $f(t)$ exists and is continuous at $t = 0$. Now we shall extend the earlier analysis to the case of a general system of M degrees of freedom defined by (8.1).

If the excitation vector is

$$x(t) = \delta(t)[0, 0, \ldots, 1, \ldots, 0]^{\mathrm{T}} \tag{8.104}$$
$$\uparrow$$
$$\text{Element } s$$

with all the elements of $x(t)$ except its sth element being zero, then we shall define the response at coordinate r as $h_{rs}(t)$, so that

$$y(t) = [h_{1s}(t), h_{2s}(t), \ldots, h_{rs}(t), \ldots, h_{Ms}(t)]^{\mathrm{T}}. \tag{8.105}$$

The $M \times M$ real matrix $h(t)$ whose elements are $h_{rs}(t)$, $r, s = 1$ to M, is called the *impulse-response function matrix* for the system.

Subject to there being $2M$ independent eigenvectors, so that (8.6) is true, the general response equation (8.11) applies. For $x(t)$ defined by (8.104), the integral with respect to time in its right-hand side is

$$\int \delta(t)[\text{diag } e^{-\lambda_i t}]dt = O, \, t < 0$$
$$= I, \, t > 0 \tag{8.106}$$

on account of (8.103). With this result, equation (8.11) gives

$$y(t) = U_{\text{upper}}[\text{diag } e^{\lambda_i t}]C, \text{ for } t < 0, \tag{8.107}$$

$$= U_{\text{upper}}[\text{diag } e^{\lambda_i t}]U_{\text{right}}^{-1}m^{-1}\begin{bmatrix} O \\ 1 \\ O \end{bmatrix} + U_{\text{upper}}[\text{diag } e^{\lambda_i t}]C, \text{ for } t > 0.$$

$$\nearrow$$
$$s\text{th element}$$

$$\tag{8.108}$$

As for the frequency-response analysis, we now assume that the system is passive so that all its eigenvalues have negative real parts (even if these are extremely small). In this case there can be no response before the impulsive excitation has been applied and so, from (8.107), the vector of arbitrary constants C must be a null vector. Then (8.108) gives, with (8.105),

$$
\begin{bmatrix} h_{1s}(t) \\ h_{2s}(t) \\ \cdots \\ \cdots \\ \cdots \\ h_{Ms}(t) \end{bmatrix} = U_{\text{upper}}[\text{diag } e^{\lambda_j t}]U_{\text{right}}^{-1}m^{-1}\begin{bmatrix} O \\ 1 \\ O \end{bmatrix}, t > 0 \qquad (8.109)
$$

sth element

and consequently the impulse-response function matrix is given by

$$
h(t) = O, \text{ for } t < 0
$$
$$
= U_{\text{upper}}[\text{diag } e^{\lambda_j t}]U_{\text{right}}^{-1}m^{-1}, \text{ for } t > 0. \qquad (8.110)
$$

Computation of impulse-response functions

The general result (8.110) is similar in form to the corresponding result (8.32) for the frequency-response function matrix $H(i\omega)$. The only difference is that the $2M \times 2M$ diagonal matrix

$$
\left[\text{diag } \frac{1}{i\omega - \lambda_j}\right]
$$

in $H(i\omega)$ is replaced by $[\text{diag } e^{\lambda_j t}]$ in $h(t)$. The expansion formula (8.39) for computing the frequency response $H_{rs}(i\omega)$ therefore holds also for the corresponding impulse-response function $h_{rs}(t)$, except that

$$
\frac{1}{i\omega - \lambda_j}
$$

is replaced by $e^{\lambda_j t}$, so that (8.39) becomes

$$
h_{rs}(t) = \sum_{j=1}^{2M} u_{rj} e^{\lambda_j t} s_{js} \qquad (8.111)
$$
$$
t > 0
$$

where, as before,

$$
s_{js} = \sum_{k=1}^{M} v_{jk} a_{ks}, \, j = 1 \text{ to } 2M, \, s = 1 \text{ to } M. \qquad (8.112)
$$

We repeat that λ_j, $j = 1$ to $2M$, are the eigenvalues, all of which are assumed to have negative real parts, u_{rj}, $r = 1$ to M, $j = 1$ to $2M$ are the elements of the upper half of U, which is the matrix of eigenvectors, all of which are assumed to be independent; v_{jk}, $j = 1$ to $2M$, $k = 1$ to M are the elements of the right-hand half of U^{-1}; and a_{ks}, $k, s = 1$ to M are the elements of m^{-1}.

Example 8.3 Impulse-response functions of the torsional system in Fig. 8.2

As an application of the general result (8.111), consider again the torsional system in Example 8.1. We have already calculated the eigenvector matrix U in (8.50) and its inverse in (8.51), and m^{-1} is given in (8.58). The eigenvalues are listed in (8.49), and so

$$[\text{diag } e^{\lambda_j t}] = \begin{bmatrix} 1 & & & \\ & e^{-10t} & & \\ & & e^{-(2.5 - i\,11.99)t} & \\ & & & e^{-(2.5 + i\,11.99)t} \end{bmatrix}. \quad (8.113)$$

Then, by identifying the elements in (8.111) and completing the summation, we get

$$h_{11}(t) = \frac{0.0889}{3} - \frac{0.0417}{3} e^{-10t} - \frac{(0.0236 + i\,0.0194)}{3} e^{-(2.5 - i\,11.99)t} -$$
$$t{>}0$$
$$- \frac{(0.0236 - i\,0.0194)}{3} e^{-(2.5 + i\,11.99)t} \quad (8.114)$$

and

$$h_{21}(t) = \frac{0.0889}{3} - 1.6 \frac{(0.0417)}{3} e^{-10t} +$$
$$t{>}0$$
$$+ (0.345 + i\,0.992)\frac{(0.0236 + i\,0.0194)}{3} e^{-(2.5 - i\,11.99)t} +$$
$$+ (0.345 - i\,0.992)\frac{(0.0236 - i\,0.0194)}{3} e^{-(2.5 + i\,11.99)t}. \quad (8.115)$$

If, as in Example 8.1, we want the response of the shaft torque $T(t)$ defined by (8.53), then

$$h_{T1}(t) = k(h_{11}(t) - h_{21}(t)) \quad (8.116)$$

where $h_{T1}(t)$ denotes the response function for the shaft torque for a unit impulsive excitation torque applied to wheel 1. From (8.114) and (8.115), this gives

$$h_{T1}(t) = k\left[\frac{0.6(0.0417)}{3} e^{-10t} - \right.$$
$$t{>}0$$
$$- (1.345 + i\,0.992)\frac{(0.0236 + i\,0.0194)}{3} e^{-(2.5 - i\,11.99)t} -$$
$$\left. - (1.345 - i\,0.992)\frac{(0.0236 - i\,0.0194)}{3} e^{-(2.5 + i\,11.99)t} \right] \quad (8.117)$$

which on sorting out the complex terms reduces to

$$h_{T1}(t)/k = 0.0083e^{-10t} + e^{-2.5t}(0.033 \sin 11.99t - 0.0083 \cos 11.99t).$$
$$t{>}0$$
$$(8.118)$$

This result is equivalent to the frequency-domain result given in equation (8.67). It is plotted in Fig. 9.4 where the impulse response function and step-response function (calculated in Ch. 9) are compared. The slope of $h_{T1}(t)$ at $t = 0$ is determined by the initial angular velocity of wheel 1. This has a moment of inertia of $3\ \mathrm{kg\,m^2}$, so that a rotary impulse of $1\ \mathrm{Nms}$ gives it an initial angular velocity of $1/3\ \mathrm{rad/s}$. Wheel 2 is stationary immediately after the impulse, and therefore the rate of twisting of the shaft is initially $1/3\ \mathrm{rad/s}$ and the initial rate of increase of shaft torque is $k/3$ which, for $k = 200\ \mathrm{N\,m/rad}$, is $66.66\ \mathrm{N\,m/s}$, as shown in Fig. 9.4.

Impulse-response functions when the eigenvector matrix is defective

When, for M degrees of freedom, there are not $2M$ independent eigenvectors, the calculation of $h(t)$ is complicated by the introduction of additional terms that do not appear in (8.110). The form of the extra terms may be seen by considering the solution of

$$\dot{q} = Jq + W^{-1}F \tag{8.119}$$

where, as before,

$$q = W^{-1}z, \tag{8.120}$$

$$W^{-1}AW = J \tag{8.121}$$

and

$$F = \begin{bmatrix} O \\ m^{-1}x(t) \end{bmatrix}. \tag{8.122}$$

On partitioning W^{-1} into left-hand and right-hand halves, we have

$$\dot{q} = Jq + W_{\mathrm{right}}^{-1}m^{-1}x(t). \tag{8.123}$$

If $x(t)$ describes a unit impulsive input applied at coordinate $x_s(t)$ with all the other inputs zero, then

$$x(t) = \delta(t)[0, 0, 0, \ldots, 1, \ldots, 0]^{\mathrm{T}}. \tag{8.124}$$
$$\uparrow$$
$$\text{element } s$$

Defining a new $2M \times M$ matrix S so that

$$S = W_{\mathrm{right}}^{-1}m^{-1} \tag{8.125}$$

and whose sth column is $s^{(s)}$, then (8.123) gives

$$\dot{q} = Jq + \delta(t)s^{(s)}. \tag{8.126}$$

The kth row of (8.126) is either

$$\dot{q}_k = \lambda_k q_k + \delta(t)s_{ks} \qquad (8.127)$$

or

$$\dot{q}_k = \lambda_k q_k + q_{k+1} + \delta(t)s_{ks} \qquad (8.128)$$

depending whether or not there is a unit element in the kth row of the Jordan matrix J. If there is not, then (8.127) applies and, on multiplying through by the integrating factor $e^{-\lambda_k t}$, this gives

$$\frac{d}{dt}(q_k e^{-\lambda_k t}) = e^{-\lambda_k t}\delta(t)s_{ks} \qquad (8.129)$$

which integrates to

$$q_k(t)e^{-\lambda_k t} = s_{ks}, \ t > 0 \qquad (8.130)$$

since we assume that the system is passive so that there is no response for $t < 0$.

Therefore, if row k of the Jordan matrix has no unit element in its super-diagonal, normal coordinate $q_k(t)$ has the response

$$q_k(t) = e^{\lambda_k t}s_{ks}, \ t > 0 \qquad (8.131)$$

Alternatively, suppose that (8.128) applies because there is a super-diagonal element of unity in row k of J. Then the solution of (8.128) depends on the solution $q_{k+1}(t)$ from the row below. Let the Jordan matrix be a diagonal matrix except for a Jordan block of order 2 occupying rows k and $(k + 1)$, so that

$$J = \begin{bmatrix} \ddots & & & & \\ & \lambda_{k-1} & & & \\ & & \lambda_k & 1 & \\ & & & \lambda_k & \\ & & & & \lambda_{k+2} \\ & & & & & \ddots \end{bmatrix} \qquad (8.132)$$

Then (8.131) applies for row $k + 1$ and

$$q_{k+1}(t) = e^{\lambda_k t}s_{k+1,s}, \ t > 0 \qquad (8.133)$$

because $\lambda_{k+1} = \lambda_k$ from (8.132). On substituting for q_{k+1} from (8.133) into (8.128) and multiplying through by the integrating factor $e^{-\lambda_k t}$, we get

$$\frac{d}{dt}[q_k(t)e^{-\lambda_k t}] = s_{k+1,s} + e^{-\lambda_k t}\delta(t)s_{ks}, \ t > 0 \qquad (8.134)$$

whose solution is

$$q_k(t) = e^{\lambda_k t}(s_{k+1,s}t + s_{ks}), \ t > 0. \qquad (8.135)$$

Now suppose that a Jordan block of order 3 occupies rows k, $(k + 1)$, $(k + 2)$ of J so that

$$J = \begin{bmatrix} \ddots & & & & & \\ & \lambda_{k-1} & & & & \\ & & \lambda_k & 1 & & \\ & & & \lambda_k & 1 & \\ & & & & \lambda_k & \\ & & & & & \lambda_{k+3} \\ & & & & & & \ddots \end{bmatrix}. \tag{8.136}$$

In this case, from (8.135),

$$q_{k+1}(t) = e^{\lambda_k t}(s_{k+2,s}t + s_{k+1,s}), \ t > 0 \tag{8.137}$$

and, corresponding to (8.134), we have

$$\frac{d}{dt}[q_k(t)e^{-\lambda_k t}] = s_{k+2,s}t + s_{k+1,s} + s_{ks}e^{-\lambda_k t}\delta(t), \ t > 0 \tag{8.138}$$

giving

$$q_k(t) = e^{\lambda_k t}(s_{k+2,s}\tfrac{1}{2}t^2 + s_{k+1,s}t + s_{ks}), \ t > 0. \tag{8.139}$$

The physical response vector $z(t)$ is obtained from the normal coordinates by the transformation

$$z(t) = Wq(t) \tag{8.140}$$

and, as before,

$$y(t) = W_{\text{upper}}q(t). \tag{8.141}$$

The response of the rth coordinate is

$$y_r(t) = h_{rs}(t) \tag{8.142}$$

since unit impulsive input was applied at coordinate s and so, from (8.142),

$$h_{rs}(t) = \sum_{j=1}^{2M} w_{rj}q_j(t). \tag{8.143}$$

If the Jordan matrix has the form of (8.132) with all the Jordan blocks of order 1 (i.e. diagonal elements) except for a Jordan block of order 2 at rows k, $(k+1)$ then, from (8.143) with (8.131) and (8.135),

$$h_{rs}(t) \atop t>0 = \sum_{j=1}^{2M} w_{rj}e^{\lambda_j t}s_{js} + w_{rk}t\,e^{\lambda_k t}s_{k+1,s} \tag{8.144}$$

which may be compared with the corresponding result (8.95) for $H_{rs}(i\omega)$.

If the Jordan matrix has the form of (8.136) with one Jordan block of order 3 occupying rows k, $(k+1)$ and $(k+2)$ then, from (8.143) with (8.137) and (8.139), we have

$$h_{rs}(t) \atop t>0 = \sum_{j=1}^{2M} w_{rj}e^{\lambda_j t}s_{js} + w_{rk}e^{\lambda_k t}(t\,s_{k+1,s} + \tfrac{1}{2}t^2 s_{k+2,s}) + w_{r,k+1}e^{\lambda_k t}(t\,s_{k+2,s}). \tag{8.145}$$

This may be compared with the corresponding result for $H_{rs}(i\omega)$ which is given in part (iv) of Problem 8.2.

The corresponding $M \times M$ matrix $h(t)$ in each of the above two cases may be obtained by assembling all the results for $h_{rs}(t)$, r, $s = 1$ to M, into a single matrix equation. For J given by (8.132), the result (8.144) is element r, s of $h(t)$ where

$$h(t) = \underset{t>0}{}$$

$$W_{\text{upper}} \begin{bmatrix} e^{\lambda_1 t} & & & & & & & & \\ & e^{\lambda_2 t} & & & & & & & \\ & & \ddots & & & & & & \\ & & & e^{\lambda_{k-1} t} & & & & & \\ & & & & e^{\lambda_k t} & t\,e^{\lambda_k t} & & & \\ & & & & & e^{\lambda_k t} & & & \\ & & & & & & e^{\lambda_{k+2} t} & & \\ & & & & & & & \ddots & \\ & & & & & & & & e^{\lambda_{2M} t} \end{bmatrix} W_{\text{right}}^{-1} m^{-1}$$

$$(8.146)$$

For J given by (8.136), the result is the same except that rows k, $(k + 1)$, $(k + 2)$ of the matrix of exponentials are changed to the sub-matrix

$$\begin{bmatrix} e^{\lambda_k t} & t\,e^{\lambda_k t} & \frac{1}{2}t^2\,e^{\lambda_k t} \\ & e^{\lambda_k t} & t\,e^{\lambda_k t} \\ & & e^{\lambda_k t} \end{bmatrix}. \qquad (8.147)$$

A pattern now becomes evident and it is shown in Problem 8.4 that if there is a 4×4 Jordan submatrix

$$\begin{bmatrix} \lambda & 1 & & \\ & \lambda & 1 & \\ & & \lambda & 1 \\ & & & \lambda \end{bmatrix}. \qquad (8.148)$$

then this leads to a sub-matrix in (8.146) which is

$$\begin{bmatrix} e^{\lambda t} & t\,e^{\lambda t} & \dfrac{t^2}{2!}e^{\lambda t} & \dfrac{t^3}{3!}e^{\lambda t} \\ & e^{\lambda t} & t\,e^{\lambda t} & \dfrac{t^2}{2!}e^{\lambda t} \\ & & e^{\lambda t} & t\,e^{\lambda t} \\ & & & e^{\lambda t} \end{bmatrix}. \qquad (8.149)$$

It is possible to express such a matrix in compact form by using the matrix exponential function, which is described below.

Use of the matrix exponential function

The exponential series

$$e^x = 1 + x + \frac{x^2}{2!} + \frac{x^3}{3!} + \dots \tag{8.150}$$

is known to converge for any x, real or complex (see, for example, Jeffreys and Jeffreys [48], Chapter 11). If x is replaced by the $2M \times 2M$ matrix X, then e^X is defined as

$$e^X = \left[I + X + \frac{X^2}{2!} + \frac{X^3}{3!} + \dots \right] \tag{8.151}$$

where by X^2 we mean XX, etc. Each of the terms in the expansion (8.151) is a $2M \times 2M$ matrix and so e^X is also a $2M \times 2M$ matrix each of whose elements is the sum of corresponding elements in I, X, $X^2/2!$, $X^3/3!$, etc.

If we put

$$X = t[\text{diag } \lambda_j] \tag{8.152}$$

then, from (8.151),

$$e^{t[\text{diag } \lambda_j]} = \left[I + t[\text{diag } \lambda_j] + \frac{t^2[\text{diag } \lambda_j]^2}{2!} + \frac{t^3[\text{diag } \lambda_j]^3}{3!} + \dots \right]$$

$$= \left[I + t[\text{diag } \lambda_j] + \frac{t^2[\text{diag } \lambda_j^2]}{2!} + \frac{t^3[\text{diag } \lambda_j^3]}{3!} + \dots \right] \tag{8.153}$$

since

$$[\text{diag } \lambda_j]^2 = [\text{diag } \lambda_j][\text{diag } \lambda_j] = [\text{diag } \lambda_j^2] \tag{8.154}$$

and so on for higher powers. Hence, collecting terms,

$$e^{t(\text{diag } \lambda_j]} = \left[\text{diag}\left(1 + \lambda_j t + \frac{\lambda_j^2 t^2}{2!} + \frac{\lambda_j^3 t^3}{3!} + \dots \right) \right], \tag{8.155}$$

so that, from (8.150),

$$e^{t[\text{diag } \lambda_j]} = [\text{diag } e^{\lambda_j t}]. \tag{8.156}$$

Now consider what happens when we replace $[\text{diag } \lambda_j]$ in (8.153) by the $2M \times 2M$ Jordan matrix J, which is almost diagonal, and is composed of Jordan blocks of arbitrary order. Instead of (8.153) we have

$$e^{tJ} = \left[I + tJ + \frac{t^2 J^2}{2!} + \frac{t^3 J^3}{3!} + \dots \right]. \tag{8.157}$$

If J consists of two Jordan blocks C_r and C_s so that

$$J = \begin{bmatrix} C_r & O \\ O & C_s \end{bmatrix} \tag{8.158}$$

then it is easy to prove (Problem 8.5) that

$$J^2 = \begin{bmatrix} C_r^2 & O \\ O & C_s^2 \end{bmatrix}. \tag{8.159}$$

The $2M \times 2M$ matrix on the right-hand side of (8.157) is therefore partitioned into the same diagonal blocks as J, and each block is a summation of the form

$$\left[I + tC_r + \frac{t^2 C_r^2}{2!} + \frac{t^3 C_r^3}{3!} + \ldots \right]. \tag{8.160}$$

If the order of the Jordan sub-matrix is 1, then

$$C_1 = \lambda \tag{8.161}$$

and the corresponding diagonal element in e^{tJ} is just

$$\left(1 + t\lambda + \frac{t^2 \lambda^2}{2!} + \frac{t^3 \lambda^3}{3!} + \ldots \right) = e^{\lambda t}. \tag{8.162}$$

If the order of C_r is 2, then

$$C_2 = \begin{bmatrix} \lambda & 1 \\ 0 & \lambda \end{bmatrix} \tag{8.163}$$

and

$$C_2^2 = \begin{bmatrix} \lambda^2 & 2\lambda \\ 0 & \lambda^2 \end{bmatrix}, \tag{8.164}$$

$$C_2^3 = \begin{bmatrix} \lambda^3 & 3\lambda^2 \\ 0 & \lambda^3 \end{bmatrix} \tag{8.165}$$

and so on. Substituting into (8.160), the corresponding diagonal block in e^{tJ} is

$$\begin{bmatrix} \left(1 + t\lambda + \dfrac{t^2}{2!}\lambda^2 + \dfrac{t^3}{3!}\lambda^3 + \ldots \right) & \left(t + t^2\lambda + \dfrac{t^3}{2!}\lambda^2 + \dfrac{t^4}{3!}\lambda^3 + \ldots \right) \\ 0 & \left(1 + t\lambda + \dfrac{t^2}{2!}\lambda^2 + \dfrac{t^3}{3!}\lambda^3 + \ldots \right) \end{bmatrix}$$

$$= \begin{bmatrix} e^{\lambda t} & t\,e^{\lambda t} \\ 0 & e^{\lambda t} \end{bmatrix}. \tag{8.166}$$

This is the diagonal block that appears in (8.146), which is a result calculated for the same Jordan block as (8.163) at rows k and $(k + 1)$.

For a third-order Jordan block

$$C_3 = \begin{bmatrix} \lambda & 1 & 0 \\ 0 & \lambda & 1 \\ 0 & 0 & \lambda \end{bmatrix} \tag{8.167}$$

it can be shown similarly that

$$\left(I + tC_3 + \frac{t^2 C_3^2}{2!} + \frac{t^3 C_3^3}{3!} + \ldots\right) = \begin{bmatrix} e^{\lambda t} & t\,e^{\lambda t} & \dfrac{t^2}{2!}e^{\lambda t} \\ 0 & e^{\lambda t} & t\,e^{\lambda t} \\ 0 & 0 & e^{\lambda t} \end{bmatrix} \quad (8.168)$$

which is the sub-matrix given in (8.147). The corresponding result for C_4 leads to the sub-matrix in (8.149). The conclusion is that the matrix exponential function e^{tJ} is a nearly diagonal matrix with the same order and the same structure as J, but with each Jordan sub-matrix replaced by a corresponding sub-matrix, as follows

$$C_1 = [\lambda] \text{ is replaced by } e^{\lambda t}[1]$$

$$C_2 = \begin{bmatrix} \lambda & 1 \\ 0 & \lambda \end{bmatrix} \text{ is replaced by } e^{\lambda t}\begin{bmatrix} 1 & t \\ 0 & 1 \end{bmatrix}$$

$$C_3 = \begin{bmatrix} \lambda & 1 & 0 \\ 0 & \lambda & 1 \\ 0 & 0 & \lambda \end{bmatrix} \text{ is replaced by } e^{\lambda t}\begin{bmatrix} 1 & t & t^2/2! \\ 0 & 1 & t \\ 0 & 0 & 1 \end{bmatrix} \quad (8.169)$$

$$C_4 = \begin{bmatrix} \lambda & 1 & 0 & 0 \\ 0 & \lambda & 1 & 0 \\ 0 & 0 & \lambda & 1 \\ 0 & 0 & 0 & \lambda \end{bmatrix} \text{ is replaced by } e^{\lambda t}\begin{bmatrix} 1 & t & t^2/2! & t^3/3! \\ 0 & 1 & t & t^2/2! \\ 0 & 0 & 1 & t \\ 0 & 0 & 0 & 1 \end{bmatrix}$$

and so on.

With these results, the expression for the impulse-response function matrix shown in (8.146) can be written in the following general form

$$h(t) = W_{\text{upper}}\, e^{tJ}\, W_{\text{right}}^{-1}\, m^{-1}. \quad (8.170)$$
$$\scriptstyle t>0$$

In this expression, which applies for an M-degree-of-freedom passive system whose A matrix is given by (8.2), the Jordan matrix J is defined by (8.70). The eigenvalues of A have to be computed in the usual way and, where there are multiple eigenvalues, there has to be an *ad hoc* investigation of the number of independent eigenvectors that are associated with each repeated eigenvalue. If necessary, there is a general method that can be used (see page 200). The Jordan matrix is then assembled so that there is a super-diagonal unit element in each column for which there is no independent eigenvector and the corresponding principal vectors are calculated as explained in Chapter 6.

Although (8.170) is an interesting compact form for $h(t)$, numerical calculations cannot be made from (8.170) conveniently. Usually, only a few of the M^2 impulse-response functions in the matrix $h(t)$ will be needed and these are calculated from the summation (8.111) if there are $2M$ independent eigenvectors, from (8.144) if there is one principal vector, from (8.145) if there are two principal vectors for a Jordan block of order 3, or from an appropriate similar summation if J has another different form.

Application to the general response equation

The result given in equation (8.11) for the response of an M-degree-of-freedom system to arbitrary excitation depends on there being a full set of independent eigenvectors so that (8.6) is true. We shall now consider how (8.11) has to be modified when the eigenvector matrix U is replaced by a principal-vector matrix W and, instead of (8.6), we have

$$W^{-1}AW = J \qquad (8.171)$$

where, for M degrees of freedom, A, W and the Jordan matrix J are all of order $2M \times 2M$.

We use the matrix exponential function defined by (8.151). This has two important properties which make the solution possible. The first is that e^{-X} is the inverse of e^X, so that

$$[e^X]^{-1} = e^{-X}. \qquad (8.172)$$

The proof derives from the form of the series expansion because, from (8.151),

$$e^{-X} = I - X + \tfrac{1}{2!}X^2 - \tfrac{1}{3!}X^3 + \ldots \qquad (8.173)$$

and

$$
\begin{aligned}
e^X e^{-X} &= (I + X + \tfrac{1}{2!}X^2 + \tfrac{1}{3!}X^3 + \ldots)(I - X + \tfrac{1}{2!}X^2 - \tfrac{1}{3!}X^3 + \ldots) \\
&= (I + X + \tfrac{1}{2!}X^2 + \tfrac{1}{3!}X^3 + \tfrac{1}{4!}X^4 + \ldots \\
&\quad - X - X^2 - \tfrac{1}{2!}X^3 - \tfrac{1}{3!}X^4 - \ldots \\
&\quad + \tfrac{1}{2!}X^2 + \tfrac{1}{2!}X^3 + \tfrac{1}{2!2!}X^4 + \ldots \\
&\quad - \tfrac{1}{3!}X^3 - \tfrac{1}{3!}X^4 - \ldots \\
&\quad + \tfrac{1}{4!}X^4 + \ldots \\
&\quad \ldots) \\
&= I.
\end{aligned}
\qquad (8.174)
$$

The second important property is that, since

$$e^{tA} = I + tA + \frac{t^2}{2!}A^2 + \frac{t^3}{3!}A^3 + \ldots, \qquad (8.175)$$

on differentiating with respect to t,

$$\frac{\mathrm{d}}{\mathrm{d}t}\mathrm{e}^{tA} = A + tA^2 + \frac{t^2}{2!}A^3 + \cdots$$

$$= A\mathrm{e}^{tA} = \mathrm{e}^{tA}A. \tag{8.176}$$

We use these two properties to obtain a completely general solution to the set of $2M$ first-order equations

$$\dot{z} = Az + F \tag{8.177}$$

which does not depend on A having $2M$ independent eigenvectors. If (8.177) is premultiplied by e^{-tA} so that

$$\mathrm{e}^{-tA}\dot{z} - \mathrm{e}^{-tA}Az = \mathrm{e}^{-tA}F \tag{8.178}$$

then, because of (8.176), the left-hand side is a perfect differential and we have

$$\frac{\mathrm{d}}{\mathrm{d}t}[\mathrm{e}^{-tA}z(t)] = \mathrm{e}^{-tA}F(t) \tag{8.179}$$

which integrates directly to give

$$\mathrm{e}^{-tA}z(t) = \int \mathrm{e}^{-tA}F(t)\,\mathrm{d}t + C' \tag{8.180}$$

where C' is a $2M \times 1$ vector of arbitrary constants of integration. On account of (8.172), we can premultiply by e^{tA} to obtain

$$z(t) = \mathrm{e}^{tA}\int \mathrm{e}^{-tA}F(t)\,\mathrm{d}t + \mathrm{e}^{tA}C' \tag{8.181}$$

as the general solution of (8.177) for arbitrary excitation $F(t)$.

The $2M \times 2M$ A-matrix is always similar to a Jordan matrix J so that (8.171) is true, and hence

$$A = WJW^{-1} \tag{8.182}$$

where W is the $2M \times 2M$ matrix of principal vectors. On substituting for A in (8.175) from (8.182), we get

$$\mathrm{e}^{tA} = I + tWJW^{-1} + \frac{t^2}{2!}(WJW^{-1})(WJW^{-1}) + \cdots$$

$$= I + tWJW^{-1} + \frac{t^2}{2!}WJ^2W^{-1} + \cdots \tag{8.183}$$

and so

$$W^{-1}\mathrm{e}^{tA}W = I + tJ + \frac{t^2}{2!}J^2 + \cdots$$

$$= \mathrm{e}^{tJ} \tag{8.184}$$

or its equivalent

$$\mathrm{e}^{tA} = W\mathrm{e}^{tJ}W^{-1}. \tag{8.185}$$

Now we can substitute for e^{tA} in (8.181) from (8.185) and find that

$$z(t) = W e^{tJ} \left[\int e^{-tJ} W^{-1} F(t) \, dt + W^{-1} C' \right] \qquad (8.186)$$

where we saw in the previous section that e^{tJ} has the same structure of diagonal blocks as J with each block of e^{tJ} being derived from the corresponding block of J according to (8.169).

For a system with M degrees of freedom defined by (8.1), with $x(t)$ being an $M \times 1$ vector of the force excitation and $y(t)$ being the $M \times 1$ displacement-response vector, then, from (8.186) with (8.3), (8.79) and (8.80),

$$y(t) = W_{\text{upper}} \, e^{tJ} \left[\int e^{-tJ} W_{\text{right}}^{-1} m^{-1} x(t) \, dt + C \right] \qquad (8.187)$$

where

$$C = W^{-1} C' \qquad (8.188)$$

is a new $2M \times 1$ vector of constants. This general result should be compared with the previous result (8.11). The latter applies only when J is a diagonal matrix so that all the Jordan blocks are of order 1. Then, according to (8.156),

$$e^{tJ} = e^{t[\text{diag } \lambda_j]} = [\text{diag } e^{\lambda_j t}] \qquad (8.189)$$

and W is replaced by a eigenvector matrix U. With these substitutions, (8.187) correctly reduces to (8.11) as a special case.

In order to determine the $2M$ constants in the vector C in (8.187), we need $2M$ equations. If all the M displacements $y(t)$ and M velocities $\dot{y}(t)$ are specified at an arbitrary time t_0, there are $2M$ initial conditions. Let the $2M \times 1$ vector $z(t)$ defined by (8.5) be called $z(t_0)$. If the lower limit of the integral in (8.186) is set at t_0, then at $t = t_0$ this integral is zero and

$$z(t_0) = W e^{t_0 J} W^{-1} C' \qquad (8.190)$$

so that

$$W^{-1} C' = e^{-t_0 J} W^{-1} z(t_0). \qquad (8.191)$$

Substituting for $W^{-1} C'$ in (8.186) from (8.191) and changing the variable of integration to τ then gives

$$z(t) = W e^{tJ} \left[\int_{t_0}^{t} e^{-\tau J} W^{-1} F(\tau) \, d\tau + e^{-t_0 J} W^{-1} z(t_0) \right]. \qquad (8.192)$$

In terms of $y(t)$ and the force excitation $x(t)$, from (8.3), (8.5), (8.79) and (8.80), we have

$$y(t) = W_{\text{upper}} \, e^{tJ} \left[\int_{t_0}^{t} e^{-\tau J} W_{\text{right}}^{-1} m^{-1} x(\tau) \, d\tau + e^{-t_0 J} W^{-1} \begin{bmatrix} y(t_0) \\ \dot{y}(t_0) \end{bmatrix} \right] \qquad (8.193)$$

where $y(t_0)$ and $\dot{y}(t_0)$ are the $M \times 1$ vectors of the displacements and velocities at t_0.

The general theoretical result (8.192) is a complete solution for the response of any linear system that is described by equation (8.4).

For an M-degree-of-freedom mechanical system whose mass matrix m is non-singular, (8.193) gives the general displacement response of the M masses. The step from (8.192) to (8.193) depends on the mass matrix being non-singular, so that m^{-1} exists. When m is singular, equations (8.1) have to be assembled into first-order form by condensing out the defective second-order equations, as explained in Chapter 6. The response vector $z(t)$ then no longer consists of M displacements followed by the corresponding M velocities, and (8.193) has to be modified accordingly. This modification can always be made once the definition of $z(t)$ has been established. Hence, in theory, we can always calculate the response of any linear system to arbitrary excitation by using (8.192) or an equivalent form like (8.193) when only the displacement response is needed.

In order to make numerical calculations in practical cases, equations (8.192) and (8.193) are not convenient in their present forms because their organization for numerical implementation is difficult, and because we rarely need to compute all the elements of a response vector. A more efficient approach is to compute the frequency-response functions for the response coordinates of interest, using the equations given earlier in this chapter, and to base a solution on a frequency-domain analysis. We consider this approach in the next chapter.

Chapter 9

Application of response functions

Fourier transforms

If $x(t)$ is a function of an independent real variable t, which we shall usually take to mean time, the Fourier transform $X(i\omega)$ of $x(t)$ is defined as

$$X(i\omega) = \frac{1}{2\pi} \int_{-\infty}^{\infty} x(t)\, e^{-i\omega t}\, dt \qquad (9.1)$$

where ω is a second independent real variable with the dimensions of $1/t$. There is a corresponding inverse Fourier transform equation

$$x(t) = \int_{-\infty}^{\infty} X(i\omega)\, e^{i\omega t}\, d\omega \qquad (9.2)$$

which allows $x(t)$ to be regained if $X(i\omega)$ is known for all values of ω, positive and negative. If t denotes time, then ω denotes angular frequency in units of radians/time.

In the author's companion book, equations (9.1) and (9.2) are developed from an initial consideration of the Fourier series expansion of periodic functions, and the reader may find it helpful to refer to that description (Newland [64], Ch. 4). For the present purpose, we shall begin with (9.1) and (9.2) and treat the properties of Fourier series as a special case of Fourier transforms. This requires delta functions to be introduced into the theory; Dirac's delta function $\delta(t)$ was the first so-called 'generalized function' to be introduced, leading eventually to the generalized theory of Fourier analysis (see, for example, Lighthill [55]).

The nomenclature for the Fourier transform of a function varies and, instead of $X(i\omega)$, may be written as $X(\omega)$. In keeping with our earlier notation for the frequency-response function $H(i\omega)$, in this book we shall use $X(i\omega)$, but $X(\omega)$ is equally valid when it is understood that $X(\omega) \equiv X(i\omega)$ means a complex function of the real variable ω. When $x(t)$ is a real function of t, as it will be in practical vibration problems, the complex form of $X(i\omega)$ arises only from the $i\omega$ term in the exponential function $e^{-i\omega t}$ in (9.1).

The definition (9.1) may be made without the $1/2\pi$, in which case this factor appears in (9.2), or both (9.1) and (9.2) may have factors of $1/\sqrt{(2\pi)}$. Also, if ω is replaced by $f = \omega/2\pi$, the pair of equations (9.1) and (9.2) can be written as

$$X(if) = \int_{-\infty}^{\infty} x(t)\, e^{-i2\pi ft}\, dt \qquad (9.3)$$

and

$$x(t) = \int_{-\infty}^{\infty} X(if)\, e^{i2\pi ft}\, df \qquad (9.4)$$

because

$$d\omega = 2\pi\, df \qquad (9.5)$$

and so the factor 2π disappears.

For a formal proof that (9.1) and (9.2) are a transform pair, and for a discussion of the conditions for their convergence, the reader is referred to the mathematical literature on generalized Fourier analysis, for example Bracewell [12] and Papoulis [79]. The conditions for convergence are extremely general and appear to include all the functions with which we are concerned except for aperiodic functions $x(t)$ of infinite duration which occur in random vibration problems (Newland [64], Ch. 5). Obviously we can only use (9.1) and (9.2) when these integrals exist.

Delta functions

The delta function $\delta(t - t_0)$ is defined as a function which is zero everywhere except at $t = t_0$. Here it is infinite in such a way that, if $x(t)$ is a continuous function of t,

$$\int_{-\infty}^{\infty} \delta(t - t_0)\, x(t)\, dt = x(t = t_0). \qquad (9.6)$$

Because of (9.6), the area under the delta function must be unity and therefore, if t is the independent variable, the units of $\delta(t - t_0)$ are those of $1/t$. It is important to remember, when checking the physical dimensions of an equation, that a delta function does have such a dimension; otherwise the dimensions of the equation will not agree.

It is possible to differentiate $\delta(t - t_0)$ in the sense that a meaning can be attached to

$$\frac{d}{dt}\delta(t - t_0) = \delta'(t - t_0)$$

as follows. From (9.6)

$$\int_{-\infty}^{\infty} \delta(t - t_0)\, x'(t)\, dt = x'(t = t_0) \qquad (9.7)$$

where the r.h.s. of (9.7) means the value of

$$\frac{dx}{dt}$$

at $t = t_0$. The l.h.s. of (9.7) can be integrated by parts using

$$\int u \, dv = uv - \int v \, du \tag{9.8}$$

where

$$u = \delta(t - t_0), \quad dv = x'(t) \, dt \tag{9.9}$$

and so

$$du = \delta'(t - t_0) \, dt, \quad v = x(t). \tag{9.10}$$

On substituting from (9.9) and (9.10) into (9.7),

$$\int_{-\infty}^{\infty} \delta(t - t_0) \, x'(t) \, dt = [\delta(t - t_0) \, x(t)]_{-\infty}^{\infty} - \int_{-\infty}^{\infty} \delta'(t - t_0) \, x(t) \, dt$$

$$= - \int_{-\infty}^{\infty} \delta'(t - t_0) \, x(t) \, dt \tag{9.11}$$

since $\delta(t - t_0) \, x(t)$ is zero at $t = \pm\infty$. Combining (9.7) and (9.11), we see that the meaning of $\delta'(t - t_0)$ is given by

$$\int_{-\infty}^{\infty} \delta'(t - t_0) \, x(t) \, dt = - x'(t = t_0). \tag{9.12}$$

The Fourier transform of a function of t may be a delta function. Suppose that we put

$$X(i\omega) = \delta(\omega - \omega_0) \tag{9.13}$$

and calculate the corresponding $x(t)$ from the inverse Fourier transform equation (9.2). In this case there is no i on the r.h.s. of (9.13); we shall see why shortly.

From (9.2) we have

$$x(t) = \int_{-\infty}^{\infty} \delta(\omega - \omega_0) \, e^{i\omega t} \, d\omega \tag{9.14}$$

and, using (9.6),

$$x(t) = e^{i\omega_0 t}. \tag{9.15}$$

Now suppose that we try to calculate the Fourier transform of the $x(t)$ in (9.15), using (9.1). We get

$$X(i\omega) = \frac{1}{2\pi} \int_{-\infty}^{\infty} e^{-i(\omega - \omega_0)t} \, dt$$

$$= \frac{1}{2\pi} \left[\frac{e^{-i(\omega - \omega_0)t}}{- i(\omega - \omega_0)} \right]_{-\infty}^{\infty} \tag{9.16}$$

which we know from (9.13) must be a delta function at $\omega = \omega_0$. The behaviour of $X(i\omega)$ in (9.16) can be seen by writing this as

$$X(i\omega) \rightarrow \frac{1}{2\pi} \left[\frac{e^{-i(\omega - \omega_0)t}}{- i(\omega - \omega_0)} \right]_{-\tau}^{\tau} \quad \text{as } \tau \rightarrow \infty. \tag{9.17}$$

Hence

$$X(i\omega) \to \frac{1}{2\pi}\left[\frac{1}{-i(\omega - \omega_0)}\left(e^{-i(\omega-\omega_0)\tau} - e^{i(\omega-\omega_0)\tau}\right)\right] \quad (9.18)$$

$$= \frac{\sin(\omega - \omega_0)\tau}{\pi(\omega - \omega_0)} \quad \text{as } \tau \to \infty \quad (9.19)$$

whose shape is shown in Fig. 9.1. The adjacent cycles pack closer together and the peak at $\omega = \omega_0$ grows higher as $\tau \to \infty$. In the limit when $\tau \to \infty$, adjacent cycles cancel each other out, except for the spike at $\omega = \omega_0$, and $X(i\omega)$ does correctly become a delta function at $\omega = \omega_0$. Hence, from (9.13) and (9.16), we see that

$$\int_{-\infty}^{\infty} e^{-i(\omega-\omega_0)t}\,dt = 2\pi\,\delta(\omega - \omega_0). \quad (9.20)$$

Although no i appears with ω on the r.h.s. of (9.20), this is because of the special properties of delta functions. A delta function is not a function in the ordinary sense but the limiting case of a sequence of ordinary functions when different, increasing values of τ are chosen. $\delta(\omega - \omega_0)$ is therefore seen as the limiting case of a sequence of functions of $i\omega$, and in that sense is still a function of $i\omega$.

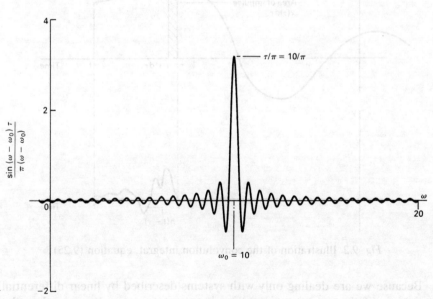

Fig. 9.1 Graph of

$$\frac{\sin(\omega - \omega_0)\tau}{\pi(\omega - \omega_0)}$$

against ω over the range $\omega = 0$ to 20 for the case when $\omega_0 = 10$ and $\tau = 10$

The convolution integral

For a passive linear system with constant parameters, with one input $x(t)$ and one output $y(t)$, Fig. 9.2, we have defined the impulse response of the system as its response $y(t) = h(t)$ when the input is a unit impulse at $t = 0$, so that $x(t) = \delta(t)$. If the impulse occurs at time τ instead of at $t = 0$, then the response begins at $t = \tau$ and is a function of the elapsed time after τ, so that it can be written as $h(t - \tau)$. In this case we have

$$h(t - \tau) = 0 \ \text{ for } t < \tau \tag{9.21}$$

because we assume that the system is passive (i.e. all its eigenvalues have negative real parts), and so the system has no response before the impulse occurs.

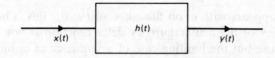

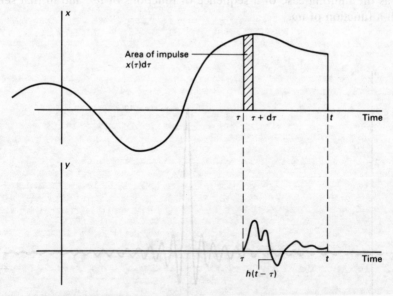

Fig. 9.2 Illustration of the convolution integral, equation (9.25)

Because we are dealing only with systems described by linear differential equations, if there are two impulsive inputs at $t = \tau_1$ and $t = \tau_2$, then the combined response for the two inputs is

$$y(t) = h(t - \tau_1) + h(t - \tau_2) \tag{9.22}$$

and if the impulses are no longer of unit magnitude but have magnitudes

$x(\tau_1)$ and $x(\tau_2)$, the corresponding response is

$$y(t) = x(\tau_1)\, h(t - \tau_1) + x(\tau_2)\, h(t - \tau_2). \qquad (9.23)$$

This result may be extended to the general case when there is a continuous input such as that illustrated in Fig. 9.2. If this is assumed to be broken down into a succession of infinitesimally small impulses, the summation (9.23) may be extended to the limit to become an integral.

Consider the response to the shaded strip of excitation of area $x(\tau)\, d\tau$ in Fig. 9.2. This may be thought of as an infinitesimal impulse represented by $x(\tau)\, d\tau\, \delta(t - \tau)$ and the response it generates at time t, $t > \tau$, is

$$x(t)\, d\tau\, h(t - \tau). \qquad (9.24)$$

Summing the response to all the similar strips of $x(\tau)$ to obtain the total response at time t, we find that

$$y(t) = \int_{-\infty}^{t} x(\tau)\, h(t - \tau)\, d\tau \qquad (9.25)$$

where the integration has to extend back in time to $-\infty$ to ensure that all the effects of past excitation have been included.

Equation (9.25) is called the convolution integral or, alternatively, Duhamel's integral or Green's integral, and is a complete solution for the response $y(t)$ in terms of the excitation $x(\tau)$, $\tau = -\infty$ to t, and the dynamic characteristics of the system represented by the impulse-response function $h(t)$.

There are three alternative versions of (9.25). The first alternative arises because of (9.21), which says that there is no response before the impulse has occurred. The integral in (9.25) may therefore be allowed to run forward in time, from $\tau = t$ to ∞, because $h(t - \tau)$ is zero for this range of values, and so alternative form 1 is

$$y(t) = \int_{-\infty}^{\infty} x(\tau)\, h(t - \tau)\, d\tau. \qquad (9.26)$$

Alternatives 2 and 3 are obtained by changing the variable of integration in (9.25) and (9.26) from τ to

$$\theta = t - \tau. \qquad (9.27)$$

In this case

$$d\theta = -d\tau \qquad (9.28)$$

since the time t at which the response is required is not a variable in the integral. The limits of θ which correspond to the limiting values of τ are obtained from (9.27), from which we see that

$\tau = -\infty$	gives $\theta = +\infty$	
$\tau = t$	gives $\theta = 0$	(9.29)
$\tau = +\infty$	gives $\theta = -\infty$.	

Hence (9.25) becomes

$$y(t) = \int_0^\infty x(t - \theta)\, h(\theta)\, d\theta \qquad (9.30)$$

and (9.26) becomes

$$y(t) = \int_{-\infty}^\infty x(t - \theta)\, h(\theta)\, d\theta. \qquad (9.31)$$

Unit step and unit pulse responses

When the system in Fig. 9.2 is subjected to a unit step input at $t = \tau$, see Fig. 9.3, we have $x(t) = 0$ for $t < \tau$ and $x(t) = 1$ for $t > \tau$. Therefore the response to this input is given, from (9.25), by

$$y(t) = \int_\tau^t h(t - \phi)\, d\phi, \; t > \tau \qquad (9.32)$$

where now ϕ replaces τ as the variable of integration in (9.25) to avoid confusion with the time that the step input is applied. We denote the unit step response by the function $r(t)$ so that, for a step at $t = \tau$,

$$r(t - \tau) = \int_\tau^t h(t - \phi)\, d\phi, \; t > \tau \qquad (9.33)$$

since the response $r(t - \tau)$ is a function only of the time $(t - \tau)$ that has elapsed after the step has been applied.

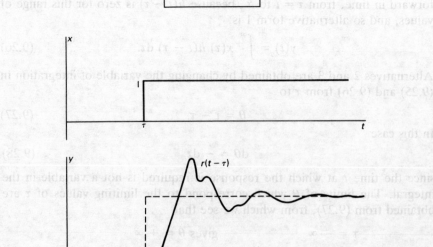

Fig. 9.3 Definition of the unit step response function, $r(t)$

When the step is applied at $\tau = 0$, from (9.33)

$$r(t) = \int_0^t h(t - \phi) \, d\phi, \ t > 0. \tag{9.34}$$

On changing the variable of integration to

$$\theta = t - \phi, \ \text{so that} \ d\theta = -d\phi \tag{9.35}$$

we find that

$$r(t) = \int_t^0 h(\theta)(-d\theta) = \int_0^t h(\theta) \, d\theta, \ t > 0 \tag{9.36}$$

and hence

$$\frac{dr(t)}{dt} = h(t), \ t > 0. \tag{9.37}$$

Example 9.1 Step response of the torsional system in Fig. 8.2

For the torsional system in Example 8.1 and Fig. 8.2, use the result of Example 8.3 to determine the shaft torque response as a result of a unit step torque applied to wheel 1 at time $t = 0$.

From equation (9.36), with the result for $h(\theta)$ from (8.117), we have

$$\underset{t>0}{r(t)/k} = \int_0^t 0.0083 \, e^{-10\theta} \, d\theta \ -$$

$$- \frac{1}{3} \int_0^t (A \, e^{-(2.5-i11.99)\theta} + B \, e^{-(2.5+i11.99)\theta}) \, d\theta$$

$$\tag{9.38}$$

where

$$A = 0.0125 + i \, 0.0495 \tag{9.39}$$
$$B = 0.0125 - i \, 0.0495.$$

Evaluating the integrals

$$\int_0^t e^{-10\theta} \, d\theta = (1 - e^{-10t})$$

$$\int_0^t e^{-(2.5-i \, 11.99)\theta} \, d\theta = \frac{1}{2.5 + i \, 11.99} [1 - e^{-(2.5-i11.99)t}] \tag{9.40}$$

$$\int_0^t e^{-(2.5+i \, 11.99)\theta} \, d\theta = \frac{1}{2.5 + i \, 11.99} [1 - e^{-(2.5+i11.99)t}].$$

On working out the arithmetic and putting $k = 200 \, \text{N m/rad}$, we find that

$$\underset{t>0}{r(t)} = 0.666 - 0.166 \, e^{-10t} - e^{-2.5t} \, (0.5 \cos 11.99t + 0.243 \sin 11.99t)$$

$$\tag{9.41}$$

with the units of $r(t)$ being N m when the step input torque applied to wheel 1 (see Fig. 8.2) is 1 N m. Notice that, at $t = 0$, the torque is zero because, instantaneously, there is angular acceleration of wheel 1 but no angular deflection of the connecting shaft. When $t \to \infty$, the torque $r(t \to \infty)$ is 0.666 N m. The total inertia of the three wheels is 9 kg m^2 so that all the wheels have a steady angular acceleration of $1/9$ rad/s^2 at $t \to \infty$. The torque transmitted through the shaft to wheels 2 and 3, whose combined moment of inertia is 6 kg m^2, is therefore $6/9 = 0.666$ N m.

Graphs of the impulse-response function $h(t)$ and step-response function $r(t)$ for this example are drawn in Fig. 9.4.

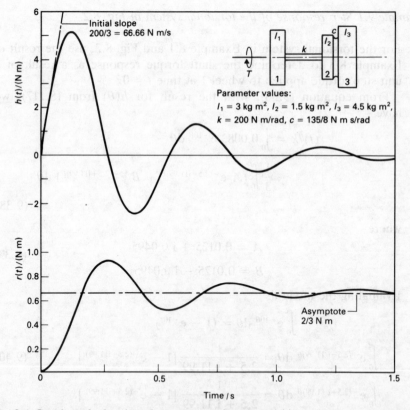

Fig. 9.4 Graphs of the impulse-response function $h(t)$ and the step-response function $r(t)$ for the torsional system shown when the input is a torque applied to wheel 1 and the output is the torque in the shaft connecting wheels 1 and 2. The magnitude of the impulse torque is 1 N m s, and the magnitude of the step torque is 1 N m. Note the different vertical scales to which the two responses are plotted

Now consider the response of a single input/single output passive, linear, time-invariant system when subjected to an input pulse of unit height lasting for time duration Δ, Fig. 9.5. From equation (9.36), the response to a unit step at $t = \tau$ can be written as

$$r(t - \tau) = \int_0^{t-\tau} h(\theta) \, d\theta, \quad t > \tau \tag{9.42}$$

and the response to a negative step at $t = \tau + \Delta$ is

$$- r(t - \tau - \Delta) = - \int_0^{t-\tau-\Delta} h(\theta) \, d\theta, \quad t > \tau + \Delta. \tag{9.43}$$

Hence, for $t > \tau + \Delta$, the response to the unit pulse is

$$r(t - \tau) - r(t - \tau - \Delta) = \int_0^{t-\tau} h(\theta) \, d\theta - \int_0^{t-\tau-\Delta} h(\theta) \, d\theta. \tag{9.44}$$

We call this response $p(t - \tau - \Delta)$ and, combining the two integrals on the r.h.s. of (9.44), we get

$$p(t - \tau - \Delta) = \int_{t-\tau-\Delta}^{t-\tau} h(\theta) \, d\theta, \quad t > \tau + \Delta. \tag{9.45}$$

This result may also be obtained directly from either (9.30) or (9.31), Problem 9.4, and is required in Chapter 10 when the approximate computation of the convolution integral is considered.

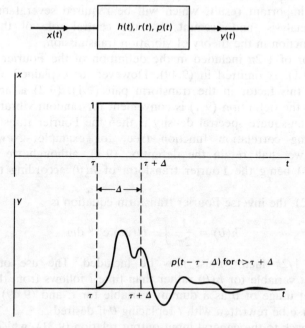

Fig. 9.5 Definition of the unit pulse response function for a pulse of duration Δ

Time-domain to frequency-domain transformations

When the input and output of a passive linear system are related by a frequency-response function $H(i\omega)$, then if the input is

$$x(t) = e^{i\omega t} \tag{9.46}$$

we know, by the definition of $H(i\omega)$, that the corresponding output is

$$y(t) = H(i\omega) \, e^{i\omega t}. \tag{9.47}$$

Consider solving the same problem by the convolution integral in its form (9.31). On substituting the input (9.46), this gives

$$y(t) = \int_{-\infty}^{\infty} e^{i\omega(t-\theta)} \, h(\theta) \, d\theta$$

$$= e^{i\omega t} \int_{-\infty}^{\infty} e^{-i\omega\theta} \, h(\theta) \, d\theta \tag{9.48}$$

since the $e^{i\omega t}$ can be brought outside the integral because it is independent of the variable of integration θ. By comparing (9.47) and (9.48), we see that

$$H(i\omega) = \int_{-\infty}^{\infty} e^{-i\omega\theta} \, h(\theta) \, d\theta \tag{9.49}$$

so that the frequency-response function $H(i\omega)$ is the Fourier transform of the impulse-response function $h(\theta)$ (except for the factor $1/2\pi$ in (9.1)). This is an important result, which will be required several times in the following analysis, and accounts for the central role of the impulse-response function in the theory of vibration transmission.

The factor of $1/2\pi$ included in the definition of the Fourier transform, equation (9.1), is omitted in (9.49). However, as explained already, the position of this factor in the transform pair (9.1), (9.2) is arbitrary. Its inclusion in the definition (9.1) is convenient for random vibration theory, because mean-square spectral density is then the Fourier transform of the corresponding correlation function (see, for example, Newland [64], Ch. 5), so we shall retain the definition (9.1), although we also speak about $H(i\omega)$ being the Fourier transform of $h(\theta)$ according to equation (9.49).

From (9.2), the inverse Fourier transform equation is

$$h(\theta) = \frac{1}{2\pi} \int_{-\infty}^{\infty} H(i\omega) \, e^{i\omega\theta} \, d\omega \tag{9.50}$$

where the $1/2\pi$ factor must now be included. The use of θ as the independent variable for $h(\theta)$ rather than time t follows from the convolution integral usage of θ as a dummy variable for t, and (9.49) and (9.50) may of course be rewritten with t replacing θ if desired.

Now go back to the general input-output relation (9.31), which is

$$y(t) = \int_{-\infty}^{\infty} x(t - \theta) \, h(\theta) \, d\theta. \tag{9.51}$$

Since we are considering only passive systems, the output $y(t)$ cannot be infinite and so this integral must converge to a limit. Consider taking Fourier transforms of both sides of (9.51). Let $Y(i\omega)$ be the Fourier transform of $y(t)$, defined by

$$Y(i\omega) = \frac{1}{2\pi} \int_{-\infty}^{\infty} y(t)\, e^{-i\omega t}\, dt. \tag{9.52}$$

We shall assume that $Y(i\omega)$ exists, either as an ordinary function or as a delta function or a series of delta functions. Then from (9.51)

$$Y(i\omega) = \frac{1}{2\pi} \int_{-\infty}^{\infty} dt\, e^{-i\omega t} \int_{-\infty}^{\infty} d\theta\, x(t - \theta)\, h(\theta)$$

$$= \frac{1}{2\pi} \int_{-\infty}^{\infty} dt \int_{-\infty}^{\infty} d\theta\, e^{-i\omega t}\, x(t - \theta)\, h(\theta) \tag{9.53}$$

since the second integral is with respect to θ, with t constant, so that $e^{-i\omega t}$ is not a function of this variable of integration. On introducing the unit factor $e^{i\omega\theta}\, e^{-i\omega\theta}$ we find that

$$Y(i\omega) = \frac{1}{2\pi} \int_{-\infty}^{\infty} dt \int_{-\infty}^{\infty} d\theta\, e^{-i\omega t(t-\theta)}\, e^{-i\omega\theta}\, x(t - \theta)\, h(\theta). \tag{9.54}$$

The integration with respect to t is with θ constant, so that changing the variable from t to

$$\phi = t - \theta \tag{9.55}$$

we have

$$d\phi = dt \tag{9.56}$$

for the first integral, and so

$$Y(i\omega) = \frac{1}{2\pi} \int_{-\infty}^{\infty} d\phi \int_{-\infty}^{\infty} d\theta\, e^{-i\omega\phi}\, e^{-i\omega\theta}\, x(\phi)\, h(\theta)$$

$$= \frac{1}{2\pi} \int_{-\infty}^{\infty} d\phi\, e^{-i\omega\phi}\, x(\phi) \int_{-\infty}^{\infty} d\theta\, e^{-i\omega\theta}\, h(\theta). \tag{9.57}$$

Now, if we define $X(i\omega)$ as the Fourier transform of $x(t)$ so that

$$X(i\omega) = \frac{1}{2\pi} \int_{-\infty}^{\infty} x(t)\, e^{-i\omega t}\, dt \tag{9.58}$$

then, with (9.49) and (9.58), equation (9.57) gives the very important result that

$$Y(i\omega) = X(i\omega)\, H(i\omega). \tag{9.59}$$

The Fourier transform of the output, $Y(i\omega)$, is the Fourier transform of the input, $X(i\omega)$, multiplied by the frequency-response function which relates the input and output concerned, $H(i\omega)$.

In order to obtain the time history of the response, $y(t)$, after calculating $Y(i\omega)$ from (9.59), we can calculate the inverse Fourier transform

$$y(t) = \int_{-\infty}^{\infty} Y(i\omega) \, e^{i\omega t} \, d\omega. \tag{9.60}$$

An additional method of finding the time response of a linear, time-invariant system is therefore (i) to calculate the Fourier transform of the input, using (9.58), (ii) to calculate the frequency-domain response $Y(i\omega)$ from (9.59), and then (iii) to make the inverse transformation to find $y(t)$ by using (9.60). This method is often a convenient practical method of computing the vibration response for a linear system.

From the general result (9.59), we see that the response $Y(i\omega)$ in the frequency domain is obtained by multiplying together $H(i\omega)$ and $X(i\omega)$, whereas from (9.31), the response $y(t)$ in the time domain is obtained by convolving $h(t)$ and $x(t)$. Multiplication in the frequency domain is therefore equivalent to convolution in the time domain, and vice versa.

General input-output relations

In Chapter 8 we analysed the response of a passive system defined by M coupled second-order linear differential equations with constant coefficients. There were assumed to be M degrees of freedom, and associated with each degree of freedom was one input (a force or its equivalent) and one output (a displacement or its equivalent). Therefore, we had M inputs and M outputs, and the $M \times M$ response matrices were, for the usual case of $2M$ independent eigenvectors, equation (8.32),

$$H(i\omega) = U_{\text{upper}} \left[\text{diag} \, \frac{1}{i\omega - \lambda_j} \right] U_{\text{right}}^{-1} \, m^{-1} \tag{9.61}$$

and, equation (8.110),

$$h(t) = U_{\text{upper}} \left[\text{diag} \, \lambda_j t \right] U_{\text{right}}^{-1} m^{-1}, \, t > 0. \tag{9.62}$$

Row j of $H(i\omega)$ and of $h(t)$ gives the response functions for output j as a result of excitation at each of the M inputs. Usually, only some of the inputs will be excited because only some of the M mass elements have forces applied to them. Also, we may be interested in only some of the M outputs. Suppose that we are concerned with m outputs as a result of n inputs. Then the response-function matrices of interest will have order $m \times n$ and can be obtained by deleting $(M - m)$ rows and $(M - n)$ columns of the parent matrices $H(i\omega)$ and $h(t)$. In (9.61) and (9.62) this is achieved by deleting the corresponding $(M - m)$ rows of U_{upper} and the corresponding $(M - n)$ columns of $U_{\text{right}}^{-1} m^{-1}$.

Consider the general multiple-input multiple-output system in Fig. 9.6, with n inputs and m outputs. Let $x_s(t)$ be a general input and $y_r(t)$ a general output, and let their Fourier transforms be $X_s(i\omega)$ and $Y_r(i\omega)$. Then the output at r due to input s alone is, from (9.59)

$$Y_r(i\omega) = H_{rs}(i\omega) \, X_s(i\omega) \tag{9.63}$$

and, from (9.31),

$$y_r(t) = \int_{-\infty}^{\infty} h_{rs}(\theta)\, x_s(t - \theta)\, d\theta \tag{9.64}$$

where, from (9.49) and (9.50),

$$H_{rs}(i\omega) = \int_{-\infty}^{\infty} e^{-i\omega\theta}\, h_{rs}(\theta)\, d\theta \tag{9.65}$$

$$h_{rs}(\theta) = \frac{1}{2\pi} \int_{-\infty}^{\infty} e^{i\omega\theta}\, H_{rs}(i\omega)\, d\omega. \tag{9.66}$$

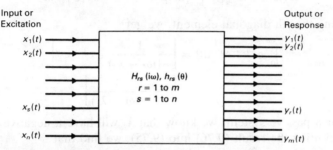

Fig. 9.6 Multiple-input, multiple-output linear system (which is assumed to be time-invariant and passive)

Hence, if

$$X(i\omega) = [X_1(i\omega),\, X_2(i\omega),\, \ldots,\, X_n(i\omega)]^T \tag{9.67}$$

and

$$Y(i\omega) = [Y_1(i\omega),\, Y_2(i\omega),\, \ldots,\, Y_m(i\omega)]^T, \tag{9.68}$$

from (9.63) we have

$$Y(i\omega) = H(i\omega)\, X(i\omega) \tag{9.69}$$

and if

$$x(t) = [x_1(t),\, x_2(t),\, \ldots,\, x_n(t)]^T \tag{9.70}$$

and

$$y(t) = [y_1(t),\, y_2(t),\, \ldots,\, y_m(t)]^T, \tag{9.71}$$

from (9.64) we have

$$y(t) = \int_{-\infty}^{\infty} h(\theta)\, x(t - \theta)\, d\theta. \tag{9.72}$$

In (9.69) and (9.72), $H(i\omega)$ and $h(\theta)$ have dimensions $m \times n$ and are derived from the parent $M \times M$ matrices as described above.

On account of (9.65), we can write

$$H(i\omega) = \int_{-\infty}^{\infty} e^{-i\omega\theta}\, h(\theta)\, d\theta \tag{9.73}$$

and this Fourier transform relationship must apply for the parent matrices defined by (9.61) and (9.62). On substituting for $h(\theta)$ from (9.62) into (9.73), we find that

$$H(i\omega) = \int_0^\infty e^{-i\omega\theta} \, U_{\text{upper}} \, [\text{diag } e^{\lambda_j\theta}] \, U_{\text{right}}^{-1} m^{-1} \, d\theta \qquad (9.74)$$

with the lower limit of integration being changed to zero, since $h(t) = O$ for $t < 0$. Hence

$$H(i\omega) = U_{\text{upper}} \int_0^\infty [\text{diag } e^{-(i\omega-\lambda_j)\theta}] \, d\theta \, U_{\text{right}}^{-1} m^{-1}. \qquad (9.75)$$

Integrating the jth diagonal element, we get

$$\int_0^\infty e^{-(i\omega-\lambda_j)\theta} \, d\theta = \left[\frac{1}{-(i\omega - \lambda_j)} e^{-(i\omega-\lambda_j)\theta} \right]_0^\infty$$

$$= \left[0 + \frac{1}{(i\omega - \lambda_j)} \right] \qquad (9.76)$$

since, for a passive system, we know that λ_j will have a negative real part. On substituting the result (9.76) into (9.75), we find that

$$H(i\omega) = U_{\text{upper}} \left[\text{diag } \frac{1}{(i\omega - \lambda_j)} \right] U_{\text{right}}^{-1} m^{-1} \qquad (9.77)$$

in agreement with (9.61). Therefore we have confirmed that the general results (9.61) and (9.62) are a Fourier transform pair, as they must be.

Case of periodic excitation

Since Fourier series can be regarded as a special case of Fourier transforms, the general input-output result (9.69) for Fourier transforms

$$Y(i\omega) = H(i\omega) \, X(i\omega) \qquad (9.69)$$

must apply equally when the input vector $x(t)$ is composed of periodic functions.

Suppose that all the elements of $x(t)$ have period T so that a typical element $x(t)$ has a Fourier series expansion

$$x(t) = \sum_{k=-\infty}^{\infty} X_k \, e^{i2\pi kt/T} \qquad (9.78)$$

where the Fourier coefficients X_k are given by

$$X_k = \frac{1}{T} \int_0^T x(t) \, e^{-i2\pi kt/T} \, dt. \qquad (9.79)$$

This is the complex form of the usual Fourier series formulae (see, for example, Newland [64], Chapter 4 and Chapter 15). The Fourier transform of the $x(t)$ in (9.78) is, from (9.1),

$$X(\mathrm{i}\omega) = \frac{1}{2\pi} \int_{-\infty}^{\infty} x(t)\, \mathrm{e}^{-\mathrm{i}\omega t}\, \mathrm{d}t$$

$$= \frac{1}{2\pi} \int_{-\infty}^{\infty} \sum_{k=-\infty}^{\infty} X_k\, \mathrm{e}^{\mathrm{i}2\pi kt/T}\, \mathrm{e}^{-\mathrm{i}\omega t}\, \mathrm{d}t$$

$$= \sum_{k=-\infty}^{\infty} \frac{1}{2\pi} X_k \int_{-\infty}^{\infty} \mathrm{e}^{-\mathrm{i}(\omega - 2\pi k/T)t}\, \mathrm{d}t \qquad (9.80)$$

and, using (9.20), this gives

$$X(\mathrm{i}\omega) = \sum_{k=-\infty}^{\infty} X_k\, \delta(\omega - 2\pi k/T). \qquad (9.81)$$

When $x(t)$ is a vector, (9.78) becomes

$$x(t) = \sum_{k=-\infty}^{\infty} X_k\, \mathrm{e}^{\mathrm{i}2\pi kt/T} \qquad (9.82)$$

and its Fourier transform is, from (9.81),

$$X(\mathrm{i}\omega) = \sum_{k=-\infty}^{\infty} X_k\, \delta(\omega - 2\pi k/T). \qquad (9.83)$$

The Fourier transform of the corresponding output vector is, from (9.69),

$$Y(\mathrm{i}\omega) = \sum_{k=-\infty}^{\infty} H(\mathrm{i}\omega)\, X_k \delta(\omega - 2\pi k/T) \qquad (9.84)$$

where the summation over k covers all the harmonics $2\pi k/T$ of the fundamental frequency $2\pi/T$. If we now express $Y(\mathrm{i}\omega)$ in terms of these harmonics by putting

$$Y(\mathrm{i}\omega) = \sum_{k=-\infty}^{\infty} Y_k\, \delta(\omega - 2\pi k/T) \qquad (9.85)$$

so that

$$\sum_{k=-\infty}^{\infty} Y_k\, \delta(\omega - 2\pi k/T) = \sum_{k=-\infty}^{\infty} H(\mathrm{i}\omega)\, X_k\, \delta(\omega - 2\pi k/T) \qquad (9.86)$$

and then integrate over frequency from $\omega = -\infty$ to $+\infty$, we get

$$\sum_{k=-\infty}^{\infty} Y_k = \sum_{k=-\infty}^{\infty} H(\mathrm{i}\, 2\pi k/T)\, X_k. \qquad (9.87)$$

Since this is true whatever the X_k, it must be true for each term in the summation separately. For the kth harmonic we have, from (9.87),

$$Y_k = H(\mathrm{i}\, 2\pi k/T)\, X_k \qquad (9.88)$$

and

$$Y_{-k} = H(-\mathrm{i}\, 2\pi k/T)\, X_{-k} \qquad (9.89)$$

where, from (9.79),

$$X_{-k} = X_k^* \tag{9.90}$$

and so, from (9.88) and (9.89),

$$Y_{-k} = Y_k^*. \tag{9.91}$$

In interpreting (9.88) and (9.89), we recall from (9.82) that the kth harmonic is represented by

$$x(t) = X_{-k}\, e^{-i2\pi kt/T} + X_k\, e^{i2\pi kt/T}$$
$$= 2\,\mathrm{Re}\{X_k\, e^{i2\pi kt/T}\} \tag{9.92}$$

on account of (9.90).

Equations (9.88) and (9.89) together give the input-output relationship for periodic functions, which is the equivalent of the general Fourier transform input-output relationship (9.69). In the next section we show an example of the application of this result to a typical problem.

Example calculation for the torsional vibration of a diesel engine

To illustrate a typical response calculation for multiple-input periodic excitation, we shall consider the torsional vibration of a diesel engine assembly. The engine is assumed to be driving a flywheel so that it may be represented by the torsional system shown in Fig. 9.7.

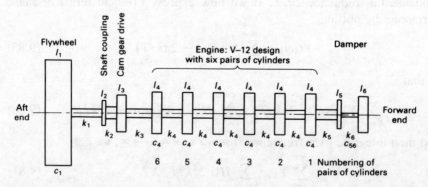

Fig. 9.7 Torsional system representing a V-12 design diesel engine which has a vibration damper at one end (wheels 5 and 6) and a flywheel at the other end (wheel 1). The system drives a ship's propeller via a fluid coupling connected to the flywheel. These parts (which are not shown) are assumed to be disconnected for the analysis in this example. Coordinates $y_1(t)$ to $y_{11}(t)$ (also not shown) give the angular displacement from static equilibrium of each wheel from an arbitrary fixed datum, with the wheels being numbered successively from the aft end. Note that damping with constants c_1 and c_4 is assumed to act between the wheels and ground, and that damping c_{56} acts between wheels 5 and 6

The engine has 12 cylinders arranged in two banks of six at 45° to each other. In the torsional model, the inertia at each pair of cylinders is represented by a rigid wheel of moment of inertia I_4. This wheel is assumed to experience a damping torque proportional to its absolute angular velocity, the coefficient of damping being c_4. The engine's flywheel has moment of inertia I_1 and damping coefficient c_1. Two wheels I_2 and I_3 represent the shaft coupling and the camshaft gear drive at the aft end of the crankshaft and have no damping. The torsional vibration damper is represented by two wheels I_5 and I_6 at the forward end of the crankshaft; these are connected by a weak torsional spring k_6 but by strong viscous coupling with coefficient c_{56}. There is assumed to be no damping to ground at I_5 and I_6, and the damping torque from c_{56} is proportional to the relative angular velocity between I_5 and I_6. The connecting shafts are all assumed to be massless.

The following numerical data, which is for a published case (Bishop, *et al.* [8]), will be used.

Moments of inertia ($\text{kg}\,\text{m}^2$):

$I_1 = 1293,\ I_2 = 26,\ I_3 = 91,\ I_4 = 95,\ I_5 = 18,\ I_6 = 64.$

Viscous damping coefficients ($\text{N}\,\text{m}\,\text{s}/\text{rad}$):

$$c_1 = 1480,\ c_4 = 778,\ c_{56} = 9355. \tag{9.93}$$

Stiffnesses ($\text{N}\,\text{m}/\text{rad}$):

$k_1 = 48 \times 10^6,\ k_2 = 222 \times 10^6,\ k_3 = 98 \times 10^6,\ k_4 = 77 \times 10^6,$

$k_5 = 101 \times 10^6,\ k_6 = 1.55 \times 10^6.$

When the engine is running due to the variation of gas pressure and the inertia of the reciprocating parts, the torque applied to the crankshaft at each pair of cylinders is irregular and is a source of torsional vibration for the whole system, (see, for example, Den Hartog [18], Chapter 5). For a four-stroke (or four-cycle) engine, which is assumed to be the case in this example, the torque goes through one period every two revolutions of the crankshaft. The fundamental component of torque is therefore called the half-order excitation, the second harmonic is the first-order excitation, and so on. In general, at each pair of cylinders, the crankshaft will experience a range of harmonic torques of the form

$$\text{Re}\{T_n\,e^{in\Omega t}\} \tag{9.94}$$

where Ω is the engine's speed (rad/s),

$$n = \tfrac{1}{2}, 1, \tfrac{3}{2}, 2, \tfrac{5}{2}, \ldots$$

is the order of the excitation, and T_n is the (complex) amplitude of the nth-order torque.

In this example we shall not be concerned with data on the magnitude of the coefficients T_n or on the relative phasing of the harmonics at each cylinder, as the following calculation will be concerned only with the harmonic response of the engine assembly to excitation of one order at a time. However, it is necessary to understand that the torque generated at each cylinder has a large peak which lasts for only a fraction of an engine revolution. Therefore harmonics of high order are significant and it may be necessary to take account of excitation torques of order up to, for example, 12 (the 24th harmonic for a four-stroke engine). Also, there will be several torsional critical speeds which can be excited by the higher-order harmonics. Therefore the torsional vibration model must allow at least for all the torsional modes whose natural frequencies lie within the range of the 12th order excitation (say) to be calculated with precision. The engine's speed range is 0 to 500 rev/min and therefore the frequency range of the excitation is 0 to 6000 rev/min = 0 to 100 Hz = 0 to 200π rad/s.

The firing order of the cylinders in both banks of the V-formation is 1, 3, 5, 6, 4, 2, where the cylinders are numbered from the forward end of the engine, see Fig. 9.7. The crank angles are at 120° to each other, so that

$$120° = \tfrac{2}{3}\pi \text{ rad}$$

of crankshaft rotation occurs between successive firings in one bank. The two number 1 cylinders fire 45° of crank angle rotation apart, and similarly for the other pairs of corresponding cylinders. The nth-order torques generated by the engine will therefore be taken to be as in the following table when measured from an arbitrary datum for $t = 0$.

Number of cylinder pair	nth-order torque: real part of
1	$T_n \, e^{in\Omega t}$
3	$T_n \, e^{in(\Omega t - 2\pi/3)}$
5	$T_n \, e^{in(\Omega t - 4\pi/3)}$
6	$T_n \, e^{in(\Omega t - 2\pi)}$
4	$T_n \, e^{in(\Omega t - 8\pi/3)}$
2	$T_n \, e^{in(\Omega t - 10\pi/3)}$

$$(9.95)$$

We shall see that the relative phasing of the exciting torques at each pair of cylinders has a big effect on the amplitude of steady-state forced vibration.

The torsional model in Fig. 9.7 has 11 wheels. The angular displacement of each wheel from static equilibrium is given by one of the coordinates $y_1(t)$ to $y_{11}(t)$, with the wheels being numbered successively from the flywheel at the aft end. Since the system is coupled to ground by viscous restraints, we cannot eliminate a degree of freedom (for rigid-body rotation of the whole assembly) and therefore the problem has 11 degrees of freedom. We shall derive the 11×11 mass, damping and stiffness matrices shortly, but consider first the 11×1 force vector $x(t)$ in equation (8.1). Wheels 1, 2, 3, 10 and 11 have no externally applied torques, while wheels 4, 5, 6, 7, 8 and 9 have the engine torques (9.95) applied to them, with the phasing of these torques being determined by the firing order. The result is that the force vector is

$$x(t) = \text{Re}\{T_n \, e^{in\Omega t}[0, 0, 0, e^{-in2\pi}, e^{-in4\pi/3}, e^{-in8\pi/3}, e^{-in2\pi/3}, e^{-in10\pi/3}, 1, 0, 0]^\text{T}\}$$

(9.96)

We shall solve the problem by applying the general results (9.88) and (9.89) for periodic excitation. We do not need to apply both these equations since, as we have seen, the second yields the complex conjugate of the result of the first. For the order of excitation n at frequency $n\Omega$, (9.88) gives

$$Y_n = H(i \, n\Omega) \, X_n$$

(9.97)

where, from (9.96),

$$X_n = T_n[0, 0, 0, e^{-in2\pi}, e^{-in4\pi/3}, e^{-in8\pi/3}, e^{-in2\pi/3}, e^{-in10\pi/3}, 1, 0, 0]^\text{T}.$$

(9.98)

We ignore the factor 2 in (9.92) because, in this example, we shall work only with positive frequencies, and thus consider X_n to represent all the excitation, rather than sharing the excitation between X_n and its complex conjugate X_{-n}.

Suppose that we want to calculate the torque $T(t)$ in the shaft which connects the engine to its flywheel, which is the shaft between wheels I_1 and I_2 in Fig. 9.7. The stiffness of this shaft is k_1 and so, in terms of the angular displacements $y_1(t)$ and $y_2(t)$ of wheels 1 and 2,

$$T(t) = k_1[y_1(t) - y_2(t)]$$

(9.99)

and, taking Fourier transforms,

$$T(i\omega) = k_1[Y_1(i\omega) - Y_2(i\omega)]$$

(9.100)

where $T(i\omega)$ is understood to mean the Fourier transform of $T(t)$. For periodic excitation of nth order we have, for positive frequencies only,

$$Y_1(i\omega) = Y_{1n} \, \delta(\omega - n\Omega)$$

$$Y_2(i\omega) = Y_{2n} \, \delta(\omega - n\Omega)$$

$$T(i\omega) = T_n \, \delta(\omega - n\Omega).$$

(9.101)

Substituting for $Y_1(i\omega)$, $Y_2(i\omega)$ and $T(i\omega)$ in (9.100) from (9.101) and integrating over ω then gives

$$T_n = k_1[Y_{1n} - Y_{2n}]$$

(9.102)

where Y_{1n}, Y_{2n} and T_n are the complex amplitudes of the nth-order displacements and torque.

Y_{1n} is the first element and Y_{2n} the second element of Y_n in (9.97), so that if $H^{(1)}(in\Omega)$ denotes the first row and $H^{(2)}(in\Omega)$ the second row of $H(in\Omega)$, then

$$Y_{1n} = H^{(1)}(in\Omega) \, X_n$$
$$Y_{2n} = H^{(2)}(in\Omega) \, X_n \tag{9.103}$$

with which (9.102) gives

$$T_n = k_1[H^{(1)}(in\Omega) - H^{(2)}(in\Omega)] \, X_n \tag{9.104}$$

This expresses the complex amplitude of the shaft torque of order n, T_n, in terms of the shaft stiffness, k_1, the first and second rows of the frequency-response function matrix $H(i\omega)$ evaluated at $\omega = n\Omega$, and the complex amplitudes of the excitation vector X_n, which are given by (9.98).

Since, from (9.98), elements 1, 2, 3, 10, 11 of X_n are zero, columns 1, 2, 3, 10, 11, of $H^{(1)}(in\Omega)$ and $H^{(2)}(in\Omega)$ can be deflated (i.e. removed) and rows 1, 2, 3, 11 of X_n can be deflated, and we only need to compute

$$H_{1k}(in\Omega) \text{ and } H_{2k}(in\Omega), \; k = 4 \text{ to } 9 \tag{9.105}$$

which, from Chapter 8, equation (8.39), can be done by using the general summations

$$H_{rs}(i\omega) = \sum_{j=1}^{22} u_{rj} \frac{1}{(i\omega - \lambda_j)} s_{js} \tag{9.106}$$

where λ_j, $j = 1$ to 22, are the eigenvalues, u_{rj} are elements of the 22×22 eigenvector matrix U, and s_{js} are defined by (8.38) in terms of the elements, v_{jk} of U_{right}^{-1} and a_{ks} of the inverse mass matrix, m^{-1}.

The method of computation is therefore to calculate the frequency-response functions in (9.105) at frequency $\omega = n\Omega$ by using (9.106) and then to compute T_n from (9.104). To do the former, we need the eigenvalues and eigenvectors of the problem, and these have to be computed as in Chapter 5. To obtain the equations of motion, consider the rotational equilibrium of each wheel to find that

$$I_1\ddot{y}_1 = k_1(y_2 - y_1) - c\dot{y}_1$$
$$I_2\ddot{y}_2 = k_2(y_3 - y_2) + k_1(y_1 - y_2)$$
$$I_3\ddot{y}_3 = k_3(y_4 - y_3) + k_2(y_2 - y_3)$$
$$I_4\ddot{y}_4 = k_4(y_5 - y_4) + k_3(y_3 - y_4) - c_4\dot{y}_4 + T_n \, e^{in(\Omega t - 2\pi)}$$
$$I_4\ddot{y}_5 = k_4(y_6 - y_5) + k_4(y_4 - y_5) - c_4\dot{y}_5 + T_n \, e^{in(\Omega t - 4\pi/3)}$$
$$I_4\ddot{y}_6 = k_4(y_7 - y_6) + k_4(y_5 - y_6) - c_4\dot{y}_6 + T_n \, e^{in(\Omega t - 8\pi/3)} \tag{9.107}$$

$$I_4\ddot{y}_7 = k_4(y_8 - y_7) + k_4(y_6 - y_7) - c_4\dot{y}_7 + T_n\, e^{in(\Omega t - 2\pi/3)}$$

$$I_4\ddot{y}_8 = k_4(y_9 - y_8) + k_4(y_7 - y_8) - c_4\dot{y}_8 + T_n\, e^{in(\Omega t - 10\pi/3)}$$

$$I_4\ddot{y}_9 = k_5(y_{10} - y_9) + k_4(y_8 - y_9) - c_4\dot{y}_9 + T_n\, e^{in\Omega t}$$

$$I_5\ddot{y}_{10} = k_6(y_{11} - y_{10}) + k_5(y_9 - y_{10}) - c_{56}(\dot{y}_{11} - \dot{y}_{10})$$

$$I_6\ddot{y}_{11} = k_6(y_{10} - y_{11}) + c_{56}(\dot{y}_{10} - \dot{y}_{11}).$$

Hence the mass matrix is the diagonal matrix:

$$m = \begin{bmatrix} I_1 \\ & I_2 \\ & & I_3 \\ & & & I_4 \\ & & & & I_4 \\ & & & & & I_4 \\ & & & & & & I_4 \\ & & & & & & & I_4 \\ & & & & & & & & I_4 \\ & & & & & & & & & I_5 \\ & & & & & & & & & & I_6 \end{bmatrix},$$

$$\text{(9.108)}$$

the damping matrix is diagonal except for a 2×2 sub-matrix in the bottom right-hand corner:

$$c = \begin{bmatrix} c_1 \\ & 0 \\ & & 0 \\ & & & c_4 \\ & & & & c_4 \\ & & & & & c_4 \\ & & & & & & c_4 \\ & & & & & & & c_4 \\ & & & & & & & & c_4 \\ & & & & & & & & & c_{56} & -c_{56} \\ & & & & & & & & & -c_{56} & c_{56} \end{bmatrix}$$

$$\text{(9.109)}$$

and the stiffness matrix is the tri-diagonal matrix

$k =$

$$
\begin{bmatrix}
k_1 & -k_1 \\
-k_1 & (k_1+k_2) & -k_2 \\
 & -k_2 & (k_2+k_3) & -k_3 \\
 & & -k_3 & (k_3+k_4) & -k_4 \\
 & & & -k_4 & 2k_4 & -k_4 \\
 & & & & -k_4 & 2k_4 & -k_4 \\
 & & & & & -k_4 & 2k_4 & -k_4 \\
 & & & & & & -k_4 & 2k_4 & -k_4 \\
 & & & & & & & -k_4 & (k_4+k_5) & -k_5 \\
 & & & & & & & & -k_5 & (k_5+k_6) & -k_6 \\
 & & & & & & & & & -k_6 & k_6
\end{bmatrix}
$$

(9.110)

For the numerical data listed as equations (9.93), the eigenvalues and eigenvectors have been found. There are 22 eigenvalues. One is zero, corresponding to the solution when there is no vibration and all the angles y have the same constant value. Another eigenvalue is $\lambda = -2.982$ (s^{-1}) in which angular rotation dies away aperiodically due to the damping c_1 and c_4 from the system to ground. The remaining 20 eigenvalues occur in ten complex-conjugate pairs, of which the four pairs with the smallest imaginary parts (i.e. the lowest frequencies) are

$$\lambda_{3,4} = -66.11 \pm i\, 149.3 \;\; s^{-1}$$

$$\lambda_{5,6} = -19.20 \pm i\, 195.2 \;\; s^{-1}$$

$$\lambda_{7,8} = -14.78 \pm i\, 502.5 \;\; s^{-1}$$

(9.111)

$$\lambda_{9,10} = -14.12 \pm i\, 821.9 \;\; s^{-1}.$$

Corresponding to these eigenvalues, the first column of the 22×22 eigenvector matrix U consists of 11 elements of unity, followed by 11 zeros. The second column has real elements only, and all the remaining 20 columns have complex elements because their eigenvalues are complex. The complex inverse matrix $V = U^{-1}$ can be computed if necessary by using the subprogram Cinv shown in Appendix 6. Also, m^{-1} has to be available. Then the elements u_{rj}, v_{jk} and a_{ks} can be extracted and the required frequency-response functions can be calculated for frequency $\omega = n\Omega$. This has been done for $n = 6$ and with Ω having a series of values in the range 0 to $100\pi/6\,\text{rad/s}$ (500 rev/min). For a sixth-order torque of amplitude $T_n = T_6 = 3\,\text{kN/m}$, the shaft torque has then to be calculated from (9.104), and its amplitude is shown plotted against speed in Fig. 9.8.

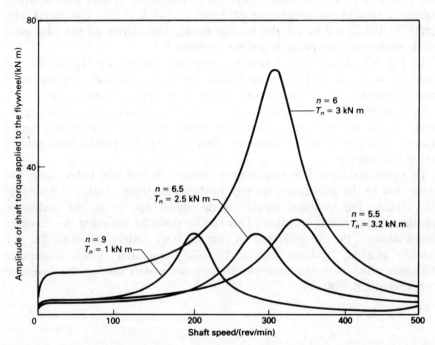

Fig. 9.8 Forced vibration-response curves for the torsional system shown in Fig. 9.7, where T_n is the amplitude of the nth-order torque harmonic applied at each pair of cylinders. The order of the excitation is the number of cycles of torque per revolution; the firing order is 1, 3, 5, 6, 4, 2 with the cylinders numbered as in Fig. 9.7. The cranks are at 120° to each other

There is a resonant peak at a speed of about 310 rev/min when the frequency of the sixth-order exciting torque coincides with the second natural frequency of the shaft which, from (9.111), is

$$195.2\,\text{rad/s} = 1864\,\text{cycles/min}.$$

We note that there is no apparent resonance of the sixth-order excitation at the first natural frequency which is, from (9.111),

$$149.3\,\text{rad/s} = 1426\,\text{cycles/min}$$

which corresponds to a shaft speed of

$$\frac{1426}{6} = 238 \text{ rev/min}.$$

The explanation for this is that the first natural frequency is for a mode in which the main motion is that of the damper assembly at the forward end, with the wheel I_6 swinging through a large amplitude but with all the other amplitudes remaining relatively small. The shaft torque at the aft end of the engine does not respond significantly. This mode is also well damped, having a logarithmic decrement of $2\pi(66.11/149.3) = 2.78$ compared with $2\pi(19.20/195.2) = 0.62$ for the second mode. Calculation of the (damped) mode shapes of the system is left for Problem 9.5.

In Fig. 9.8 three other harmonic response curves are shown for the orders $n = 5\frac{1}{2}$, $6\frac{1}{2}$ and 9. In each case there are different amplitudes of exciting torque. These have been chosen to be representative values for a typical engine. We see that resonance at the second natural frequency again dominates the response, and the peaks all occur at an engine speed which corresponds to a frequency close to the 1864 cycles/min second natural frequency.

In a practical case, it is important to ensure that fatigue failure does not occur due to the alternating stresses in the drive shafts, and it is necessary to calculate the resultant torque in the shafts due to all the orders of exciting torque acting together. This can be done by summing the complex amplitudes of the torques due to the separate orders, allowing for the relative phasing between orders, by using equation (9.86). Computer packages which complete such calculations are widely used in the design of reciprocating machinery.

Chapter 10

Discrete response calculations

Discrete Fourier transforms

If $x(t) = x(t + T)$ is a periodic function, this may be expressed in the Fourier expansion

$$x(t) = \sum_{k=-\infty}^{\infty} X_k \, e^{i2\pi kt/T} \tag{10.1}$$

where

$$X_k = \frac{1}{T} \int_0^T x(t) \, e^{-i2\pi kt/T} \, dt. \tag{10.2}$$

When only sampled values of $x(t)$ are known, the integral in (10.2) can be replaced by a summation. If sampling occurs at a regular time spacing Δ, see Fig. 10.1, so that

$$N\Delta = T \tag{10.3}$$

and we write

$$x(t = r\Delta) = x_r, \tag{10.4}$$

then (10.2) gives

$$X_k = \frac{1}{N\Delta} \sum_{r=0}^{N-1} [x_r \, e^{-i2\pi kr/N}]\Delta$$

$$= \frac{1}{N} \sum_{r=0}^{N-1} x_r \, e^{-i2\pi kr/N}. \tag{10.5}$$

This is the definition of the discrete Fourier transform (DFT) of the sequence $\{x_r\}$, $r = 0$ to $N - 1$. Provided that the sampling interval Δ is small enough, the X_k calculated from (10.5) are approximations for the exact Fourier coefficients calculated by (10.2).

When the integer k exceeds $N - 1$, the coefficients X_k in (10.5) repeat themselves and, if k is replaced by $N + k$,

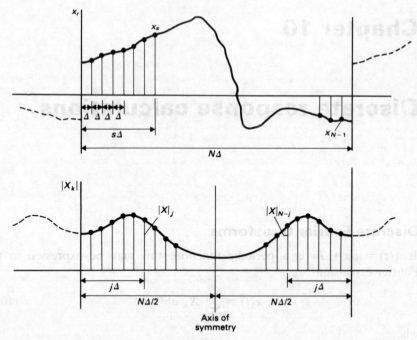

Fig. 10.1 Sampled data $x(t = r\Delta) = x_r$, $r = 0$ to $N - 1$, and the magnitude of its discrete Fourier transform X_k, $k = 0$ to $N - 1$

$$X_{N+k} = \frac{1}{N} \sum_{r=0}^{N-1} x_r \, e^{-i2\pi(N+k)r/N}$$

$$= \frac{1}{N} \sum_{r=0}^{N-1} x_r \, e^{-i2\pi r} \, e^{-i2\pi kr/N} \tag{10.6}$$

which, since

$$e^{-i2\pi r} = 1 \tag{10.7}$$

for all integer values r, gives

$$X_{N+k} = X_k. \tag{10.8}$$

Similarly, if k is replaced by $N - k$, then

$$X_{N-k} = \frac{1}{N} \sum_{r=0}^{N-1} x_r \, e^{i2\pi kr/N} \tag{10.9}$$

with the only difference from X_k in (10.5) being the sign of the exponent of the complex exponential function. If the sequence $\{x_r\}$ is a sequence of real numbers, it follows from (10.9) that

$$X_{N-k} = X_k^*. \tag{10.10}$$

Also, if the x_r are real, then from (10.5),

$$X_0 = X_N \qquad (10.11)$$

is real and, if N is even, $X_{N/2}$ is real.

In Fig. 10.1, a possible sequence of real numbers $\{x_r\}$ is shown plotted on a base of the integers $r = 0$ to $N - 1$ with, below it, a sequence of $|X_k|$ plotted on a base of $k = 0$ to $N - 1$. Because of (10.10), there is a central axis of symmetry in the $|X_k|$ diagram. The diagram reflects about a vertical axis at the position $k = N/2$.

The range of k in equation (10.1) is therefore restricted to harmonics up to $k = N/2$ (N assumed even), so that (10.1) becomes

$$x(t = r\Delta) \simeq \sum_{k=-N/2}^{N/2} X_k \, e^{i2\pi kr/N} \qquad (10.12)$$

which, because of (10.7) and (10.8), is the same as

$$x(t = r\Delta) \simeq \sum_{k=0}^{N-1} X_k \, e^{i2\pi kr/N}. \qquad (10.13)$$

In fact, the sequence $\{x_r\}$, $r = 0$ to $N - 1$, is exactly recovered from the sequence $\{X_k\}$, $k = 0$ to $N - 1$. This can be proved by substituting in (10.13) from (10.5), after changing the variable integer r to s (say) in (10.5) to avoid confusion with the r in (10.13) (see Problem 10.3). The discrete Fourier transform pair of equations is therefore

$$X_k = \frac{1}{N} \sum_{r=0}^{N-1} x_r \, e^{-i2\pi kr/N}, \, k = 0 \text{ to } N - 1 \qquad (10.14)$$

$$x_r = \sum_{k=0}^{N-1} X_k \, e^{i2\pi kr/N}, \, r = 0 \text{ to } N - 1. \qquad (10.15)$$

When continuous records are analysed by discrete sampling, these two equations replace the Fourier series pair

$$X_k = \frac{1}{T} \int_0^T x(t) \, e^{-i2\pi kt/T} \, dt \qquad (10.16)$$

$$x(t) = \sum_{k=-\infty}^{\infty} X_k \, e^{i2\pi kt/T} \qquad (10.17)$$

if the data is periodic so that $x(t) = x(t + T)$, or, if the data is not periodic, they replace the Fourier transform pair

$$X(i\omega) = \frac{1}{2\pi} \int_{-\infty}^{\infty} x(t) \, e^{-i\omega t} \, dt \qquad (10.18)$$

$$x(t) = \int_{-\infty}^{\infty} X(i\omega) \, e^{i\omega t} \, d\omega. \qquad (10.19)$$

Properties of the DFT

Consider using the discrete Fourier transform to calculate approximately the frequency composition of a continuous periodic signal $x(t) = x(t + T)$.

It is most important that the sampling interval Δ is small enough. We have seen that a graph of $|X_k|$ against k reflects about $k = N/2$ (Fig. 10.1). This corresponds to an angular frequency given by

$$\omega_0 = 2\pi k/T \qquad (10.20)$$

when $k = N/2$ and $T = N\Delta$, so that

$$\omega_0 = \pi/\Delta. \qquad (10.21)$$

Therefore the maximum frequency of the harmonics that can be represented by the DFT is limited by the size of the sampling interval Δ. This maximum frequency ω_0 is called the *folding frequency* or sometimes the *Nyquist frequency*. For an accurate representation, Δ must be small enough that ω_0 exceeds the highest frequency harmonic of the signal being analysed. If it does not, higher frequency components present in $x(t)$ will corrupt the coefficients X_k calculated by the DFT and lead to errors. This distortion of the values of the X_k is usually called *aliasing distortion*. It is important to ensure, when using (10.14), that the sampling interval is small enough that $\omega_0 = \pi/\Delta$ is a high enough frequency to include all the significant harmonic components of $x(t)$.

The lowest-frequency harmonic that is represented by the DFT is the fundamental frequency

$$2\pi/T = 2\pi/N\Delta. \qquad (10.22)$$

Application of the DFT to an aperiodic signal has the effect of assuming that this signal is periodic with period $T = N\Delta$ where N is the sequence length and Δ is the sampling interval. In response calculations, use of the DFT will generate the response to a periodic input $x(t) = x(t + T)$ and, if $x(t)$ is not periodic, this will lead to errors. These errors have been studied extensively in the subject of random vibrations, and the application of the DFT in random vibration theory is discussed at length in the author's other book on random vibrations and spectral analysis (Newland [64]). For non-random problems, when a specific aperiodic excitation time-history is prescribed, the sampling interval Δ and sequence length N must be chosen to ensure that a sufficient length of record is analysed (having regard to the time response of the system concerned). This will normally include the whole duration of the excitation and a sufficient following period for the response to decay away after the excitation has ceased. The record length can then be thought of as one period of a periodic excitation and response history. The sampling interval must be sufficiently small that all the high-frequency components of the excitation and of the response are modelled with sufficient accuracy. The practical approach to the selection of N and Δ is to continue to increase N and reduce Δ until the computed time response becomes substantially invariant to further changes in N and Δ.

An important property of the DFT is given by Parseval's theorem, which says that

$$\frac{1}{N} \sum_{r=0}^{N-1} x_r^2 = \sum_{k=0}^{N-1} X_k X_k^*. \tag{10.23}$$

The mean-square value of x_r (taken over the full sequence length, N) is equal to the sum of the squares of the frequency coefficients, $|X_k|^2$. This is the discrete analogue of the usual result for Fourier series that

$$\frac{1}{T} \int_0^T x^2(t) \, \mathrm{d}t = \sum_{k=-\infty}^{\infty} X_k X_k^* \tag{10.24}$$

and the corresponding result from Fourier transform theory that

$$\frac{1}{2\pi} \int_{-\infty}^{\infty} x^2(t) \, \mathrm{d}t = \int_{-\infty}^{\infty} X(\mathrm{i}\omega) \, X^*(\mathrm{i}\omega) \, \mathrm{d}\omega. \tag{10.25}$$

All these results are proved in Problem 10.3.

In order to compute the DFT of a sequence $\{x_r\}$, $r = 0$ to $N - 1$, it is simple in principle to devise an algorithm to implement equation (10.14). However, for each X_k there have to be N complex multiplications, and for $N/2$ independent coefficients there have to be $N^2/2$ complex multiplications. Since, for a realistic sequence length, N can easily be of the order of 10^6, a considerable amount of computer time may be required. Furthermore, such a large number of operations leads to the accumulation of errors due to round-off in the computer.

The fast Fourier transform (FFT) algorithm is an ingenious way of implementing the DFT (10.14) and its inverse (10.15) without requiring nearly so many operations as a straightforward calculation would require. The number of complex multiplications can be shown to be reduced from $N^2/2$ to $(N \log_2 N)/2$ by a typical FFT algorithm (see, for example, Newland [64], Ch. 12), which for $N = 2^{20} = 1\,048\,576$ amounts to a reduction by a factor of

$$\frac{N^2}{N \log_2 N} = 52\,429 \tag{10.26}$$

or a potential reduction in processing time for multiplications of over $50\,000$. For this reason the FFT algorithm, of which there are various alternative forms, is always used for practical calculations requiring Fourier analysis.

The detailed logic of the FFT and a typical program in both Basic and Fortran are given in the author's other book [64], Chapter 12 and Appendix 2. Similar programs are also now available in most computer program libraries. The reader may find it helpful at this point to use such a program to work Problem 10.2.

Relationship between the discrete and continuous Fourier transforms

Suppose that we want to compute the continuous Fourier transform of a function $x(t)$ by using the discrete Fourier transform. It will be necessary to consider a time-span long enough that $x(t)$ is negligible at both ends of this 'window' which we shall assume lasts from $t = -T/2$ to $t = +T/2$. The DFT calculates approximations for the first $N/2$ Fourier coefficients of a periodic function for which $x(t)$, $-T/2 < t < T/2$, is one period. The exact coefficients of such a periodic function are given from (10.16) by

$$X_k = \frac{1}{T} \int_{-T/2}^{T/2} x(t) \, e^{-i2\pi kt/T} \, dt \tag{10.27}$$

where the limits of the integration can be altered from 0 to T to $-T/2$ to $+T/2$ because $x(t)$ is assumed to have period T.

The exact Fourier transform of the truncated function $x(t)$, $-T/2 < t < T/2$, is given, from (10.18), by

$$X(i\omega) = \frac{1}{2\pi} \int_{-T/2}^{T/2} x(t) \, e^{-i\omega t} \, dt \tag{10.28}$$

where the limits of integration are $\pm T/2$, because $x(t)$ is assumed to be zero outside this range.

By comparing (10.27) and (10.28), we see that

$$X_k = \frac{2\pi}{T} \, X(i\omega = i2\pi k/T) \tag{10.29}$$

and the discrete Fourier coefficient X_k is equal to $T/2\pi$ times the value of $X(i\omega)$ at frequency

$$\omega = 2\pi k/T \tag{10.30}$$

which is the kth harmonic of the fundamental frequency $2\pi/T$.

This is an important result that is illustrated in Fig. 10.2. $X(i\omega)$ is the exact (continuous) Fourier transform of the truncated signal in view (b). X_k is an exact Fourier coefficient for the periodic signal in view (c) which is made up of the same $x(t)$ as in view (b). These two quantities, $X(i\omega)$ and X_k, are exactly related by (10.29).

In practice, the DFT produces an approximation for X_k and $X(i\omega)$ is itself an approximation for the FT of the original continuous signal $x(t)$ when there is no truncation. Therefore (10.29) is also an approximate relation between the DFT and the underlying continuous Fourier transform. The approximation may be made as close as we like by increasing the record length $T = N\Delta$ (by increasing the sequence length N) and by reducing the sampling interval Δ (to ensure that the Nyquist frequency π/Δ exceeds all significant frequencies in $x(t)$) provided that the continuous signal $x(t)$ remains zero outside the window $-T/2 < t < T/2$. For many vibration problems this condition is met because the excitation exists for only a limited period of time. However for random vibration problems it is generally not the case and consideration has then to be given to the errors introduced by windowing. This is a specialized topic for which the reader is referred to the author's other book [64].

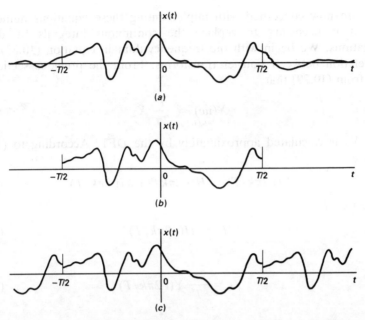

Fig. 10.2 Illustrating equation (10.29) that relates the continuous Fourier transform of a truncated signal to the Fourier coefficients of a corresponding periodic function: (*a*) original signal for analysis; (*b*) truncated signal, whose Fourier transform is $X(i\omega)$; and (*c*) periodic signal, of which (*b*) is one period, whose Fourier coefficients are X_k defined by (10.29)

Discrete calculations in the frequency domain

For a passive, linear, time-invariant system with input $x(t)$ and output $y(t)$, the input-output relations are, from (9.25),

$$y(t) = \int_{-\infty}^{t} x(\tau)\, h(t - \tau)\, d\tau \qquad (10.31)$$

in the time domain, and from (9.59)

$$Y(i\omega) = H(i\omega)\, X(i\omega) \qquad (10.32)$$

in the frequency domain, where $X(i\omega)$ and $Y(i\omega)$ are the Fourier transforms of $x(t)$ and $y(t)$ respectively, and $h(\theta)$ and $H(i\omega)$ are the impulse-response and frequency-response functions which are related from (9.49) and (9.50) by

$$H(i\omega) = \int_{-\infty}^{\infty} h(\theta)\, e^{-i\omega}\, d\theta \qquad (10.33)$$

and

$$h(\theta) = \frac{1}{2\pi} \int_{-\infty}^{\infty} H(i\omega) \, e^{i\omega\theta} \, d\omega. \tag{10.34}$$

We are now concerned with implementing these equations numerically when it is necessary to replace the continuous integrals by discrete summations. We begin with the frequency-domain equation (10.32) which is a relation between Fourier transforms. From the previous section, we know from (10.29) that

$$X(i\omega) \Big|_{\omega=2\pi k/T} = \frac{T}{2\pi} X_k \tag{10.35}$$

when X_k is calculated approximately by the DFT. According to (10.32), we have

$$Y(i \, 2\pi k/T) = H(i \, 2\pi k/T) \, X(i \, 2\pi k/T) \tag{10.36}$$

and hence, if

$$H_k = H(i \, 2\pi k/T) \tag{10.37}$$

and

$$Y_k = \frac{2\pi}{T} \, Y(i \, 2\pi k/T) \tag{10.38}$$

then

$$Y_k = H_k X_k. \tag{10.39}$$

This equation (10.39) is exact when the X_k and Y_k are Fourier coefficients defined by (10.16), and the original $x(t)$ is zero outside time span T. When X_k and Y_k are approximations for the Fourier coefficients, calculated approximately by the DFT, and when $x(t)$ has been truncated (see Fig. 10.2), then (10.39) is an approximate relationship. However, as we have seen, if the sequence length N is large enough and the sampling interval Δ is small enough, the approximation can be made a very close one.

When X_k is part of a sequence $\{X_k\}$, $k = 0$ to $N - 1$, calculated by the DFT, we recall from (10.10) that

$$X_{N-k} = X_k^*. \tag{10.40}$$

because of the symmetry properties of the DFT when X_k is derived from a sequence of real numbers $\{x_r\}$, repesenting the real input signal $x(t = r\Delta)$. In order to maintain this symmetry in $\{Y_k\}$, $k = 0$ to $N - 1$, only the first half of the sequence $\{H_k\}$, $k = 0$ to $N - 1$, can be defined by (10.37). The remaining terms in the sequence must satisfy the symmetry requirement that

$$H_{N-k} = H_k^*. \tag{10.41}$$

When N is even, (10.37) is expressed more fully by

$$H_k = H(\text{i } 2\pi k/T), \; k = 0 \text{ to } N/2$$

and

$$H_k = H^*_{N-k}, \; k = \frac{N}{2} + 1 \text{ to } N - 1 \tag{10.42}$$

and then $\{Y_k\}$ calculated from (10.41) has the same symmetry as $\{X_k\}$.

When selecting the sampling interval Δ and the time span $T = N\Delta$ before applying (10.41), it is important that period T is long enough not only to include all of the significant input signal $x(t)$ (see Fig. 10.2) but also to ensure that the frequency spacing between harmonics $2\pi/T$ is close enough to discriminate between all the important frequency characteristics of $H(\text{i}\omega)$ as well as of $X(\text{i}\omega)$. In addition, the sampling interval Δ must be small enough that the Nyquist frequency π/Δ is greater than the highest significant frequency of the input signal, having regard to possible resonances of $H(\text{i}\omega)$ at the upper end of the frequency range of the calculation.

Discrete calculations in the time domain

Now consider the time-domain integral (10.31). If the value of $y(t)$ at $t = 0$ is

$$y(t = 0) = y_0 \tag{10.43}$$

then (10.31) becomes

$$y(t) = y_0 + \int_0^t x(\tau) \, h(t - \tau) \, d\tau. \tag{10.44}$$

The integral can be approximated by a summation in the same way as the integral in (10.2) was approximated by the summation (10.5). Putting

$$\tau = r\Delta \text{ and } t = s\Delta \tag{10.45}$$

where Δ is the sampling interval, then if

$$x(\tau = r\Delta) = x_r$$
$$y(t = s\Delta) = y_s \tag{10.46}$$

and

$$h[t - \tau = (s - r)\Delta] = h_{s-r},$$

(10.44) gives

$$y_s - y_0 = \Delta \sum_{r=0}^{s-1} x_r h_{s-r}. \tag{10.47}$$

The accuracy of this approximation can be improved by replacing discrete values of the impulse response function $h(t - \tau)$ by corresponding values of the pulse-response functions $p(t - \tau - \Delta)$. Consider the response of the shaded pulse of $x(t)$ in Fig. 10.3. From Chapter 9, Fig. 9.5, the response to a pulse of unit magnitude occupying the timespan τ to $\tau + \Delta$ is $p(t - \tau - \Delta)$, $t > \tau + \Delta$. In Fig. 10.3 the shaded pulse has magnitude x_r because its height is $x(t = r\Delta)$ (instead of unity in Fig. 9.5). Hence the response to this shaded pulse for $t > \tau + \Delta$ is

$$x_r p(t - \tau - \Delta) \tag{10.48}$$

which, on account of (10.43), is

$$x_r p_{s-r-1}. \tag{10.49}$$

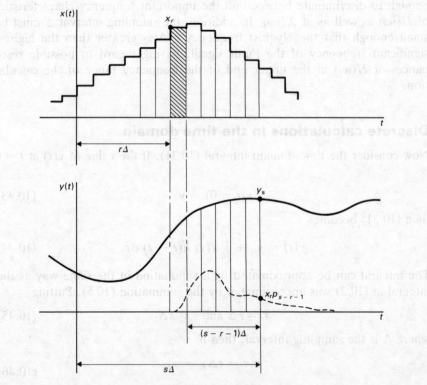

Fig. 10.3 Illustrating equation (10.50) for discrete response calculations in the time domain using the pulse-response function

Notice the index of p in (10.49) is determined by the number of time intervals Δ which occur after the pulse has ended before the present time $t = s\Delta$ is reached. The total response at $t = s\Delta$ is the sum of all the responses to the pulses that have occurred before $t = s\Delta$, and so, instead of (10.47), we have

$$y_s - y_0 = \sum_{r=0}^{s-1} x_r p_{s-r-1} \tag{10.50}$$

where, from (9.45),

$$p_{s-r-1} = \int_{(s-r-1)\Delta}^{(s-r)\Delta} h(\theta) \, d\theta, \ s \geqslant r + 1. \tag{10.51}$$

The equality sign in $s \geqslant r + 1$ appears in (10.51) because the summation (10.50) includes a term p_0. We interpret p_0 as meaning the response immediately after a pulse of excitation has ended. If $x(t)$ has the staircase shape in Fig. 10.3, then (10.50) is an exact result; when $x(t)$ is continuous, (10.50) is approximate but it is closer to the exact result than is (10.47).

The discrete convolutions (10.47) and (10.50) require substantial computing power to put into practical effect. To compute a single discrete response parameter y_s requires s multiplications, and so to find N values of y_s, $s = 1$ to N, requires

$$\sum_{s=1}^{N} s = \frac{1}{2} N(N + 1) \tag{10.52}$$

multiplications. This has to be compared with the number of multiplications required by a discrete frequency-domain calculation. To calculate the DFT X_k, $k = 0$ to $N - 1$, using a typical FFT algorithm requires $\frac{1}{2} N \log_2 N$ complex multiplications; to find Y_k from X_k using (10.39) requires $N/2$ complex multiplications (only half of the Y_k have to be computed because $Y_{N-k} = Y_k^*$); and to generate the output y_s, $s = 0$ to $N - 1$, using the inverse FFT requires a further $\frac{1}{2} N \log_2 N$ complex multiplications. Therefore there are $\frac{1}{2} N(N + 1)$ real multiplications for discrete convolution in the time domain compared with $\frac{1}{2} N(2 \log_2 N + 1)$ complex multiplications for the same discrete calculation in the frequency domain. As already mentioned in a previous section, when $N = 2^{20} = 1\,048\,576$, the ratio $N/\log_2 N = 52\,429$, so that it becomes increasingly economical to make a discrete calculation in the frequency domain rather than in the time domain as the sequence length N increases.

Discrete finite-difference calculations

An alternative method of computing the time-domain response of a system is to use a finite-difference model.

Suppose that a continuous response parameter $y(t)$ is related to continuous excitation $x(t)$ by the usual response equation

$$a_n \frac{d^n y}{dt^n} + a_{n-1} \frac{d^{n-1} y}{dt^{n-1}} + \ldots + a_1 \frac{dy}{dt} + a_0 y$$

$$= b_m \frac{d^m x}{dt^m} + b_{m-1} \frac{d^{m-1} x}{dt^{m-1}} + \ldots + b_1 \frac{dx}{dt} + b_0 x \tag{10.53}$$

where we assume that the a's and b's are constants, that the system is passive, and that $n > m$. Consider replacing the derivatives in (10.53) by finite-difference approximations. If the time spacing is Δ, so that the discrete values of $y(t)$ are $y(t = r\Delta) = y_r$, and we use backward differences then, at $t = r\Delta$,

$$\left(\frac{dy}{dt}\right)_{t=r\Delta} \simeq \frac{y(t = r\Delta) - y(t = (r - 1)\Delta)}{\Delta} = \frac{y_r - y_{r-1}}{\Delta} \quad (10.54)$$

and

$$\left(\frac{d^2y}{dt^2}\right)_{t=r\Delta} \simeq \frac{y(t = r\Delta) - 2y(t = (r - 1)\Delta) + y(t = (r - 2)\Delta)}{\Delta^2}$$

$$= \frac{y_r - 2y_{r-1} + y_{r-2}}{\Delta^2} \quad (10.55)$$

and so on for higher derivatives and for the derivatives of x. Then on substituting into (10.53) we find that

$$y_r + c_1 y_{r-1} + \ldots + c_{n-1} y_{r-n+1} + c_n y_{r-n}$$

$$= d_0 x_r + d_1 x_{r-1} + \ldots + d_{m-1} x_{r-m+1} + d_m x_{r-m} \quad (10.56)$$

where the c's and d's are new constants which depend on the a's and b's, respectively, and on the time interval Δ. Hence

$$y_r = -\sum_{s=1}^{n} c_s y_{r-s} + \sum_{k=0}^{m} d_k x_{r-k}. \quad (10.57)$$

The response $y_r = y(t = r\Delta)$ is expressed as a summation of the n previous values of y and $m + 1$ values of x. This is illustrated in Fig. 10.4.

If the coefficients a and b in the nth-order differential equation (10.53) are known, then in principle the c's and d's can be calculated from the finite-difference approximations. In practice, (10.53) is not usually known. We are more likely to know the coefficients of the mass, damping and stiffness matrices for a set of coupled second-order equations

$$m\ddot{y} + c\dot{y} + ky = x. \quad (10.58)$$

If there are M equations in this set, the order n of the l.h.s. of the corresponding version of (10.53) will be

$$n = 2M \quad (10.59)$$

and that of the r.h.s. will be

$$m = 2(M - 1) = n - 2 \quad (10.60)$$

(Problem 10.4). The n coefficients c_s, $s = 1$ to n, and the $m + 1$ coefficients d_k, $k = 0$ to m, can then be found directly from (10.58) without ever deriving (10.53). The method is as follows.

For the particular input x and output y specified, the impulse-response function $h(t)$ can be found from (8.111) if the eigenvalues are distinct, or

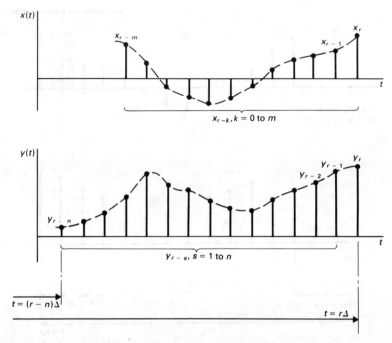

Fig. 10.4 Illustrating the calculation of $y_r = y(t = r\Delta)$ by application of the finite-difference equation (10.57)

from an equation like (8.144) or (8.145) if there are repeated eigenvalues. From the appropriate equation, $2n$ discrete values of $h(t)$ are computed for

$$t = 0, \Delta, 2\Delta, \ldots, (2n - 1)\Delta \qquad (10.61)$$

and the results stored. These give the response $y(t)$ at time intervals $0, \Delta, 2\Delta, \ldots, (2n - 1)\Delta$ after a unit impulsive input at $t = 0$ with the system initially dormant and with no ongoing response.

Now refer to Fig. 10.5. The response value $y_r = y(t = r\Delta)$ depends on n previous values of y and $n - 1$ values of x. Suppose that all the x's in Fig. 10.5 are zero except for a single unit impulse which occurred at $t = (r - n)\Delta$. The immediate response to this impulse is $h(t = 0) = h_0$, so that for this input $y_{r-n} = h_0$. One interval Δ later, the response is $h(t = \Delta) = h_1$, so that $y_{r-n+1} = h_1$, and similarly $y_{r-n+2} = h_2$, and so on. It follows that $y_r = h_n$. But y_r can also be obtained from the n preceding values by applying equation (10.57). Since, for the case we have chosen all the x's in (10.57) are zero, we find that

$$h_n = -\sum_{s=1}^{n} c_s h_{n-s}. \qquad (10.62)$$

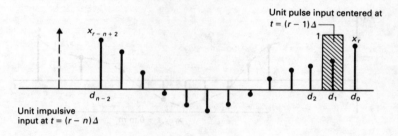

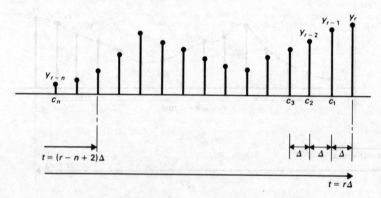

Fig. 10.5 Calculation of the coefficients c_s, $s = 1$ to n, and d_k, $k = 0$ to $n - 2$, in the finite-difference equation (10.57) when $m = n - 2$. The upper graph shows discrete values of the excitation, the lower discrete values of the response, on a time base. Corresponding constants in Equation (10.57) are identified below each of the discrete x and y.

With no further excitation, this result is repeated as we step forward in time, and one interval Δ later we have

$$h_{n+1} = - \sum_{s=1}^{n} c_s h_{n-s+1} \qquad (10.63)$$

and r intervals later,

$$h_{n+r} = - \sum_{s=1}^{n} c_s h_{n-s+r}. \qquad (10.64)$$

In this way we can generate n linear equations which may be solved for the n unknown coefficients c_s, $s = 0$ to $n - 1$. In matrix form we have

$$\begin{bmatrix} h_0 & h_1 & h_2 & \dots & h_{n-1} \\ h_1 & h_2 & h_3 & \dots & h_n \\ h_2 & h_3 & \vdots & & \vdots \\ \vdots & \vdots & \vdots & & \vdots \\ h_{n-1} & h_n & \dots & & h_{2n-2} \end{bmatrix} \begin{bmatrix} c_n \\ c_{n-1} \\ c_{n-2} \\ \vdots \\ c_1 \end{bmatrix} = - \begin{bmatrix} h_n \\ h_{n+1} \\ h_{n+2} \\ \vdots \\ h_{2n-1} \end{bmatrix} \qquad (10.65)$$

which can be solved by an appropriate computer program, for example

Gaussian elimination with interchanges as discussed in Chapter 7. The $n \times n$ matrix of values of the unit impulse-response function (10.65) is called the *Hankel* matrix and it has an important role in linear control theory (see, for example, Reid [84]). For our purposes, it provides a method of computing the unknown coefficients, c_s, $s = 0$ to $n - 1$, in the finite-difference equation (10.55).

All that we have done is to set the system in free vibration by applying a unit impulse. With no further excitation, the response is the unit impulse-response $h(t)$ and we obtain n sets of $(n + 1)$ equally spaced response values by sampling $h(t)$ at intervals of Δ. These n sets of values of y allow (10.57) to be written n times. The resulting n simultaneous equations (10.65) can then be solved to find the required finite-difference coefficients c_s, $s = 1$ to n.

We still have to find the other set of coefficients d_k, $k = 0$ to $m = n - 2$ in (10.57). This can be done by applying $n - 1$ different excitations $x(t)$ for which the response $y(t)$ is known and then working back to find the unknown d's. We cannot use impulsive inputs because we need finite values to substitute for the x's in (10.57); instead it is convenient to consider the responses which result from unit pulse inputs of duration Δ applied at different times. For example, with reference to Fig. 10.5, let the only input be a pulse of unit height and duration Δ which lasts from $t = (r - 3/2)\Delta$ to $t = (r - 1/2)\Delta$. The response to this input is y_{r-1} at $t = (r - 1)\Delta$ and y_r at $t = r\Delta$. We now change the notation used in the previous section and call these responses p_0 and p_1, respectively, as shown in Fig. 10.6. Notice that p_0 means the response when the unit pulse is only half complete, p_1 means the response at time $\Delta/2$ after the pulse has ended, p_2 means the response at time $3\Delta/2$ after the pulse has ended, and so on. Previously p_0 meant the response immediately after the unit pulse had ended, p_1 meant the response at time Δ after the pulse had ended, and so on. With these new definitions we have

$$y_{r-1} = p_0 \tag{10.66}$$

and

$$y_r = p_1. \tag{10.67}$$

On substituting from (10.66) and (10.67) into (10.57), with x_{r-1} equal to unity, we find that

$$p_1 = -c_1 p_0 + d_1 \tag{10.68}$$

which can be solved directly for d_1.

If the unit pulse input occurs one time step Δ later, the equation is even simpler and becomes

$$p_0 = d_0. \tag{10.69}$$

Equations of similar form, but with more terms, can be obtained for all the other d's by putting the unit pulse inputs at different positions, stepping progressively further back in time until the last pulse straddles the time $t = (r - n + 2)\Delta$ (see Fig. 10.5), when equation (10.57) becomes

$$p_{n-2} = - \sum_{s=1}^{n-2} c_s p_{n-2-s} + d_{n-2}. \qquad (10.70)$$

The values of the unit pulse-response function that appear in these equations are defined by Fig. 10.6 and can be calculated from the corresponding impulse response function via equation (9.45), which gives

$$p(t - \Delta) = \int_{t-\Delta}^{t} h(\theta), \; t > \Delta \qquad (10.71)$$

where $t = 3\Delta/2$ for p_1, $t = 5\Delta/2$ for p_2, and so on. For p_0 the pulse has not been completed, and so p_0 is the response to a unit step at $t = 0$, which is given by equation (9.36) with $t = \Delta/2$.

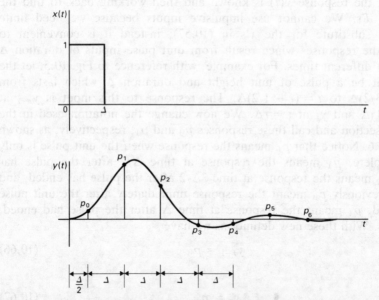

Fig. 10.6 Definitions of the discrete unit pulse-response functions p_k, $k = 0$ to $n - 2$, used to determine the unknown coefficients d_k in the finite-difference equation (10.57) (with $m = n - 2$)

Once the coefficients in (10.57) have been computed, each successive value of the discrete response $y_r = y(t = r\Delta)$ can be calculated by the finite-difference model from knowledge of the n previous values of y and $m + 1 = n - 1$ values of the excitation x. This is a much more compact computation than is the discrete convolution (10.50). Its accuracy as an approximate model of the continuous system represented by (10.58) depends (i) on the time interval Δ being small enough that (10.57) is a satisfactory model of (10.53) and (ii) on the set of equations (10.65) being well conditioned for the accurate computation of the coefficients c_s, $s = 1$ to n. The practical method of ensuring that both these conditions are met appears to be to carry out the required simulation more than once, using decreasing values of Δ, and confirm that substantially the same result is obtained as Δ is progressively reduced.

Numerical integration

Finite-difference methods are applied in various other ways to generate time-domain responses by numerically integrating the equations of motion. It is usual to begin with the equations in their first-order form

$$\frac{dz}{dt} = Az + F \tag{10.72}$$

where $z \equiv z(t)$ is the usual vector of displacements and velocities defined by (8.5) and $F \equiv F(t)$ is the excitation vector (8.3). If z_r is the response at $t = t_r$ and z_{r+1} is an approximation for z at $t = t_{r+1} = t_r + \Delta$, then using forward differences (rather than backward differences as in (10.54) and (10.55))

$$\frac{z_{r+1} - z_r}{\Delta} = \left(\frac{dz}{dt}\right)_{t=t_r} \tag{10.73}$$

which, with (10.72), gives

$$z_{r+1} = (I + \Delta A)z_r + \Delta F_r. \tag{10.74}$$

Similarly,

$$z_{r+2} = (I + \Delta A)z_{r+1} + \Delta F_{r+1} \tag{10.75}$$

and, combining (10.74) and (10.75),

$$z_{r+2} = (I + \Delta A)^2 z_r + (I + \Delta A) \Delta F_r + \Delta F_{r+1}. \tag{10.76}$$

Each new value of z_r comes from the previous value by multiplying by $(I + \Delta A)$ and adding the appropriate contributions from the excitation. This is called Euler's method. Later we shall consider a more complicated method in which the slope vector on the r.h.s. of (10.73) is computed more accurately. But first we investigate the problem of numerical stability by using (10.73) to see how small errors can accumulate if the step size Δ is too large.

Stability

For no excitation, $F = 0$, after n steps starting from $r = 0$ we have

$$z_n = (I + \Delta A)^n z_0 \tag{10.77}$$

which has to be compared with the exact value which, from (8.181), is

$$z(t = n\Delta) = e^{n\Delta A}z_0. \tag{10.78}$$

Suppose that time t is fixed, but we take many very small steps by letting $n \to \infty$ as $\Delta \to 0$. Equation (10.78) can be written as

$$z(t) = e^{tA}z_0 \tag{10.79}$$

and we know that the exact response will be stable provided that the eigenvalues of A all have negative real parts. If the $z(t)$ are normal coordinates, A will be a diagonal matrix of eigenvalues, λ_j, which are assumed distinct. Then $(I + \Delta A)$ will also be diagonal, and its eigenvalues are

$$\mu_j = 1 + \Delta\lambda_j. \tag{10.80}$$

The difference equation (10.77) will be *stable* provided that, for all the eigenvalues,

$$|\mu_j| < 1 \tag{10.81}$$

because then $\mu_j^n \to 0$ as $n \to \infty$. If (10.81) is not true, the finite-difference calculation blows up because $\mu_j^n \to \infty$ as $n \to \infty$, which we know it should not do. Suppose that a typical eigenvalue is

$$\lambda = -\alpha + i\beta \tag{10.82}$$

where α and β are real and positive. Then (10.81) gives

$$|1 - \Delta\alpha + \Delta i\beta| < 1$$

or

$$(1 - \Delta\alpha)^2 + (\Delta\beta)^2 < 1. \tag{10.83}$$

In order for the finite-difference approximation to be stable, the step length Δ must be small enough that (10.83) is satisfied. This means that the size of Δ has to be chosen with regard to those eigenvalues for which α and/or β are large, even though, if α is large, the effect of these eigenvalues may die out rapidly in the true solution. This may make practical computations difficult for so-called *stiff systems* which have eigenvalues of very different magnitudes. If there is an eigenvalue with a large negative real part (very strong damping) or a large imaginary part (high-frequency oscillation) it will be necessary to keep the step length very small even though the response of interest may be developing much more slowly.

Problems of stability arise when forward differences, rather than backward differences, are being used (see Problem 10.5). The advantage of forward differences for initial-value problems is that each new response vector z_n can be calculated from knowledge of the previous vector z_{n-1} without inverting a matrix or, in the case of nonlinear problems, solving a set of nonlinear equations (Problem 10.5). This is a major computational advantage, but it brings the penalty that the step size Δ may have to be very small when there are large eigenvalues.

Fourth-order Runge-Kutta method

In addition to being *stable*, the finite-difference approximation must be *accurate* and this requires the error vector

$$z(t = n\Delta) - z_n \qquad (10.84)$$

to be small. To help achieve this, the finite-difference equation (10.73) is modified so that its r.h.s. is a closer approximation to the vector of average slopes between $t = t_r$ and $t = t_r + \Delta$. In the fourth-order *Runge–Kutta* method this average slope k is expressed as

$$k = \frac{k_1}{6} + \frac{k_2}{3} + \frac{k_3}{3} + \frac{k_4}{6} \qquad (10.85)$$

where

$$k_1 = \left(\frac{dz}{dt}\right)_{t=t_r},$$

k_2 and k_3 are two different estimates of the slopes at $t = t_r + \Delta/2$, and k_4 is an estimate of the slopes at $t = t_r + \Delta$.

The calculation of these slopes is illustrated in Fig. 10.7. Assume that we know the vector z_r at $t = t_r$. From (10.72), the exact vector of slopes here is

$$\left(\frac{dz}{dt}\right)_{t=t_r} = Az_r + F_r = k_1. \qquad (10.86)$$

The value of z at the mid-point of the next step is then given approximately by

$$z_{r+1/2} = z_r + \frac{\Delta}{2}\left(\frac{dz}{dt}\right)_{t=t_r}$$

$$= z_r + \frac{\Delta}{2} k_1. \qquad (10.87)$$

A first estimate for the mid-point slope is therefore

$$\left(\frac{dz}{dt}\right)_{t=t_r+\Delta/2} = Az_{r+1/2} + F_{r+1/2} \qquad (10.88)$$

and so, from (10.87),

$$k_2 = A\left(z_r + \frac{\Delta}{2} k_1\right) + F_{r+1/2}. \qquad (10.89)$$

Using this new slope k_2, a second estimate for the mid-point's location is

$$z_{r+1/2} = z_r + \frac{\Delta}{2} k_2 \qquad (10.90)$$

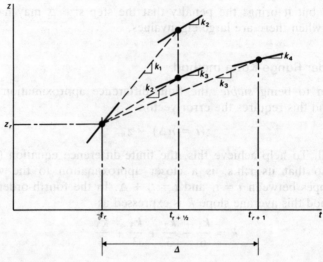

Fig. 10.7 Calculation of four slopes k_1, k_2, k_3 and k_4 in the fourth-order Runge–Kutta method

with which (10.88) gives

$$k_3 = A\left(z_r + \frac{\Delta}{2} k_2\right) + F_{r+1/2}. \tag{10.91}$$

If k_3 is taken to be the vector of average slopes over the full step, then

$$z_{r+1} = z_r + \Delta k_3 \tag{10.92}$$

and so

$$k_4 = \left(\frac{dz}{dt}\right)_{t=t_r+\Delta} = A(z_r + \Delta k_3) + F_{r+1}. \tag{10.93}$$

Collecting these results, fourth-order Runge–Kutta calculates

$$z_{r+1} = z_r + \Delta k \tag{10.94}$$

where

$$k = \tfrac{1}{6}(k_1 + 2k_2 + 2k_3 + k_4) \tag{10.95}$$

and the k's are compounded so that

$$
\begin{aligned}
k_1 &= Az_r + F_r \\
k_2 &= A\left(z_r + \frac{\Delta}{2} k_1\right) + F_{r+1/2} \\
k_3 &= A\left(z_r + \frac{\Delta}{2} k_2\right) + F_{r+1/2} \\
k_4 &= A(z_r + \Delta k_3) + F_{r+1}.
\end{aligned}
\tag{10.96}
$$

The result is accurate to the fourth order in Δ. This may be seen by substituting for k_1 in k_2, k_2 in k_3 and k_3 in k_4 and then substituting for all the k's in (10.95) to get, from (10.94),

$$z_{r+1} = (I + \Delta A + \tfrac{1}{2}\Delta^2 A^2 + \tfrac{1}{6}\Delta^3 A^3 + \tfrac{1}{24}\Delta^4 A^4)z_r$$
$$+ \tfrac{1}{6}\Delta(I + \Delta A + \tfrac{1}{2}\Delta^2 A^2 + \tfrac{1}{4}\Delta^3 A^3)F_r$$
$$+ \tfrac{2}{3}\Delta(I + \tfrac{1}{2}\Delta A + \tfrac{1}{8}\Delta^2 A^2)F_{r+1/2} + \tfrac{1}{6}\Delta F_{r+1}. \tag{10.97}$$

The terms in brackets in the first line of (10.97) agree with the expansion of $e^{\Delta A}$ as far as the term in Δ^4 (compare equation (10.79)).

This has been found to be an efficient algorithm for integrating sets of differential equations starting from specified initial conditions. Each step forward in time depends only on the conditions at the start of the step (and on the known excitation), and so changes in step size can be made as the calculation progresses. For a gradually changing response, the step size Δ can be large. When there are sudden changes, Δ can be reduced without difficulty. Although there is no guarantee of stability, the method has been found to be highly accurate and it can be programmed quite easily.

Variable step size

In order to vary the step size, it is necessary to have a suitable criterion against which to judge whether a step is too large. One method is to calculate the vector $z_{r+1}^{(1)}$ by a full-length step Δ from z_r and then to repeat the calculation in two half-steps to obtain $z_{r+1}^{(2)}$. The magnitudes of the differences between corresponding elements of $z_{r+1}^{(1)}$ and $z_{r+1}^{(2)}$ are then compared with a preset standard to see whether the step size Δ is too large. If the errors fall within acceptable limits, $z_{r+1}^{(1)}$ is accepted and the calculation proceeds to its next step. For this new step, the step size is scaled up to a value for which the largest error in the previous step would have been close to its limit. The method of scaling is explained below. If, at the end of the new step, the errors fall outside acceptable limits, Δ is scaled down appropriately and the step is repeated.

The procedure for scaling is as follows. For the most sensitive element of the vector z, let the result of making a step Δ be $z_{r+1}^{(1)}$. Assuming that z_r is exact, then $z_{r+1}^{(1)}$ will differ from its exact value $z(t = (r + 1)\Delta)$ by terms of order Δ^5 and smaller, so that

$$z_{r+1}^{(1)} = z(t = (r + 1)\Delta) + c\Delta^5 + 0(\Delta^6). \tag{10.98}$$

Now imagine making a half-step from the same starting point. This gives

$$z_{r+1/2} = z(t = (r + 1/2)\Delta) + c\left(\frac{\Delta}{2}\right)^5 + 0(\Delta^6). \tag{10.99}$$

A second half-step, starting from $z(t = (r+1/2)\Delta$, would produce

$$z^{(2)}_{r+1} = z(t = (r + 1)\Delta) + c\left(\frac{\Delta}{2}\right)^5 + 0(\Delta^6) \qquad (10.100)$$

and so on a second step starting from $z_{r+1/2}$ gives

$$z^{(2)}_{r+1} = z(t = (r + 1)\Delta) + 2c\left(\frac{\Delta}{2}\right)^5 + 0(\Delta^6). \qquad (10.101)$$

Hence we see that

$$z^{(1)}_{r+1} - z^{(2)}_{r+1} = c\Delta^5 - 2c\left(\frac{\Delta}{2}\right)^5 + 0(\Delta^6)$$

$$= \frac{15}{16} c\Delta^5 + 0(\Delta^6)$$

$$= e \text{ (say)} \qquad (10.102)$$

where e denotes the difference between the result of a calculation by one step and the result of a calculation by two half-steps. Therefore, if e is the error for step length Δ and e_0 for step Δ_0, we have

$$\frac{\Delta}{\Delta_0} = \left(\frac{e}{e_0}\right)^{1/5} \qquad (10.103)$$

so that the step size has to be scaled in proportion to $e^{1/5}$.

Knowing the error e, we can use (10.102) to substitute for $c\Delta^5$ in (10.101) and so obtain

$$z^{(2)}_{r+1} = z(t = (r + 1)\Delta) + \frac{e}{15} + 0(\Delta^6). \qquad (10.104)$$

The true value $z(t = (r + 1)\Delta)$ at the end of the step is then given by

$$z(t = (r + 1)\Delta) = z^{(2)}_{r+1} - \frac{e}{15} + 0(\Delta^6). \qquad (10.105)$$

If we define $z^{(3)}_{r+1}$ so that

$$z^{(3)}_{r+1} = z^{(2)}_{r+1} - \frac{e}{15}, \qquad (10.106)$$

then $z^{(3)}_{r+1}$ will be accurate to order Δ^5. Alternatively, on account of (10.102),

$$z^{(3)}_{r+1} = z^{(1)}_{r+1} - \frac{16}{15} e. \qquad (10.107)$$

These results hold for all the elements of the vectors, so that if the vector e is defined by

$$e = z^{(1)}_{r+1} - z^{(2)}_{r+1} \qquad (10.108)$$

then

$$z_{r+1}^{(3)} = z_{r+1}^{(2)} - \frac{1}{15} e = z_{r+1}^{(1)} - \frac{16}{15} e. \tag{10.109}$$

Before proceeding to the next step, the accuracy of the calculated vector z_{r+1} can be brought up to order Δ^5 by making this correction.

We have still to say what is an acceptable error vector e for the difference between the result of a single step and two half-steps. A number of strategies are described in Press *et al.* [82]. For vibration problems we are generally concerned with oscillations whose amplitudes (of displacement and velocity) are bounded and for which an approximate estimate of the maximum values can usually be made. Then the vector e can be set as a small fraction of a vector of maxima, z_{max}. For example

$$e = 10^{-6} z_{max}. \tag{10.110}$$

In the limit, the precision of the computer controls the accuracy achievable and there is no point in taking infinitely many infinitesimal steps which lead nowhere.

A logical flow diagram for a fourth-order Runge–Kutta integration step is given in Appendix 7. Programs based on this diagram have been used to compute the results given in Chapter 3 for the response of a system which is accelerated through resonance and the results in Chapter 14 for the same problem when the system has a nonlinear spring. Also, a fourth-order Runge–Kutta program has been used in Chapter 14 to compute the chaotic response of a system with gross nonlinearity and large-amplitude harmonic excitation.

If nonlinear problems can be written as a set of first-order equations

$$\frac{dz_i}{dt} = f_i(z, t), \ i = 1 \text{ to } N \tag{10.111}$$

then equations (10.94) and (10.95) still apply provided that the elements of the slope vectors k_1, k_2, k_3 and k_4 are now computed from

$$k_{1i} = f_i(z_r, t_r)$$

$$k_{2i} = f_i\left(z_r + \frac{\Delta}{2} k_1, t_r + \frac{\Delta}{2}\right)$$

$$k_{3i} = f_i\left(z_r + \frac{\Delta}{2} k_2, t_r + \frac{\Delta}{2}\right) \qquad i = 1 \text{ to } N \tag{10.112}$$

$$k_{4i} = f_i(z_r + \Delta k_3, t_r + \Delta)$$

which correspond to equations (10.96).

Implementations of the fourth-order Runge–Kutta routines with variable step size are available in many computer program libraries. More sophisticated routines involve the extrapolation of trial functions and include the *predictor-corrector methods* and the *Bulirsch–Stoer method* (see Press *et al.*

306   *Discrete response calculations*

[82] and Stoer and Bulirsch [92]). There is a good discussion in the book *Numerical Recipes* by Press *et al.* [82], but the selection of the 'best' numerical integration routine for a particular problem may be extremely difficult, and there are no general rules. Apparently reliable methods can fail on unusual problems and it is definitely recommended that programs should give a warning when unusually small step sizes are being used.

Chapter 11

Systems with symmetric matrices

Introduction

In Chapter 5 we calculated the eigenvalues and eigenvectors of a general undamped system whose free motion is described by

$$m\ddot{y}(t) + ky(t) = O. \tag{11.1}$$

For a solution

$$y(t) = e^{i\omega t}y \tag{11.2}$$

we must have

$$[-\omega^2 m + k]y = O \tag{11.3}$$

and, provided that m is not singular,

$$[-\omega^2 I + m^{-1}k]\,y = O. \tag{11.4}$$

If there are M degrees of freedom, so that m and k have order $M \times M$, we can then say that if

$$\lambda_j, j = 1 \text{ to } M \tag{11.5}$$

are the eigenvalues of

$$A = m^{-1}k \tag{11.6}$$

then the characteristic values of ω_j are given by

$$\omega_j^2 = \lambda_j, j = 1 \text{ to } M. \tag{11.7}$$

In many applications, equation (11.1) describes the small-amplitude vibration of an undamped system of masses and springs. For such systems we shall show now that, subject to very general conditions, both the mass matrix m and the stiffness matrix k are symmetric and positive definite. Also, the eigenvalues λ_j are always real and positive, and there is always a full set of independent eigenvectors. Because of the symmetric properties of m and k, a simplification of the general vibration-response equation is possible, and this has important computational advantages.

The generation of symmetric, positive definite **m** and **k** matrices depends on the form of the kinetic-energy and potential-energy functions for a mechanical system. In order to derive the equations of motion directly from these energy functions we need Lagrange's formulation of the general equations of three-dimensional motion. Lagrange's equations are also helpful for deriving the equations of motion for specific vibration problems, so the next section is about the basis and application of Lagrange's equations. We shall then go on to consider the special properties of systems with symmetric matrices. This involves some fairly detailed matrix algebra. For readers who are willing to take these properties without proof and who do not need Lagrange's equations, it is possible to leave out the next 12 sections and turn to the section *Alternative proof of orthogonality when the eigenvalues are distinct*, which begins on p. 325.

Lagrange's equations

Lagrange's equations of motion are an alternative statement in energy terms of Newton's laws of motion. Their derivation, starting either from the axiom of Newton's laws or from the equivalent variational statement of Hamilton's principle, is given in books on advanced dynamics, for example Synge and Griffith [96] and Crandall *et al.* [16]. For the purposes of this chapter we shall consider only systems that are (i) scleronomic and (ii) holonomic. Restriction (i) excludes systems with moving supports. The geometrical configuration of a system is then given when the values of the response parameters $y_1, y_2, \ldots, y_M$ are all specified. Restriction (ii) means that arbitrary, independent changes in the y's can always be made without violating any geometrical constraints. This is not possible in certain problems of rolling contact without slip (see, for example, Synge and Griffith [96], Ch. 15), and these and similar problems are therefore excluded by restriction (ii).

Subject to these two restrictions, Lagrange's equations for a system with M degrees of freedom can be expressed in the form

$$\frac{d}{dt}\left(\frac{\partial T}{\partial \dot{y}_r}\right) - \frac{\partial T}{\partial y_r} + \frac{\partial V}{\partial y_r} = Q_r, \quad r = 1 \text{ to } M, \qquad (11.8)$$

where the meanings of the various terms are as follows:

$T = T(y_1, y_2, \ldots, y_M, \dot{y}_1, \dot{y}_2, \ldots, \dot{y}_M)$ is the total kinetic energy of the system which, in general, is a function of all the displacements y_r and all the velocities $\dot{y}_r$, $r = 1$ to M. $V = V(y_1, y_2, \ldots, y_M)$ is the total potential energy of the system and is a function of all the displacements y_r, $r = 1$ to M.

$$\frac{\partial}{\partial y_r}$$

means the partial derivative with respect to y_r, with all the other y's and all the $\dot{y}$'s held constant.

$$\frac{\partial}{\partial \dot{y}_r}$$

means the partial derivative with respect to $\dot{y}_r$, with all the other $\dot{y}$'s and all the y's held constant.

Q_r is the rth non-conservative generalized force, which is defined so that, if the configuration of the system changes by δy_r, with all the other y's constant, the work done on the system by all the non-conservative forces is $Q_r \delta y_r$. By definition, a non-conservative force is any force whose work increment cannot be described by the change in a potential-energy function, and so is not included already by the potential-energy term in (11.8).

For rheonomic systems (systems with moving supports), there is no potential energy function (because all the forces may depend on time as well as on position) so V is eliminated from (11.8). Instead all the forces are included in Q_r. The kinetic energy T is now a function of time as well as of the M generalized coordinates and their derivatives; its partial derivatives are calulated at a fixed instant of time. For the non-holonomic case (which is rare in practice), there are significant complications, although a modified version of Lagrange's equations still applies ([96], Ch. 15). We shall restrict ourselves to the simpler holonomic case with fixed supports, which describes most structural vibration problems and many mechanical problems.

Example 11.1 Application of Lagrange's equations

Derive the equations of motion of the three-degree-of-freedom system in Fig. 2.7 by using Lagrange's equations.

The kinetic energy of the three masses is

$$T = \tfrac{1}{2} m(\dot{y}_1^2 + \dot{y}_2^2 + \dot{y}_3^2) \tag{11.9}$$

and so

$$\frac{\partial T}{\partial \dot{y}_1} = m\dot{y}_1, \quad \frac{\partial T}{\partial \dot{y}_2} = m\dot{y}_2, \quad \frac{\partial T}{\partial \dot{y}_3} = m\dot{y}_3 \tag{11.10}$$

and

$$\frac{\mathrm{d}}{\mathrm{d}t}\left(\frac{\partial T}{\partial \dot{y}_1}\right) = m\ddot{y}_1, \quad \frac{\mathrm{d}}{\mathrm{d}t}\left(\frac{\partial T}{\partial \dot{y}_2}\right) = m\ddot{y}_2, \quad \frac{\mathrm{d}}{\mathrm{d}t}\left(\frac{\partial T}{\partial \dot{y}_3}\right) = m\ddot{y}_3. \tag{11.11}$$

Also, since T is independent of the displacements in this example,

$$\frac{\partial T}{\partial y_1} = \frac{\partial T}{\partial y_2} = \frac{\partial T}{\partial y_3} = 0. \tag{11.12}$$

The potential energy of the four springs is

$$V = \tfrac{1}{2} k[y_1^2 + (y_2 - y_1)^2 + (y_3 - y_2)^2 + y_3^2] \qquad (11.13)$$

so that

$$\frac{\partial V}{\partial y_1} = k[y_1 - (y_2 - y_1)] = k[2y_1 - y_2]$$

$$\frac{\partial V}{\partial y_2} = k[(y_2 - y_1) - (y_3 - y_2)] = k[-y_1 + 2y_2 - y_3] \qquad (11.14)$$

$$\frac{\partial V}{\partial y_3} = k[(y_3 - y_2) + y_3] = k[-y_2 + 2y_3].$$

The non-conservative forces are the excitation force $x(t)$ and the viscous-damping force $c\dot{y}_2$, which pushes to the left on the middle mass. When y_1 is incremented by δy_1, with y_2 and y_3 constant, the work input is $x(t)\delta y_1$. Hence

$$Q_1 \delta y_1 = x(t)\,\delta y_1$$

and

$$Q_1 = x(t). \qquad (11.15)$$

When y_2 is incremented with y_1 and y_3 constant, the work input is $-c\dot{y}_2\,\delta y_2$, and so

$$Q_2 = -c\dot{y}_2. \qquad (11.16)$$

No non-conservative force acts on the third mass, and so

$$Q_3 = 0. \qquad (11.17)$$

Substituting these results into (11.8), we have, for $r = 1$, 2 and 3, in turn,

$$m\ddot{y}_1 + k(2y_1 - y_2) = x(t)$$
$$m\ddot{y}_2 + k(-y_1 + 2y_2 - y_3) = -c\dot{y}_2 \qquad (11.18)$$
$$m\ddot{y}_3 + k(-y_2 + 2y_3) = 0.$$

Combining these into a single matrix equation then gives

$$\begin{bmatrix} m & 0 & 0 \\ 0 & m & 0 \\ 0 & 0 & m \end{bmatrix} \begin{bmatrix} \ddot{y}_1 \\ \ddot{y}_2 \\ \ddot{y}_3 \end{bmatrix} + \begin{bmatrix} 0 & 0 & 0 \\ 0 & c & 0 \\ 0 & 0 & 0 \end{bmatrix} \begin{bmatrix} \dot{y}_1 \\ \dot{y}_2 \\ \dot{y}_3 \end{bmatrix} +$$

$$+ \begin{bmatrix} 2k & -k & 0 \\ -k & 2k & -k \\ 0 & -k & 2k \end{bmatrix} \begin{bmatrix} y_1 \\ y_2 \\ y_3 \end{bmatrix} = \begin{bmatrix} x(t) \\ 0 \\ 0 \end{bmatrix} \qquad (11.19)$$

which agrees with our previous result.

Potential energy of a linear elastic system

Figure 11.1 shows a general linear elastic system secured to fixed supports. Suppose that it has M degrees of freedom so that its geometrical configuration is completely specified by M displacement coordinates y_r, $r = 1$ to M. When all these displacements are zero, the system is assumed to be in a state of stable equilibrium. Let a set of externally applied generalized forces x_r, $r = 1$ to M, act on the system at the coordinates y_r. By 'generalized force' we understand a linear force in the direction of y_r if y_r is a linear displacement, or a rotational torque in the direction of y_r if y_r is an angular displacement. Also, let α_{rs}, r, $s = 1$ to M, be a set of influence coefficients defined so that the deflection of coordinate y_r due to generalized force x_s is given by

$$y_r = \alpha_{rs}x_s. \tag{11.20}$$

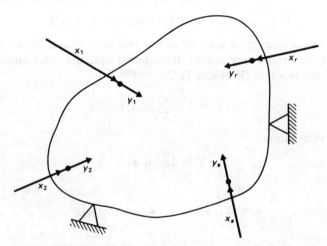

Fig. 11.1 Elastic body with fixed supports whose configuration is defined by generalized displacement coordinates y_1, y_2, y_r, y_s. The generalized forces x_1, x_2, x_r, x_s each act in the direction of the corresponding generalized displacement

Suppose that, initially, no forces are applied, so that the system is at rest with all the displacements y_r, $r = 1$ to M, equal to zero. Let force x_r be applied slowly and the resulting static displacement be y_r. The elastic-strain energy stored by the body is then

$$V = \tfrac{1}{2}x_r y_r = \tfrac{1}{2}\alpha_{rr}x_r^2 \tag{11.21}$$

from (11.20). Now let force x_s be applied also (slowly), with x_r remaining in action. The deflection under x_s is then $\alpha_{ss}x_s$, and the extra deflection under x_r is $\alpha_{rs}x_s$. The total work done on the system is therefore

$$\tfrac{1}{2}\alpha_{ss}x_s^2 + \alpha_{rs}x_r x_s \tag{11.22}$$

and the strain energy increases to

$$V = \tfrac{1}{2}\alpha_{rr}x_r^2 + \alpha_{rs}x_rx_s + \tfrac{1}{2}\alpha_{ss}x_s^2. \tag{11.23}$$

If the order in which the two forces are applied is reversed, so that x_s is applied first, followed by x_r, the corresponding result is

$$V = \tfrac{1}{2}\alpha_{ss}x_s^2 + \alpha_{sr}x_sx_r + \tfrac{1}{2}\alpha_{rr}x_r^2. \tag{11.24}$$

Since the elastic-strain energy of a linear system is independent of the order in which the loads are applied, these two results (11.23) and (11.24) must be the same, and so

$$\alpha_{rs} = \alpha_{sr}, \ r \neq s. \tag{11.25}$$

This is Maxwell's reciprocity relationship and it holds for any system for which the principle of linear superposition applies.

As a result of (11.25), the energy expression (11.23) can be written as

$$V = \tfrac{1}{2}(\alpha_{rr}x_r^2 + \alpha_{rs}x_rx_s + \alpha_{sr}x_sx_r + \alpha_{ss}x_s^2). \tag{11.26}$$

This is the strain energy as a result of the two generalized forces x_r and x_s only. When the remaining forces are applied and the total strain energy calculated, the result is (Problem 11.2).

$$V = \tfrac{1}{2}\sum_{r=1}^{M} \sum_{s=1}^{M} \alpha_{rs}x_rx_s \tag{11.27}$$

or, in matrix notation,

$$V = \tfrac{1}{2}x^{\mathrm{T}} \, \alpha \, x \tag{11.28}$$

where

$$x = [x_1, x_2, \ldots, x_r, \ldots, x_M]^{\mathrm{T}} \tag{11.29}$$

and

$$\alpha = \begin{bmatrix} \alpha_{11} & \alpha_{12} & \cdots & \alpha_{1M} \\ \alpha_{21} & \alpha_{22} & \cdots & \alpha_{2M} \\ & & \cdot & \\ & & \cdot & \\ & & \cdot & \\ \alpha_{M1} & \alpha_{M2} & \cdots & \alpha_{MM} \end{bmatrix} \tag{11.30}$$

Let k be the $M \times M$ stiffness matrix which relates the $M \times 1$ static-displacement vector

$$y = [y_1, y_2, \ldots, y_r, \ldots, y_M]^{\mathrm{T}} \tag{11.31}$$

to the force vector x defined by (11.29), so that

$$x = k \, y. \tag{11.32}$$

By the reversal law for transposed products we then have

$$x^T = y^T k^T \qquad (11.33)$$

and, substituting for x and x^T in (11.28), the strain energy U can be expressed as

$$V = \tfrac{1}{2} y^T k^T \alpha \, k \, y. \qquad (11.34)$$

The influence coefficient matrix α is the inverse of the stiffness matrix, since, from (11.20)

$$y = \alpha \, x \qquad (11.35)$$

and so, by comparing (11.32) and (11.35), we have

$$\alpha k = I \qquad (11.36)$$

and, taking the transpose of this equation,

$$k^T \alpha^T = I. \qquad (11.37)$$

On account of Maxwell's theorem, equation (11.25),

$$\alpha = \alpha^T \qquad (11.38)$$

and so, from (11.37),

$$k^T \alpha = I. \qquad (11.39)$$

On substituting this result into (11.34), we then find that an alternative expression for the strain energy is

$$V = \tfrac{1}{2} y^T k \, y \qquad (11.40)$$

where k is the $M \times M$ stiffness matrix and y is the displacement vector defined by (11.31). From (11.39)

$$k^T = \alpha^{-1} \qquad (11.41)$$

so, using (11.36),

$$k^T = k. \qquad (11.42)$$

Therefore the stiffness matrix k is also a symmetric matrix.

Potential energy is an essentially positive quantity. Unless some of the springs have zero stiffness (for example, if the system is not firmly attached to its supports or has disconnected parts), there is always an increase in the system's potential energy V when its displacements change from zero. Hence, V, as given by (11.40), is always positive or, in the exceptional case of zero stiffness, it is zero. The real, symmetric matrix k in (11.40) is therefore a *positive semi-definite* matrix. By definition, a positive definite matrix is a real, symmetric matrix, for example k, for which $y^T k y$ is always positive, whatever the real vector y. A positive semi-definite matrix is one for which $y^T k y$ is always positive or zero, but is never negative; it is also called a *non-negative definite* matrix.

We conclude that the general stiffness matrix k for a linear elastic system is a real, symmetric matrix which is positive definite or, occasionally, positive semi-definite. The only restriction is that the system, in addition to being linearly elastic, must also be scleronomic and holonomic so that its configuration can be completely defined by M independent generalized coordinates y_r, $r = 1$ to M.

Kinetic energy for small-amplitude vibrations

Consider the kinetic energy of a system subject to the same conditions as in the last section. The total kinetic energy is the sum of the kinetic energy of the component parts. If every part is thought to be composed of mass particles, the total kinetic energy T is the sum of the kinetic energies of the particles, so that

$$T = \tfrac{1}{2} \sum_i m_i v_i^2 \tag{11.43}$$

where v_i is the absolute velocity of the ith particle of mass m_i. If position vector r_i locates m_i from a fixed origin, then

$$v_i = \frac{\mathrm{d}}{\mathrm{d}t} r_i, \tag{11.44}$$

where r_i is a function of the generalized coordinates. Suppose that there are M degrees of freedom so that there are M independent generalized coordinates y_r, $r = 1$ to M. Then

$$r_i = r_i(y_1, y_2, \ldots, y_M) \tag{11.45}$$

and

$$\frac{\mathrm{d}}{\mathrm{d}t} r_i = \sum_{r=1}^{M} \frac{\partial r_i}{\partial y_r} \frac{\mathrm{d}y_r}{\mathrm{d}t}. \tag{11.46}$$

Hence, from (11.44) and (11.46),

$$v_i^2 = \sum_{r=1}^{M} \sum_{s=1}^{M} \frac{\partial r_i}{\partial y_r} \frac{\partial r_i}{\partial y_s} \frac{\mathrm{d}y_r}{\mathrm{d}t} \frac{\mathrm{d}y_s}{\mathrm{d}t} \tag{11.47}$$

or, putting

$$a_{rs}^{(i)}(y_1, y_2, \ldots, y_M) = a_{sr}^{(i)}(y_1, y_2, \ldots, y_M) = \frac{\partial r_i}{\partial y_r} \cdot \frac{\partial r_i}{\partial y_s} \tag{11.48}$$

we get

$$v_i^2 = \sum_{r=1}^{M} \sum_{s=1}^{M} a_{rs}^{(i)} \dot{y}_r \dot{y}_s. \tag{11.49}$$

The coefficients $a_{rs}^{(i)}$ in (11.49) are functions of the coordinates y_1, y_2, $\ldots$, y_M and may be expressed in a Taylor expansion, so that

$$a_{rs}^{(i)}(y_1, y_2, \ldots, y_M) = a_{rs}^{(i)}(0, 0, \ldots, 0) + \frac{\partial}{\partial y_1} a_{rs}^{(i)}(0, 0, \ldots, 0) \, dy_1 +$$

$$+ \ldots + \frac{\partial}{\partial y_M} a_{rs}^{(i)}(0, 0, \ldots, 0) \, dy_M +$$

+ higher-order terms in $dy_1, dy_2, \ldots, dy_M$. (11.50)

We shall now assume that the system is vibrating about a position of stable equilibrium at

$$y_1 = y_2 = \ldots = y_M = 0 \qquad (11.51)$$

and that the amplitudes of vibration are small. Then the derivatives $\dot{y}_r$, $r = 1$ to M, are all small and v_i^2 defined by (11.49) is of the second order in small quantities. Hence we get v_i^2 to second-order accuracy by retaining only the constant terms in the Taylor expansions (11.50). Therefore the $a_{rs}^{(i)}(y_1, y_2, \ldots, y_M)$ in (11.49) may be replaced by constant values $a_{rs}^{(i)}(0, 0, \ldots, 0)$. On substituting for v_i from (11.49) into (11.43), we then find that

$$T = \tfrac{1}{2} \sum_i m_i \sum_{r=1}^{M} \sum_{s=1}^{M} a_{rs}^{(i)} \dot{y}_r \dot{y}_s \qquad (11.52)$$

$$= \tfrac{1}{2} \sum_{r=1}^{M} \sum_{s=1}^{M} \dot{y}_r \dot{y}_s \sum_i m_i a_{rs}^{(i)} \qquad (11.53)$$

and after defining new constants

$$m_{rs} = \sum_i m_i a_{rs}^{(i)} \qquad (11.54)$$

this gives

$$T = \tfrac{1}{2} \sum_{r=1}^{M} \sum_{s=1}^{M} \dot{y}_r \dot{y}_s m_{rs} \qquad (11.55)$$

for the total kinetic energy of the system where, from (11.48),

$$m_{rs} = m_{sr}. \qquad (11.56)$$

If the $M \times M$ mass matrix is defined by m, where element m_{rs} is defined by (11.54), and if $\dot{y}$ is the $M \times 1$ vector defined by

$$\dot{y} = [\dot{y}_1, \dot{y}_2, \ldots, \dot{y}_M]^T \qquad (11.57)$$

then (11.55) may be written in the matrix form

$$T = \tfrac{1}{2} \dot{y}^T m \dot{y}. \qquad (11.58)$$

We conclude that (11.58) is a general description of the total kinetic energy of an M-degree-of-freedom system for small movements from its position of static equilibrium. The configuration of the system must be completely defined by its M independent generalized coordinates y_r, $r = 1$

to M (so that the system must be scleronomic and holonomic). Also, the deflections from static equilibrium must be small enough that the derivatives $\dot{y}_r$, $r = 1$ to M, are all small. Under this condition (11.58) has second-order accuracy, but it must be remembered that it is an approximate equation and applies only for the small-amplitude vibration of a system about its position of stable static equilibrium.

Because of (11.56), the $M \times M$ mass matrix m is always symmetric. Also, since kinetic energy cannot be negative, the product $\dot{y}^T m \dot{y}$ can never be negative. Provided that none of the degrees of freedom has zero mass, $\dot{y}^T m \dot{y}$ is never zero unless $\dot{y}$ is a null vector, and so m must be a positive definite matrix. If there is a coordinate with zero mass, then that coordinate may be given a rate of change without altering the kinetic energy, and in that case m is a positive semi-definite matrix because $\dot{y}^T m \dot{y}$ can be zero without $\dot{y}$ having all its elements zero. We conclude that m is a real, symmetric matrix which is either positive definite or positive semi-definite.

General equations of small-amplitude vibration

We can now use Lagrange's equations to derive general equations of motion for the small-amplitude vibration of a linear elastic system with fixed supports. For such a system, the kinetic energy T is given by (11.58) and the potential energy V is given by (11.40), so that, if y is the vector of displacement responses,

$$T = \tfrac{1}{2}\dot{y}^T m \dot{y} \tag{11.59}$$

and

$$V = \tfrac{1}{2}y^T k\, y. \tag{11.60}$$

If there are M degrees of freedom, m and k have order $M \times M$ and they are both real, symmetric matrices. Usually they are both positive definite, although either may be positive semi-definite if the system includes particles of zero mass or springs of zero stiffness.

To apply Lagrange's equations (11.8), we have to differentiate (11.59) and (11.60), and to do so it is convenient to write T and V in the double-summation forms

$$T = \tfrac{1}{2}\sum_{j=1}^{M} \sum_{k=1}^{M} m_{jk}\dot{y}_j\dot{y}_k \tag{11.61}$$

and

$$V = \tfrac{1}{2}\sum_{j=1}^{M} \sum_{k=1}^{M} k_{jk}y_j y_k \tag{11.62}$$

which are equivalent to (11.59) and (11.60). Suppose, for example, that $M = 2$. Then (11.61) and (11.62) give

$$T = \tfrac{1}{2}(m_{11}\dot{y}_1^2 + m_{12}\dot{y}_1\dot{y}_2 + m_{21}\dot{y}_2\dot{y}_1 + m_{22}\dot{y}_2^2) \tag{11.63}$$

and

$$V = \tfrac{1}{2}(k_{11}y_1^2 + k_{12}y_1y_2 + k_{21}y_2y_1 + k_{22}y_2^2). \tag{11.64}$$

On differentiating T with respect to $\dot{y}_1$ and V with respect to y_1, we get

$$\frac{\partial T}{\partial \dot{y}_1} = \tfrac{1}{2}(2m_{11}\dot{y}_1 + m_{12}\dot{y}_2 + m_{21}\dot{y}_2) \tag{11.65}$$

and

$$\frac{\partial V}{\partial y_1} = \tfrac{1}{2}(2k_{11}y_1 + k_{12}y_2 + k_{21}y_2) \tag{11.66}$$

or, since m and k are symmetric so that

$$m_{21} = m_{12}$$
$$k_{21} = k_{12}, \tag{11.67}$$

we have

$$\frac{\partial T}{\partial \dot{y}_1} = (m_{11}\dot{y}_1 + m_{12}\dot{y}_2) \tag{11.68}$$

and

$$\frac{\partial V}{\partial y_1} = (k_{11}y_1 + k_{12}y_2). \tag{11.69}$$

These results may easily be extended to the general case (Problem 11.2) to prove that

$$\frac{\partial T}{\partial \dot{y}_r} = \sum_{j=1}^{M} m_{rj}\,\dot{y}_j \tag{11.70}$$

and

$$\frac{\partial V}{\partial y_r} = \sum_{j=1}^{M} k_{rj}\,y_j. \tag{11.71}$$

For substitution into Lagrange's equations (11.8), we need the derivative of (11.70), which is

$$\frac{d}{dt}\left(\frac{\partial T}{\partial \dot{y}_r}\right) = \sum_{j=1}^{M} m_{rj}\ddot{y}_j \tag{11.72}$$

provided that the mass distribution remains fixed so that the m_{rj} are constants. Also, the derivative $\partial T/\partial y_r$ in (11.8) is zero for small-amplitude oscillations because, according to (11.59), T is independent of the (small) displacements y_r. Hence on substituting from (11.71) and (11.72) into (11.8), the general equations of motion are

$$\sum_{j=1}^{M} m_{rj}\ddot{y}_j + \sum_{j=1}^{M} k_{rj}\,y_j = Q_r, \; r = 1 \text{ to } M. \tag{11.73}$$

In terms of the response vector

$$y = [y_1, y_2, \ldots, y_M]^\mathrm{T} \tag{11.74}$$

and a vector generalized forces Q defined by

$$Q = [Q_1, Q_2, \ldots, Q_M]^\mathrm{T} \tag{11.75}$$

this may be written in the standard matrix form

$$m\ddot{y} + k\,y = Q \tag{11.76}$$

where m and k are the $M \times M$ mass and stiffness matrices in (11.59) and (11.60) which, for a linear elastic system secured to fixed supports, are symmetric and positive definite (or semi-definite) matrices. The elements of the vector Q include all the non-conservative forces which cannot be represented by the potential energy V, and include both damping terms and externally-applied excitation forces.

Special properties of systems with symmetric matrices

We now consider some of the special properties of the eigenvalues and eigenvectors of a general M-degree-of-freedom system described by the set of equations

$$m\ddot{y}(t) + k\,y(t) = O \tag{11.77}$$

where m and k are both real, symmetric matrices. First, we give the results of three theorems of linear algebra that will be needed in the later analysis.

Three important theorems

Definition
An orthogonal matrix R is a real, square matrix whose inverse is the same as its transpose so that

$$R^\mathrm{T}R = I \tag{11.78}$$

where I is the identity matrix.

Theorem 1
If A is a *real, symmetric* matrix of order $M \times M$, it is always possible to find an orthogonal matrix R such that

$$R^\mathrm{T}AR = [\mathrm{diag}\,\lambda_j] \tag{11.79}$$

where λ_j, $j = 1$ to M, are the eigenvalues of A which are always all real. Also, the eigenvectors of A are real and orthogonal and there are always M independent eigenvectors even if there are repeated (multiple) eigenvalues. The eigenvector matrix therefore satisfies (11.78).

Theorem 2

If A is a *real, symmetric* matrix which is also *positive definite*, then, in addition to being real, the eigenvalues of A are always positive. Hence, it is always possible to write (11.79) as

$$R^{T}AR = [\text{diag } \alpha_j^2] \qquad (11.80)$$

where, if A has order $M \times M$, α_j^2, $j = 1$ to M, are the M positive, real eigenvalues of A.

Theorem 3

If A, H and P are all matrices of order $M \times M$ (not necessarily real or symmetrical) which are related by

$$P = H^{-1}AH. \qquad (11.81)$$

then A and P have the same eigenvalues and, if U is the matrix of (column) eigenvectors of A, then $H^{-1}U$ is the corresponding matrix of eigenvectors of P.

The proofs of these theorems are given in, for example, Wilkinson [110], Ch. 1.

Standard forms of the equations of motion

We now apply these theorems to the system defined by (11.77). Starting from equation (11.77), let the free-vibration solution be

$$y(t) = e^{i\omega t}y \qquad (11.82)$$

so that, on substituting for $y(t)$ in (11.77),

$$[-\omega^2 m + k]y = O. \qquad (11.83)$$

Putting

$$\lambda = \omega^2 \qquad (11.84)$$

this can be written as

$$k\,y = \lambda\,m\,y \qquad (11.85)$$

or, on pre-multiplying by m^{-1}, as

$$m^{-1}k\,y = \lambda\,y. \qquad (11.86)$$

This is the standard eigenvalue problem

$$A\,y = \lambda\,y \qquad (11.87)$$

where A is the real matrix given by

$$A = m^{-1}k. \qquad (11.88)$$

Alternatively, if

$$\mu = \frac{1}{\omega^2}, \tag{11.89}$$

(11.83) can be written as

$$k^{-1}m\,y = \mu\,y \tag{11.90}$$

which is also in the standard form (11.87), but with

$$A = k^{-1}m. \tag{11.91}$$

Because the classical results of eigenvalue theory apply to the standard form (11.87), it is helpful to rewrite equation (11.83) either in the standard form (11.86) or in the standard form (11.90). The first requires m^{-1} to exist, the second requires k^{-1} to exist. We shall show next that, if a matrix is positive definite, then its inverse always exists. To reduce the general equation (11.83) to standard form therefore requires either m or k to be positive definite (but not both).

Proof that a positive-definite matrix always has an inverse

Let A be a positive definite matrix which, by definition, is also real and symmetric. Then, from theorem 2, we can always write

$$R^{\mathrm{T}}A\,R = [\mathrm{diag}\,\alpha_j^2] \tag{11.92}$$

where R is an orthogonal matrix (by definition real) for which, from (11.78),

$$R^{-1} = R^{\mathrm{T}}. \tag{11.93}$$

Taking the inverse of both sides of (11.92) using the reversal rule for the inverse of a product, gives

$$R^{-1}A^{-1}\,(R^{\mathrm{T}})^{-1} = [\mathrm{diag}\,1/\alpha_j^2] \tag{11.94}$$

or, from (11.93),

$$R^{\mathrm{T}}A^{-1}R = [\mathrm{diag}\,1/\alpha_j^2]. \tag{11.95}$$

On pre- and post-multiplying by R and R^{T}, respectively, we then get

$$A^{-1} = R[\mathrm{diag}\,1/\alpha_j^2]R^{\mathrm{T}}. \tag{11.96}$$

By definition, the orthogonal matrix R and its transpose R^{T} both exist, and the α_j^2, $j = 1$ to M, are all real, positive quantities. Since none of the α_j^2 is zero, none of the $1/\alpha_j^2$ is infinite, and so $[\mathrm{diag}\,1/\alpha_j^2]$ exists. We conclude from (11.96) that A^{-1} exists. Therefore a real, symmetric matrix A always has an inverse if A is positive definite.

In the following analysis we shall assume that m is the positive-definite matrix, so that m^{-1} always exists, and use the standard form (11.87) with

A defined by (11.88). However, a similar analysis can be carried out for the alternative case when k is positive definite and the standard form has A defined by (11.91). The eigenvalues μ in the latter case are the inverse of the eigenvalues λ when (11.88) is used for A.

Similarity transformation to find a symmetric matrix that is similar to $m^{-1}k$

We now investigate the eigenvalues and eigenvectors of the matrix $m^{-1}k$, where both m and k are real, symmetric matrices and m is positive definite.

We have seen that, because m is positive definite, m^{-1} always exists. It is easy to see that m^{-1} is also a symmetric, positive-definite matrix. Replacing A by m in (11.96)

$$m^{-1} = R[\operatorname{diag} 1/\alpha_j^2]\, R^{\mathrm{T}} \tag{11.97}$$

and, taking the transpose of both sides of this equation, using the reversal law for transposed products, gives

$$(m^{-1})^{\mathrm{T}} = R[\operatorname{diag} 1/\alpha_j^2]\, R^{\mathrm{T}} = m^{-1}. \tag{11.98}$$

Therefore the transpose of m^{-1} is equal to m^{-1}, and hence m^{-1} must be symmetric. On pre- and post-multiplying (11.97) by R^{T} and R, respectively, and using (11.78), we find that

$$R^{\mathrm{T}}m^{-1}R = [\operatorname{diag} 1/\alpha_j^2] \tag{11.99}$$

which has the standard form (11.80) of theorem 2. The conclusion is that, if m is real, symmetric and positive definite, then so is m^{-1}.

However, because m^{-1} and k are both symmetric, it does not follow that $m^{-1}k$ will be symmetric. In general, it will not be (as the reader can easily check by multiplying together two small symmetric matrices). But although $m^{-1}k$ is not symmetric, it is possible to use theorem 3 to find a real, symmetric matrix P which is derived from $m^{-1}k$ by a similarity transformation like (11.81). Since P is similar to $m^{-1}k$, by theorem 3 its eigenvalues will be the same as those of $m^{-1}k$ and its eigenvectors will be related to the eigenvectors of $m^{-1}k$. Since P is real and symmetric, from theorem 1, its eigenvalues will always be real and it will have a full set of orthogonal eigenvectors. Therefore we can conclude that the eigenvalues of $m^{-1}k$ will always be real and that $m^{-1}k$ will have a full set of eigenvectors that can be calculated from the orthogonal eigenvectors of P. These properties simplify the later analysis considerably.

We want to find a transformation matrix H such that

$$H^{-1}m^{-1}k\,H = P \tag{11.100}$$

where P is real and symmetric. From (11.97), we know that m^{-1} may be written as

$$m^{-1} = R D^2 R^T \qquad (11.101)$$

where R is a (real) orthogonal matrix and

$$D = [\text{diag } 1/\alpha_j] \qquad (11.102)$$

where the α_j are all real and positive. On substituting from (11.101),

$$m^{-1}k = R D^2 R^T k. \qquad (11.103)$$

Pre-multiplying by $D^{-1}R^T$ and post-multiplying by

$$(D^{-1}R^T)^{-1} = RD \qquad (11.104)$$

from (11.93), (11.103) gives

$$(D^{-1}R^T) (m^{-1}k) (D^{-1}R^T)^{-1} = (D^{-1}R^T) (RD^2R^Tk) (RD)$$
$$= D R^T k R D \qquad (11.105)$$

after using (11.78). The r.h.s. of (11.105) is a symmetric matrix because

$$(DR^T k R D)^T = D^T R^T k^T R D^T$$
$$= D R^T k R D \qquad (11.106)$$

so that the operation of transposition leaves the r.h.s. unchanged. We conclude that the transformation matrix H in (11.100) is the real matrix

$$H = RD \qquad (11.107)$$

where, from (11.101),

$$m^{-1} = HH^T. \qquad (11.108)$$

Eigenvectors of $m^{-1} k$

We have now reached the position that, if m is positive definite, $m^{-1} k$ has only real eigenvalues and a full set of eigenvectors. Alternatively, if k is positive definite, we can show in the same way that $k^{-1} m$ has only real eigenvalues and a full set of eigenvectors. Let V be the $M \times M$ matrix of real (column) eigenvectors of the real, symmetric matrix P defined by (11.100) when H is given by (11.107). Then, from theorem 1, V is an orthogonal matrix so that

$$V^T V = I. \qquad (11.109)$$

Also, let U be the $M \times M$ matrix of eigenvectors of $m^{-1}k$. From theorem 3, U is related to V by

$$U = HV \qquad (11.110)$$

so that, from (11.107),

$$U = RDV. \tag{11.111}$$

Since R, D and V are real matrices, we see that U is real, and so the eigenvectors of $m^{-1}k$ are all real. Also, from (11.111) and (11.78),

$$V = D^{-1}R^{T}U \tag{11.112}$$

and, substituting for V in (11.109) from (11.112),

$$(U^{T}RD^{-1})(D^{-1}R^{T}U) = I \tag{11.113}$$

so that

$$U^{T}RD^{-2}R^{T}U = I. \tag{11.114}$$

But, from (11.101),

$$m = RD^{-2}R^{T} \tag{11.115}$$

and so (11.114) gives

$$U^{T}m\,U = I. \tag{11.116}$$

Hence the eigenvector matrix U of $m^{-1}k$ is always a real matrix which is *orthogonal with respect to* m.

Proof that the eigenvalues of $m^{-1}k$ cannot be negative

From (11.85) we have

$$k\,y_j = \lambda_j m\,y_j, \; j = 1 \text{ to } M \tag{11.117}$$

and, on pre-multiplying by y_j^{T}, we get

$$y_j^{T}k\,y_j = \lambda_j y_j^{T}m\,y_j \tag{11.118}$$

so that

$$\lambda_j = \frac{y_j^{T}k\,y_j}{y_j^{T}m\,y_j}. \tag{11.119}$$

If m is a positive-definite matrix, we always have

$$y_j^{T}my_j > 0 \tag{11.120}$$

and, since k is positive definite or semi-definite,

$$y_j^{T}ky_j \geqslant 0 \tag{11.121}$$

so that the λ_j defined by (11.119) are always positive or possibly zero, but never negative.

If k, rather than m, is the positive-definite matrix, with m positive semi-definite, then the same argument may be used to show that the eigenvalues μ of $k^{-1}m$ can never be negative.

If m is positive definite, we conclude from (11.84) that a conservative system with M degrees of freedom always has M natural frequencies (some of which may be repeated and some of which may be zero). If k is positive definite, the system also always has M eigenvalues, but if some of these are zero the corresponding natural frequencies will then be infinite on account of (11.89).

If neither m nor k is positive definite, we can no longer say for certain that there will be a full set of eigenvectors. If there are not, it will be necessary to fall back on the more general analysis discussed in Chapters 6 and 8 and to find a matrix of principal vectors by which $m^{-1}k$ or $k^{-1}m$ may be reduced to its Jordan form. The advantages of the analysis using an orthogonal eigenvector matrix like (11.116) are then lost. For the rest of this chapter we shall assume that the system being studied has a full set of eigenvectors, and it is convenient to assume that the mass matrix m is positive definite because then there are no infinite natural frequencies.

Other orthogonality conditions

Reverting to the general analysis with m positive definite, equation (11.117) is true for each of the M independent eigenvectors y_j, $j = 1$ to M. Each y_j is a column of the eigenvector matrix U, and combining the M separate equations (11.117) into a single matrix equation, we have

$$kU = mU \, [\text{diag} \, \lambda_j] \tag{11.122}$$

or, in terms of the natural frequencies ω_j defined by

$$\omega_j^2 = \lambda_j, \tag{11.123}$$

(11.122) becomes

$$k \, U = mU \, [\text{diag} \, \omega_j^2]. \tag{11.124}$$

On pre-multiplying this equation by U^T,

$$U^T k \, U = U^T mU \, [\text{diag} \, \omega_j^2] \tag{11.125}$$

or, on account of (11.116),

$$U^T k \, U = [\text{diag} \, \omega_j^2]. \tag{11.126}$$

Therefore the eigenvector matrix U is also *orthogonal with respect to k*.

The form of the diagonal matrix on the right-hand sides of (11.116) and (11.126) depends on the (arbitrary) scaling that is adopted for the eigenvectors, y_j, $j = 1$ to M, which are the columns of U. In the general case that we have considered in previous chapters, the eigenvector matrix U is not an orthogonal matrix, and so we could adopt any convenient scaling for the columns of U because we automatically have

$$U^{-1}U = I. \tag{11.127}$$

Now that U is a matrix with special properties of orthogonality, it is convenient to normalize U so as to take maximum benefit of the advantages of m and k being symmetrical. The best approach seems to be to adopt the convention of normalizing to satisfy (11.116), which means that each eigenvector must be scaled to satisfy†

$$y_j^T m y_j = 1 \qquad (11.128)$$

or, in summation form,

$$\sum_{r=1}^{M} \sum_{s=1}^{M} m_{rs} \, y_{rj} \, y_{sj} = 1 \qquad (11.129)$$

where y_{rj}, y_{sj} are the rth and sth elements of the jth eigenvector.

However, we note that other authors use different conventions. The most popular seems to be to replace (11.116) by

$$U^T m \, U = \bar{m} \qquad (11.130)$$

where $\bar{m}$ is the total mass of the vibration system. With this convention, (11.126) becomes

$$U^T k \, U = \bar{m} \, [\text{diag } \omega_j^2]. \qquad (11.131)$$

There is then a factor of $\bar{m}$ or $1/\bar{m}$ entering into the response formulae that use (11.130) and (11.131). We are normalizing so that

$$\bar{m} = 1 \qquad (11.132)$$

which is possible since the choice of $\bar{m}$ is arbitrary.

Alternative proof of orthogonality when the eigenvalues are distinct

The preceding general analysis depends on m and k being symmetric and on one of them being positive definite. Under these conditions there will always be a full set of eigenvectors. If m is the matrix which is positive definite, all the natural frequencies are finite, and the eigenvector matrix U will satisfy the orthogonality conditions (11.116) and (11.126). It does not matter whether the eigenvalues are distinct or not. They can be repeated any number of times.

However, if the eigenvalues are distinct, a simpler proof of the orthogonality of the eigenvectors is possible, as follows.

Let eigenvector y_j correspond to eigenvalue ω_j^2 and eigenvector y_k to eigenvalue ω_k^2. Then, from (11.83),

$$\omega_j^2 m y_j = k \, y_j \qquad (11.133)$$

† Following our previous nomenclature, y_j is the jth column of the eigenvector matrix U. The reader is reminded that this convention was adopted originally because Y had been used for the amplitudes of $y(t)$.

and

$$\omega_k^2 m y_k = k y_k \tag{11.134}$$

where all the quantities are real and k and m are symmetric. Taking the transpose of (11.133) gives

$$\omega_j^2 y_j^T m = y_j^T k. \tag{11.135}$$

Now pre-multiplying (11.134) by y_j^T and post-multiplying (11.135) by y_k, we get

$$\omega_k^2 y_j^T m y_k = y_j^T k y_k \tag{11.136}$$

and

$$\omega_j^2 y_j^T m y_k = y_j^T k y_k. \tag{11.137}$$

The right-hand sides of these last two equations are the same, and subtracting (11.137) from (11.136) gives

$$(\omega_k^2 - \omega_j^2) y_j^T m y_k = 0. \tag{11.138}$$

Provided that ω_k and ω_j are different, we conclude from (11.138) that

$$y_j^T m y_k = 0, j \neq k. \tag{11.139}$$

Each vector y_j may be normalized arbitrarily, but if we normalize as before, so that

$$y_j^T m y_j = 1, j = 1 \text{ to } M, \tag{11.140}$$

then if U is the $M \times M$ eigenvector matrix each of whose columns is one of the y_j, equations (11.139) and (11.140) give

$$U^T m U = I \tag{11.141}$$

in agreement with (11.116).

Also from (11.136), we have, with (11.139),

$$y_j^T k y_k = 0, j \neq k, \tag{11.142}$$

and, from (11.140),

$$y_j^T k y_j = \omega_j^2 \tag{11.143}$$

so that

$$U^T k U = [\text{diag } \omega_j^2] \tag{11.144}$$

in agreement with (11.126).

Time response of lightly-damped symmetric systems

We shall now consider the time response of a system with M degrees of freedom represented by the general equation (11.76). Let the vector of non-conservative forces Q be split into two parts, one representing viscous damping forces arising within the system, $c\dot{y}$, and the other representing externally applied forces x, so that

$$Q = -c\dot{y} + x. \tag{11.145}$$

In this case, (11.76) becomes

$$m\ddot{y} + c\dot{y} + ky = x \tag{11.146}$$

where c is a new $M \times M$ real matrix determined by the characteristics of the system being studied. For the moment we say nothing about the form of c except that it is real. We shall assume that m and k are real and symmetrical and that m is positive definite.

Let the natural frequencies of the conservative system

$$m\ddot{y} + ky = O \tag{11.147}$$

be ω_j, $j = 1$ to M, and let its $M \times M$ matrix of real eigenvalues be U, where

$$U^T m U = I \tag{11.148}$$

and

$$U^T k U = [\text{diag } \omega_j^2] \tag{11.149}$$

in agreement with the results of the previous sections.

In order to solve (11.146), we make a change of coordinates from y to normal coordinates q where

$$y = Uq. \tag{11.150}$$

On substituting for y in (11.146) and then pre-multiplying by U^T, we get

$$U^T m U\ddot{q} + U^T c U\dot{q} + U^T k Uq = U^T x. \tag{11.151}$$

Then, using (11.148) and (11.149), this reduces to

$$\ddot{q} + U^T c U\dot{q} + [\text{diag } \omega_j^2] q = U^T x. \tag{11.152}$$

The M equations for q_j, $j = 1$ to M, will be uncoupled if $U^T c U$ is a diagonal matrix. This will be the case if

$$c = \alpha m \tag{11.153}$$

or

$$c = \beta k \tag{11.154}$$

or a linear combination of both, where α and β are real constants. In problems of the small-amplitude vibration of elastic systems with low damping, motion will be dominated by the mass and stiffness terms, except in the vicinity of each resonance, and it is then customary to assume that $U^T c U$ is diagonal in such a way that

$$U^{\mathrm{T}} c \, U = [\mathrm{diag}\, 2\zeta_j \omega_j] \tag{11.155}$$

where ζ_j is the damping ratio of the jth mode. We shall discuss the consequences of the assumptions (11.153) or (11.154) shortly, but for the present we shall assume that (11.155) is true. Under this assumption, (11.152) gives

$$\ddot{q} + [\mathrm{diag}\, 2\zeta_j \omega_j] \, \dot{q} + [\mathrm{diag}\, \omega_j^2] \, q = U^{\mathrm{T}} x \tag{11.156}$$

and motion in each of the M normal coordinates q_j, $j = 1$ to M, is then uncoupled from motion in all the other normal coordinates.

Consider the jth of the M equations (11.156), which may be written

$$\ddot{q}_j + 2\zeta_j \omega_j \dot{q}_j + \omega_j^2 q_j = \phi_j(t) \tag{11.157}$$

where $\phi_j(t)$ is the jth element of the excitation vector

$$U^{\mathrm{T}} x(t) \equiv U^{\mathrm{T}} x. \tag{11.158}$$

Let $h_j(t)$ be the unit impulse-response function for $q_j(t)$ when $\phi_j(t)$ is replaced by a delta function at $t = 0$. Then the solution of (11.157) is given by the usual convolution integral (9.25) as

$$q_j(t) = \int_{-\infty}^{t} h_j(t - \tau) \, \phi_j(\tau) \, \mathrm{d}\tau. \tag{11.159}$$

There is a similar equation for each of the other rows of (11.156) and, combining all these back into a single matrix equation, we get

$$q(t) = \int_{-\infty}^{t} [\mathrm{diag}\, h_j(t - \tau)] \, U^{\mathrm{T}} x(\tau) \, \mathrm{d}\tau \tag{11.160}$$

or, reverting to the vector of physical-response coordinates $y(t)$ by using (11.150),

$$y(t) = \int_{-\infty}^{t} U[\mathrm{diag}\, h_j(t - \tau)] \, U^{\mathrm{T}} x(\tau) \, \mathrm{d}\tau. \tag{11.161}$$

This is a general solution for the set of M second-order equations (11.146) when subjected to arbitrary excitation $x(\tau)$. U is the $M \times M$ eigenvector matrix for the (real) displacements of the M coordinates, normalized to satisfy (11.148). $[\mathrm{diag}\, h_j(t - \tau)]$ is an $M \times M$ diagonal matrix of the modal impulse-response functions, which from (11.157) are the solutions of

$$\ddot{h}_j + 2\zeta_j \omega_j h_j + \omega_j^2 h_j = \delta(t - \tau). \tag{11.162}$$

and which, from equation (1.56), are given by

$$h_j(t - \tau) = \frac{1}{\omega_j \sqrt{1 - \zeta_j^2}} \, \mathrm{e}^{-\zeta_j \omega_j (t - \tau)} \sin{(\omega_j \sqrt{1 - \zeta_j^2}(t - \tau))},$$
$$t > \tau, \, j = 1 \text{ to } M. \tag{11.163}$$

This solution is subject to the condition on damping given by (11.155) and it also assumes that m and k are real symmetric matrices and that m is positive definite. If m is positive semi-definite, we expect that some of the natural frequencies ω_j will not exist (i.e. they will be infinite), and the solution (11.163) then fails. Provided that k is positive definite, this problem can be overcome by putting the A-matrix in the form (11.91) instead of (11.88), so that the eigenvalues are $1/\omega_j^2$ instead of ω_j^2. The normalizations (11.116) and (11.126) and equations (11.162) and (11.163) are then modified (see Problem 11.5).

Frequency response of lightly-damped symmetric systems

Returning to the normal-mode equation (11.157), let $H_j(i\omega)$ be the frequency-response function for the jth normal coordinate q_j, so that if

$$\phi_j(t) = e^{i\omega t} \tag{11.164}$$

then the corresponding steady-state solution is

$$q_j(t) = H_j(i\omega)\, e^{i\omega t}. \tag{11.165}$$

On substituting from (11.164) and (11.165) into (11.157), we find that

$$H_j(i\omega) = \frac{1}{(i\omega)^2 + 2\zeta_j\omega_j(i\omega) + \omega_j^2}. \tag{11.166}$$

Then, if $Q_j(i\omega)$ is the Fourier transform of $q_j(t)$ and $\Phi_j(i\omega)$ is the Fourier transform of $\phi_j(t)$, by taking Fourier transforms of both sides of (11.157), we get

$$Q_j(i\omega) = H_j(i\omega)\, \Phi_j(i\omega) \tag{11.167}$$

(see Problem 11.4). Also defining $X(i\omega)$ as the vector whose elements are the Fourier transforms of the corresponding elements in $x(t)$, and $Q(i\omega)$ as the vector whose elements are $Q_j(i\omega)$, the M equations like (11.167) can be combined into the single matrix equation

$$Q(i\omega) = [\operatorname{diag} H_j(i\omega)]\, U^{\mathrm{T}} X(i\omega). \tag{11.168}$$

Lastly, if the vector $Y(i\omega)$ is the Fourier transform of $y(t)$, then from (11.150)

$$Y(i\omega) = U[\operatorname{diag} H_j(i\omega)]\, U^{\mathrm{T}} X(i\omega) \tag{11.169}$$

which is the frequency-domain equivalent of (11.161) (see Problem (11.5). It is subject to the same restrictions as (11.161), namely that m and k are real symmetric matrices and that m is positive definite, so that all the natural frequencies exist and there is a full set of eigenvectors, and that the (real) damping matrix c satisfies (11.155). The orthogonal eigenvector matrix U must be normalized to satisfy (11.141).

Impulse-response and frequency-response matrices

In interpreting (11.161) and (11.169), it is important to remember that $h_j(t)$ and $H_j(i\omega)$ are modal-response functions for a unit impulse and a unit harmonic input to mode j. They must be distinguished from the elements of the $M \times M$ matrices of the physical-response functions $h(t)$ and $H(i\omega)$. The latter may be found as follows.

If $x(\tau)$ in (11.162) is given by

$$x(\tau) = [\delta(\tau), 0, 0, \ldots, 0]^T \tag{11.170}$$

the response vector $y(t)$ will be, by definition,

$$y(t) = [h_{11}(t), h_{21}(t), \ldots, h_{M1}(t)]^T. \tag{11.171}$$

On substituting for $x(\tau)$ and $y(t)$ from (11.170) and (11.171) into (11.161) and completing the integral we find that

$$
\begin{bmatrix} h_{11}(t) \\ h_{21}(t) \\ \vdots \\ h_{M1}(t) \end{bmatrix} = \int_{-\infty}^{t} U[\operatorname{diag} h_j(t - \tau)] \, a^{(1)} \, \delta(\tau) \, d\tau
$$

$$= U[\operatorname{diag} h_j(t)] \, a^{(1)}. \tag{11.172}$$

where $a^{(1)}$ is the first column of U^T. When, instead of (11.170),

$$x(\tau) = [0, \delta(\tau), 0, 0, \ldots, 0]^T \tag{11.173}$$

then, instead of (11.171),

$$y(t) = [h_{21}(t), h_{22}(t), \ldots, h_{M2}(t)]^T \tag{11.174}$$

a result similar to (11.172) is obtained except that $a^{(1)}$ is replaced by $a^{(2)}$, the second column of U^T. Combining the results for the impulsive input $\delta(\tau)$ in all its M positions in the vector $x(\tau)$, we then find that the $M \times M$ matrix of impulse-response functions is

$$h(t) = U[\operatorname{diag} h_j(t)] \, U^T. \tag{11.175}$$

This has the same form as the previous general result (8.110). There is no inverse-mass matrix on the r.h.s. of (11.175) as there is in (8.110), because the eigenvector matrix U in (11.175) is orthogonal with respect to m according to (11.116). The effect of m^{-1} is therefore accounted for automatically in the simpler expression (11.175).

Similarly, the $M \times M$ matrix of frequency-response functions for the vector of displacements y, which are the physical coordinates of the problem, can be obtained from (11.169). When

$$X(i\omega) = [1, 0, 0, \ldots, 0]^T \tag{11.176}$$

the response is

$$Y(i\omega) = [H_{11}(i\omega), H_{21}(i\omega), \ldots, H_{M1}(i\omega)]^{\text{T}}. \tag{11.177}$$

When

$$X(i\omega) = [0, 1, 0, \ldots, 0]^{\text{T}} \tag{11.178}$$

it is

$$Y(i\omega) = [H_{12}(i\omega), H_{22}(i\omega), \ldots, H_{M2}(i\omega)]^{\text{T}}. \tag{11.179}$$

and so on. Hence, as for $h(t)$, we find that the $M \times M$ matrix of frequency-response functions is

$$H(i\omega) = U[\text{diag } H_j(i\omega)] \, U^{\text{T}} \tag{11.180}$$

instead of the more general result (8.32).

The general expansions (8.111) for $h_{rs}(t)$ and (8.39) for $H_{rs}(i\omega)$ can be adapted easily to the symmetric case. Corresponding to (8.111), we have from (11.175)

$$h_{rs}(t) = \sum_{j=1}^{M} u_{rj} \, h_j(t) \, v_{js} \tag{11.181}$$

where v_{js}, $j = 1$ to M, are the elements in the sth column of U^{T}. These are the same elements as in the sth row of U, so that putting

$$v_{js} = u_{sj} \tag{11.182}$$

we find that

$$h_{rs}(t) = \sum_{j=1}^{M} u_{rj} \, u_{sj} \, h_j(t). \tag{11.183}$$

In this important result for a symmetric system, the unit impulse response for output $y_r(t)$ and input $x_s(t)$ is given by a summation of the modal impulse-response functions defined by (11.163) and elements of the jth eigenvector which is the jth column of U when U is normalized according to (11.116).

Corresponding to (8.39), for the frequency-response function $H_{rs}(i\omega)$ we have, similarly, that

$$H_{rs}(i\omega) = \sum_{j=1}^{M} u_{rj} \, u_{sj} \, H_j(i\omega) \tag{11.184}$$

where $H_j(i\omega)$ is given by (11.166).

On substituting in (11.183) from (11.163), we get

$$h_{rs}(t) \underset{t>0}{=} \sum_{j=1}^{M} u_{rj} \, u_{sj} \, \frac{1}{\omega_j \sqrt{1 - \xi_j^2}} \, e^{-\zeta_j \omega_j t} \sin \omega_j \sqrt{1 - \xi_j^2} \, t \tag{11.185}$$

and on substituting in (11.184) from (11.166), we get

$$H_{rs}(i\omega) = \sum_{j=1}^{M} u_{rj} \, u_{sj} \, \frac{1}{(i\omega)^2 + 2\xi_j \omega_j(i\omega) + \omega_j^2}. \tag{11.186}$$

Reciprocity relations

It can be seen from equations (11.185) and (11.186) that $h_{rs}(t)$ and $H_{rs}(i\omega)$ remain the same when the order of their subscripts is reversed. This confirms the reciprocal property of the frequency-response function discussed in Chapter 3 and proves a similar result for the impulse-response function. These results apply only to systems which satisfy the restrictions given at the beginning of this chapter, namely that they are (i) scleronomic and (ii) holonomic. Furthermore, it is assumed that the input consists of a set of forces and the output a set of geometrical response parameters. We have taken the latter to be displacement parameters, but they could equally be velocities or accelerations provided that the outputs are all displacements, or all velocities, or all accelerations.

Equations (11.185) and (11.186) apply only to systems with damping distributed according to a relation which satisfies equation (11.155). Then, as we have seen, the undamped mode shapes are unaltered by the presence of damping. However, this damping assumption (11.155) is not a condition for the reciprocal property of $h_{rs}(t)$ and $H_{rs}(i\omega)$. It can be seen by the following argument that reciprocity applies for any general arrangement of linear viscous dampers.

Suppose that there is no damping. Then $h_{rs}(t)$ and $H_{rs}(i\omega)$ are special cases of (11.185) and (11.186), and reciprocity applies so that $h_{rs}(t)$ and $H_{rs}(i\omega)$ are the same as $h_{sr}(t)$ and $H_{sr}(i\omega)$, respectively. Consider the frequency-response function $H_{rs}(i\omega)$. If linear viscous dampers are added to the undamped system by positioning these in parallel with springs (if necessary, springs of zero stiffness) the relevant stiffness terms k in $H_{rs}(i\omega)$ are replaced by $k + ic\omega$ in each case. The alteration is the same for $H_{sr}(i\omega)$ as for $H_{rs}(i\omega)$ and the reciprocal property of the undamped frequency-response function is retained. Since we know from Chapter 9 that each function $h_{rs}(t)$ is the inverse Fourier transform of $H_{rs}(i\omega)$, it follows that if there is a reciprocal property for $H_{rs}(i\omega)$ then there must be the same reciprocal property for $h_{rs}(t)$.

Modal truncation

The response calculations in the previous sections of this chapter depend on devising a transformation which uncouples the normal coordinates q_j, $j = 1$ to M, each of which may then be solved separately as a one-degree-of-freedom problem. There are often practical cases when only a limited number of the M modes participate significantly in the response. When this is so, the expansion of each physical-response coordinate in terms of its normal coordinates may be restricted to the significant modes only. These modes are not necessarily successive modes, and need be only those modes which significantly affect the response. The eigenvector matrix U then has less than M columns.

Suppose that N modes are thought to be of interest, and that these have have eigenvalues ω_j^2 and corresponding column eigenvectors y_j, $j = 1$ to N. The eigenvector matrix U is then of order $M \times N$ ($M > N$), where the N columns of U are the N vectors y_j. We still have

$$U^{T}m\,U = I \qquad (11.187)$$

except that the identity matrix I has order $N \times N$ instead of $M \times M$.

Also, the $M \times 1$ response vector y is still related to the N significant normal coordinates in the $N \times 1$ vector q by

$$y = Uq \qquad (11.188)$$

except that U is now the $M \times N$ truncated eigenvector matrix instead of the full $M \times M$ matrix used before. On substituting for y from (11.188) into the general second-order equation (11.146) we arrive at (11.156) in exactly the same way as before, except that

$$[\text{diag}\,2\zeta_j\omega_j] \text{ and } [\text{diag}\,\omega_j^2]$$

are reduced in order to $N \times N$, where ω_j^2, $j = 1$ to N, are the eigenvalues corresponding to the eigenvectors in U and, of course, are in the same order as the columns of U. All the analysis following (11.156) then holds good, leading to the same general expressions for the $M \times M$ impulse-response function matrix $h(t)$, equation (11.175), and frequency-response function matrix $H(i\omega)$, equation (11.180). The orders of $[\text{diag}\,h_j(t)]$ and $[\text{diag}\,H_j(i\omega)]$ are reduced to $N \times N$, corresponding to the modes of interest only, while U is of order $M \times N$ and U^{T} is of order $N \times M$.

This method of excluding unwanted modes from a solution is an important practical procedure, particularly for the manipulation of large finite-element models of structures when there may be a very large number of degrees of freedom. It works conveniently only when the eigenvector matrix U satisfies the orthogonality condition (11.116), so that U^{T} appears in the general equations rather than U^{-1} as in (8.32) and (8.110). When only some of the columns of U are available, the corresponding rows of U^{T} can be found immediately. The same is not true when U^{-1} is needed in the general case, because U^{-1} can be computed only if U is known in full. All the elements of U have to be computed, which means that all the eigenvectors of the problem have to be computed in order to find the required rows of U^{-1}. Although U and U^{-1} could then be truncated in the same way as in the orthogonal case, the limited saving in computation time that this will achieve (having previously calculated all the eigenvalues and eigenvectors) does not appear to justify such a move.

Computational aspects

There are a number of different strategies for computing the eigenvalues ω_j^2 and eigenvectors y_j of the M-degree-of-freedom system for which, from (11.3),

$$k\, y_j = \omega_j^2 m\, y_j, \, j = 1 \text{ to } M, \qquad (11.189)$$

where k and m are both real and symmetric. To take advantage of symmetry, one method is to use equation (11.100) to find a symmetric matrix P that is similar to $m^{-1}k$ (if m is positive definite) or similar to $k^{-1}m$ (if k is positive definite). The eigenvalues and eigenvectors of the real symmetric P can then be found by a sequence of orthogonal similarity transformations in the *Jacobi method* or by reducing P to tri-diagonal form by *Givens' method* or *Householder's method* from which the eigenvalues can be extracted by a simplified version of the QR algorithm or its companion the QL algorithm. In these methods the eigenvectors are generated progressively at the same time as the eigenvalues. The QL algorithm is a variation of the QR algorithm in which, instead of A being decomposed into the form

$$A = QR \qquad (11.190)$$

where Q is orthogonal and R is an upper triangular matrix (a right-side triangle), A is decomposed to

$$A = QL \qquad (11.191)$$

where L is a lower triangular matrix (a left-side triangle). When combined with Householder's reduction to tri-diagonal form, the ordering of operations is such that using a lower-triangle decomposition of the tri-diagonal matrix is likely to introduce smaller round-off errors than an upper-triangular decomposition (Wilkinson [110], Wilkinson and Reinsch [111] and Press *et al* [82]).

When a general QR algorithm for obtaining the eigenvalues of any real, non-symmetric matrix is available (such as that described in Chapter 7 and Appendix 2) this can be used directly to compute the eigenvalues of $m^{-1}k$ or $k^{-1}m$. Although such a program is more complicated than a program for the symmetric case and involves more operations for matrices whose order is greater than, typically, 10×10, in the author's experience it is perfectly satisfactory to use the general-purpose QR algorithm (for the non-symmetric case) for most problems of mechanical vibration. The exception is for structural problems represented by finite-element models involving large, symmetric mass and stiffness matrices. Then it may be better to follow the method outlined above, first finding a symmetric matrix P, then transforming this to tri-diagonal form and then using the QL transform to extract its eigenvalues. However, a problem with this approach is that the transformation from $m^{-1}k$ (or $k^{-1}m$) to the symmetric form P may be ill conditioned (see Bathe [4]). In that case, a generalized Jacobi method can be used which works directly on the unmodified equation (11.189). This generates all the eigenvalues and eigenvectors simultaneously, but it is not as efficient as the QL algorithm. Large finite-element models therefore present special problems and there does not appear to be any one 'best' algorithm. Since only a limited number of the lowest eigenvalues and their corresponding eigenvectors are usually required in finite-element analyses, special solution methods have been developed for this purpose. Two of these methods, the determinant search method and the subspace iteration method, are described in Bathe [4], Chapter 12.

Scaling of eigenvectors

When general-purpose eigenvalue and eigenvector programs are used, the eigenvectors may be normalized in a number of different ways. In the program illustrated by the logical flow diagram in Appendix 5, each eigenvector is normalized so that its first element is real and of magnitude unity. However, in order to satisfy

$$U^{\mathrm{T}}m\,U = I \qquad (11.192)$$

so that the general response equations given in this chapter apply, each eigenvector must be scaled appropriately. If u_{rj}, $r = 1$ to M, are the elements of the jth eigenvector as generated by the eigenvector program, and if all the elements are to be scaled by γ_j, then from (11.192) we must have

$$\gamma_j^2 \sum_{r=1}^{M} \sum_{s=1}^{M} m_{rs} u_{rj} u_{sj} = 1, \, j = 1 \text{ to } M. \qquad (11.193)$$

Hence the scaling factors are given by

$$\gamma_j = \frac{1}{(\sum_{r=1}^{M} \sum_{s=1}^{M} m_{rs} u_{rj} u_{sj})^{1/2}}, \, j = 1 \text{ to } M. \qquad (11.194)$$

For a positive-definite mass matrix, we know that the double summation in the denominator of (11.194) will always be positive (see equation (11.120)), and so γ_j is always real. Its sign is arbitrary. All the elements in each eigenvector must be multiplied by the appropriate scaling factor γ_j before proceeding with response calculations which depend on the truth of (11.192).

When the eigenvectors are normalized according to (11.192), their physical dimensions in units of mass, length and time sometimes cause confusion. This is because the dimensions of the eigenvectors are not the same as the dimensions of the response vector y in (11.146). For example, let all the elements of each of m, y and x have the dimensions of mass, length and force, respectively. Then, from (11.148), the dimensions of the elements of U must be $(\text{mass})^{-1/2}$ and, from either (11.150) or (11.152), the dimensions of the elements of the normal coordinate vector q are $(\text{length}) \times (\text{mass})^{1/2}$. If a reference mass is included on the r.h.s. of the normalization equation, as in (11.130), the elements of U become non-dimensional, but, as noted already, the reference mass appears in all the response formulae. Provided that numerical parameter values are expressed in a consistent set of dimensional units, as they must be, no computation difficulties arise from using (11.192), and the resulting equations are then simpler.

Damping assumptions

The M coupled second-order equations which describe an M-degree-of-freedom system can only be uncoupled by a transformation to undamped normal coordinates q if, according to (11.155), $U^T c\, U$ is a diagonal matrix. Since we know that, according to (11.148) and (11.149), both $U^T m\, U$ and $U^T k\, U$ are diagonal, we know that $U^T c\, U$ will be diagonal if c is proportional to m or k according to (11.153) or (11.154).

Suppose that (11.153) is true, so that

$$c = \alpha m. \tag{11.195}$$

This will be the case if each mass element is connected to a viscous damping element whose other end is secured to ground. Every inertia force $m_{jk}\ddot{y}$ is then accompanied by a damping force $c_{jk}\dot{y}$ with all the viscous-damping coefficients c_{jk} being in the same proportion α to their respective masses m_{jk}. If (11.195) is true, then, on account of (11.148),

$$U^T c\, U = \alpha U^T m\, U = \alpha I \tag{11.196}$$

and, from (11.155), this gives

$$[\mathrm{diag}\, 2\zeta_j\omega_j] = \alpha I \tag{11.197}$$

so that

$$2\zeta_j\omega_j = \alpha,\ j = 1 \text{ to } M. \tag{11.198}$$

In Chapter 3, the modal bandwidth $\Delta\omega_j$ is defined by Fig. 3.4(b) and it is given, for small damping, by equation (3.49). Therefore (11.198) means that the modal bandwidth will be the same for all modes, and it is called the *constant modal bandwidth* assumption.

The alternative damping assumption (11.154) is that

$$c = \beta k. \tag{11.199}$$

This will be the case if each spring element has a viscous-damping element in parallel with it and corresponding damping and spring elements are in the same proportion β. Then, from (11.149),

$$U^T c\, U = \beta U^T k\, U = \beta[\mathrm{diag}\,\omega_j^2] \tag{11.200}$$

and, from (11.155),

$$[\mathrm{diag}\, 2\zeta_j\omega_j] = \beta[\mathrm{diag}\,\omega_j^2] \tag{11.201}$$

so that

$$2\zeta_j\omega_j = \beta\omega_j^2,\ j = 1 \text{ to } M. \tag{11.202}$$

The modal bandwidth is now proportional to ω_j^2. As frequency increases, the viscous damping elements progressively dominate the force produced by each parallel spring/damper combination, and as a result high-frequency modes are heavily damped.

A further damping possibility arises from combining (11.195) and (11.199), to put

$$c = \alpha m + \beta k \qquad (11.203)$$

which would be the case if every mass element were connected to ground by a viscous damper and every spring element had a viscous damper in parallel with it, the proportions of damping to mass being α and damping to stiffness being β. Then

$$U^T c \, U = \alpha I + \beta[\text{diag } \omega_j^2] \qquad (11.204)$$

so that

$$2\zeta_j\omega_j = \alpha + \beta\omega_j^2, \, j = 1 \text{ to } M. \qquad (11.205)$$

The modal bandwidth is then approximately constant for low-frequency modes but increases for high-frequency modes.

Since there are two constants in (11.205), in a practical simulation these can be chosen to give specified damping ratios for two different modes. The remaining modes have damping ratios which are then determined by (11.205).

The assumption that $U^T c \, U$ is a diagonal matrix is used widely in finite-element analyses of the vibration properties of structural systems (see e.g. Bathe [4]). Since the present state of knowledge of structural energy dissipation does not allow the damping matrix c for such a system to be constructed by a finite-element analysis, the assumption that (11.205) is true is often the only means of analysing a problem, and it is usually satisfactory for lightly-damped structures.

However, not all structural vibration problems should be treated in this way. The damped chimney in Example 5.5 is such an example, where the undamped normal modes are not retained in the presence of added damping concentrated at the base of the chimney. As can be seen from Fig. 5.15, the 'shape' of the second damped natural mode differs significantly from what it would be for the undamped case. An eigenvector matrix which is orthogonal with respect to m cannot then be found and it is necessary to revert to the general method of analysis based on the $2M \times 2M$ A-matrix given by

$$A = \begin{bmatrix} O & I \\ -m^{-1}k & -m^{-1}c \end{bmatrix}. \qquad (11.206)$$

Both this solution and that for the symmetric case are based on the assumption of linear viscous damping. They do not include the use of a complex stiffness such as

$$k(1 + i\eta) \tag{11.207}$$

which is a form often used to model viscoelastic elements (see Ch. 3). If, instead of

$$m\ddot{y} + c\dot{y} + k\,y = x, \tag{11.208}$$

we have

$$m\ddot{y} + k(1 + i\eta)\,y = x \tag{11.209}$$

as the equations of motion, then these equations may be uncoupled by the usual undamped normal coordinates to give

$$\ddot{q} + [\mathrm{diag}(1 + i\eta)\,\omega_j^2]\,q = U^{\mathrm{T}}x \tag{11.210}$$

provided that η is a constant. The modal frequency-response function for such a system is then

$$H_j(i\omega) = \frac{1}{(i\omega)^2 + (1 + i\eta)\,\omega_j^2}. \tag{11.211}$$

Causality conditions

In order for the frequency-domain-to-time-domain transformations of linear theory to apply, it is necessary for $H_j(i\omega)$ to be the Fourier transform of an impulse-response function $h_j(t)$, so that, from (9.49),

$$H_j(i\omega) = \int_{-\infty}^{\infty} h_j(t)\,e^{-i\omega t}\,dt. \tag{11.212}$$

For a passive, linear, time-invariant system, $h_j(t)$ must be a real function of time t with the properties that

$$h_j(t) = 0, \text{ for } t < 0 \tag{11.213}$$

and

$$h_j(t) \to 0, \text{ when } t \to \infty. \tag{11.214}$$

The second condition (11.214) is necessary for the existence of the integral (11.212) as an ordinary function and does not present a problem. However the first condition (11.213) has significant consequences. It says that the response cannot occur before the excitation (which in this case is a unit impulse) has been applied at $t = 0$. A function which satisfies (11.213) is said to be a *causal* function because the output is caused by the input and does not anticipate it. By the inverse Fourier transform, if (11.212) is true, then

$$h(t) = \frac{1}{2\pi} \int_{-\infty}^{\infty} H(i\omega)\,e^{i\omega t}\,d\omega. \tag{11.215}$$

Therefore a frequency-response function for a passive system that is valid for the application of linear frequency/time transformations must be such that, when its inverse Fourier transform is calculated by (11.215), the resulting $h_j(t)$ is a real function that satisfies the conditions (11.213) and (11.214).

For $h_j(t)$ to be real, we must have

$$H_j(i\omega) = H_j^*(-i\omega) \tag{11.216}$$

which is not satisfied by the function defined in (11.211). For this reason (11.211) is modified to

$$H_j(i\omega) = \cfrac{1}{(i\omega)^2 + \left[1 + i\eta \cfrac{\omega}{|\omega|}\right]\omega_j^2}. \tag{11.217}$$

It turns out that this modified function is still not acceptable because, when its inverse Fourier transform is calculated by applying (11.215), the resulting $h_j(t)$ does not satisfy (11.213) (see, for example, Nashif *et al.* [62] Ch. 4) and so is not a causal function. The $H_j(i\omega)$ in (11.217) does not satisfy the requirement of *causality*. It is the Fourier transform of an impulse-response function that is not capable of realization in practice.

The conclusion is that the loss factor η appearing in (11.217) cannot be constant. Consider what happens if it is a function of frequency. Also, let the stiffness be frequency dependent so that, for a single-degree-of-freedom system,

$$H(i\omega) = \cfrac{1}{-m\omega^2 + k(\omega)\left[1 + i\eta(\omega)\cfrac{\omega}{|\omega|}\right]} \tag{11.218}$$

where $k(\omega)$ and $\eta(\omega)$ are even functions of ω. This is the frequency-response function that would be obtained from an 'equation' of the form

$$m\ddot{y} + k(\omega)\left[1 + i\eta(\omega)\frac{\omega}{|\omega|}\right]y = x. \tag{11.219}$$

The latter is not a valid equation because we cannot have frequency-dependent coefficients in an equation describing a time-domain solution. Therefore the general theory for the response of linear differential equations with constant coefficients no longer applies to the $H(i\omega)$ in (11.218). However, the frequency/time transformations implied by linear theory will still be applicable if this $H(i\omega)$ is the Fourier transform of a causal impulse-response function.

Although there are various theorems which relate to analytic functions in complex variable theory (see Papoulis [79], Ch. 10), it appears that there is no completely general solution to the problem of determining the conditions that a given $H(i\omega)$ must satisfy in order to be the Fourier transform of a causal $h(t)$. However, it is always possible to integrate (11.215) numerically for specified frequency-dependent terms in $H(i\omega)$ to find how closely the $h(t)$ that derives from this $H(i\omega)$ satisfies the condition (11.213). The results of such a calculation for some representative functions are given in Nashif *et al.* [62], where it is demonstrated that, for small damping ($\eta < 0.1$), the $H(i\omega)$ in (11.217) is almost causal in the sense that $h(t) \simeq 0$ for $t < 0$. The same conclusion holds when the frequency-dependent stiffness and damping terms, $k(\omega)$ and $\eta(\omega)$, represent typical viscoelastic materials with light damping. Therefore the viscoelastic behaviour of lightly damped materials is sometimes represented by (11.218) even though this function does not satisfy the causality condition (11.213).

Chapter 12

Continuous systems I

Normal mode functions

For an elastic system with fixed supports whose position is defined
completely by its M (generalized) coordinates, and which is in a position of
stable static equilibrium, the equations for small-amplitude vibration are

$$m\ddot{y} + c\dot{y} + ky = x \qquad (12.1)$$

where $y(t)$ is its $M \times 1$ displacement-response vector and $x(t)$ is the $M \times 1$
force-excitation vector. We have seen in Chapter 11 that m and k are real,
symmetric matrices of order $M \times M$, and that m is positive definite unless
some parts of the system have zero mass (when m is positive semi-
definite), and k is positive definite unless parts of the system are
disconnected from the rest (when k is positive semi-definite).

In this chapter we shall consider how (12.1) can be extended to the
continuous case by allowing the number of degrees of freedom, M, to
become infinite. Then the column eigenvector for the discrete case is
replaced by a continuous normal mode function and the discrete orthogonality relations (11.141) and (11.144) are replaced by corresponding
integral relations. We begin by investigating the form of these orthogonality conditions for the normal mode functions of a continuous system.

For an M-degree-of-freedom system, we have seen in the last chapter
that, if U is the $M \times M$ matrix of (real) eigenvectors of the undamped
system, then it is possible to transform (12.1) from its physical coordinates
y to normal coordinates q, where

$$y = Uq \qquad (12.2)$$

to obtain

$$\ddot{q} + [\text{diag}\, 2\zeta_j\omega_j]\dot{q} + [\text{diag}\, \omega_j^2]q = U^T x \qquad (12.3)$$

subject to the following conditions. The eigenvectors must be normalised
so that

$$U^T m\, U = I \qquad (12.4)$$

in which case we also have

$$U^T k U = [\text{diag } \omega_j^2], \tag{12.5}$$

and the damping matrix must satisfy (11.203), so that we also have

$$U^T c U = [\text{diag } 2\zeta_j \omega_j]. \tag{12.6}$$

If u_{rs} is the element of U in row r and column s, i.e. it is the rth element of the sth eigenvector, then (12.4) can also be written as

$$\sum_{r=1}^{M} \sum_{s=1}^{M} m_{rs} u_{rj} u_{sk} = \delta_{jk}, \quad j, k = 1 \text{ to } M, \tag{12.7}$$

where δ_{jk} is zero except when $j = k$, when it is unity. Similarly, (12.5) and (12.6) can be written as

$$\sum_{r=1}^{M} \sum_{s=1}^{M} k_{rs} u_{rj} u_{sk} = \omega_j^2 \delta_{jk}, \quad j, k = 1 \text{ to } M \tag{12.8}$$

and

$$\sum_{r=1}^{M} \sum_{s=1}^{M} c_{rs} u_{rj} u_{sk} = 2\zeta_j \omega_j \delta_{jk}, \quad j, k = 1 \text{ to } M. \tag{12.9}$$

Now consider a continuous system with distributed mass and elasticity. This may take many forms, for example a slender member like a rod or beam, or a two-dimensional thin plate (which may be flat or curved), or it may be a general three-dimensional body. To illustrate the following analysis, Fig. 12.1 shows a 'structure' consisting of a flat plate on fixed supports. Let position vector z locate a point on the plate and let the magnitude of the displacement of this point from its static equilibrium position be $y(z, t)$. The direction of $y(z, t)$ is perpendicular to the plate. No displacements are assumed to occur in the plane of the plate. Later in the chapter we shall remove this restriction and allow the displacement at position z to be a three-dimensional vector $\mathbf{y}(z, t)$ instead of the scalar $y(z, t)$. However, the equations are simplified when there is deflection only in a known direction, and there are many simple continuous systems for which this assumption is a satisfactory approximation.

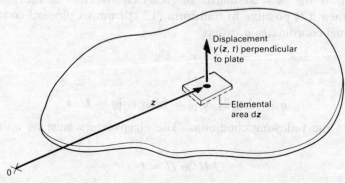

Fig. 12.1 Part of a continuous system consisting of a flat plate on fixed supports (not shown). The origin of coordinates is fixed at point 0

If we define dz to mean the scalar elemental area at position z as shown in Fig. 12.1, the total kinetic energy of the system can be written as

$$T = \int_R dz \; \tfrac{1}{2} m(z) \; \dot{y}^2(z, t) \tag{12.10}$$

where the integration is taken over the whole surface R of the structure, which in this case is the whole surface of the plate. The kinetic energy of each elemental area dz of the structure is determined by its mass $m(z)dz$ and its absolute velocity $\dot{y}(z, t)$. In effect, the structure is modelled by infinitely many infinitesimally-small point masses, with one point mass at each coordinate of absolute displacement.

For a discrete system with M degrees of freedom, the assumption that there is a point mass at each coordinate means that the mass matrix m in (12.1) is a diagonal matrix, in which case the double summation in (12.7) can be replaced by the single summation

$$\sum_{r=1}^{M} m_{rr} u_{rj} u_{rk} = \delta_{jk}, \quad j, k = 1 \text{ to } M, \tag{12.11}$$

since

$$m_{rs} = 0 \text{ for } r \neq s. \tag{12.12}$$

When, for a continuous system, M becomes infinite, the summation in (12.11) may be replaced by an integral. If $m(z)$ is the distributed mass per unit area, and we define a continuous function $U_j(z)$ to give the displacement of the jth mode at position z, then by putting

$$m_{rr} = m(z) \; dz$$
$$u_{rj} = U_j(z) \tag{12.13}$$
$$u_{rk} = U_k(z),$$

(12.11) gives

$$\int_R dz \; m(z) \; U_j(z) \; U_k(z) = \delta_{jk}, \quad j, k = 1 \text{ to } \infty \tag{12.14}$$

in the limit when $M \to \infty$. The jth normal mode of the undamped structure is described by the continuous *normal mode function $U_j(z)$*, which replaces the jth column of the eigenvector matrix U. This is orthogonal with respect to the distributed mass function $m(z)$ according to (12.14).

We shall see next that, subject to the restraining force on area dz at position z depending only on the values of $y(z, t)$ and its derivatives evaluated at z, the second orthogonality condition (12.8) for M degrees of freedom, which is a consequence of (12.7), can be replaced by the integral equation

$$\int_R dz \; L\{U_j(z)\} \; U_k(z) = \omega_j^2 \; \delta_{jk}, \quad j, k = 1 \text{ to } \infty \tag{12.15}$$

where $L\{\;\}$ denotes a linear differential operator in the spatial coordinates which cover the surface of the structure.

Consider the case when the stiffness of the structure may be modelled by infinitely many linear springs. Assume that each elemental mass $m(z)dz$ is supported by a separate spring. Then the elastic restraining force at position z depends only on the displacement of one spring and is independent of the displacements of all the other springs. In the discrete case, the stiffness matrix k would be diagonal. In the continuous case, if we call the stiffness per unit area $k(z)$ then, from (12.8) and by analogy with (12.14), we have

$$\int_R dz\, k(z)\, U_j(z)\, U_k(z) = \omega_j^2\, \delta_{jk}, \quad j, k = 1 \text{ to } \infty \qquad (12.16)$$

as the second orthogonality condition for the normal mode function $U_j(z)$.

In practice, we do not have infinitely many independent springs giving a restraining force

$$k(z)\{y(z, t)\}\, dz \qquad (12.17)$$

but instead we often have a restraining force of the form

$$L\{y(z, t)\}\, dz \qquad (12.18)$$

where $L\{\ \}$ is a linear differential operator with respect to the spatial variables.

For example, for the transverse vibration of a stretched string under tension T,

$$L\{y(z, t)\} = -T \frac{\partial^2}{\partial z^2}\, y(z, t); \qquad (12.19)$$

for the longitudinal vibration of an elastic column of cross-sectional area A and modulus E,

$$L\{y(z, t)\} = -\, EA\, \frac{\partial^2}{\partial z^2}\, y(z, t); \qquad (12.20)$$

for the transverse vibration of an Euler beam of bending stiffness EI,

$$L\{y(z, t)\} = EI\, \frac{\partial^4}{\partial z^4}\, y(z, t); \qquad (12.21)$$

and for the transverse vibration of an isotropic flat plate,

$$L\{y(z, t)\} =$$

$$L\{y(z_1, z_2, t)\} = D\!\left(\frac{\partial^4}{\partial z_1^4} + 2\, \frac{\partial^4}{\partial z_1^2 \partial z_2^2} + \frac{\partial^4}{\partial z_2^4}\right) y(z_1, z_2, t) \quad (12.22)$$

where D is the plate stiffness defined by

$$D = \frac{Et^3}{12(1 - v^2)} \qquad (12.23)$$

with Young's modulus E, thickness t and Poisson's ratio v (Problem 12.1). Notice that in all cases the restraining force on area dz at position z

depends only on the values of the spatial derivatives of $y(z, t)$ when evaluated at z. Therefore the restraining force on dz depends only on the derivatives of the structure's deflection at position z, not on the deflected shape at positions other than z. By analogy with the discrete case, the stiffness matrix k has become an infinite diagonal matrix with the differential operator $L\{\ \}$ replacing its diagonal elements.

We conclude, by comparing (12.17) and (12.18), that the terms $k(z)U_j(z)$ in (12.16) may be replaced by $L\{U_j(z)\}$, thereby obtaining the orthogonality condition (12.15).

For the normal coordinates of the undamped case to hold also when damping is present, we know that, for M degrees of freedom, the damping matrix c must be such that (12.6) and its equivalent (12.9) are true. The same restriction on the form of damping applies for a continuous structure. By analogy with (11.203), the required orthogonality condition will be satisfied if

$$c(z)\ \dot{y}(z, t) = \alpha m(z)\ \dot{y}(z, t) + \beta\ L\{\dot{y}(z, t)\} \qquad (12.24)$$

where α and β are arbitrary constants.

Equations of motion

Having shown how the properties of continuous normal mode functions may be deduced from corresponding properties in the discrete case, we consider next the equation of motion that describes the vibration of many simple continuous systems. In terms of the differential stiffness operator $L\{\ \}$, and for damping terms defined by (12.24), this general partial linear differential equation is

$$m(z)\ \frac{\partial^2}{\partial t^2}\ y(z, t) + \alpha\ m(z)\ \frac{\partial}{\partial t}\ y(z, t) + \beta\ L\left\{\frac{\partial}{\partial t}\ y(z, t)\right\} + L\{y(z, t)\}$$
$$= x(z, t) \quad (12.25)$$

where $y(z, t)$ is the response and $x(z, t)$ is the distributed excitation at position z and time t. If $q_j(t)$, $j = 1$ to ∞, are the normal coordinates, the equivalent of equation (12.2) is

$$y(z, t) = \sum_{j=1}^{\infty} U_j(z)\ q_j(t) \qquad (12.26)$$

where $U_j(z)$, $j = 1$ to ∞, are the normal mode functions for undamped free vibration. Substituting for $y(z, t)$ in (12.25) from (12.26), multiplying by $U_j(z)$ and integrating over the whole system, region R, then gives

$$\ddot{q}_j + 2\zeta_j\omega_j\dot{q}_j + \omega_j^2 q_j = \int_R U_j(z)\ x(z, t)\ dz \qquad (12.27)$$

on account of the orthogonality conditions (12.14) and (12.15) and where ζ_j is given by (Problem 12.2)

$$2\zeta_j\omega_j = \alpha + \beta\omega_j^2. \tag{12.28}$$

In order to determine the natural frequencies ω_j and their corresponding normal mode functions $U_j(z)$, we substitute the single mode solution

$$y(z, t) = U_j(z)\, e^{i\omega_j t} \tag{12.29}$$

into the free-vibration equation

$$m(z)\,\frac{\partial^2}{\partial t^2}\, y(z, t) + L\{y(z, t)\} = 0. \tag{12.30}$$

This gives

$$- \omega_j^2\, m(z)\, U_j(z) + L\{U_j(z)\} = 0 \tag{12.31}$$

which is a linear differential equation for $U_j(z)$ that may be solved subject to the appropriate boundary conditions. The natural frequency ω_j is included in the general solution for $U_j(z)$ and, in order to satisfy the boundary conditions, both the eigenvalues ω_j and the normal mode functions $U_j(z)$ are discovered. This procedure is illustrated in the following example.

Longitudinal vibration of an elastic bar

Consider, as an example, the longitudinal vibration of a homogeneous elastic bar of density ρ, Young's modulus E and cross-sectional area A. The bar is in the form of a rectangular prism and is assumed to be subjected to one-dimensional stresses only. The effect of Poisson's ratio is neglected. There is no gravity and there are no externally-applied forces. With reference to Fig. 12.2, let $y(z, t)$ be the longitudinal displacement of the cross-section of the bar that is at distance z from the left-hand end when at rest. The longitudinal strain of the elemental section of length dz is then $\partial y/\partial z$, and so the tension force at section z is

$$EA\,\frac{\partial y}{\partial z}.$$

For dynamic equilibrium of the slice dz, we then have

$$\rho A\,\frac{\partial^2 y}{\partial t^2} = \frac{\partial}{\partial z}\left(EA\,\frac{\partial y}{\partial z}\right) \tag{12.32}$$

which gives the equation of motion

$$m\,\frac{\partial^2 y}{\partial t^2} - EA\,\frac{\partial^2 y}{\partial z^2} = 0 \tag{12.33}$$

where

$$m = \rho A \tag{12.34}$$

is the mass per unit length. The operator L in this example is therefore

$$L = - EA \frac{\partial^2}{\partial z^2} \qquad (12.35)$$

in agreement with (12.20).

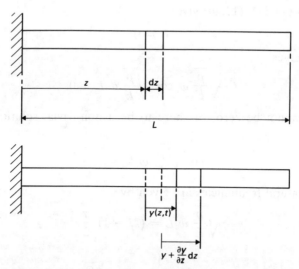

Fig. 12.2 Displacement coordinate $y(z, t)$ for the longitudinal vibration of a homogenous elastic bar of length L. The effects of gravity and of lateral deformation due to Poisson's ratio are neglected

On substituting the normal mode solution (12.29), we find that

$$- \omega_j^2 \, mU_j(z) - EA \frac{d^2}{dz^2} U_j(z) = 0 \qquad (12.36)$$

whose solution gives

$$U_j(z) = B \cos \sqrt{\frac{\rho}{E}} \, \omega_j z + C \sin \sqrt{\frac{\rho}{E}} \, \omega_j z \qquad (12.37)$$

where B and C are arbitrary constants. These depend on the boundary conditions at the two ends of the column.

Suppose that the column is fixed at its left-hand end and free at its right-hand end. Then the boundary conditions are

$$y = 0 \text{ at } z = 0 \qquad (12.38)$$

and

$$\frac{\partial y}{\partial z} = 0 \text{ at } z = L \qquad (12.39)$$

since there can be no strain at a free end. With (12.29), they give

$$U_j = 0 \text{ at } z = 0 \tag{12.40}$$

and

$$\frac{d}{dz} U_j = 0 \text{ at } z = L \tag{12.41}$$

and so, from (12.37), (12.40) gives

$$B = 0 \tag{12.42}$$

and (12.41) gives

$$C \sqrt{\frac{\rho}{E}} \, \omega_j \cos \sqrt{\frac{\rho}{E}} \, \omega_j L = 0. \tag{12.43}$$

Since C cannot be zero for there to be a non-trivial solution, we must have

$$\cos \sqrt{\frac{\rho}{E}} \, \omega_j L = 0 \tag{12.44}$$

and so the natural frequencies are given by

$$\sqrt{\frac{\rho}{E}} \, \omega_j L = (2j - 1) \frac{\pi}{2} \tag{12.45}$$

so that

$$\omega_j = (2j - 1) \frac{\pi}{2L} \sqrt{\frac{E}{\rho}}. \tag{12.46}$$

The corresponding normal mode function is, from (12.37) and (12.46)

$$U_j(z) = C \sin(2j - 1) \frac{\pi}{2L} z \tag{12.47}$$

where C is arbitrary.

In order to satisfy the normalization condition in (12.14), we want

$$\int_0^L dz \rho A C^2 \sin^2(2j - 1) \frac{\pi}{2L} z = 1 \tag{12.48}$$

so that

$$\rho A C^2 \frac{L}{2} = 1 \tag{12.49}$$

and

$$C = \sqrt{\frac{2}{\rho A L}}. \tag{12.50}$$

We conclude that the natural frequencies and their corresponding normalized normal mode functions are

$$\omega_j = (2j - 1) \frac{\pi}{2L} \sqrt{\frac{E}{\rho}} \quad \text{and} \quad U_j(z) = \sqrt{\frac{2}{\rho A L}} \sin(2j - 1) \frac{\pi}{2L} z,$$

$$j = 1 \text{ to } \infty. \tag{12.51}$$

The first four normal mode functions are drawn in Fig. 12.3.

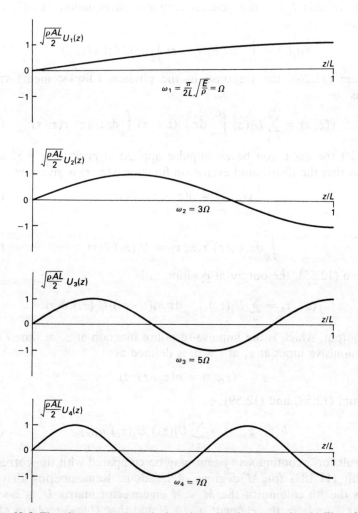

Fig. 12.3 First four normal mode functions for the elastic bar in Fig. 12.2

Impulse-response and frequency-response functions

Consider equation (12.27) for the jth normal coordinate $q_j(t)$. When the r.h.s. of (12.27) is $\delta(t)$, the response $q_j(t) = h_j(t)$ is the modal impulse-response function. Hence $h_j(t)$ is the solution of

$$\ddot{h}_j + 2\zeta_j\omega_j\,\dot{h}_j + \omega_j^2\,h_j = \delta(t) \tag{12.52}$$

which, from Chapter 1, equation (1.56) is

$$h_j(t) = \frac{1}{\omega_j \sqrt{1 - \zeta_j^2}}\, e^{-\zeta_j \omega_j t} \sin \omega_j \sqrt{1 - \zeta_j^2}\, t, \quad t > 0, \, j = 1 \text{ to } \infty. \quad (12.53)$$

In terms of this $h_j(t)$, the general response of equation (12.27) can be written as

$$q_j(t) = \int_{-\infty}^{t} d\tau\, h_j(t - \tau) \int_R dz\, U_j(z)\, x(z, \tau) \quad (12.54)$$

and, from (12.26), the response in the physical (displacement) variable $y(z, t)$ is

$$y(z, t) = \sum_{j=1}^{\infty} U_j(z) \int_{-\infty}^{t} d\tau\, h_j(t - \tau) \int_R dz\, U_j(z)\, x(z, \tau). \quad (12.55)$$

Now let the excitation be an impulse applied at position $z = z_s$ at time $\tau = 0$, so that the distributed excitation function $x(z, \tau)$ is given by

$$x(z, \tau) = \delta(z - z_s)\, \delta(\tau). \quad (12.56)$$

Then

$$\int_R dz\, U_j(z)\, x(z, \tau) = U_j(z_s)\, \delta(\tau) \quad (12.57)$$

and, from (12.55), the output at position z_r is

$$y(z_r, t) = \sum_{j=1}^{\infty} U_j(z_r) \int_{-\infty}^{t} d\tau\, h_j(t - \tau)\, U_j(z_s)\, \delta(\tau). \quad (12.58)$$

If this output, which is the impulse-response function at z_r at time t due to a unit impulsive input at z_s at $t = 0$, is defined as

$$y(z_r, t) = h(z_r, z_s, t) \quad (12.59)$$

then, from (12.58) and (12.59),

$$h(z_r, z_s, t) = \sum_{j=1}^{\infty} U_j(z_r)\, U_j(z_s)\, h_j(t). \quad (12.60)$$

This result for a continuous system may be compared with the corresponding result (11.183) for M degrees of freedom. Remembering that $U_j(z)$ replaces the jth column of the $M \times M$ eigenvector matrix U, it is evident that $U_j(z_r)$ replaces the element u_{rj} of U and that $U_j(z_s)$ replaces element u_{sj} of U, so that (12.60) and (11.183) agree.

The corresponding frequency-domain response can be obtained as follows. Let $H_j(i\omega)$ be the modal frequency-response function defined, from (12.27), by

$$H_j(i\omega) = \frac{1}{(i\omega)^2 + 2\zeta_j \omega_j(i\omega) + \omega_j^2}. \quad (12.61)$$

Then, if a unit harmonic input force is applied at $z = z_s$, we have

$$x(z, t) = \delta(z - z_s)\, e^{i\omega t}. \quad (12.62)$$

If the normal coordinate response is

$$q_j(t) = Q_j(i\omega)\,e^{i\omega t} \tag{12.63}$$

then, from (12.27),

$$Q_j(i\omega) = H_j(i\omega) \int_R U_j(z)\,\delta(z - z_s)\,dz$$

$$= H_j(i\omega)\,U_j(z_s). \tag{12.64}$$

Also if the corresponding response in the physical coordinates at position z_r is

$$y(z_r,\,t) = H(z_r,\,z_s,\,i\omega)\,e^{i\omega t} \tag{12.65}$$

then, from (12.26),

$$H(z_r,\,z_s,\,i\omega) = \sum_{j=1}^{\infty} U_j(z_r)\,U_j(z_s)\,H_j(i\omega) \tag{12.66}$$

which can be seen to be in agreement with equation (11.184) for the case of M degrees of freedom.

The frequency-response function $H(z_r, z_s, i\omega)$ gives the harmonic response at z_r for unit harmonic excitation applied at z_s. The point of application of the steady-state harmonic excitaion is assumed to be a fixed point so that the vector z_s is a constant vector. If z_s is a function of time, $z_s(t)$, then (12.66) no longer applies. This is because steady-state harmonic conditions are never established if the location of the excitation is continually changing.

In order to calculate the response of a structure to moving excitation, for example the response of a bridge to a moving load, the general response equation (12.55) can be used directly provided that the general excitation $x(z, \tau)$ represents the moving load properly (see problem 12.10).

Application to an elastic bar: I

To illustrate the application of the results in the previous section, consider the undamped elastic bar in Fig. 12.2. Suppose that we want the response at the free end, $z = L$, to a unit impulse applied at this end in the direction of positive z.

For no damping, the modal impulse-response function is, from (12.53) with $\zeta_j = 0$,

$$h_j(t) = \frac{1}{\omega_j}\sin \omega_j t, \quad t > 0. \tag{12.67}$$

Then, on substituting into (12.60) with $z_r = z_s = L$, we have

$$h(L,\,L,\,t) = \sum_{j=1}^{\infty} U_j^2(L)\,h_j(t) \tag{12.68}$$

and, from (12.51) and (12.67),

$$h(L, L, t) = \sum_{j=1}^{\infty} \left(\frac{2}{\rho AL}\right) \frac{1}{\omega_j} \sin \omega_j t, \quad t > 0. \tag{12.69}$$

On substituting for ω_j from (12.51)

$$h(L, L, t) = \frac{4}{\pi \sqrt{(E\rho)} A} \sum_{j=1}^{\infty} \frac{1}{(2j-1)} \sin (2j-1) \frac{\pi}{2L} \sqrt{\frac{E}{\rho}} t, \quad t > 0. \tag{12.70}$$

The corresponding result for the frequency-response function is, from (12.66),

$$H(L, L, i\omega) = \sum_{j=1}^{\infty} U_j^2(L) H_j(i\omega)$$

$$= \frac{2}{\rho AL} \sum_{j=1}^{\infty} \frac{1}{(i\omega)^2 + \omega_j^2} \tag{12.71}$$

from (12.51) and (12.61). On substituting for ω_j from (12.51), this gives

$$H(L, L, i\omega) = \frac{2}{\rho AL} \sum_{j=1}^{\infty} \frac{1}{\left[(2j-1)^2 \left(\frac{\pi}{2L}\right)^2 \frac{E}{\rho} - \omega^2\right]}. \tag{12.72}$$

If there is damping present which satisfies (12.24), so that the normal mode functions remain those for the undamped case, then $h_j(t)$ in (12.67) is replaced by (12.53), and $H_j(i\omega)$ in (12.71) is replaced by the $H_j(i\omega)$ in (12.61). The corresponding series expansion for $h(L, L, t)$ is

$$h(L, L, t) = \frac{4}{\pi \sqrt{(E\rho)} A} \sum_{j=1}^{\infty} \frac{1}{(2j-1)\sqrt{(1-\zeta_j^2)}} \times$$

$$\times e^{-(2j-1)\zeta_j(\pi/2L)\sqrt{(E/\rho)}t} \sin (2j-1) \frac{\pi}{2L} \sqrt{\frac{E}{\rho}} (1 - \zeta_j^2) t, \quad t > 0 \tag{12.73}$$

instead of (12.70), and for $H(L, L, i\omega)$ is

$$H(L, L, i\omega) =$$

$$\frac{2}{\rho AL} \sum_{j=1}^{\infty} \frac{1}{\left\{(2j-1)^2 \left(\frac{\pi}{2L}\right)^2 \frac{E}{\rho} + (2j-1) \left(\frac{\pi}{L}\right) \zeta_j \sqrt{\frac{E}{\rho}} i\omega - \omega^2\right\}} \tag{12.74}$$

instead of (12.72).

In both of these results (12.73) and (12.74), ζ_j is the modal damping ratio for the jth mode. For two modes, ζ_j may be chosen arbitrarily, but the remaining ζ_j then have to satisfy (12.28), where the constants α and β

in (12.28) are determined by the first two chosen values of ζ_j. For $\zeta_j > 1$, (12.73) and (12.74) still apply but the argument of the sine function in (12.73) is then imaginary and we need the result that, for ϕ real,

$$\sin i\phi = \frac{i}{2}(e^{\phi} - e^{-\phi}). \tag{12.75}$$

This follows from the usual complex exponential form

$$e^{i\theta} = \cos\theta + i\sin\theta \tag{12.76}$$

by replacing θ by $i\phi$ and then by $-i\phi$ and subtracting the results. The factor i in $\sin i\phi$ in the numerator of (12.73) cancels with the corresponding factor i arising from $\sqrt{1 - \zeta_j^2}$ in its denominator, so that $h(L, L, t)$ always remains real.

Alternative closed-form solution for frequency response

The response equations we have just obtained were derived by solving for the undamped case to find the natural frequencies ω_j and normal mode functions $U_j(z)$ and then using the result that the expansion

$$y(z, t) = \sum_{j=1}^{\infty} U_j(z)\, q_j(t) \tag{12.77}$$

is always a solution of the equation of motion (12.25) for general excitation. This allows the frequency-response function $H(z_r, z_s, i\omega)$ to be found in its general series-expanded form (12.66) with $H_j(i\omega)$ given by (12.61) and the modal damping ratios satisfying (12.28).

An alternative closed-form solution for the frequency-response of a continuous system can also be found from the knowledge that, if there is harmonic excitation so that

$$x(z, t) = X(z, i\omega)\, e^{i\omega t}, \tag{12.78}$$

there will always be a steady-state harmonic response

$$y(z, t) = Y(z, i\omega)\, e^{i\omega t}, \tag{12.79}$$

provided that there is positive damping. On substituting (12.78) and (12.79) into the general equation (12.25), we get

$$(i\omega)^2\, m(z)\, Y(z, i\omega) + i\omega\, \alpha\, m(z)\, Y(z, i\omega) + i\omega\beta L\{Y(z, i\omega)\} +$$
$$+ L\{Y(z, i\omega)\} = X(z, i\omega) \tag{12.80}$$

with the harmonic time function $e^{i\omega t}$ cancelling from both sides. This is a linear differential equation in $Y(z, i\omega)$ that may be solved subject to the boundary conditions.

The frequency-response function $H(z_r, z_s, i\omega)$ is the harmonic response at $z = z_r$ for a discrete harmonic force applied at $z = z_s$, so that, if

$$X(z, i\omega) = \delta(z - z_s) \tag{12.81}$$

then the response at z_r is the required frequency-response function, i.e.

$$Y(z_r, i\omega) = H(z_r, z_s, i\omega). \tag{12.82}$$

Application to an elastic bar: II

We shall apply this approach to the elastic bar problem, starting with the undamped case. Let there be a distributed force per unit length $x(z, t)$ acting in the direction of positive z. Then the equation of motion is

$$\rho A \frac{\partial^2}{\partial t^2} y(z, t) - EA \frac{\partial^2}{\partial z^2} y(z, t) = x(z, t). \tag{12.83}$$

If we want the frequency-response function for input and output at the free end of the column, then for input

$$x(z, t) = \delta(z - L)\, e^{i\omega t} \tag{12.84}$$

we have a general response

$$y(z, t) = Y(z, i\omega)\, e^{i\omega t} \tag{12.85}$$

and, at the free end,

$$H(L, L, i\omega) = Y(L, i\omega). \tag{12.86}$$

On substituting (12.84) and (12.85) into (12.83), we get

$$(i\omega)^2 \rho A Y(z, i\omega) - EA \frac{d^2}{dz^2} Y(z, i\omega) = \delta(z - L). \tag{12.87}$$

Subject to the boundary conditions, this gives

$$\frac{d^2 Y}{dz^2} + \omega^2 \left(\frac{\rho}{E}\right) Y = 0 \tag{12.88}$$

which has the general solution

$$Y(z, i\omega) = B \cos \sqrt{\frac{\rho}{E}}\, \omega z + C \sin \sqrt{\frac{\rho}{E}}\, \omega z. \tag{12.89}$$

As remarked previously, although ω rather than $i\omega$ appears on the r.h.s. of (12.89), the cosine and sine functions that appear here are the real and imaginary parts of $e^{\sqrt{(\rho/E)}i\omega z}$ so that, in that sense, the r.h.s. is a function of $i\omega$.

At the left-hand end of the column there is no displacement, so that $B = 0$ and, to satisfy force equilibrium at the right-hand end, we must have

$$EA \frac{dY}{dz} = 1 \tag{12.90}$$

because the excitation is a force of unit amplitude. This result may be confirmed by integrating (12.87) from $z = L-$ to $z = L+$ noting that d^2Y/dz^2 will be infinite at $z = L$ but that dY/dz will be finite. The integration gives

$$- EA \left[\frac{dY}{dz_{L+}} - \frac{dY}{dz_{L-}} \right] = 1. \tag{12.91}$$

The bar ends at $z = L$, so $EA\,dY/dz$ must be zero at $L+$ and we conclude that

$$EA \frac{dY}{dz_{L-}} = 1 \tag{12.92}$$

which is in agreement with (12.90).

This condition gives, from (12.89),

$$C\omega \sqrt{\frac{\rho}{E}} \cos \sqrt{\frac{\rho}{E}}\, \omega L = \frac{1}{EA} \tag{12.93}$$

so that, since $B = 0$,

$$Y(z, i\omega) = \frac{1}{\omega A \sqrt{E\rho}} \frac{\sin \sqrt{\dfrac{\rho}{E}}\, \omega z}{\cos \sqrt{\dfrac{\rho}{E}}\, \omega L} \tag{12.94}$$

and, from (12.86),

$$H(L, L, i\omega) = \frac{1}{\omega A \sqrt{E\rho}} \tan \sqrt{\frac{\rho}{E}}\, \omega L. \tag{12.95}$$

If k is the static longitudinal stiffness of the column, measured at its free end, then, from (12.95) with $\omega = 0$,

$$\frac{1}{k} = H(L, L, i\omega = 0) = \frac{L}{EA}. \tag{12.96}$$

By defining an additional parameter

$$a = \sqrt{\frac{\rho}{E}}\, L \tag{12.97}$$

the result (12.95) can then be written as

$$H(L, L, i\omega) = \frac{1}{k} \frac{\tan \omega a}{\omega a}. \tag{12.98}$$

In Fig. 12.4, $kH(L, L, i\omega)$ is plotted against ωa over a range which includes the first three natural frequencies.

We now have two expressions for $H(L, L, i\omega)$. The closed form (12.98) obtained above must yield exactly the same result as the series expansion (12.72). In terms of k and a defined by (12.96) and (12.97), the latter reads

$$H(L, L, i\omega) = \frac{2}{k} \sum_{j=1}^{\infty} \frac{1}{(2j - 1)^2 \left(\frac{\pi}{2}\right)^2 - \omega^2 a^2}. \tag{12.99}$$

It is clear that the r.h.s. of (12.99) is infinite at $\omega a = \pi/2, 3\pi/2, 5\pi/2, \ldots,$ in agreement with Fig. 12.4, but it is not at all obvious that (12.98) and (12.99) are identical in all respects. The proof depends on a standard result from the summation of series which is given in Problem 12.3.

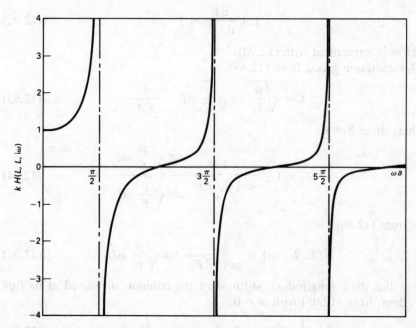

Fig. 12.4 Graph of the displacement frequency response of a homogenous elastic bar when subjected to a harmonic force at one end, with the other end fixed (see Fig. 12.2). The frequency-response function $H(L, L, i\omega)$ is multiplied by the static stiffness of the block k and is plotted against non-dimensional frequency ωa, where a is defined by equation (12.97)

Frequency-response functions for general damping

The method of normal mode analysis for a continuous system depends on the distributed damping $[c_1(z)\dot{y}(z, t) + c_2(z) L\{(\dot{y}(z, t)\}]$ being such that

$$\int_R dz[c_1(z)\ U_j(z) + c_2(z)\ L\{U_j(z)\}]\ U_k(z) = 2\zeta_j\omega_j\ \delta_{jk}, \quad j, k = 1 \text{ to } \infty, \tag{12.100}$$

where $U_j(z)$ is the (undamped) normal mode function for the jth mode. The general method of finding a closed-form solution for the frequency response does not have this restriction. For a general equation of motion

$$m(z) \frac{\partial^2}{\partial t^2} y(z, t) + c_1(z) \frac{\partial}{\partial t} y(z, t) + c_2(z) L\left\{\frac{\partial}{\partial t} y(z, t)\right\} + L\{y(z, t)\}$$

$$= x(z, t) \quad (12.101)$$

we can always substitute the assumed steady-state harmonic solution (12.78) and (12.79) to find

$$(i\omega)^2 m(z) Y(z, i\omega) + (i\omega) c_1(z) Y(z, i\omega) + i\omega c_2(z) L\{Y(z, i\omega)\} +$$

$$+ L\{Y(z, i\omega)\} = X(z, i\omega). \quad (12.102)$$

No particular restrictions need to be imposed on $c_1(z)$ and $c_2(z)$. Once the differential operator $L\{\ \}$ is specified, in principle $Y(z, i\omega)$ can be solved in terms of $X(z, i\omega)$ in the usual way, subject to the appropriate boundary conditions. If $x(z, t)$ is harmonic force excitation applied at a point, then $X(z, i\omega)$ is given by (12.81) and the frequency-response function $H(z_r, z_s, i\omega)$ by (12.82).

At any given frequency ω, equation (12.102) is a linear ordinary differential equation with constant but complex coefficients. The consequence of the complex coefficients is that a complete analytical solution often proves impossible and values of $Y(z, i\omega)$ at chosen values of z and ω have to be computed numerically.

Frequency-response functions for moving supports

As explained in Chapter 11, the standard form of Lagrange's equations (11.8) is limited to systems which are scleronomic (have fixed supports) and holonomic (have their configurations completely determined by independent coordinates). The general theory in Chapter 11 depends on these assumptions. It is assumed that the excitation consists of arbitrary forces, and the response is the set of resulting displacements. Lagrange's equations then lead to the conclusions that the mass and stiffness matrices are symmetrical, with the important consequence that the eigenvector matrix has the orthogonality properties (11.116) and (11.126).

Sometimes it is necessary to consider vibration problems when there is movement of the supports. Then the excitation vector may consist of a mixture of forces and displacements (of the supports that are moved), and the response vector will be a corresponding mixture of displacements and of forces (needed at the supports for their assumed displacements). In that case, the standard equation (11.76) no longer occurs (see Problem 12.4) and, in general, orthogonal normal mode functions satisfying (12.14) and (12.15) cannot be obtained. The result is that solutions are no longer possible by the series expansion of orthogonal modes. However, closed-form solutions of frequency-response functions can still be found by the method described previously.

To calculate any chosen frequency-response function $H(z_r, z_s, i\omega)$, a unit harmonic input is applied at $z = z_s$ and the resulting steady-state harmonic response is calculated at $z = z_r$. The input may be a displacement or force or any other appropriate variable (for example, a velocity or acceleration) and the output may be the same or a different variable. The specified input is a boundary condition that, with the other boundary conditions, must be satisfied by the spatial response function $Y(z, i\omega)$ defined by (12.79). The required frequency-response function is the value of $Y(z, i\omega)$ at the required output location z_r.

This calculation procedure is illustrated in the next section.

Application to an elastic column with a moving support

Consider a vertical elastic column of length L which is subjected to a unit harmonic displacement excitation at its lower end, Fig. 12.5. The column is taken to be vertical because in the next section we shall use it to represent flexible building which is subjected to a vibration input from the ground. There is no force excitation, so that the governing differential equation is assumed, from (12.33), to be

$$m \frac{\partial^2 y}{\partial t^2} + c \frac{\partial y}{\partial t} - EA \frac{\partial^2 y}{\partial z^2} = 0 \qquad (12.103)$$

where

$$m = \rho A \qquad (12.104)$$

is the mass per unit length, c is the viscous damping coefficient per unit length, E is Young's modulus and A is the column's cross-sectional area. All these parameters are assumed to be constants. The boundary conditions are the prescribed displacement at $z = 0$, which is

$$y(z = 0, t) = x(t) = e^{i\omega t} \qquad (12.105)$$

and the absence of an applied force at the free end $z = L$, so that

$$\frac{\partial y(z, t)}{\partial z} = 0, \quad z = L. \qquad (12.106)$$

The steady-state harmonic response is

$$y(z, t) = Y(z, i\omega) e^{i\omega t} \qquad (12.107)$$

and substituting this into the equation of motion (12.103) gives

$$[(i\omega)^2 m + (i\omega) c] Y - EA \frac{d^2 Y}{dz^2} = 0 \qquad (12.108)$$

or, after rearranging the terms,

$$\frac{d^2 Y}{dz^2} + \left(\frac{\rho \omega^2}{E} - i \frac{\mu \omega}{E} \right) Y = 0 \qquad (12.109)$$

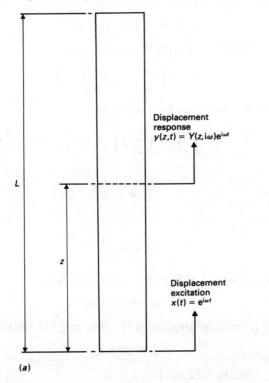

(a)

Displacement
response
$y(z,t) = Y(z, i\omega)e^{i\omega t}$

Displacement
excitation
$x(t) = e^{i\omega t}$

L

z

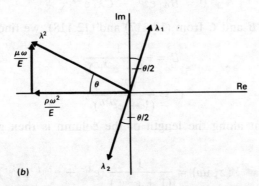

(b)

Fig. 12.5 (a) Vertical elastic column of length L subjected to unit harmonic displacement excitation at its lower end. (*b*) Solutions of equation (12.112) for the eigenvalues of the response function $Y(z, i\omega)$ defined by (12.111)

where

$$\mu = \frac{c}{A}. \tag{12.110}$$

The general solution for $Y(z, i\omega)$ is

$$Y = B e^{\lambda_1 z} + C e^{\lambda_2 z} \tag{12.111}$$

where, from (12.109), λ_1, λ_2 are the solutions of

$$\lambda^2 + \left(\frac{\rho \omega^2}{E} - i \frac{\mu \omega}{E} \right) = 0. \tag{12.112}$$

From Fig. 12.5(*b*), these can be seen to be

$$\lambda_1 = \left[\left(\frac{\rho \omega^2}{E} \right)^2 + \left(\frac{\mu \omega}{E} \right)^2 \right]^{1/4} \left(\sin \frac{\theta}{2} + i \cos \frac{\theta}{2} \right) \tag{12.113}$$

and

$$\lambda_2 = - \lambda_1 \tag{12.114}$$

where

$$\tan \theta = \frac{\mu}{\rho \omega}. \tag{12.115}$$

On substituting from (12.114) into (12.111), we have

$$Y = B e^{\lambda_1 z} + C e^{-\lambda_1 z}. \tag{12.116}$$

The boundary conditions give, from (12.105) and (12.107) at $z = 0$,

$$1 = B + C \tag{12.117}$$

and, from (12.106) and (12.107) at $z = L$,

$$0 = B \lambda_1 e^{\lambda_1 L} - C \lambda_1 e^{-\lambda_1 L} \tag{12.118}$$

and, solving for B and C from (12.117) and (12.118), we find that

$$B = \frac{1}{(1 + e^{2\lambda_1 L})} \tag{12.119}$$

$$C = \frac{e^{2\lambda_1 L}}{(1 + e^{2\lambda_1 L})}. \tag{12.120}$$

The displacement along the length of the column is then given by, from (12.111),

$$Y \equiv Y(z, i\omega) = \frac{1}{(1 + e^{2\lambda_1 L})} (e^{\lambda_1 z} + e^{2\lambda_1 L} e^{-\lambda_1 z})$$

$$= \frac{e^{\lambda_1(L-z)} + e^{-\lambda_1(L-z)}}{e^{\lambda_1 L} + e^{-\lambda_1 L}} \tag{12.121}$$

where $\lambda_1 \equiv \lambda_1(i\omega)$ is given by (12.113). Since λ_1 is a complex quantity, it is convenient to put

$$\lambda_1 = \alpha + i\beta \tag{12.122}$$

where α and β are real. After separating the real and imaginary parts of each term in (12.121), we then arrive at the result that

$$Y(z, i\omega) = \frac{\cosh \alpha(L - z)\cos \beta(L - z) + i \sinh \alpha(L - z)\sin \beta(L - z)}{\cosh \alpha L \cos \beta L + i \sinh \alpha L \sin \beta L}.$$

$$(12.123)$$

This gives the (complex) amplitude of the displacement at position z for a unit amplitude harmonic displacement with frequency ω applied at $z = 0$. If we are interested in the force transmitted along the column, $f(z, t)$ where, for steady-state harmonic conditions,

$$f(z, t) = F(z, i\omega)\, e^{i\omega t} \qquad (12.124)$$

we know that, if $f(z, t)$ is a tension force,

$$f(z, t) = EA \frac{\partial}{\partial z} y(z, t) \qquad (12.125)$$

so that

$$F(z, i\omega) = EA \frac{d}{dz} Y(z, i\omega). \qquad (12.126)$$

By differentiating (12.121), this gives

$$F(z, i\omega) = EA\left(\frac{-\lambda_1 e^{\lambda_1(L-z)} + \lambda_1 e^{-\lambda_1(L-z)}}{e^{\lambda_1 L} + e^{-\lambda_1 L}}\right). \qquad (12.127)$$

Using the static stiffness k defined by (12.96), and replacing λ_1 by $(\alpha + i\beta)$ according to (12.122), we find that

$$\frac{F(z, i\omega)}{k} = -(\alpha + i\beta)L \times$$

$$\times \left(\frac{\sinh \alpha(L - z)\cos \beta(L - z) + i \cosh \alpha(L - z)\sin \beta(L - z)}{\cosh \alpha L \cos \beta L + i \sinh \alpha L \sin \beta L}\right). \qquad (12.128)$$

Notice that the physical dimensions of $F(z, i\omega)$ are force/length since $F(z, i\omega)$ is the tensile force at position z and frequency ω for a unit displacement input at $z = 0$.

If the output is defined as the compressive force in the column (rather than the tensile force), the column's frequency response is

$$H(z, 0, i\omega) = -F(z, i\omega). \qquad (12.129)$$

The force that has to be applied at the base of the column to give the prescribed displacement input here is then given by $H(0, 0, i\omega)$.

In Fig. 12.6, $|H(0, 0, i\omega)|/k$ is plotted against ωa for the range $\omega a = 0$ to $6.5(\pi/2)$ for the case when $E = 10^{10}$ N/m^2, $\rho = 2400$ kg/m^3, $\mu = 5 \times 10^4$ N s/m^4, $L = 30$ m. It can be seen that the output force has peaks at $\omega a = \pi/2, 3\pi/2, 5\pi/2, \ldots$, which are the resonant frequencies for the free vibration of an elastic column with one end fixed, Fig. 12.4. However, notice that in Fig. 12.6 it is the applied force (not the displacement) which has resonant peaks. In the limit of zero damping, an infinite force is required at the lower end of the column, Fig. 12.5(a), to give a unit harmonic displacement at the lower end when $\omega a = \pi/2, \, 3\pi/2, \, 5\pi/2$, etc. This is because, at these frequencies, the column is acting as a dynamic vibration absorber† which restrains motion at its lower end (see Problem 12.6). In the undamped case, motion at a nodal point for free vibration cannot be excited because the system acts as a perfect vibration absorber for this input. In the presence of damping, motion of a support which also happens to be a node can occur, but the dynamic stiffness is high so that a large force is required to give only a small movement of the support.

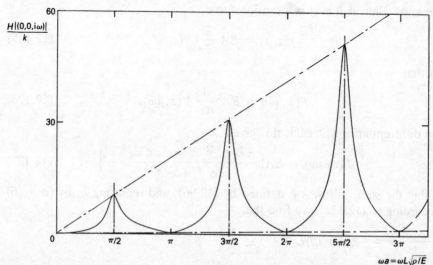

Fig. 12.6 Magnitude of the frequency-response function for the elastic column in Fig. 12.5 when the input is a unit amplitude displacement applied at the lower end of the column and the output is the force required at the lower end to give this displacement. The parameter values are $E = 10^{10} \, \text{N/m}^2$, $\rho = 2400 \, \text{kg/m}^3$, $\mu = 5 \times 10^4 \, \text{N s/m}^4$ and $L = 30 \, \text{m}$. The stiffness k is defined by equation (12.96)

For small damping, the magnitude of the peak resonance at $\omega a = (2j - 1)\pi/2$ can be calculated from (12.128). From Fig. 12.5(b), if there is a small damping, angle θ is small, and

$$\theta \simeq \frac{\mu}{\rho \omega}. \tag{12.130}$$

In this case

$$|\lambda_1| \simeq \omega \sqrt{\frac{\rho}{E}} \tag{12.131}$$

† A dynamic vibration absorber acts, not by dissipating energy, but by applying a reactive force of the correct frequency and phase to minimize vibration at a particular location (see, for example, Den Hartog [18], Chapter 3).

and, if

$$\lambda_1 = \alpha + i\beta \qquad (12.132)$$

we have

$$\alpha \simeq |\lambda_1| \frac{\theta}{2} = \omega \sqrt{\frac{\rho}{E}} \left(\frac{\mu}{2\rho\omega} \right) = \frac{\mu}{2 \sqrt{\rho E}} \qquad (12.133)$$

and

$$\beta \simeq |\lambda_1| = \omega \sqrt{\frac{\rho}{E}} = \omega \frac{a}{L} \qquad (12.134)$$

from (12.97). Hence, for $\omega a = (2j - 1)\pi/2$, we have

$$\beta L = (2j - 1) \pi/2 \qquad (12.135)$$

for which

$$\cos \beta L = 0 \text{ and } \sin \beta L = \pm 1. \qquad (12.136)$$

On substituting into (12.128) with $z = 0$, we then have, with (12.129),

$$\frac{H(0, 0, i\omega)}{k} = (\alpha + i\beta)L \left(\frac{1}{\tanh \alpha L} \right). \qquad (12.137)$$

For small damping we know from (12.133) that α is small so that

$$\frac{H(0, 0, i\omega)}{k} \simeq i \frac{\beta}{\alpha} = i \frac{(2j - 1)\pi}{2\alpha L} \qquad (12.138)$$

from (12.135) and so the resonant peaks are given approximately by

$$\frac{|H(0, 0, i\omega)|}{k} = \frac{(2j - 1)\pi}{2\alpha L}, j = 1, 2, 3, \ldots \qquad (12.139)$$

Therefore the heights of the resonant peaks in Fig. 12.6 increase linearly with frequency (subject to the approximation of small damping). Also, similarly, the magnitudes of the minimum responses at $\omega a = \pi, 2\pi, 3\pi, \ldots$ increase linearly with frequency (subject to the same assumption of small damping).

The applied force is a minimum at $\omega a = \pi, 2\pi, 3\pi, \ldots$ because these are the resonant frequencies of an undamped elastic column with both ends free (Problem 12.6). For these modes there is an anti-node (point of maximum amplitude) at the lower end of the column, and so the dynamic stiffness for displacement excitation at this point is then a minimum.

The variation of displacement along the length of the column can be calculated from equation (12.123). This applies for unit displacement excitation

$$x(t) = \text{Re}\{e^{i\omega t}\} \qquad (12.140)$$

where we now (arbitrarily) identify $x(t)$ as the real part of the complex exponential. The displacement response is then

$$y(z, t) = \text{Re}\{Y(z, i\omega)\, e^{i\omega t}\} \qquad (12.141)$$

from which $y(z, t)$ can be calculated as a function of longitudinal position z when ω and t are specified. In Figs 12.7 and 12.8, $y(z, t)$ is plotted against z, for $\omega a = \pi$ in Fig. 12.7 and for $\omega a = 2\pi$ in Fig. 12.8, in each case for nine values of time, covering a half-period. Each figure shows nine snapshots of the column's displacement during forced excitation at the first resonant frequency (Fig. 12.7) and second resonant frequency (Fig. 12.8) of the free–free column. The deflection of the vibrating column at these two frequencies is very similar to the mode shapes of the free–free beam. Note, however, that the nodal points are not fixed points; their longitudinal position changes as the column passes through each period of its forced motion.

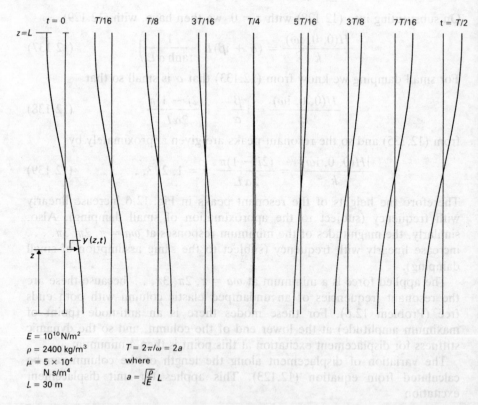

$E = 10^{10}\,\text{N/m}^2$
$\rho = 2400\,\text{kg/m}^3$
$\mu = 5 \times 10^4$
$\quad$ N s/m^4
$L = 30$ m

$T = 2\pi/\omega = 2a$
where
$a = \sqrt{\dfrac{\rho}{E}}\,L$

Fig. 12.7 Successive positions of the longitudinal deflection of the damped elastic column in Fig. 12.5(a) when subjected to displacement excitation at its lower end at its lowest natural frequency for undamped free–free vibration, $\omega a = \pi$

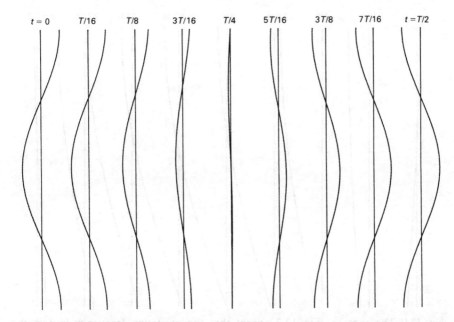

$t = 0$ $T/16$ $T/8$ $3T/16$ $T/4$ $5T/16$ $3T/8$ $7T/16$ $t = T/2$

Fig. 12.8 The same as Fig. 12.7 except that the excitation frequency is now the second natural frequency of the undamped free–free column, $\omega a = 2\pi$

In Figs 12.9 and 12.10 the same graphs are shown for $\omega a = \pi/2$ in Fig. 12.9 and for $\omega a = 3\pi/2$ in Fig. 12.10. Now the column is being forced at frequencies that are natural frequencies for an undamped elastic column which is fixed at its lower end. In the absence of damping, we have seen above that it is not possible to have displacement excitation at the lower end of the column at these frequencies because infinite amplitudes of force would be required to achieve this. In the presence of damping, displacement excitation of the lower end of the column is possible but large forces are needed to achieve these displacements. In consequence, the displacement of the rest of the column is much greater than the forced displacement. In Fig. 12.9, the column moves in its roughly half-sine shape for undamped resonance, but almost exactly 90° out of phase with the excitation. In Fig. 12.10, when the excitation frequency is that for the second undamped fixed–free mode, the conclusion is the same. The column responds to displacement excitation at this frequency and at the lower end (where there should be a node) by vibrating through a much larger amplitude than the lower end's forced amplitude and almost exactly 90° out of phase with the forcing displacement.

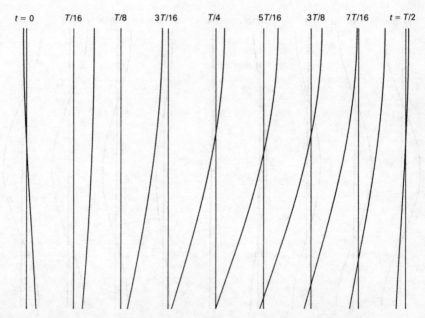

Fig. 12.9 The same as Fig. 12.7 except that the excitation frequency is now the lowest natural frequency for undamped fixed–free vibration, $\omega a = \pi/2$

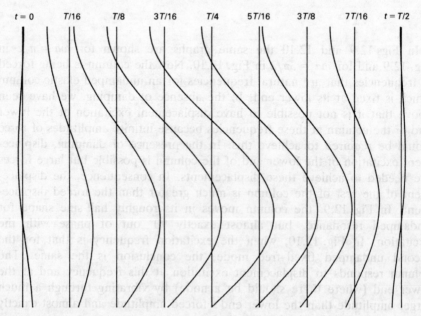

Fig. 12.10 The same as Fig. 12.7 except that the excitation frequency is now the second natural frequency for undamped fixed–free vibration, $\omega a = 3\pi/2$

Example of a flexible column on a resilient foundation

A practical example concerns the transmission of vertical vibration from the ground to a flexible building. In order to reduce the transmission of ground-borne vibration from road and rail traffic, particularly underground railways, a new building may be constructed on a flexible elastomeric base layer. The ability of such a resilient interface to attenuate the transmission of vibration depends on the stiffness and damping of the material used and on the vibration characteristics of the building that is isolated. Consider the idealized model shown in Fig. 12.11(*a*). The resilient base layer is modelled as a linear spring of stiffness k and viscous damping c, and the building as a homogeneous resilient block of height L, modulus of elasticity E, density ρ and viscous damping per unit volume μ.

We shall consider only the transmission of vertical vibration from the ground, represented by input displacement $x(t)$, and the resulting vertical vibration of the elastic column. As output, initially we take the displacement response $y(t)$ at the base of the column.

Consider breaking the composite system into the components shown in Fig. 12.11(*b*). Let the total dynamic force exerted on the base of the building be $f(t)$, as shown. For equilibrium of the spring and damper

$$c(\dot{x} - \dot{y}) + k(x - y) = f \tag{12.142}$$

and so, for steady-state harmonic excitation at frequency ω, if

$$x(t) = X(i\omega)\,e^{i\omega t},\ y(t) = Y(i\omega)\,e^{i\omega t},\ f(t) = F(i\omega)\,e^{i\omega t} \tag{12.143}$$

then

$$X(i\omega)[i\omega c + k] - Y(i\omega)[i\omega c + k] = F(i\omega). \tag{12.144}$$

Also, if $H(i\omega)$ denotes the frequency-response function for force output/displacement input at the base of the elastic column, then

$$F(i\omega) = H(i\omega)\,Y(i\omega). \tag{12.145}$$

On eliminating $F(i\omega)$ between (12.144) and (12.145), we get

$$\frac{Y(i\omega)}{X(i\omega)} = \frac{i\omega c + k}{H(i\omega) + i\omega c + k}. \tag{12.146}$$

This is the frequency-response function for displacement output $y(t)$ at the base of the column and displacement input $x(t)$ at the ground. Denoting

$$\frac{Y(i\omega)}{X(i\omega)}$$

by $H_{yx}(i\omega)$, we have

$$H_{yx}(i\omega) = \frac{i\omega c + k}{H(i\omega) + i\omega c + k} \tag{12.147}$$

and the transmissibility from the ground to the base of the building is

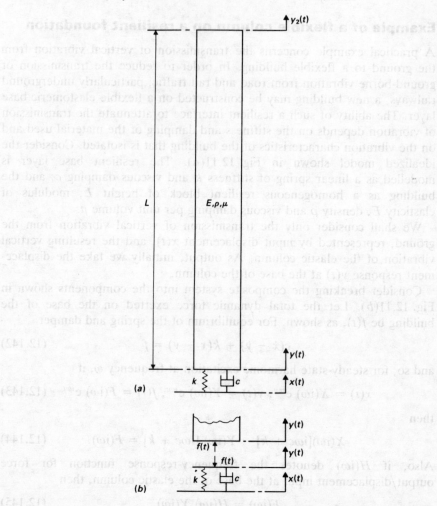

Fig. 12.11 (a) Idealized model of a building on a resilient foundation to reduce the transmission of ground-borne vertical vibration. (b) Free-body diagram of the resilient foundation shown separated from the base of the building

$$T = 20 \log_{10}|H_{yx}(i\omega)| = 20 \log_{10}\left|\frac{i\omega c + k}{H(i\omega) + i\omega c + k}\right|. \quad (12.148)$$

$H(i\omega)$ is the response of the building at its base for force output and displacement input where, from Fig. 12.11, the force is compressive. Hence, from (12.129),

$$H(i\omega) = H(0, 0, i\omega) = - F(0, i\omega) \quad (12.149)$$

which, with (12.128) and (12.96), gives

$$H(i\omega) = EA(\alpha + i\beta)\left(\frac{\sinh \alpha L \cos \beta L + i \cosh \alpha L \sin \beta L}{\cosh \alpha L \cos \beta L + i \sinh \alpha L \sin \beta L}\right). \quad (12.150)$$

The procedure for computing the transmissibility T is to begin by choosing a frequency ω and then to compute the real and imaginary parts α and β of eigenvalue λ_1 from equations (12.113) and (12.115). With these values of α and β, the real and imaginary parts of $H(i\omega)$ are computed from (12.150), and then the transmissibility is found from (12.148). A logical flow diagram is given in Fig. 12.12.

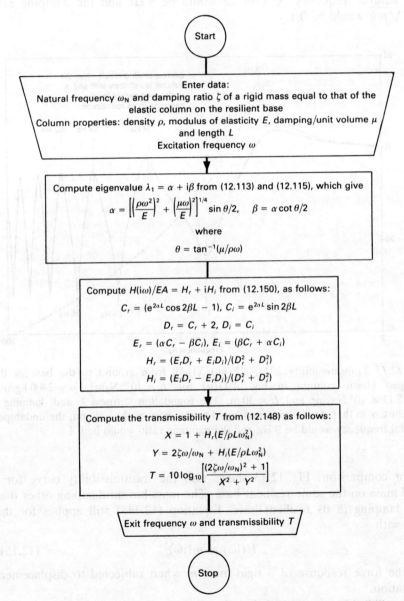

Start

Enter data:
Natural frequency ω_N and damping ratio ζ of a rigid mass equal to that of the elastic column on the resilient base
Column properties: density ρ, modulus of elasticity E, damping/unit volume μ and length L
Excitation frequency ω

Compute eigenvalue $\lambda_1 = \alpha + i\beta$ from (12.113) and (12.115), which give

$$\alpha = \left[\left(\frac{\rho\omega^2}{E} \right)^2 + \left| \frac{\mu\omega}{E} \right|^2 \right]^{1/4} \sin \theta/2, \quad \beta = \alpha \cot \theta/2$$

where

$$\theta = \tan^{-1}(\mu/\rho\omega)$$

Compute $H(i\omega)/EA = H_r + iH_i$ from (12.150), as follows:

$$C_r = (e^{2\alpha L} \cos 2\beta L - 1), \quad C_i = e^{2\alpha L} \sin 2\beta L$$

$$D_r = C_r + 2, \quad D_i = C_i$$

$$E_r = (\alpha C_r - \beta C_i), \quad E_i = (\beta C_r + \alpha C_i)$$

$$H_r = (E_r D_r + E_i D_i)/(D_r^2 + D_i^2)$$

$$H_i = (E_i D_r - E_r D_i)/(D_r^2 + D_i^2)$$

Compute the transmissibility T from (12.148) as follows:

$$X = 1 + H_r(E/\rho L\omega_N^2)$$

$$Y = 2\zeta\omega/\omega_N + H_i(E/\rho L\omega_N^2)$$

$$T = 10 \log_{10} \left[\frac{(2\zeta\omega/\omega_N)^2 + 1}{X^2 + Y^2} \right]$$

Exit frequency ω and transmissibility T

Stop

Fig. 12.12 Logical flow diagram to compute the displacement transmissibility given by equation (12.150) using real arithmetic only

In Fig. 12.13, results are plotted for a typical case with $E = 10^{10}$ N/m^2 $\rho = 2400$ kg/m^3, $\mu = 5.13 \times 10^4$ N s/m^4, $L = 30$ m. This represents a column of concrete 30 m high. The damping value is chosen to give a damping ratio of 0.1 for the lowest mode of the column alone when its lower end is fixed. The properties of the resilient foundation, stiffness k and damping c, are chosen so that, if the column were rigid with mass m, the natural frequency $\sqrt{k/m}/2\pi$ would be 9 Hz and the damping ratio $c/2\sqrt{mk}$ would be 0.1.

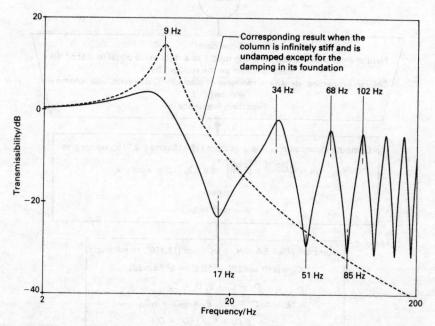

Fig. 12.13 Transmissibility $20 \log_{10} |Y(i\omega)/X(i\omega)|$ from ground to the base of the damped elastic column in Fig. 12.11(a) for $E = 10^{10}$ N/m^2, $\rho = 2400$ kg/m^3, $\mu = 5.13 \times 10^4$ N s/m^4 and $L = 30$ m. The foundation stiffness k and damping c are chosen so that, for a rigid mass equal to the mass of the column, the undamped natural frequency would be 9 Hz and the damping ratio would be 0.1

For comparison, Fig. 12.13 shows also the transmissibility curve for a rigid mass on the same resilient base. The mass has no damping other than the damping in its resilient base. Equation (12.148) still applies for this case with

$$H(i\omega) = m(i\omega)^2 \tag{12.151}$$

for the force response of a rigid mass m when subjected to displacement excitation.

The natural frequencies of an elastic column with a fixed base are given by (12.51) and, for the values of E, ρ and L given above, the first three natural frequencies are

$$f_1 = 17 \text{ Hz}, f_2 = 51 \text{ Hz}, f_3 = 85 \text{ Hz} \tag{12.152}$$

approximately. In Fig. 12.13, these can be seen to be frequencies at which the column acts as a vibration absorber for displacement inputs at its base, and the transmissibility reaches a local minimum close to each of these frequencies. However, the free–free column has natural frequencies (see Problem 12.6 (ii)) given by

$$\omega_j = j \frac{\pi}{L} \sqrt{\frac{E}{\rho}} \tag{12.153}$$

and, for the parameter values above, the first three natural frequencies of the free–free column are

$$f_1 = 34 \text{ Hz}, f_2 = 68 \text{ Hz}, f_3 = 102 \text{ Hz}. \tag{12.154}$$

In Fig. 12.13 these can be seen to be frequencies close to local maxima in the transmissibility curve. The resonant frequencies of the combined system are close to the natural frequencies of the free–free column.

Response at the top of the column

As well as calculating the displacement response at the bottom of the flexible column in Fig. 12.13, the same method may be used to find the response at any other position on the column. For example, suppose that we want the displacement response at the top of the column, coordinate $y_2(t)$ in Fig. 12.11(a).

From Fig. 12.5, the displacement frequency-response function for the displacement at height z for unit harmonic displacement input at the bottom of the column is $Y(z, i\omega)$, where $Y(z, i\omega)$ has been found to be given by (12.123). At the top of the column $z = L$ and then, from (12.123),

$$Y(L, i\omega) = \frac{1}{\cosh \alpha L \cos \beta L + i \sinh \alpha L \sin \beta L}. \tag{12.155}$$

If the amplitude of the displacement input at $z = 0$ is

$$Y(0, i\omega) = Y(i\omega) \tag{12.156}$$

instead of unity in Fig. 12.5(a), then the amplitude of the response at the top of the column is

$$Y_2(i\omega) = Y(L, i\omega) \, Y(i\omega) \tag{12.157}$$

and the transmissibility to the top of the column is

$$T_2 = 20 \log_{10} \left| \frac{Y_2(i\omega)}{X(i\omega)} \right|$$

$$= 20 \log_{10} \left(|Y(L, i\omega)| \left| \frac{Y(i\omega)}{X(i\omega)} \right| \right)$$

$$= 20 \log_{10} |Y(L, i\omega)| + T \qquad (12.158)$$

where T is the transmissibility to the bottom of the column given by (12.148). Hence the transmissibility to the top, T_2, is obtained by adding $20 \log_{10} |Y(L, i\omega)|$ to the transmissibility to the bottom, T.

This has been done for the parameter values of the curves in Fig. 12.13 and the results are plotted in Fig. 12.14. The transmissibility to the bottom of the column, from Fig. 12.13, is plotted as the broken-line curve for comparison with the new results for the top of the column, plotted as the continuous curve. At the frequencies at which there are minima in Fig. 12.13, there are still minima (approximately) but the transmissibility is higher at these minima than before. This is because these are the frequencies at which the column behaves as a vibration absorber acting to prevent motion of its base. This is effective at the base, but less so at the top of the column since the column must vibrate in order to exert the necessary oscillatory reaction force at its base. At the resonant frequencies of the column/resilient base assembly, which are close to the resonant frequencies of a free–free column, the peak amplitudes of the the top and

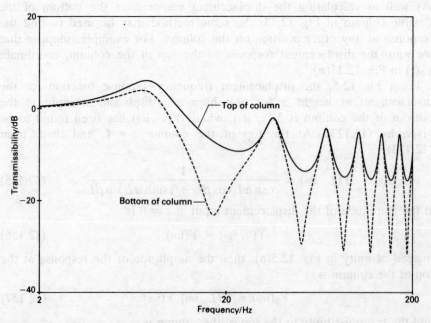

Fig. 12.14 Transmissibility $20 \log_{10} |Y_2(i\omega)/X(i\omega)|$ from ground to the top of the damped elastic column in Fig. 12.11(a) for the same parameter values as Fig. 12.13

bottom of the column are (very nearly) the same. This is because in the (undamped) free–free modes the amplitudes of the top and bottom of the column are the same.

This conclusion depends on there being small damping. For Figs 12.13 and 12.14, the damping is chosen to give a damping ratio of 0.1 for the lowest mode of the fixed–free column, which has a natural frequency of 17 Hz. The damping model assumed by (12.103) involves a constant modal bandwidth assumption (see equation (3.49)) with

$$\zeta_j \omega_j = \text{constant.} \tag{12.159}$$

This may be seen from (12.25) and (12.28) because the equation of motion (12.103) is a special case of (12.25) with $\beta = 0$. Hence the damping ratio for frequencies higher than 17 Hz is less than 0.1, decreasing inversely as frequency increases. If instead of assuming that

$$\zeta_j \propto 1/\omega_j \tag{12.160}$$

by putting $\beta = 0$ in (12.25), we put $\alpha = 0$ so that

$$\zeta_j \propto \omega_j, \tag{12.161}$$

completely different results are obtained for the transmissibility curves. This alternative damping assumption is considered in the next section.

Alternative damping model

For the results in Figs 12.13 and 12.14, the equation of motion of the column in Fig. 12.11(a) has been taken to be

$$\frac{\partial^2 y}{\partial t^2} + \frac{\mu}{\rho} \frac{\partial y}{\partial t} - \frac{E}{\rho} \frac{\partial^2 y}{\partial z^2} = 0 \tag{12.162}$$

where $\mu = c/A$ is the viscous damping per unit volume. On substituting the modal expansion (12.26) and using (12.14) and (12.15), we have

$$\ddot{q}_j + \frac{\mu}{\rho} \dot{q}_j + \omega_j^2 q_j = 0 \tag{12.163}$$

where q_j is the jth normal coordinate. Putting

$$2\zeta_j \omega_j = \mu/\rho \tag{12.164}$$

this can be written in the standard form

$$\ddot{q}_j + 2\zeta_j \omega_j \dot{q}_j + \omega_j^2 q_j = 0. \tag{12.165}$$

The modal bandwidth is $2\zeta_j \omega_j$ and, from (12.164), is constant for all modes.

Instead of (12.162), consider the alternative equation of motion

$$\frac{\partial^2 y}{\partial t^2} - \eta \frac{E}{\rho} \frac{\partial^3 y}{\partial z^2 \partial t} - \frac{E}{\rho} \frac{\partial^2 y}{\partial z^2} = 0. \tag{12.166}$$

This is a particular case of the general equation (12.25) with $\alpha = 0$ and $\beta = \eta$. In comparison, (12.162) is a different particular case of (12.25), with $\alpha = \mu/\rho$ and $\beta = 0$. For a steady-state harmonic response

$$y(z, t) = Y(z, i\omega) \, e^{i\omega t} \tag{12.167}$$

and, on substituting in (12.166), this gives

$$(i\omega)^2 Y - \eta \frac{E}{\rho} (i\omega) \frac{d^2 Y}{dz^2} - \frac{E}{\rho} \frac{d^2 Y}{dz^2} = 0. \tag{12.168}$$

After multiplying through by ρ/E and collecting terms, we then have

$$\frac{d^2 Y}{dz^2} (1 + \eta i\omega) + \frac{\rho\omega^2}{E} Y = 0. \tag{12.169}$$

This equation corresponds to (12.109) in the previous analysis and, for the same general solution (12.111), we have

$$\lambda^2 (1 + \eta i\omega) + \frac{\rho\omega^2}{E} = 0 \tag{12.170}$$

instead of (12.112). The solutions for λ_1, λ_2 can be seen from Fig. 12.15 and, instead of (12.113) to (12.115), we now have

$$\lambda_1 = \sqrt{\frac{\rho}{E}} \, \omega(1 + \eta^2\omega^2)^{-1/4} \left(\sin\frac{\theta}{2} + i\cos\frac{\theta}{2} \right) \tag{12.171}$$

$$\lambda_2 = -\lambda_1 \tag{12.172}$$

and

$$\tan\theta = \eta\omega. \tag{12.173}$$

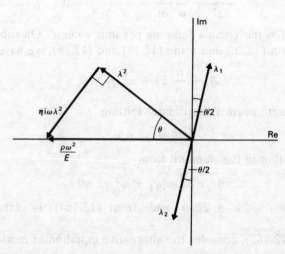

Fig. 12.15 Solutions of equations (12.170) for the eigenvalues of the response function $Y(z, i\omega)$ defined by (12.167)

On account of (12.172), which is the same as (12.114), the same results as for the previous case apply, and so (12.121), (12.123), (12.127) and (12.128) apply unaltered. The difference is that α and β, which are the real and imaginary parts of λ_1 now have to be calculated from (12.171) and (12.173) instead of from (12.113) and (12.115).

Figures 12.16 and 12.17 are comparable results to those plotted in Figs 12.13 and 12.14 for the original damping assumption. The parameter values are $E = 10^{10}\,\text{N/m}^2$, $\rho = 2400\,\text{kg/m}^3$ and $L = 30\,\text{m}$, as before, with the new damping coefficient η set at $\eta = 1.87 \times 10^{-4}\,\text{s}$ (the units being seconds). This value of damping is chosen so that the lowest-frequency mode of the column with one end fixed has a damping ratio of 0.01. That this is so may be seen by substituting the modal expansion (12.26) into (12.166), using (12.14) and (12.15), to get

$$\ddot{q}_j + \eta\omega_j^2\dot{q}_j + \omega_j^2\,q_j = 0. \tag{12.174}$$

In the standard form (12.165), we then have

$$2\zeta_j\omega_j = \eta\omega_j^2 \tag{12.175}$$

and the modal bandwidth is proportional to ω_j^2. The lowest natural frequency of the fixed–free column is, from (12.152), $f_1 = 17\,\text{Hz}$, at which

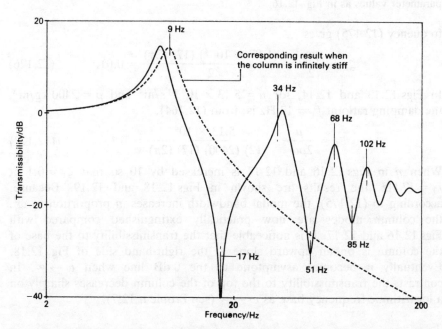

Fig. 12.16 The same graph as in Fig. 12.13 for displacement transmissibility from ground to column base, except that the damping model defined by equation (12.166) is used instead of equation (12.162). Parameter values E, ρ, L, k and c as for Fig. 12.13. Damping coefficient $\eta = 1.87 \times 10^{-4}\,\text{s}$

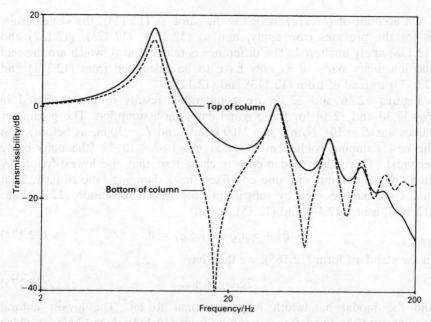

Fig. 12.17 Displacement transmissibility from ground to column top for the same parameter values as in Fig. 12.16

frequency (12.175) gives

$$\zeta_1 = \frac{\eta\omega_1}{2} = \frac{(1.87 \times 10^{-4})\,(17)\,(2\pi)}{2} = 0.01. \qquad (12.176)$$

In Figs 12.13 and 12.14, for $\mu = 5.13 \times 10^4\,\mathrm{N\,s/m^4}$ and $\rho = 2400\,\mathrm{kg/m^3}$, the damping ratio at $f_1 = 17\,\mathrm{Hz}$ is, from (12.164),

$$\zeta_1 = \frac{\mu}{2\rho\omega_1} = \frac{5.13 \times 10^4}{(2)\,(2400)\,(17)\,(2\pi)} = 0.1. \qquad (12.177)$$

When η in Figs 12.16 and 12.17 is increased by 10 so that $\zeta_1 = 0.1$ at $f_1 = 17\,\mathrm{Hz}$, the results are shown in Figs 12.18 and 12.19. Because, according to (12.175), the modal bandwidth increases in proportion to ω_j^2, the column modes are now practically extinguished compared with Figs 12.16 and 12.17. It is noticeable that the transmissibility to the base of the column is on an upward slope at the right-hand side of Fig. 12.18. Eventually it becomes asymptotic to the 0 dB line when $\omega \to \infty$. In contrast, the transmissibility to the top of the column decreases sharply on a logarithmic frequency base as $\omega \to \infty$ (see Problem 12.7).

Discussion of damping models

The essential difference between the two different damping models (12.162) and (12.166) is illustrated in Fig. 12.20. In the left-hand lumped-

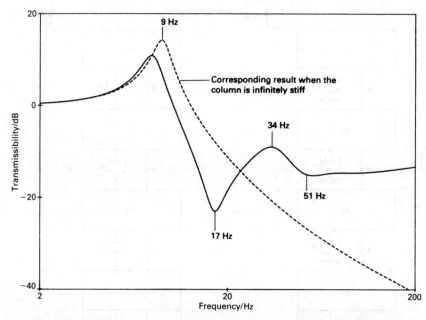

Fig. 12.18 The same graph as Fig. 12.16, except that the column damping has been increased by a factor of 10 to $\eta = 1.87 \times 10^{-3}$ s

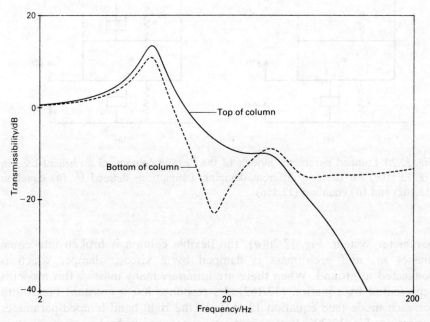

Fig. 12.19 The same graph as Fig. 12.17, except that the column damping η has been increased by a factor of 10 to $\eta = 1.87 \times 10^{-3}$ s

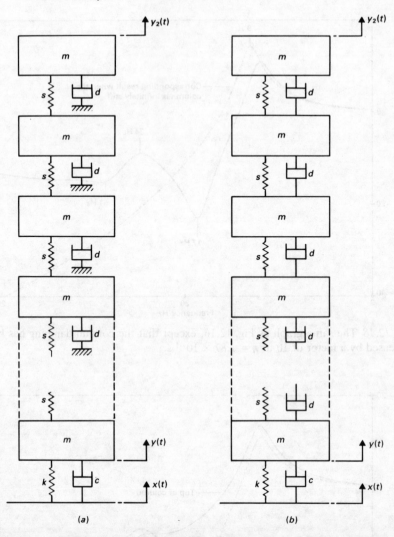

Fig. 12.20 Lumped parameter models of the flexible column on a resilient base in Fig. 12.11(*a*) for the two different damping assumptions defined by (*a*) equation (12.162) and (*b*) equation (12.166)

parameter system, Fig. 12.20(*a*), the flexible column is broken into equal masses *m*, and each mass is damped by a viscous damper which is connected to ground. When there are infinitely many masses, this model is represented by equation (12.162). Its response has a constant bandwidth for each mode (see equation 12.164). In the right-hand lumped-parameter system in Fig. 12.20(*b*), the continuous column is broken into discrete masses in the same way but each viscous damper is now connected to the adjacent mass instead of to ground. For an infinite number of masses, this becomes the continuous model defined by (12.166). The response of the latter has a modal bandwidth which increases in proportion to frequency squared (see equation (12.175)).

Figures 12.13 and 12.14 apply for the model based on Fig. 12.20(a). Figures 12.16, 12.17, 12.18 and 12.19 apply for the model based on Fig. 12.20(b). Except for the column's damping, all of the numerical parameters are the same for all these graphs. The column is always 30 m high and is assumed to have the density and stiffness of concrete with $\rho = 2400 \text{ kg/m}^3$ and $E = 10^{10} \text{ N/m}^2$. The fixed–free longitudinal modes of the column then have natural frequencies at 17 Hz, 51 Hz, 85 Hz, etc., and the free–free longitudinal modes have natural frequencies at 34 Hz, 68 Hz, 102 Hz, etc. The resilient foundation always has its stiffness per unit area and damping per unit area such that, if the column were rigid, the natural frequency of the system would be 9 Hz and its damping ratio would be 0.1.

The column's damping is chosen as follows. For Figs 12.13 and 12.14, which are for the constant-bandwidth column, the parameter $\mu = 5.13 \times 10^4 \text{ N s/m}^4$. From equation (12.164), this gives $\zeta_1 = 0.1$ for the lowest mode of the fixed–free column for which $\omega_1/2\pi = 17 \text{ Hz}$. Figures 12.16 and 12.17, which are for the model with bandwidth proportional to frequency squared, have parameter $\eta = 1.87 \times 10^{-4} \text{ s}$. From equation (12.175), this gives $\zeta_1 = 0.01$ when $\omega_1/2\pi = 17 \text{ Hz}$. For Figs 12.18 and 12.19, which are for the same model, $\eta = 1.87 \times 10^{-3} \text{ s}$, giving $\zeta_1 = 0.1$ at $\omega_1/2\pi = 17 \text{ Hz}$.

These two damping models represent extreme cases. They can be combined by including the damping terms

$$\frac{\mu}{\rho} \frac{\partial y}{\partial t}$$

from (12.162) and

$$-\eta \frac{E}{\rho} \frac{\partial^3 y}{\partial z^2 \partial t}$$

from (12.166) in one equation of motion and solving this new equation in the same way as described above for equations (12.162) and (12.166). The column's bandwidth is then given by

$$\frac{\mu}{\rho} + \eta \omega_j^2$$

instead of (12.164) or (12.175). A further alternative is to include a complex modulus E to give a damping term of the form

$$-i\eta \frac{E}{\rho} \frac{\partial^2 y}{\partial z^2}$$

instead of

$$-\eta \frac{E}{\rho} \frac{\partial^3 y}{\partial z^2 \partial t}$$

(the dimensions of η being different in these two terms). In the frequency-domain this gives a modal bandwidth proportional to frequency. However, as explained in the last section of Chapter 11, such a damping model does not satisfy the requirement of causality and cannot be used for exact solutions in the time domain.

General response equations for continuous systems

The equation of motion (12.25) and results which stem from it depend on the assumption that, at position z, deflection occurs only in a known reference direction. For many simple continuous systems this will give an adequate approximation, but for more complex systems it is not a valid assumption. The deflection of a curved shell may have significant components in the tangential plane of the shell as well as normal to it; the deflection of a point in a three-dimensional elastic body may be in any direction. Then the scalar response variable $y(z, t)$ must be replaced by the vector $y(z, t)$ with components $y_1(z, t)$, $y_2(z, t)$, $y_3(z, t)$ in three orthogonal reference directions. Also, the stiffness operator $L\{ \ \}$ becomes a vector operator $L\{ \ \}$ with components $L_1\{ \ \}$, $L_2\{ \ \}$, $L_3\{ \ \}$ in the reference directions. As a result, the equation of motion (12.25) is replaced by an equivalent vector equation

$$m(z)\frac{\partial^2}{\partial t^2}y(z, t) + \alpha m(z)\frac{\partial}{\partial t}y(z, t) + \beta L\left\{\frac{\partial}{\partial t}y(z, t)\right\} + L\{y(z, t)\}$$

$$= x(z, t) \quad (12.178)$$

where the response vector

$$y(z, t) = \begin{bmatrix} y_1(z, t) \\ y_2(z, t) \\ y_3(z, t) \end{bmatrix}, \quad (12.179)$$

the stiffness operator

$$L\{y(z, t)\} = \begin{bmatrix} L_1\{y(z, t)\} \\ L_2\{y(z, t)\} \\ L_3\{y(z, t)\} \end{bmatrix} = \begin{bmatrix} L_1\{y_1(z, t), y_2(z, t), y_3(z, t)\} \\ L_2\{y_1(z, t), y_2(z, t), y_3(z, t)\} \\ L_3\{y_1(z, t), y_2(z, t), y_3(z, t)\} \end{bmatrix}$$

$$(12.180)$$

and the three-dimensional excitation vector

$$x(z, t) = \begin{bmatrix} x_1(z, t) \\ x_2(z, t) \\ x_3(z, t) \end{bmatrix}. \quad (12.181)$$

As before, the response vector can be expanded in terms of normal coordinates $q_j(t)$ and normal mode functions $U_j(z)$, which are now vectors defined by

$$U_j(z) = \begin{bmatrix} U_{1j}(z) \\ U_{2j}(z) \\ U_{3j}(z) \end{bmatrix} \qquad (12.182)$$

so that, instead of (12.26), we have

$$y(z, t) = \sum_{j=1}^{\infty} q_j(t)\, U_j(z) . \qquad (12.183)$$

Corresponding to (12.14), the normal mode functions $U_j(z)$ satisfy the orthogonality condition

$$\int_R dz\, m(z)\, U_j^{\mathrm{T}}(z)\, U_k(z) = \delta_{jk},\, j,\, k = 1 \text{ to } \infty \qquad (12.184)$$

which, on expansion, gives

$$\int_R dz\, m(z)\, \{U_{1j}(z)\, U_{1k}(z) + U_{2j}(z)\, U_{2k}(z) + U_{3j}(z)\, U_{3k}(z)\}$$
$$= \delta_{jk},\quad j,\, k = 1 \text{ to } \infty. \quad (12.185)$$

The integration in (12.184) and (12.185) extends over the whole region occupied by the system. For a curved shell it is a surface integral over the area of the shell, and dz is an elemental area; for a general solid body it is a volume integral over the volume of the body, and dz is an elemental volume. By comparison with equation (12.11), it can be seen that (12.185) is an extension of the discrete result from Chapter 11 to this more complicated continuous case.

Consider the modal solution of (12.178) for undamped, free vibration. For the jth mode the response is

$$y(z, t) = e^{i\omega_j t}\, U_j(z) \qquad (12.186)$$

where ω_j is the jth natural frequency. On substituting into (12.178) with $\alpha = \beta = 0$ and for no excitation, we get

$$-\,\omega_j^2\, m(z)\, U_j(z) + L\{U_j(z)\} = O. \qquad (12.187)$$

Taking the transpose of (12.187), post-multiplying by $U_k(z)$ and integrating over the structure then gives

$$-\,\omega_j^2 \int_R dz\, m(z)\, U_j^{\mathrm{T}}(z)\, U_k(z) + \int_R dz\, L^{\mathrm{T}}\{U_j(z)\}\, U_k(z) = 0. \quad (12.188)$$

Therefore, on account of (12.184), the normal mode functions must satisfy also the second orthogonality condition

$$\int_R dz\, L^{\mathrm{T}}\{U_j(z)\}\, U_k(z) = \omega_j^2\, \delta_{jk},\, j,\, k = 1 \text{ to } \infty, \qquad (12.189)$$

which is a more general form of our previous result (12.15).

On substituting for $y(z, t)$ from (12.183) into (12.178) and using the orthogonality conditions (12.184) and (12.189), we get, instead of (12.27),

$$\ddot{q}_j + 2\zeta_j\omega_j\dot{q}_j + \omega_j^2 q_j = \int_R dz\, U_j^{\mathrm{T}}(z)\, x(z, t) \qquad (12.190)$$

where the modal damping ratio is again given by (12.28).

We can use (12.190) to derive the vector of impulse response functions $h(z_r, z_s, t)$ which, corresponding to (12.60), becomes

$$h(z_r, z_s, t) = \sum_{j=1}^{\infty} h_j(t)\, U_j(z_r) U_j^{\mathrm{T}}(z_z) e_s \tag{12.191}$$

where e_s is a unit vector defining the direction of the unit impulsive excitation applied at $z = z_s$ at $t = 0$ and $h_j(t)$ is given by (12.53). The derivation of (12.191) from (12.190) follows closely the steps in the derivation of (12.60) from (12.27).

By taking Fourier transforms of both sides of (12.191), we get, corresponding to (12.66),

$$H(z_r, z_s, i\omega) = \sum_{j=1}^{\infty} H_j(i\omega)\, U_j(z_r) U_j^{\mathrm{T}}(z_s) e_s \tag{12.192}$$

where $H_j(i\omega)$ is given by (12.61). The components of $H(z_s, z_s, i\omega)$ are the frequency responses in the three coordinate directions at z_r for unit harmonic excitation applied at z_s in direction e_s.

To find the natural frequencies and mode shapes for a particular problem, we have to find the solutions to (12.187). This set of three scalar equations

$$- \omega_j^2\, m(z)\, U_{1j}(z) + L_1\{U_{1j}(z), U_{2j}(z), U_{3j}(z)\} = 0$$
$$- \omega_j^2\, m(z)\, U_{2j}(z) + L_2\{U_{1j}(z), U_{2j}(z), U_{3j}(z)\} = 0 \tag{12.193}$$
$$- \omega_j^2\, m(z)\, U_{3j}(z) + L_3\{U_{1j}(z), U_{2j}(z), U_{3j}(z)\} = 0$$

must be solved subject to the appropriate boundary conditions and allows the components of the normal mode functions $U_{1j}(z)$, $U_{2j}(z)$, $U_{3j}(z)$ and the natural frequencies ω_j, $j = 1$ to ∞, to be determined. However, in order to implement these results we need to derive the vector stiffness operator $L\{\ \}$ in the equation of motion (12.178) and we need to be able to solve the set of equations (12.193). Both these calculations may present formidable analytical difficulties. Also, a real system will usually consist of several connected subsystems, each with a different stiffness operator $L\{\ \}$. The result is that, in practice, the analysis of continuous systems is generally carried out by using a finite-element model to reduce the continuous problem to a discrete system which can be studied by applying the general results given in the previous chapters. We shall therefore not pursue these general response equations for continuous systems any further, but in the next chapter we go back to some simpler cases for which there are complete solutions of considerable value.

Chapter 13

Continuous systems II

Properties of Euler beams

The equation of motion for the small-amplitude lateral vibration of an undamped uniform beam whose shear deflection can be neglected (an Euler beam) is (Problem 12.1(iii))

$$m \frac{\partial^2 y}{\partial t^2} + EI \frac{\partial^4 y}{\partial z^4} = 0 \tag{13.1}$$

where m is the beam's mass per unit length and EI is its bending stiffness (both of which are assumed constant). The lateral deflection of the beam is $y(z, t)$, which is a function of longitudinal position z and time t.

This equation (13.1) may be obtained by considering the lateral equilibrium of a small element dz of the beam. The net lateral force on the element is the difference between the opposing shear forces on its faces and these are related to the curvature of the beam by Euler beam theory. The net lateral force must be equal to the mass of the element $m\, dz$ multiplied by its lateral acceleration $\partial^2 y / \partial t^2$.

If $U_j(z)$ is the normal mode function for the jth mode

$$y(z, t) = U_j(z)\, e^{i\omega_j t} \tag{13.2}$$

for free motion at the jth natural frequency and, on substituting (13.2) into (13.1),

$$m(i\omega_j)^2\, U_j(z) + EI \frac{d^4}{dz^4} U_j(z) = 0. \tag{13.3}$$

This has a general solution

$$U_j(z) = e^{\lambda_j z} \tag{13.4}$$

where, on substituting (13.4) into (13.3),

$$EI\, \lambda_j^4 = m\omega_j^2 \tag{13.5}$$

so that

$$\lambda_j^2 = \pm \left(\frac{m}{EI} \right)^{1/2} \omega_j = \pm a^2 \tag{13.6}$$

and

$$\lambda_j = \pm\, a \text{ and } \pm\, ia \tag{13.7}$$

where

$$a^4 = \frac{m\omega_j^2}{EI}. \tag{13.8}$$

The corresponding jth normal mode function is

$$U_j(z) = C_1\, e^{az} + C_2\, e^{-az} + C_3\, e^{iaz} + C_4\, e^{-iaz} \tag{13.9}$$

where C_1, C_2, C_3, C_4 are arbitrary constants to be determined by the boundary conditions. Alternatively, using the results that

$$\sinh\theta = \tfrac{1}{2}(e^{\theta} - e^{-\theta}), \quad \cosh\theta = \tfrac{1}{2}(e^{\theta} + e^{-\theta}) \tag{13.10}$$

and

$$\sin\theta = \frac{1}{2i}\,(e^{i\theta} - e^{-i\theta}), \quad \cos\theta = \frac{1}{2}\,(e^{i\theta} + e^{-i\theta}), \tag{13.11}$$

we can write the normal mode function as

$$U_j(z) = A\cos az + B\sin az + C\cosh az + D\sinh az \tag{13.12}$$

where A, B, C, D is a new set of constants. The latter form proves more convenient in the following analysis.

Simply-supported beam

Consider a simply-supported beam of length L which is hinged to supports at $z = 0$ and $z = L$. There is no deflection at the two ends so that

$$U_j(z) = 0 \text{ at } z = 0,\ z = L, \tag{13.13}$$

and there is no bending moment at the two hinges, so that

$$\frac{d^2U_j(z)}{dz^2} = 0 \text{ at } z = 0,\ z = L. \tag{13.14}$$

On substituting the conditions at $z = 0$ into (13.12), we get

$$0 = A + C \tag{13.15}$$

for no deflection, and

$$0 = -A + C \tag{13.16}$$

for no bending moment. Hence we must have

$$A = C = 0 \tag{13.17}$$

and, for this problem, the normal mode function is

$$U_j(z) = B\sin az + D\sinh az. \tag{13.18}$$

On substituting the boundary conditions at $z = L$ into (12.196), we have

$$0 = B \sin aL + D \sinh aL \tag{13.19}$$

for no deflection, and

$$0 = - B \sin aL + D \sinh aL \tag{13.20}$$

for no bending moment. For these two equations to have a solution other than $B = D = 0$, we must have

$$\det \begin{bmatrix} \sin aL & \sinh aL \\ - \sin aL & \sinh aL \end{bmatrix} = 0 \tag{13.21}$$

which gives

$$2 \sin aL \sinh aL = 0. \tag{13.22}$$

The hyperbolic function $\sinh aL$ is not zero unless $aL = 0$, and so the only solution for which all the constants in $U_j(z)$ are not zero is, from (13.22), when

$$\sin aL = 0 \tag{13.23}$$

so that

$$aL = \pi, 2\pi, 3\pi, \ldots \tag{13.24}$$

and so the jth natural frequency is given by

$$aL = j\pi \tag{13.25}$$

and therefore, from (13.8),

$$\frac{m\omega_j^2}{EI} = j^4 \left(\frac{\pi}{L}\right)^4 \tag{13.26}$$

so that

$$\omega_j = j^2 \left(\frac{\pi}{L}\right)^2 \sqrt{\frac{EI}{m}}. \tag{13.27}$$

From (13.19), B can be arbitrary, but D must be zero (since $\sinh aL$ is not zero), and so the corresponding normal mode function is, from (13.18),

$$U_j(z) = B \sin(j\pi z/L). \tag{13.28}$$

The constant B must be chosen to normalize $U_j(z)$ according to (12.14), and so we find that

$$\int_0^L dz\, m\, B^2 \sin^2(j\pi z/L) = 1 \tag{13.29}$$

which gives

$$B = \sqrt{2/mL}. \tag{13.30}$$

The conclusion for an undamped simply-supported beam is that the natural frequencies are given by

$$\omega_j = j^2 \left(\frac{\pi}{L} \right)^2 \sqrt{EI/m}, \quad j = 1 \text{ to } \infty, \qquad (13.31)$$

and the normal mode functions by

$$U_j(z) = \sqrt{2/mL} \sin(j\pi z/L). \qquad (13.32)$$

A solution of (13.23) that we have not included in (13.24) is the solution that aL is zero. This is because $\sinh aL$ is then also zero. Consider the case when $aL \to 0$. Then $\sin aL$ and $\sinh aL$ become indistinguishable, and so the only solution of (13.19) and (13.20) is

$$B = D = 0 \qquad (13.33)$$

in which case there is no vibration. Therefore $aL = 0$ is not an eigenvalue for the problem, which is of course obvious because a simply-supported beam of finite stiffness cannot have a zero natural frequency.

Beams with other boundary conditions

The natural frequencies and normal mode functions for other end conditions can be obtained in the same way. On substituting for $U_j(z)$ from (13.12) into the appropriate boundary conditions, four equations are obtained for the unknown constants A, B, C and D. For the case of an initially straight beam whose ends are free or pinned or clamped, all of the four equations have right-hand sides which are zero so that they form a homogeneous set of equations for which there is only a non-trivial solution when aL is an eigenvalue. The amplitude of the displacement function $U_j(z)$ is arbitrary and, subject to normalization to satisfy (12.14), $U_j(z)$ is one of the beam's normal mode functions. The corresponding natural frequency is obtained from the eigenvalue aL by (13.8).

When the beam is clamped at $z = 0$ and free at $z = L$, the boundary conditions are

$$U_j(z) = \frac{\mathrm{d}}{\mathrm{d}z} U_j(z) = 0 \text{ at } z = 0 \qquad (13.34)$$

and

$$\frac{\mathrm{d}^2 U_j(z)}{\mathrm{d}z^2} = \frac{\mathrm{d}^3 U_j(z)}{\mathrm{d}z^3} = 0 \text{ at } z = L \qquad (13.35)$$

which is the condition for no bending moment and no shear force at the free end. The reader can check (Problem 13.1) that the eigenvalues are then the solutions of

$$\cosh aL \cos aL = -1. \qquad (13.36)$$

When both ends are clamped, or alternatively, when both ends are free, the corresponding equation is

$$\cosh aL \cos aL = + 1 \qquad (13.37)$$

and, when one end is clamped and the other pinned, or alternatively, when one end is free and the other pinned, the frequency equation is

$$\tanh aL = \tan aL. \qquad (13.38)$$

The solutions for all these cases are illustrated in Fig. 13.1. It is interesting that the natural frequencies for different boundary conditions can be the same. The clamped–clamped case and the free–free case have the same frequency equation, as do the clamped–pinned and pinned–free cases. Notice, however, that although their frequency equation is the same, the free–free beam has two zero natural frequencies which are not eigenvalues for the clamped–clamped case. Similarly, the pinned–free beam has a zero natural frequency which the clamped–pinned beam does not have. This is because a floating beam can move sideways and rotate without restraint and a pinned–free beam can rotate about its pinned end without restraint.†

The presence of zero-frequency eigenvalues in these two cases and their absence in the two corresponding cases with the same frequency equation (see Fig. 13.1) can be confirmed by considering the limiting form of the normal mode functions when $a \to 0$ (Problem 13.1). For the clamped–clamped and clamped–pinned cases, $U_j(z)$ becomes zero when $a \to 0$, and so there is no solution possible at zero frequency, even though $a = 0$ is a solution of their frequency equation.

From Fig. 13.1 it can be seen that the increase in aL from one eigenvalue to the next becomes approximately π for modes other than the first two or three. But from (13.8) the natural frequency ω_j is proportional to $(a_j L)^2$, from which we see that the frequency interval $\Delta \omega_j$ between adjacent natural frequencies becomes progressively larger at higher frequencies. From (13.8)

$$\omega_j = (a_j L)^2 \sqrt{\frac{EI}{mL^4}} \qquad (13.39)$$

so that

$$\omega_{j+1} = \omega_j + \Delta \omega_j = (a_j L + \pi)^2 \sqrt{\frac{EI}{mL^4}}$$

$$= [(a_j L)^2 + 2(a_j L)\,\pi + \pi^2] \sqrt{\frac{EI}{mL^4}}$$

$$\simeq [(a_j L)^2 + 2(a_j L)\,\pi] \sqrt{\frac{EI}{mL^4}} \qquad (13.40)$$

---

† A uniform free–free beam is an example of a system with a repeated (zero) eigenvalue which has two different eigenvectors: these are (i) translation with no rotation and (ii) rotation about the beam's centre, or any two different combinations of (i) and (ii). Since only lateral deflections are considered, translation must occur perpendicular to the beam's axis.

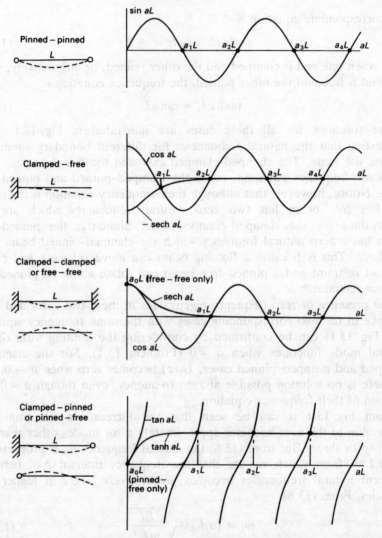

Fig. 13.1 Calculation of eigenvalues for Euler beams with different end conditions

for a natural frequency which is high enough that

$$a_j L \gg \pi. \tag{13.41}$$

Therefore, from (13.40),

$$\Delta \omega_j \simeq 2(a_j L) \pi \sqrt{\frac{EI}{mL^4}} \tag{13.42}$$

and, with (13.39), we conclude that

$$\Delta \omega_j \propto \omega_j \tag{13.43}$$

for high natural frequencies. This progressively larger spacing between natural frequencies applies only for beams. For plates we shall see below that the natural frequencies are spaced evenly (on average) along a linear base of frequency.

Simply-supported rectangular plates

Subject to the same assumptions as for an Euler beam, the equation of motion for the small deflection of an initially-flat thin isotropic plate with no damping is

$$m \frac{\partial^2 y}{\partial t^2} + D\left(\frac{\partial^4 y}{\partial z_1^4} + 2 \frac{\partial^4 y}{\partial z_1^2 \partial z_2^2} + \frac{\partial^4 y}{\partial z_2^4}\right) = 0 \qquad (13.44)$$

where $y(z_1, z_2, t)$ is the deflection of the plate at a position defined by the rectangular coordinate system z_1, z_2, m is the mass per unit area, and D is the flexural rigidity of the plate defined by

$$D = \frac{Et^3}{12(1 - \mu^2)} \qquad (13.45)$$

where E is Young's modulus, μ is Poisson's ratio and t is the plate's thickness (Problem 12.1(iv)).

If $U_j(z_1, z_2)$ is the normal mode function of the jth mode which has natural frequency ω_j,

$$y(z_1, z_2, t) = U_j(z_1, z_2) \, e^{i\omega_j t} \qquad (13.46)$$

and, on substituting this solution into (13.44), we find that

$$m(i\omega_j)^2 \, U_j + D\left(\frac{\partial^4 U_j}{\partial z_1^4} + 2 \frac{\partial^4 U_j}{\partial z_1^2 \partial z_2^2} + \frac{\partial^4 U_j}{\partial z_2^4}\right) = 0. \qquad (13.47)$$

A possible solution is

$$U_j(z_1, z_2) = \sin \lambda_{j1} z_1 \sin \lambda_{j2} z_2 \qquad (13.48)$$

which, on substitution into (13.47), gives

$$m(i\omega_j)^2 + D(\lambda_{j1}^4 + 2\lambda_{j1}^2 \lambda_{j2}^2 + \lambda_{j2}^4) = 0 \qquad (13.49)$$

or, after rearrangement,

$$(\lambda_{j1}^2 + \lambda_{j2}^2)^2 = \frac{m}{D} \omega_j^2. \qquad (13.50)$$

Hence, from (13.50),

$$\lambda_{j1}^2 + \lambda_{j2}^2 = \pm \sqrt{\frac{m}{D}} \, \omega_j. \qquad (13.51)$$

Suppose that the plate, which is assumed to be simply supported, has length L_1 in the z_1 direction and length L_2 in the z_2 direction. In order to satisfy the displacement boundary conditions, each of the normal mode functions $U_j(z_1, z_2)$ must be zero at the four edges and must give rise to zero bending moment about axes along each of the edges. For zero displacement along the edges we have

$$U_j(z_1, z_2) = 0 \quad \text{for edge 1: } z_1 = 0$$

$$\text{edge 2: } z_2 = 0 \tag{13.52}$$

$$\text{edge 3: } z_1 = L_1$$

$$\text{edge 4: } z_2 = L_2.$$

For edges 1 and 3, $z_1 = 0$ and L_1, the bending moment about an axis parallel to these edges is

$$D\left(\frac{\partial^2 U_j}{\partial z_1^2} + \mu \frac{\partial^2 U_j}{\partial z_2^2}\right)$$

but since, from (13.52),

$$\frac{\partial^2 U_j}{\partial z_2^2}$$

is zero along $z_1 = 0$ and L_1, it follows that the zero bending moment condition reduces to

$$\frac{\partial^2 U_j}{\partial z_1^2} = 0 \text{ at } z_1 = 0 \text{ and } L_1. \tag{13.53}$$

Similarly for edges 2 and 4, $z_2 = 0$ and L_2, there will be zero bending moment if

$$\frac{\partial^2 U_j}{\partial z_2^2} = 0 \text{ at } z_2 = 0 \text{ and } L_2. \tag{13.54}$$

The assumed solution (13.48) fits these boundary conditions at $z_1 = z_2 = 0$, and will do so at $z_1 = L_1$, $z_2 = L_2$ if

$$\lambda_{j1} L_1 = j_1 \pi \quad \text{and} \quad \lambda_{j2} L_2 = j_2 \pi. \tag{13.55}$$

A solution which satisfies the equation of motion and all the boundary conditions must be the correct solution, and so the normal mode function for the plate is, after normalization to satisfy (12.14),

$$U_j(z_1, z_2) = \frac{2}{\sqrt{m L_1 L_2}} \sin\left(j_1 \frac{\pi z_1}{L_1}\right) \sin\left(j_2 \frac{\pi z_2}{L_2}\right) \tag{13.56}$$

corresponding to the natural frequency of, from (13.51),

$$\omega_j = \sqrt{\frac{D}{m}\left[\left(\frac{j_1 \pi}{L_1}\right)^2 + \left(\frac{j_2 \pi}{L_2}\right)^2\right]} \tag{13.57}$$

where j_1 and j_2 are positive integers. They give the number of half wavelengths of the normal mode function in the z_1 and z_2 directions, respectively; $j_1\pi/L_1$ and $j_2\pi/L_2$ are called the *wavenumbers* in the z_1 and z_2 directions.

From (13.57), the natural frequency ω_j depends on the sum of the squares of the two wavenumbers, and this relationship is illustrated graphically in Fig. 13.2. The area on the wavenumber diagram occupied by a single mode, for example the cross-hatched area shown, is π^2/L_1L_2. The total area bounded by a circle whose radius corresponds to a frequency ω_j is

$$A = \frac{\pi}{4} \omega_j \sqrt{\frac{m}{D}} \tag{13.58}$$

and so the approximate number of modes whose natural frequency is less than ω_j is

$$A/(\pi^2/L_1L_2) = \frac{L_1L_2}{4\pi} \omega_j \sqrt{\frac{m}{D}}. \tag{13.59}$$

This calculation is only approximate, but it becomes more accurate as ω_j becomes larger. The number of modes per unit frequency, or the *modal density*, is then

$$\frac{L_1L_2}{4\pi} \sqrt{\frac{m}{D}} \tag{13.60}$$

which is independent of frequency. This constant modal density is characteristic of plates, and differs from beams, for which, from (13.43), the modal density is inversely proportional to ω_j.

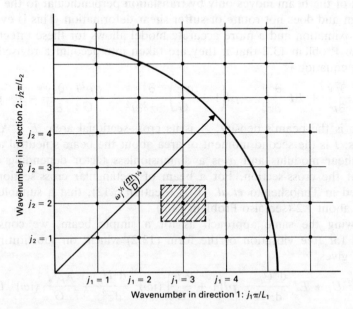

Fig. 13.2 Wavenumber diagram for the free undamped vibration of a uniform rectangular plate with hinged edges to illustrate the calculation of modal density

The above analysis is restricted to a uniform rectangular plate with simply-supported edges. There are complete solutions for a few other special cases, for example circular plates with a variety of boundary conditions and rectangular plates when two opposite edges are simply supported and the other two opposite edges are either clamped or free (see, for example, Gorman [37]), but a general analytical solution for a flat plate with an irregular boundary has not been found. For these and more complicated structural vibration problems the *finite element method* permits numerical solutions to be obtained by modelling the continuum as an assembly of separate finite elements. Each element is analysed as a separate continuous system with an interpolation function to describe the variation of its displacement. The nodal forces (i.e. the forces at the nodes or junctions of the finite element) are calculated from the assumed interpolation function and then the elements are assembled together, ensuring geometrical compatibility and force equilibrium at the nodes. The system's equations then have the standard form of Chapter 11 and can be solved as described there. There is now an extensive literature on finite-element procedures including, for example, Huebner [46], Zienkiewicz [113] and Bathe [4]. The first is written at an introductory level compared with the more specialized treatments of the second and third.

Timoshenko beam

The equation of motion (13.1) of simple beam theory assumes that each element of the beam moves only by translation perpendicular to the axis of the beam and does not rotate or suffer shear deformation. This is evidently an approximation and a more accurate model allows for these effects. It is shown in Problem 13.2 that if they are taken into account a revised beam bending equation is

$$\rho A \frac{\partial^2 y}{\partial t^2} + EI \frac{\partial^4 y}{\partial z^4} - \rho I \left(1 + \frac{\alpha E}{G}\right) \frac{\partial^4 y}{\partial z^2 \partial t^2} + \frac{\alpha \rho^2 I}{G} \frac{\partial^4 y}{\partial t^4} = 0 \quad (13.61)$$

where ρ is the beam's density, A is its cross-sectional area, E is Young's modulus, I is the second moment of area about the beam's neutral axis, G is the shear modulus and α is a dimensionless factor depending on the shape of the cross-section. For a beam of rectangular cross-section, it is suggested in Timoshenko *et al.* [101] (Section 5.12), that a suitable value for α is about 1.2 (see also Problem 13.3).

Following the same approach as for a simple beam, we consider a solution for free vibration of the form (13.2) which, on substituting into (13.61), gives

$$\rho A (i\omega)^2 \, U_j + EI \frac{d^4 U_j}{dz^4} - \rho I \left(1 + \frac{\alpha E}{G}\right) (i\omega)^2 \frac{d^2 U_j}{dz^2} + \frac{\alpha \rho^2 I}{G} (i\omega)^4 \, U_j = 0$$

$$(13.62)$$

or, after collecting terms,

$$\frac{d^4 U_j}{dz^4} + \frac{\rho}{E}\left(1 + \frac{\alpha E}{G}\right)\omega^2 \frac{d^2 U_j}{dz^2} + \left(\frac{\alpha\rho^2}{EG}\omega^4 - \frac{\rho A}{EI}\omega^2\right)U_j = 0. \quad (13.63)$$

This fourth-order differential equation for the normal mode function $U_j(z)$ can be solved if the boundary conditions are specified. Consider a simply-supported beam of length L with zero deflection and zero bending moment at each end. A function

$$U_j(z) = \sin\left(j\frac{\pi z}{L}\right) \quad (13.64)$$

nearly satisfies these boundary conditions provided that the rotary inertia and shear effects are small. It does not exactly satisfy the requirement for zero bending moment at the ends of the beam because $U_j(z)$ gives the total deflection due to bending and shear taken together, so that

$$EI\frac{d^2 U_j(z)}{dz^2}$$

is no longer an exact expression for the bending moment (see Problem 13.2). However, (13.64) nearly satisfies the boundary conditions and it also satisfies the differential equation (13.63) if, on substituting (13.64) into (13.63),

$$\left(j\frac{\pi}{L}\right)^4 - \frac{\rho}{E}\left(1 + \frac{\alpha E}{G}\right)\omega^2\left(j\frac{\pi}{L}\right)^2 + \left(\frac{\alpha\rho^2}{EG}\omega^4 - \frac{\rho A}{EI}\omega^2\right) = 0. \quad (13.65)$$

Therefore, on rearrangement of (13.65), we see that the natural frequencies of a simply-supported Timoshenko beam of length L are given approximately by the solutions ω_j of

$$\frac{\alpha\rho^2}{EG}\omega_j^4 - \left[\frac{\rho}{E}\left(1 + \frac{\alpha E}{G}\right)\left(j\frac{\pi}{L}\right)^2 + \frac{\rho A}{EI}\right]\omega_j^2 + \left(j\frac{\pi}{L}\right)^4 = 0. \quad (13.66)$$

Effect of rotary inertia alone

If the shear deflection of the beam is zero, $\alpha = 0$, in which case (13.66) gives

$$\omega_j^2 = \frac{(j\pi/L)^4}{\left[\frac{\rho}{E}\left(j\frac{\pi}{L}\right)^2 + \frac{\rho A}{EI}\right]}. \quad (13.67)$$

This result, which includes the effect of rotary inertia, should be compared with (13.31) for the case without rotary inertia. Using the symbol Ω_j for the natural frequency in the absence of rotary inertia, from (13.31)

$$\Omega_j = j^2(\pi/L)^2\sqrt{EI/\rho A} \quad (13.68)$$

since the mass m per unit length is given by

$$m = \rho A. \tag{13.69}$$

On substituting (13.68) into (13.67), we get

$$\omega_j^2 = \frac{\Omega_j^2}{\frac{I}{A}\left(j\frac{\pi}{L}\right)^2 + 1} \tag{13.70}$$

and if r is the radius of gyration of the second moment of area, so that

$$I = Ar^2 \tag{13.71}$$

then (13.70) gives

$$\omega_j^2 = \frac{\Omega_j^2}{\left(j\pi\frac{r}{L}\right)^2 + 1}. \tag{13.72}$$

From (13.32), we know that the wavelength of the jth normal mode function is

$$\lambda_j = 2\pi/(j\pi/L) = 2L/j \tag{13.73}$$

and, in terms of λ_j, (13.72) becomes

$$\omega_j^2 = \frac{\Omega_j^2}{\left(\dfrac{2\pi r}{\lambda_j}\right)^2 + 1}. \tag{13.74}$$

The effect of rotary inertia is therefore to lower the beam's natural frequencies, with the reduction only becoming significant for modes whose wavelength is comparable to the depth of the beam (and therefore comparable to its radius of gyration r). If b is the width of the beam and h is its depth

$$I = \frac{1}{12} bh^3 = Ar^2 \tag{13.75}$$

where $A = bh$, and so

$$r = h/\sqrt{12}. \tag{13.76}$$

Hence for a beam of depth 25 mm, the radius of gyration is $r = 7.2$ mm. Suppose that the beam's length is 1 m and we consider the fourth mode. From (13.73)

$$\lambda_4 = 0.5 \text{ m} \tag{13.77}$$

and (13.73) then gives

$$\frac{\omega_4}{\Omega_4} = 0.996 \tag{13.78}$$

which is a very small reduction in frequency of 0.4%.

For this case of rotary inertia only, there is no shear deflection of the beam, and so (13.65) is an exact mode shape and (13.74) is an exact result.

Effect of rotary inertia and shear together

When the effect of shear is included, in addition to rotary inertia, the approximate natural frequency has to be obtained by solving the quadratic equation (13.66). Taking a typical case for

$$E = 2 \times 10^{11}\,\text{N/m}^2,\; G = 8 \times 10^{10}\,\text{N/m}^2,\; \alpha = 1.2$$
$$\rho = 7800\,\text{kg/m}^3,\; L = 1\,\text{m},\; h = 0.025\,\text{m},\; j = 4 \tag{13.79}$$

and substituting these numbers into (13.66), on solving the quadratic we get

$$\omega_4 = 5678.9\,\text{rad/s} \text{ or } 4.12 \times 10^5\,\text{rad/s}. \tag{13.80}$$

The lower value is an approximation for the fourth natural frequency in the presence of rotary inertia and shear. From (13.68), the corresponding value in the absence of these effects is

$$\Omega_4 = 5770.8\,\text{rad/s} \tag{13.81}$$

so that we now have

$$\frac{\omega_4}{\Omega_4} = \frac{5678.9}{5770.8} = 0.984 \tag{13.82}$$

which is a reduction of 1.6% in the value obtained from simple beam theory. On comparison with (13.78), from which the reduction in natural frequency due to rotary inertia only is 0.4%, we see that in this example the reduction in natural frequency due to shear is three times the reduction due to rotary inertia. This result depends on the ratio between the depth of the beam and the wavelength of the normal mode function for the mode in question.

Although the quadratic equation (13.66) suggests that there are two natural frequencies which have the same normal mode function (13.64), in practice this is not so and the second natural frequency listed in (13.80) is a spurious value. It arises because the normal mode function (13.64) is an approximate function only. At high frequencies, when there is significant shearing of the beam, the assumed normal mode function becomes inaccurate because the boundary conditions at $z = 0$ and $z = L$ are no longer

$$\frac{\partial^2 y}{\partial z^2} = 0.$$

Then the frequency equation (13.66) is no longer correct because it relates to the wrong normal mode function.

Beam with a travelling load

The Timoshenko beam equation (13.61) cannot be written in the standard form (12.25). Equation (13.61) includes terms in

$$\frac{\partial^4 y}{\partial t^4} \quad \text{and} \quad \frac{\partial^4 y}{\partial z^2 \partial t^2}$$

which are not present in (12.25). This is because (12.25) applies to slender or plate-like structures whose elemental masses $m(z)dz$ are assumed not to shear or rotate. A number of other important beam problems have equations which do not conform to (12.25), for example the vibration of a pipe carrying flowing fluid (Paidoussis [77]) and the instability of an elastically-supported beam with a travelling inertia load (Newland [68] and Problem 13.3). These are essentially similar problems and we shall now use the latter to illustrate the complicated response that may occur in systems described by beam equations which do not have the standard form (12.25).

The elastically-supported beam problem has been considered in the context of the buckling of railway track as a result of its thermal expansion in hot weather. Suppose that the track is represented by a straight beam of mass m per unit length and bending stiffness EI supported on an elastic foundation of lateral spring stiffness γ per unit length, and an axial compressive load P acts in the beam as a result of thermal expansion. If $y(z, t)$ is the lateral deflection of the centre-line of the beam at longitudinal coordinate z and time t, the equation of the beam is

$$m \frac{\partial^2 y}{\partial t^2} + EI \frac{\partial^4 y}{\partial z^4} + P \frac{\partial^2 y}{\partial z^2} + \gamma y = 0 \qquad (13.83)$$

which does have the standard form (12.25). However, when a train is travelling along the track, the equation becomes more complicated. Let an infinitely long train of mass M per unit length and zero stiffness be travelling along the track at speed U. It is shown in Problem 13.3 that the lateral force F per unit length exerted by the train on the track is

$$F = M \left(\frac{\partial^2 y}{\partial t^2} + 2U \frac{\partial^2 y}{\partial z \partial t} + U^2 \frac{\partial^2 y}{\partial z^2} \right) \qquad (13.84)$$

and then the beam equation for the combination of the track and train becomes

$$(m + M) \frac{\partial^2 y}{\partial t^2} + 2MU \frac{\partial^2 y}{\partial z \partial t} + EI \frac{\partial^4 y}{\partial z^4} + (P + MU^2) \frac{\partial^2 y}{\partial z^2} + \gamma y = 0$$

$$(13.85)$$

which differs from (12.25) on account of the term

$$2MU \frac{\partial^2 y}{\partial z \partial t}.$$

This is a linear equation and we can search in the usual way for a harmonic solution

$$y(z, t) = Y(z, i\omega) e^{i\omega t} \tag{13.86}$$

by substituting (13.86) into (13.85) and solving the resulting fourth-order ordinary differential equation for $Y(z, i\omega)$ subject to the appropriate boundary conditions. An analytical solution appears to be impossible and values of $Y(z, i\omega)$ have to be calculated numerically for particular cases. If, as in (13.85), there is no forcing function, non-zero solutions of $Y(z, i\omega)$ will only be possible when ω is an eigenvalue, and the numerical determination of these eigenvalues, so that $Y(z, i\omega)$ may fit the differential equation and its boundary conditions, becomes extremely complicated. However, for an infinitely long track-and-train combination, a simple solution is possible.

On substituting (13.86) into (13.85), we get

$$EI \frac{d^4Y}{dz^4} + (P + MU^2) \frac{d^2Y}{dz^2} + 2MU (i\omega) \frac{dY}{dz} + [\gamma - (m + M) \omega^2] Y = 0 \tag{13.87}$$

and putting

$$Y = Y(z, i\omega) = e^{\lambda(i\omega)z} = e^{\lambda z} \tag{13.88}$$

where $\lambda(i\omega) \equiv \lambda$ is a complex function of frequency, we find that

$$EI\lambda^4 + (P + MU^2) \lambda^2 + 2MU (i\omega) \lambda + [\gamma - (m + M) \omega^2] = 0 \tag{13.89}$$

which can be solved to give four solutions for λ. Generally these will be complex, with real and imaginary parts. If one of the λ's has a positive real part, it means that the deflection $Y(z, i\omega)$ at $z = \infty$ must be infinite. If one of the λ's has a negative real part, it means that $Y(z, i\omega)$ will be infinite at $z = -\infty$. For a solution which is not infinite, the λ's must therefore all be entirely imaginary, in which case $Y(z, i\omega)$ will be a combination of sine and cosine functions, and we can put

$$\lambda = ik \tag{13.90}$$

where k is always real. With this substitution, (13.89) becomes

$$EI k^4 - (P + MU^2) k^2 - 2MU k\omega + [\gamma - (m + M) \omega^2] = 0. \tag{13.91}$$

Instead of solving (13.91) for k in terms of ω, consider solving for ω in terms of k. This involves solving the quadratic equation

$$(m + M) \omega^2 + 2MU k\omega + [(P + MU^2) k^2 - EI k^4 - \gamma] = 0 \tag{13.92}$$

for which we see that ω will have a complex pair of values if

$$(2MU\,k)^2 < 4(m + M)\,[(P + MU^2)\,k^2 - EI\,k^4 - \gamma].\qquad(13.93)$$

On dividing through by k^2 and rearranging the terms, this says that the frequency ω in (13.86) will be complex if

$$\left(P + \frac{mM}{m + M}\,U^2\right) > EI\,k^2 + \frac{\gamma}{k^2}.\qquad(13.94)$$

If ω is complex, from (13.92) there will be a complex-conjugate pair of solutions

$$\omega = \alpha \pm i\beta\qquad(13.95)$$

where α and β are real. The exponent $i\omega t$ in (13.86) will then have two values

$$i\omega t = i\alpha t \pm \beta t\qquad(13.96)$$

one of which will have a positive real part denoting a solution which increases exponentially with time. In this case, for the chosen value of wavenumber k, there will be an unstable solution with an exponentially increasing amplitude so that $y(z, t)$ has the form (Problem 13.3)

$$y(z, t) = e^{\beta t}\sin(kz + \alpha t).\qquad(13.97)$$

In this example of an infinitely long beam, the wavenumber k is not determined by any boundary conditions and may have any value. The value it will take in practice is the value at which instability first occurs. This may be obtained by differentiating the r.h.s. of (13.94) to find the value of k for which

$$\left(P + \frac{mM}{m + M}\,U^2\right)$$

is a minimum. On differentiating with respect to k

$$\frac{\mathrm{d}}{\mathrm{d}k}\left(EI\,k^2 + \frac{\gamma}{k^2}\right) = 2EI\,k - \frac{2\gamma}{k^3}\qquad(13.98)$$

which is zero when

$$k = \left(\frac{\gamma}{EI}\right)^{1/4}.\qquad(13.99)$$

Therefore the limiting condition for the onset of instability is, from (13.94), when

$$P + \frac{mM}{m + M}\,U^2 = 2\sqrt{EI\gamma}.\qquad(13.100)$$

The conclusion is that an infinitely long beam with a travelling inertia load will become unstable when the axial compressive load P is too high, or the speed of an (infinitely long) train U is too high, or some combination of both, to satisfy (13.100). When there is no moving train, so that $U = 0$, the axial buckling load is

$$P = 2\sqrt{EI\gamma} \qquad (13.101)$$

in agreement with static analyses (see, for example, Hetényi [43]). When the velocity is not zero, the inertial loading of the moving train interacts with the forces in the track to reduce the axial buckling load.

From (13.86), (13.88) and (13.90), the solution we have obtained is the travelling-wave solution

$$y(z, t) = e^{i(kz+\omega t)} \qquad (13.102)$$

which, for k and ω real, defines a wave of unit amplitude travelling in the $-z$ direction at speed ω/k (Problem 13.3). At the limit of stability, we know from (13.92) that both the solutions for ω are

$$\omega = -\frac{MUk}{m + M} \qquad (13.103)$$

since the remaining part of the solution is zero when the inequality sign in (13.93) is replaced by an equals sign. Hence the wave speed (phase velocity) c in the direction of positive z is

$$c = -\omega/k = \frac{MU}{m + M} \qquad (13.104)$$

so that the unstable wave travels in the same direction as the train but at a slower speed than the train travels.

Approximate natural frequencies

It is sometime helpful to calculate natural frequencies approximately. We shall now discuss how this may be done. The calculation involves equating the kinetic and potential energy of vibration assuming that, for small damping, there is negligible energy loss per cycle. It applies to systems of any type, whether discrete or continuous or composed of a mixture of discrete and continuous elements. We begin by considering the discrete case.

In Chapter 11 we demonstrated that, for systems with symmetric mass and stiffness matrices, the kinetic energy T is given by (11.58) as

$$T = \tfrac{1}{2}\dot{y}^T m \dot{y} \qquad (13.105)$$

and the potential energy V is given by (11.40) as

$$V = \tfrac{1}{2}y^T k y. \qquad (13.106)$$

For M degrees of freedom, m and k have order $M \times M$ and y is an $M \times 1$ vector of the displacements of the generalized coordinates. If ω_j is the natural frequency of the jth mode, with real eigenvector y_j so that

$$y(t) = e^{i\omega_j t} y_j, \tag{13.107}$$

then

$$\dot{y}(t) = i\omega_j e^{i\omega_j t} y_j. \tag{13.108}$$

The vector of maximum displacements is therefore y_j and the vector of maximum velocities is $\omega_j y_j$, so that the maximum kinetic energy is

$$T_{max} = \omega_j^2 \tfrac{1}{2} y_j^T m y_j \tag{13.109}$$

and the maximum potential energy is

$$V_{max} = \tfrac{1}{2} y_j^T k y_j. \tag{13.110}$$

For the free vibration of a system with zero damping these must be the same, and so we must have

$$\omega_j^2 = \frac{y_j^T k y_j}{y_j^T m y_j}. \tag{13.111}$$

The r.h.s. of (13.111) is called *Rayleigh's quotient* and, if the real eigenvector y_j is known exactly, it allows the corresponding natural frequency ω_j to be calculated exactly.

There are sometimes cases when y_j is not known exactly, but there is enough information about the vibrating system to allow an approximation to be obtained for y_j. Rayleigh's quotient provides a good method of using this approximate y_j to obtain an approximate value for the corresponding natural frequency ω_j. In the next section we consider the accuracy of this approximation.

Rayleigh's method

We shall now prove that, if y_j is accurate to order ε, then ω_j will be accurate to order ε^2. Also, in the case of the lowest natural frequency ω_1 (only), Rayleigh's quotient always gives an upper bound approximation, so that the true value of ω_1 will always be slightly less than the calculated value.

Suppose that y is an approximation for y_1 which satisfies the boundary conditions and consists of the true vector y_1 plus small contributions from all the other eigenvectors, so that

$$y = \alpha(y_1 + \varepsilon_2 y_2 + \varepsilon_3 y_3 + \ldots + \varepsilon_M y_M) \tag{13.112}$$

where ε_1, ε_2, .., ε_M are small non-dimensional parameters and the eigenvectors are all real. The scaling factor α is introduced to show that y does not have to satisfy the same normalization as the eigenvectors, which are assumed to satisfy (11.140) and (11.143). On substituting for y from (13.112)

$$y^{\mathrm{T}}ky = \alpha^2[y_1 + \varepsilon_2 y_2 + \ldots]^{\mathrm{T}} \, k \, [y_1 + \varepsilon_2 y_2 + \ldots]$$

$$= \alpha^2[y_1 + \varepsilon_2 y_2 + \ldots]^{\mathrm{T}} \, [ky_1 + \varepsilon_2 ky_2 + \ldots]$$

$$= \alpha^2(y_1^{\mathrm{T}}ky_1 + \varepsilon_2^2 y_2^{\mathrm{T}}ky_2 + \ldots) \tag{13.113}$$

since all the terms like $\varepsilon_2 y_2^{\mathrm{T}}ky_1$ disappear on account of the orthogonality condition (11.142). Also, from (11.143),

$$y_j^{\mathrm{T}}ky_j = \omega_j^2 \tag{13.114}$$

with which (13.113) becomes

$$y^{\mathrm{T}}ky = \alpha^2(\omega_1^2 + \varepsilon_2^2 \omega_2^2 + \varepsilon_3^2 \omega_3^2 + \ldots). \tag{13.115}$$

On using (13.112) and (11.139) we find that

$$y^{\mathrm{T}}my = \alpha^2(y_1^{\mathrm{T}}my_1 + \varepsilon_2^2 y_2^{\mathrm{T}}my_2 + \ldots) \tag{13.116}$$

which with (11.140) becomes

$$y^{\mathrm{T}}my = \alpha^2(1 + \varepsilon_2^2 + \varepsilon_3^2 + \ldots). \tag{13.117}$$

Therefore Rayleigh's quotient gives

$$\frac{y^{\mathrm{T}}ky}{y^{\mathrm{T}}my} = \frac{\omega_1^2 + \varepsilon_2^2 \omega_2^2 + \varepsilon_3^2 \omega_3^2 + \ldots}{1 + \varepsilon_2^2 + \varepsilon_3^2 + \ldots}$$

$$= \omega_1^2 \left[\frac{1 + \varepsilon_2^2 \left(\dfrac{\omega_2}{\omega_1}\right)^2 + \varepsilon_3^2 \left(\dfrac{\omega_3}{\omega_1}\right)^2 + \ldots + \varepsilon_M^2 \left(\dfrac{\omega_M}{\omega_1}\right)^2}{1 + \varepsilon_2^2 + \varepsilon_3^2 + \ldots + \varepsilon_M^2} \right]. \tag{13.118}$$

Hence if y is an approximation to the true eigenvector y_1 to order ε, Rayleigh's quotient will give an approximation to ω_1^2 (and therefore to ω_1) to order ε^2. Also, since ω_1 is the lowest natural frequency, all the terms like

$$\left(\frac{\omega_2}{\omega_1}\right)^2$$

will be greater than one and so the numerator in [ ] brackets on the r.h.s. of (13.118) will always be greater than the denominator, and the approximation obtained for ω_1 will always be greater than the true value.

When the assumed eigenvector y is an approximation to order ε for a higher-order eigenvector y_j, Rayleigh's quotient still gives a value for the jth natural frequency, ω_j, which is correct to order ε^2, but the reader can check that the approximate natural frequency is no longer always larger than the true natural frequency (see Problem 13.8(i)). The result that Rayleigh's quotient gives an upper bound applies only to calculations of the lowest natural frequency.

The same conclusions apply for continuous systems. Consider a system whose equation of motion for free undamped vibration has the standard form (12.30). For a single-mode solution (12.29), this leads to equation (12.31) which gives

$$\omega_j^2(z)m(z)U_j(z) = L\{U_j(z)\}. \tag{13.119}$$

On multiplying by $U_j(z)$ and integrating over the surface R we get

$$\omega_j^2 \int_R dz\, U_j(z)m(z)U_j(z) = \int_R dz\, U_j(z)\, L\{U_j(z)\} \tag{13.120}$$

so that

$$\omega_j^2 = \frac{\int_R dz\, U_j(z)\, L\{U_j(z)\}}{\int_R dz\, U_j(z)\, m(z)\, U_j(z)} = \frac{\int dz\, U_j(z) L\{U_j(z)\}}{\int_R dz\, m(z) U_j^2(z)} \tag{13.121}$$

which is an alternative form of Rayleigh's quotient for a continuous system defined by (12.30). Since, according to (12.18), $L\{U_j(z)\}\, dz$ is the static force required per unit area to deflect the system through displacement $U_j(z)$ at position z, the numerator of (13.121) is twice the maximum strain energy of the system. Also, since $m(z)$ is the mass per unit area at z, the denominator of (13.121) is twice the maximum kinetic energy divided by ω_j^2.

By replacing the exact normal mode function for the lowest frequency mode, $U_1(z)$, by the approximation

$$U(z) = U_1(z) + \varepsilon_2 U_2(z) + \varepsilon_3 U_3(z) + \ldots \tag{13.122}$$

and using the orthogonality relations (12.14) and (12.15) we find, as for the analysis above for the discrete case, that

$$\frac{\int_R dz\, U(z)\, L\{U(z)\}}{\int_R dz\, m(z)\, U^2(z)} = \omega_1^2 + 0(\varepsilon^2) \tag{13.123}$$

where $0(\varepsilon^2)$ means terms of order ε^2 and smaller. This last result can be very helpful in obtaining approximate values of the lowest natural frequency of continuous systems. The approximate normal mode function must be one that can be expressed as the sum of the true normal mode functions, each of which will satisfy the problem's boundary conditions. Therefore the approximate function $U(z)$ must satisfy the boundary conditions.

We have seen that Rayleigh's quotient arises by equating the kinetic and potential energies of vibration. For systems composed of both discrete and continuous elements, it is convenient to leave the quotient expressed in terms of energies. For the assumed mode shape and amplitude of vibration, let T_{max} be the maximum kinetic energy and V_{max} the maximum potential energy. Also let T'_{max} be the maximum kinetic energy that the vibrating system would have in the same assumed mode shape and amplitude if it were vibrating at a frequency of $\omega = 1$ rad/s, so that

$$T'_{max} = \frac{T_{max}}{\omega_j^2}. \tag{13.124}$$

In terms of T'_{max} and V_{max}, Rayleigh's quotient can then be written as

$$\omega_j^2 \pm 0(\varepsilon^2) = \frac{V_{max}}{T'_{max}} \qquad (13.125)$$

provided that the assumed mode shape satisfies the boundary conditions and differs from the actual mode shape only by terms of order ε. This applies to systems with both discrete and distributed properties, and combinations of both. The proof of (13.125) for the combined case is best done by using the discrete approach and considering continuous elements to be modelled by many discrete lumped elements which, in the limit, become infinitely many small elements. As before, for the lowest natural frequency, the r.h.s. of (13.125) always gives an upper bound for ω_1^2 so that for $j = 1$ the plus sign always applies on the l.h.s. of (13.125).

For continuous systems there will be an infinite number of modes, so that $U(z)$ is then expanded as an infinite series in (13.122). The expression of Rayleigh's quotient in a form like (13.118) therefore has an infinite series in its numerator and another in its denominator. This raises the question of the convergence of these infinite series. It is shown in Problem 13.6 that, provided that the approximate normal mode function $U(z)$ satisfies the equation of motion to order ε and that the natural frequency being calculated is well separated from adjacent natural frequencies, then these infinite series always converge to make (13.125) true. The statement that the equation of motion must be satisfied to order ε means that there is a restriction on the higher-order terms in the assumed normal mode function $U(z)$. The higher the mode, the less that can be included in $U(z)$ if an accurate approximation is to be obtained for the desired natural frequency.

We want to begin with a normal mode function that is as close to the exact function as possible. Since the normal mode functions $U_j(z)$ satisfy all the boundary conditions, the approximate function $U(z)$ should also do so. However, when the energy form of Rayleigh's quotient (13.125) is used, some of the boundary conditions may relate to higher-order derivatives that do not appear in the energy expressions for V_{max} and T'_{max}. In that case, ignoring the boundary conditions on these higher-order derivatives may make very little difference to the calculated V_{max} and T'_{max}.

Example of the whirling of a shaft subjected to external pressure

As an example of the application of Rayleigh's method, we consider the effect of external pressure on the vibration of a rotating cantilever shaft.[†] This is a problem that has been considered in connection with the design of extruders for plastics in which a rotating screwed shaft is used to extrude molten plastic from a heated cylindrical barrel. The shaft is

† Simpler applications of Rayleigh's method are given in Problem 13.5, part (iii).

unsupported except at its driven end, and there is a tendency for whirling to occur if the shaft's rotational speed approaches the lowest natural frequency for bending vibration of the stationary shaft. Because of the high pressure that is built up in the plastic melt as it is forced down the barrel of the extruder, large forces act on the screwed shaft and these reduce significantly the shaft's natural frequencies. In order to predict the rotational speed at which whirling occurs, it is necessary to calculate the lowest natural frequency of the shaft when subjected to the appropriate pressure field.

The deflection equation for an initially-straight elastic column of variable area $A(z)$ when subjected to a variable external pressure field $p(z)$ is given by (Newland [71]),

$$\frac{d^2}{dz^2}\left(EI\frac{d^2y}{dz^2}\right) + (P - pA)\frac{d^2y}{dz^2} - A\frac{dp}{dz}\frac{dy}{dz} = 0 \quad (13.126)$$

where $P(z)$ is the axial compressive load in the column at section z and $EI(z)$ is the variable bending stiffness of the column. The equation for bending vibrations is therefore

$$m\frac{\partial^2 y}{\partial t^2} + \frac{\partial^2}{\partial z^2}\left(EI\frac{\partial^2 y}{\partial z^2}\right) + (P - pA)\frac{\partial^2 y}{\partial z^2} - A\frac{dp}{dz}\frac{\partial y}{\partial z} = 0 \quad (13.127)$$

when it is assumed that the pressure field varies only with z and that $m(z)$ is the mass of the shaft per unit length. It can be shown (Newland [70] and [71]) that the axial compressive force at section z is

$$P = pA + \int_z^L \left(A\frac{dp}{dz}\right)_{z=\xi} d\xi \quad (13.128)$$

where the shaft has length L and z is the distance from the fixed end, Fig. 13.3. This integral occurs because, if a fluid column is imagined to replace the shaft, a distributed body force

$$A\frac{dp}{dz}dz$$

would have to be applied to each section dz of the fluid column to hold it in equilibrium in the surrounding pressure field. The force at section z would then be just pA where p and A are the pressure and area at z. Since no body forces are applied, the total force at section z is given by (13.128).

On substituting the free vibration solution

$$y(z, t) = U(z)\, e^{i\omega t} \quad (13.129)$$

into (13.127), we get

$$-m\omega^2 U + \frac{d^2}{dz^2}\left(EI\frac{d^2 U}{dz^2}\right) + (P - pA)\frac{d^2 U}{dz^2} - A\frac{dp}{dz}\frac{dU}{dz} = 0 \quad (13.130)$$

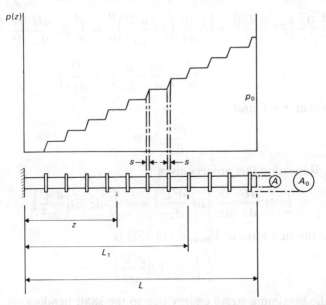

Fig. 13.3 Model of the shaft of a plastics extruder consisting of a cantilever elastic shaft with equally spaced rings subjected to the external pressure field shown. (*Reprinted by permission of the Council of the Institution of Mechanical Engineers from Ref. [70]*)

which in principle can be solved for $U(z)$ subject to $p(z)$, $A(z)$ and $I(z)$ being specified. The boundary conditions are zero deflection and slope at $z = 0$ and zero bending moment and shear force at the free end (the deflections are assumed to be small enough that the pressure is constant over each transverse section of the beam). In practice, this solution proves to be extremely complicated to work out and an approximate solution by Rayleigh's method is very much easier.

The reference kinetic energy $T'_{\max}$, which is the denominator of Rayleigh's quotient (13.125), is given, from (13.123), by

$$T'_{\max} = \frac{1}{2} \int_0^L dz\, m(z) U^2(z). \tag{13.131}$$

The maximum potential energy is, from the numerator of (13.123),

$$V_{\max} = \frac{1}{2} \int_0^L dz\, U(z) \left[\frac{d^2}{dz^2} \left(EI \frac{d^2 U}{dz^2} \right) + (P - pA) \frac{d^2 U}{dz^2} - A \frac{dp}{dz} \frac{dU}{dz} \right] \tag{13.132}$$

where all the terms in [ ] brackets may be functions of z.

Consider the first integral on the r.h.s. of (13.132). On integrating by parts we get

$$\int_0^L dz\, U\left[\frac{d^2}{dz^2}\left(EI\frac{d^2U}{dz^2}\right)\right] = \left[U\frac{d}{dz}\left(EI\frac{d^2U}{dz^2}\right)\right]_0^L - \int_0^L dz\,\frac{dU}{dz}\frac{d}{dz}\left(EI\frac{d^2U}{dz^2}\right)$$

$$= -\int_0^L dz\,\frac{dU}{dz}\frac{d}{dz}\left(EI\frac{d^2U}{dz^2}\right) \qquad (13.133)$$

since $U = 0$ at $z = 0$ and

$$\frac{d^2U}{dz^2} = 0$$

at $z = L$. Repeating this process gives

$$\int_0^L dz\,\frac{dU}{dz}\frac{d}{dz}\left(EI\frac{d^2U}{dz^2}\right) = -\int_0^L dz\, EI\left(\frac{d^2U}{dz^2}\right)^2. \qquad (13.134)$$

and hence the first term in $V_{\max}$ in (13.132) is

$$\frac{1}{2}\int_0^L dz\, EI\left(\frac{d^2U}{dz^2}\right)^2 \qquad (13.135)$$

which is the maximum strain energy due to the shaft bending.

The remaining terms in equation (13.132) for $V_{\max}$ give the change of potential energy of the shaft in the pressure field to which it is subjected. An analogy is with a flagpole in the earth's gravity field. When the flagpole deflects from the vertical, its potential energy is decreased because there is a reduction in the height of the column. According to (13.132), the increase in potential energy of the extruder shaft due to its change of position is

$$\frac{1}{2}\int_0^L dz\, U\left[(P - pA)\frac{d^2U}{dz^2} - A\frac{dp}{dz}\frac{dU}{dz}\right]. \qquad (13.136)$$

After substituting for $(P - pA)$ from (13.128) and using the boundary condition that

$$U = 0 \text{ at } z = 0, \qquad (13.137)$$

the integral in (13.136) may be reduced to (Problem 13.7)

$$-\frac{1}{2}\int_0^L dz\, A\frac{dp}{dz}\left[\int_0^z\left(\frac{dU}{dz}\right)^2 d\xi\right]_{z=\xi}. \qquad (13.138)$$

The negative sign is because the potential energy of the shaft in the pressure field decreases. Due to the deflection $U(z)$ of the shaft, section z moves axially a (small) distance

$$\frac{1}{2}\int_0^z\left(\frac{dU}{dz}\right)^2 d\xi \bigg|_{z=\xi}$$

towards the fixed end (see Problem 13.7). The body force on an element of length dz at z is

$$A \frac{dp}{dz} dz$$

and so the work done by the pressure field on the shaft, which is the same as the decrease in the potential energy of the shaft, is given correctly by (13.138).

On substituting the results (13.135) and (13.138) into (13.132), the maximum potential energy of the shaft (when deflected according to the function $U(z)$) is

$$V_{max} = \frac{1}{2} \int_0^L dz \ EI \left(\frac{d^2 U}{dz^2}\right)^2 - \frac{1}{2} \int_0^L dz \ A \frac{dp}{dz} \left[\int_0^z \left(\frac{dU}{dz}\right)^2 d\xi\right]_{z=\xi}. \quad (13.139)$$

On substituting for V_{max} and T'_{max} from (13.139) and (13.131), into (13.125) we then find that an approximate expression for the lowest natural frequency of the shaft is given by

$$\omega_1^2 = \frac{\displaystyle\int_0^L dz \ EI \left(\frac{d^2 U}{dz^2}\right)^2 - \int_0^L dz \ A \frac{dp}{dz} \left[\int_0^z \left(\frac{du}{dz}\right)^2 d\xi\right]_{z=\xi}}{\displaystyle\int_0^L dz \ m \ U^2}. \quad (13.140)$$

If we knew what the normal mode function $U_1(z)$ for the first mode was, equation (13.140) would give the exact value of the lowest natural frequency, ω_1. We do not know $U_1(z)$, so we use instead a function for $U_1(z)$ that we hope is a good approximation for the real function. There are two geometric boundary conditions to satisfy, which are that there is zero deflection and slope at $z = 0$ so that

$$U = \frac{dU}{dz} = 0 \text{ at } z = 0, \quad (13.141)$$

and there are two natural (or force) boundary conditions that

$$\frac{d^2 U}{dz^2} = \frac{d^3 U}{dz^3} = 0 \text{ at } z = L \quad (13.142)$$

because there can be no bending moment and no shear force at the free end of the beam.

We shall choose the approximate function

$$U(z) = \delta(1 - \cos \pi z/2L) \quad (13.143)$$

which satisfies both of (13.141) and the zero bending condition of (13.142) but not the zero shear force condition. The advantage of using the simple function (13.143) in spite of it not satisfying both of the natural boundary conditions is that it allows the integrals in (13.140) to be evaluated easily. The loss of accuracy because the shear force condition is not satisfied will not be significant within the overall accuracy of this simplified model of a real extruder because the energy integrals in (13.140) do not involve any d^3U/dz^3 terms explicitly.

To complete this example, we apply (13.140) with the displacement function (13.143) to calculate the lowest natural frequency of the shaft shown in Fig. 13.3. This is a shaft with many equally-spaced rings with the progressively-increasing pressure distribution shown. The pressure is assumed to be constant between the rings but to increase linearly across the width, s, of each ring. The shaft cross-sectional area is A and the cross-sectional area of the rings is A_0. Each ring is supposed to be small in axial length compared with the intervening lengths of shaft. The rings then contribute little to the stiffness and weight of the shaft so that the integrals

$$\int_0^L dz\ EI\left(\frac{d^2U}{dz^2}\right)^2 \quad \text{and} \quad \int_0^L dz\ m\ U^2 \tag{13.144}$$

can be found with sufficient accuracy by neglecting the rings and assuming that the shaft has constant area A. In that case,

$$\int_0^L dz\ EI\left(\frac{d^2U}{dz^2}\right)^2 = EI\delta^2\pi^4/32L^3 \tag{13.145}$$

and

$$\int_0^L dz\ m\ U^2 = \rho AL\delta^2(3/2 - 4/\pi). \tag{13.146}$$

The second integral in the numerator of (13.140) is zero where dp/dz is zero. Hence it has to be evaluated only over the length of the rings, where the pressure is changing (see Fig. 13.3). After substituting for $U(z)$ from (13.143) and evaluating the integral in square brackets, the contribution to the integral of one ring, distance L_1 from the fixed end, is

$$\int_{L_1}^{L_1+s} dz\ A_0\left(\frac{p_0}{ns}\right)\left(\frac{\pi^2\delta^2}{8L^2}\right)\left(z - \frac{L}{\pi}\sin\frac{\pi z}{L}\right) = \frac{A_0p_0}{n}\left(\frac{\pi^2\delta^2}{8L^2}\right)\left(L_1 - \frac{L}{\pi}\sin\frac{L_1}{L}\right) \tag{13.147}$$

where n is the number of rings. There are $n - 1$ similar terms, and so

$$\int_0^L dz\ A\ \frac{dp}{dz}\left[\int_0^z\left(\frac{dU}{dz}\right)^2 d\xi\right]_{z=\xi} = \frac{A_0p_0}{n}\left(\frac{\pi^2\delta^2}{8L^2}\right)\left[\sum_{m=1}^n \frac{mL}{n} - \left(\frac{L}{\pi}\right)\sum_{m=1}^n \sin\frac{\pi m}{n}\right]. \tag{13.148}$$

The two series in (13.148) may be summed using the results in Jolley [51], series 18 and 417, and hence

$$\int_0^L dz\ A\ \frac{dp}{dz}\left[\int_0^z\left(\frac{dU}{dz}\right)^2 d\xi\right]_{z=\xi} = \frac{A_0p_0}{n}\left(\frac{\pi^2\delta^2}{8L^2}\right)\left[\left(\frac{n+1}{2}\right)L - \left(\frac{L}{\pi}\right)\cot\frac{\pi}{2n}\right] \tag{13.149}$$

and, when there are many rings so that $n \to \infty$, this becomes

$$\int_0^L dz \, A \, \frac{dp}{dz} \left[\int_0^z \left(\frac{dU}{dz} \right)^2 d\xi \right]_{z=\xi} = A_0 p_0 \left(\frac{\pi^2 \delta^2}{4L} \right) \left(\frac{1}{4} - \frac{1}{\pi^2} \right). \quad (13.150)$$

On substituting the results (13.145), (13.146) and (13.150) into Rayleigh's quotient (13.140), the lowest natural frequency ω_1 is given by

$$\omega_1^2 = \Omega^2 \left[1 - \frac{8A_0 p_0 L^2}{\pi^2 EI} \left(\frac{1}{4} - \frac{1}{\pi^2} \right) \right] \quad (13.151)$$

where

$$\Omega^2 = \frac{EI}{\rho A} \frac{(\pi/2L)^4}{(3 - 8/\pi)}. \quad (13.152)$$

The natural frequency in the absence of external pressure is Ω and, on working out the numerical factor in (13.152), is

$$\Omega = \frac{3.66}{L^2} \sqrt{\frac{EI}{\rho A}} \quad (13.153)$$

compared with the exact figure for a cantilever elastic shaft which is (Problem 13.7)

$$\Omega = \frac{3.53}{L^2} \sqrt{\frac{EI}{\rho A}}. \quad (13.154)$$

The approximation obtained by using Rayleigh's method with the assumed mode function (13.143) is therefore about 4% higher than the exact value.

The presence of external pressure reduces this frequency according to the approximate results (13.151), and the natural frequency is reduced to zero when

$$\frac{8A_0 p_0 L^2}{\pi^2 EI} \left(\frac{1}{4} - \frac{1}{\pi^2} \right) = 1 \quad (13.155)$$

so that a cantilever with this pressure distribution buckles when

$$p_0 A_0 = 8.30 \frac{EI}{L^2}. \quad (13.156)$$

This is analogous to the well-known problem of a flagpole buckling under its own weight, for which the exact solution is (Timoshenko and Gere [100], p. 101)

$$p_0 A_0 = 7.84 \frac{EI}{L^2} \quad (13.157)$$

and the approximate buckling pressure comes out to be some 6% too high when calculated approximately in this way. Note that the effective area of the shaft for the pressure calculation is A_0, which is the area of the rings, rather than the area of the shaft, A, because all the pressure difference is assumed to occur across the width of the rings. The shaft stiffness EI is calculated for the shaft length between the (thin) rings, where the cross-sectional area is A.

For a steel shaft 6 m long and 0.2 m diameter, the natural frequency for zero external pressure is, from (13.153),

$$\omega_1 = \Omega = 25.8 \text{ rad/s (4.1 Hz)}. \tag{13.158}$$

For a typical extrusion pressure $p_0 = 35 \text{ MN/m}^2$ and a ring diameter of 0.24 m, the factor

$$\left[1 - \frac{8A_0p_0L^2}{\pi^2 EI}\left(\frac{1}{4} - \frac{1}{\pi^2}\right)\right] = 0.56 \tag{13.159}$$

so that the natural frequency is reduced from 25.8 rad/s to

$$\omega_1 = \Omega \sqrt{0.56} = 19.3 \text{ rad/s (3.1 Hz)}. \tag{13.160}$$

The theoretical first whirling speed is therefore reduced from 246 rev/min to 184 rev/min.

The Rayleigh–Ritz method

We have seen that Rayleigh's method gives an upper bound for a system's lowest natural frequency. If the assumed modal function $U(z)$ contains one or more variable parameters, so that the shape of $U(z)$ depends on the values of these parameters, the approximate natural frequency ω_1 obtained by Rayleigh's method can be improved by differentiating with respect to the variable parameters to seek the minimum value of ω_1. This minimum will be the best approximation that the trial function allows.

The Rayleigh–Ritz method of calculating approximately the undamped natural frequencies and mode shapes of a system with many (usually infinitely many) degrees of freedom depends on this idea. As an illustration of the method, suppose that it is required to find approximately the first two natural frequencies and modes of an undamped continuous system for which Rayleigh's quotient is defined by (13.123).

The approximate modal function $U(z)$ is chosen so that

$$U(z) = q_1\psi_1(z) + q_2\psi_2(z) \tag{13.161}$$

where q_1 and q_2 are arbitrary (real) parameters to be determined and the functions $\psi_1(z)$ and $\psi_2(z)$ are chosen to be as close to the first and second normal mode functions $U_1(z)$ and $U_2(z)$ as possible. Both $\psi_1(z)$ and $\psi_2(z)$ must satisfy the boundary conditions, for all derivatives if possible but at least for those derivatives that appear in the kinetic-energy and potential-energy functions in Rayleigh's quotient. The accuracy of the calculation depends on how close $\psi_1(z)$ is to $U_1(z)$ and $\psi_2(z)$ is to $U_2(z)$ and we shall assume in the following analysis that each is accurate enough that we can write

$$\psi_1(z) = U_1(z) + \varepsilon_{12}U_2(z) + \varepsilon_{13}U_3(z) + \ldots \tag{13.162}$$

and

$$\psi_2(z) = \varepsilon_{21} U_1(z) + U_2(z) + \varepsilon_{23} U_3(z) + \dots \quad (13.163)$$

We shall now substitute the assumed function $U(z)$ defined by (13.161) into Rayleigh's quotient (13.123). First we work out the integral in the denominator of (13.123) using the orthogonality condition (12.14) to find that

$$\int_R dz\, m(z)\, U^2(z) = q_1^2(1 + \varepsilon_{12}^2 + \varepsilon_{13}^2 + \dots) +$$
$$+ 2q_1 q_2(\varepsilon_{21} + \varepsilon_{12} + \varepsilon_{13}\varepsilon_{23} + \varepsilon_{14}\varepsilon_{24} + \dots) +$$
$$+ q_2^2(\varepsilon_{21}^2 + 1 + \varepsilon_{23}^2 + \dots). \quad (13.164)$$

Secondly, substituting (13.161) into the numerator of (13.123) and using the orthogonality condition (12.15), we get

$$\int_R dz\, U(z)\, L\{U(z)\} = q_1^2(\omega_1^2 + \varepsilon_{12}^2\omega_2^2 + \varepsilon_{13}^2\omega_3^2 + \dots) +$$
$$+ 2q_1 q_2(\varepsilon_{21}\omega_1^2 + \varepsilon_{12}\omega_2^2 + \varepsilon_{13}\varepsilon_{23}\omega_3^2 + \varepsilon_{14}\varepsilon_{24}\omega_4^2 + \dots) +$$
$$+ q_2^2(\varepsilon_{21}^2\omega_1^2 + \omega_2^2 + \varepsilon_{23}^2\omega_3^2 + \dots). \quad (13.165)$$

If we call the r.h.s. of (13.164) $2T'(q_1, q_2)$ and the r.h.s. of (13.165) $2V(q_1, q_2)$, then on substituting into Rayleigh's quotient (13.123)

$$\omega^2 = \frac{V(q_1, q_2)}{T'(q_1, q_2)} \quad (13.166)$$

where we replace ω_1 in (13.123) by ω without a subscript for the reason that we shall see in a moment. We want ω to be a minimum. Writing (13.166) as

$$\omega^2 T'(q_1, q_2) = V(q_1, q_2) \quad (13.167)$$

and differentiating with respect to q_1 and q_2 gives

$$\frac{\partial \omega^2}{\partial q_1} T'(q_1, q_2) + \omega^2 \frac{\partial T'(q_1, q_2)}{\partial q_1} = \frac{\partial V(q_1, q_2)}{\partial q_1} \quad (13.168)$$

and

$$\frac{\partial \omega^2}{\partial q_2} T'(q_1, q_2) + \omega^2 \frac{\partial T'(q_1, q_2)}{\partial q_2} = \frac{\partial V(q_1, q_2)}{\partial q_2}. \quad (13.169)$$

The approximate natural frequency ω will be a minimum when

$$\frac{\partial \omega^2}{\partial q_1} = \frac{\partial \omega^2}{\partial q_2} = 0 \quad (13.170)$$

which, from (13.168) and (13.169), will occur when

$$\frac{\partial V(q_1, q_2)}{\partial q_1} - \omega^2 \frac{\partial T'(q_1, q_2)}{\partial q_1} = 0 \quad (13.171)$$

and

$$\frac{\partial V(q_1, q_2)}{\partial q_2} - \omega^2 \frac{\partial T'(q_1, q_2)}{\partial q_2} = 0. \tag{13.172}$$

From (13.164) and (13.165), the derivatives of T' and V in (13.171) and (13.172) are

$$\frac{\partial T'}{\partial q_1} = q_1(1 + \varepsilon_{12}^2 + \varepsilon_{13}^2 + \ldots) + q_2(\varepsilon_{21} + \varepsilon_{12} + \varepsilon_{13}\varepsilon_{23} + \ldots)$$

$$\frac{\partial T'}{\partial q_2} = q_1(\varepsilon_{21} + \varepsilon_{12} + \varepsilon_{13}\varepsilon_{23} + \ldots) + q_2(\varepsilon_{21}^2 + 1 + \varepsilon_{23}^2 + \ldots)$$

$$\frac{\partial V}{\partial q_1} =$$

$$q_1(\omega_1^2 + \varepsilon_{12}^2\omega_2^2 + \varepsilon_{13}^2\omega_3^2 + \ldots) + q_2(\varepsilon_{21}\omega_1^2 + \varepsilon_{12}\omega_2^2 + \varepsilon_{13}\varepsilon_{23}\omega_3^2 + \ldots)$$

$$\frac{\partial V}{\partial q_2} =$$

$$q_1(\varepsilon_{21}\omega_1^2 + \varepsilon_{12}\omega_2^2 + \varepsilon_{13}\varepsilon_{23}\omega_3^2 + \ldots) + q_2(\varepsilon_{21}^2\omega_1^2 + \omega_2^2 + \varepsilon_{23}^2\omega_3^2 + \ldots)$$

$$\tag{13.173}$$

with which (13.171) gives

$$q_1[(\omega_1^2 - \omega^2) + \varepsilon_{12}^2(\omega_2^2 - \omega^2) + \varepsilon_{13}^2(\omega_3^2 - \omega^2) + \ldots] +$$

$$+ q_2[\varepsilon_{21}(\omega_1^2 - \omega^2) + \varepsilon_{12}(\omega_2^2 - \omega^2) + \varepsilon_{13}\varepsilon_{23}(\omega_3^2 - \omega^2) + \ldots] = 0$$

$$\tag{13.174}$$

and (13.172) gives

$$q_1[\varepsilon_{21}(\omega_1^2 - \omega^2) + \varepsilon_{12}(\omega_2^2 - \omega^2) + \varepsilon_{13}\varepsilon_{23}(\omega_3^2 - \omega^2) + \ldots] +$$

$$+ q_2[\varepsilon_{21}^2(\omega_1^2 - \omega^2) + (\omega_2^2 - \omega^2) + \varepsilon_{23}^2(\omega_3^2 - \omega^2) + \ldots] = 0. \tag{13.175}$$

These two simultaneous linear equations in q_1 and q_2 have the trivial solution

$$q_1 = q_2 = 0 \tag{13.176}$$

unless the determinant of the coefficients of q_1 and q_2 is zero, so that

$$[(\omega_1^2 - \omega^2) + \varepsilon_{12}^2(\omega_2^2 - \omega^2) + \varepsilon_{13}^2(\omega_3^2 - \omega^2) + \ldots] \times$$

$$\times [\varepsilon_{21}^2(\omega_1^2 - \omega^2) + (\omega_2^2 - \omega^2) + \varepsilon_{23}^2(\omega_3^2 - \omega^2) + \ldots] =$$

$$= [\varepsilon_{21}(\omega_1^2 - \omega^2) + \varepsilon_{12}(\omega_2^2 - \omega^2) + \varepsilon_{13}\varepsilon_{23}(\omega_2^2 - \omega^2) + \ldots]^2. \tag{13.177}$$

On multiplying out the brackets in (13.177), retaining only those terms of order ε^2 and larger, we get

$$(\omega_1^2 - \omega^2)(\omega_2^2 - \omega^2) + (\omega_1^2 - \omega^2)[\varepsilon_{21}^2(\omega_1^2 - \omega^2) + \varepsilon_{23}^2(\omega_3^2 - \omega^2) + \ldots] +$$

$$+ (\omega_2^2 - \omega^2)[\varepsilon_{12}^2(\omega_2^2 - \omega^2) + \varepsilon_{13}^2(\omega_3^2 - \omega^2) + \ldots] =$$

$$= \varepsilon_{21}^2(\omega_1^2 - \omega^2)^2 + 2\varepsilon_{12}\varepsilon_{21}(\omega_1^2 - \omega^2)(\omega_2^2 - \omega^2) + \varepsilon_{12}^2(\omega_2^2 - \omega^2)^2. \tag{13.178}$$

This is a quadratic equation for ω^2. In the limit when all the ε's are zero, so that the trial solution is, from (13.161)–(13.163),

$$U(z) = q_1 U_1(z) + q_2 U_2(z) \tag{13.179}$$

we see from (13.178), that

$$(\omega_1^2 - \omega^2)(\omega_2^2 - \omega^2) = 0. \tag{13.180}$$

The natural frequencies calculated by the Rayleigh–Ritz method are then the exact values of the first and second natural frequencies.

When the ε's are not zero, but they are all small, then one solution for ω will be close to ω_1 and the other close to ω_2. If we assume that

$$\omega^2 = \omega_1^2 + 0(\varepsilon) \tag{13.181}$$

is one solution, then $(\omega_1^2 - \omega^2)$ has order ε and some of the terms in (13.178) can be removed because they are of order ε^3. The remaining terms are

$$(\omega_1^2 - \omega^2)(\omega_2^2 - \omega^2) + (\omega_2^2 - \omega^2)[\varepsilon_{12}^2(\omega_2^2 - \omega^2) + \varepsilon_{13}^2(\omega_3^2 - \omega^2) + \ldots] =$$
$$= \varepsilon_{12}^2(\omega_2^2 - \omega^2)^2. \tag{13.182}$$

Hence, on rearrangement, and cancelling the factor $(\omega_2^2 - \omega^2)$ which we assume is a term of zero order (since we assume that the natural frequencies are distinct and sufficiently well separated),

$$\omega^2 = \frac{\omega_1^2 + \varepsilon_{13}^2\omega_3^2 + \varepsilon_{14}^2\omega_4^2 + \ldots}{1 + \varepsilon_{13}^2 + \varepsilon_{14}^2 + \ldots} \tag{13.183}$$

which may be compared with the result (13.118) obtained previously by using Rayleigh's method.

Similarly, if we start by assuming that

$$\omega^2 = \omega_2^2 + 0(\varepsilon) \tag{13.184}$$

is a solution, (13.178) gives to order ε^2

$$(\omega_1^2 - \omega^2)(\omega_2^2 - \omega^2) + (\omega_1^2 - \omega^2)[\varepsilon_{21}^2(\omega_1^2 - \omega^2) + \varepsilon_{23}^2(\omega_3^2 - \omega^2) + \ldots] =$$
$$= \varepsilon_{21}^2(\omega_1^2 - \omega^2). \tag{13.185}$$

On rearranging the terms in (13.185), the second natural frequency is given approximately by the solution

$$\omega^2 = \frac{\omega_2^2 + \varepsilon_{23}^2\omega_3^2 + \varepsilon_{24}^2\omega_4^2 + \ldots}{1 + \varepsilon_{23}^2 + \varepsilon_{24}^2 + \ldots} \tag{13.186}$$

The conclusion is that the Rayleigh–Ritz method with a two-term solution produces two natural frequencies which, from (13.183) and (13.186), are upper-bound solutions for the first and second natural frequencies. Provided that the approximate modal function $U(z)$ has only small contributions to order ε from modes other than the first two, the two natural frequencies will be accurate to order ε^2. The ratio q_1/q_2 from

(13.174) or (13.175) gives, on substitution into (13.161), the approximate modal functions for each of the calculated natural frequencies.

The effect of differentiating with respect to q_1 and q_2 is to eliminate the contribution of the second mode to (13.183) and the first mode to (13.186). The result (13.183) is more accurate than the corresponding result from Rayleigh's method which, from (13.118), would be

$$\omega^2 = \frac{\omega_1^2 + \varepsilon_{12}^2 \omega_2^2 + \varepsilon_{13}^2 \omega_3^2 + \varepsilon_{14}^2 \omega_4^2 + \ldots}{1 + \varepsilon_{12}^2 + \varepsilon_{13}^2 + \varepsilon_{14}^2 + \ldots} \tag{13.187}$$

instead of (13.183) because $\omega_2^2 > \omega_1^2$ (see Problem 13.8).

The above results for a trial modal function with two variable parameters q_1 and q_2 can be extended to the general case of N variables. It is shown in Collatz [15] that the frequencies obtained by the Rayleigh–Ritz method using N variable parameters are upper-bound approximations for the first N natural frequencies. In practice, the method relies on choosing an assumed modal function which includes accurate representations of the higher modes that are included. Otherwise, the higher natural frequencies and mode shapes will also be inaccurate (see Bisplinghoff *et al.* [9]).

Corollaries of Rayleigh's principle

By using Rayleigh's principle, it is possible to derive six important theorems. They stem from the original work of Rayleigh on the theory of sound [83, section 88] and are discussed in the form presented here by Temple & Bickley [97]. The theorems relate changes in the natural frequencies of an undamped system to changes in the magnitude and distribution of its mass and stiffness. They apply for any general conservative system for which Rayleigh's quotient applies. In the case of a discrete system, this means that the kinetic and potential energies must be able to be written in the forms (13.109) and (13.110). From chapter 11, it follows that the system has to be scleronomic (have fixed supports) and holonomic (have independent coordinates). Also its motion has to be restricted to small-amplitude vibration about a position of stable equilibrium (otherwise the kinetic energy cannot be written as (11.55) and therefore as (13.109)). Similar requirements apply for continuous systems. We shall consider the continuous case and prove the theorems by reference to the quotient in its form (13.121). The first two theorems follow.

Theorem 1
If the mass of such an undamped linear system is increased by increasing a constituent mass of the system, the stiffness remaining unchanged, all the natural frequencies of the system will decrease apart from the exceptional natural frequency that may remain unchanged.

Theorem 2

If the stiffness of such an undamped linear system is increased by increasing a constituent stiffness of the system, the mass remaining unchanged, all the natural frequencies will increase apart from the exceptional natural frequency that may remain unchanged.

The proofs depend on the property of Rayleigh's quotient that, if an assumed mode function is accurate to order ε, the quotient gives a natural frequency that is accurate to order ε^2.

For example, suppose that the jth natural frequency of a continuous system is given exactly by (13.121), which is

$$\omega_j^2 = \frac{\int_R dz\, U_j(z)\, L\{U_j(z)\}}{\int_R dz\, m(z)\, U_j^2(z)}. \tag{13.188}$$

Now let $m(z)$ be increased to $m'(z)$ by a change of order ε. We expect that the corresponding change in the modal function from $U_j(z)$ to $U_j'(z)$ will also be of order ε (or less). This was proved in Problem 11.6 for the case of a small change in stiffness; a corresponding result applies when the mass is given a small change. By Rayleigh's principle, an approximation for the new natural frequency ω_j' is given from (13.123) by

$$\omega_j'^2 \pm 0(\varepsilon^2) = \frac{\int_R dz\, U_j(z)\, L\{U_j(z)\}}{\int_R dz\, m'(z)\, U_j^2(z)} \tag{13.189}$$

where the original modal function $U_j(z)$ is used as an approximation to order ε for the new modal function $U_j'(z)$. For the lowest natural frequency we have shown that Rayleigh's quotient always gives an upper bound for the natural frequency, but for other, higher, natural frequencies the same proof no longer applies (Problem 13.8). However, the natural frequency will still be correct to order ε^2 if the approximate function $U_j(z)$ only differs from the exact function $U_j'(z)$ by order ε.

By comparing the r.h.s. of (13.188) and the r.h.s. of (13.189), these are seen to be the same except for $m(z)$ in (13.188) being replaced by $m'(z)$ in (13.189). Since $m'(z)$ is greater than $m(z)$ by an amount of order ε, we expect, from (13.188), that

$$\frac{\int_R dz\, U_j(z)\, L\{U_j(z)\}}{\int_R dz\, m'(z)\, U_j^2(z)} = \omega_j^2 - 0(\varepsilon) \tag{13.190}$$

where $0(\varepsilon)$ means 'including terms of order ε (and smaller)'. Combining (13.189) and (13.190), we see that

$$\omega_j'^2 = \omega_j^2 - 0(\varepsilon) \tag{13.191}$$

because the terms of order ε will always swamp those of order ε^2 when ε is made small enough. The natural frequency of mode j is then reduced by a term of order ε.

In the exceptional case we may find that

$$\int_R \mathrm{d}z\, m'(z)\, U_j^2(z) \tag{13.192}$$

will be the same as

$$\int_R \mathrm{d}z\, m(z)\, U_j^2(z). \tag{13.193}$$

This would be the case if an additional point mass were placed at the node of the system, where $U_j(z)$ is zero. In that case, eqn. (13.119) is still satisfied by the same ω_j and the same $U_j(z)$ as for the original mass distribution and there is no change in the natural frequency (or its mode shape).

We conclude that the effect of increasing the mass of a vibrating system of the type defined above is always to decrease its natural frequencies (or leave the exceptional natural frequency unchanged) and never to cause any natural frequency to increase. By integration of this result, it can be seen that the same result (theorem 1) applies for large changes of mass as well as for small changes, provided that corresponding pairs of natural frequencies are correctly identified when the modified system is compared with the original system.

Exactly the same method may be used to prove theorem 2. Increasing the stiffness of any system of the type defined above always causes its natural frequencies to increase (or leave the exceptional natural frequency unchanged) and never causes any natural frequency to decrease. The theorem is true for large changes in stiffness as well as for small changes.

An additional result which is sometimes useful is the following.

Theorem 3

If the mass of a system, for example a string or a beam, is distributed non-uniformly, the natural frequencies of this system will fall between the corresponding natural frequencies of systems (a) and (b), where (a) is a similar uniform system whose distributed mass is the maximum mass per unit length (or volume) of the non-uniform system, and (b) is a similar uniform system whose distributed mass is the minimum mass per unit length (or volume) of the non-uniform system.

The proof follows directly from theorem 1. Theorem 3 applies also when the system is an assembly of which a particular subsystem has a non-uniform mass distribution. The natural frequencies of the assembly will fall between the corresponding natural frequencies of assembly (a) and assembly (b), where (a) includes the subsystem with its maximum distributed mass everywhere and (b) includes the subsystem with its minimum distributed mass everywhere. There is a similar theorem for stiffness.

Theorem 4

If the stiffness of a system or part of a system is distributed non-uniformly, the natural frequencies of this system will fall between the corresponding natural frequencies of systems (*a*) and (*b*) when these are defined as follows. For system (*a*), the member with non-uniformly distributed stiffness is replaced by a corresponding member with uniformly distributed stiffness whose magnitude is equal to the maximum local stiffness of the non-uniform member. For system (*b*), the member with non-uniformly distributed stiffness is replaced by a corresponding member with uniformly distributed stiffness whose magnitude is equal to the minimum local value of the non-uniform member.

Rayleigh's principle also leads to two more useful results expressed in the following theorems 5 and 6. Theorem 5 concerns the case when the mass of a vibrating system may be divided into two or more parts, for example a floor of girders with a distributed mass loading on the floor. The mass of the girders can be separated from the mass on top of the floor. Let $m_1(z)$ denote the distributed mass of the girders and $m_2(z)$ that of the loading on the floor. The total distributed mass is then $m(z)$ where

$$m(z) = m_1(z) + m_2(z). \tag{13.194}$$

Call the lowest natural frequency of the assembly ω_1, the lowest natural frequency of the girders with no load on the floor Ω_1, and the lowest natural frequency of the floor loading on massless girders of the same stiffness as the real girders Ω_2. Let $U_1(z)$ be the exact normal mode function for the assembly, so that, from (13.121),

$$\omega_1^2 = \frac{\int_R dz\, U_1(z)\, L\{U_1(z)\}}{\int_R dz\, m(z)\, U_1^2(z)}. \tag{13.195}$$

Also, using $U_1(z)$ as an approximation for the normal mode function in both cases of partial mass loading of the floor, we have from (13.123)

$$\Omega_1^2 \leqslant \frac{\int_R dz\, U_1(z)\, L\{U_1(z)\}}{\int_R dz\, m_1(z)\, U_1^2(z)} \tag{13.196}$$

and

$$\Omega_2^2 \leqslant \frac{\int_R dz\, U_1(z)\, L\{U_1(z)\}}{\int_R dz\, m_2(z)\, U_1^2(z)}. \tag{13.197}$$

On inverting (13.195)–(13.197) and using (13.194), we then see that

$$\frac{1}{\omega_1^2} \leqslant \frac{1}{\Omega_1^2} + \frac{1}{\Omega_2^2}. \tag{13.198}$$

The equals sign applies only in the exceptional case when the mode shapes for the partial mass problems are the same as the mode shape for the combined problem. For modes higher than the first, the inequality signs in (13.196) to (13.198) have to be replaced by approximately-equals signs, but the result (13.198) becomes unreliable for high modes unless the normal mode function for the mode concerned is altered only slightly by changing the mass distribution from $m(z)$ to $m_1(z)$ to $m_2(z)$.

The result (13.198) may be extended to the case when $m(z)$ may be broken down into more than two parts, and theorem 5 may then be written as follows.

Theorem 5

If a linear elastic system has a mass distribution which may be separated into several parts $m_1(z)$, $m_2(z)$, $m_3(z)$, ..., and the lowest natural frequencies of the system with each of these mass distributions alone are Ω_1, Ω_2, Ω_3, ..., respectively, then if ω_1 is the lowest natural frequency of the combined system,

$$\frac{1}{\omega_1^2} \leqslant \frac{1}{\Omega_1^2} + \frac{1}{\Omega_2^2} + \frac{1}{\Omega_3^2} + \ldots \tag{13.199}$$

There is a corresponding theorem 6 for the case when the stiffness of a system may be considered to be broken down into separate components. This theorem was used by Southwell [91] in connection with the lateral vibrations of spinning disks. Southwell calculated the lowest natural frequency of a non-rotating disk, Ω_1, and of a rotating disk with no stiffness, Ω_2. For the real case of a rotating disk with stiffness due to both the inherent stiffness of the plate and the additional stiffness due to the effect of centrifugal force, the stiffness operator $L\{U(z)\}$ is the sum of the operators in the two separate cases so that

$$L\{U(z)\} = L_1\{U(z)\} + L_2\{U(z)\}. \tag{13.200}$$

Therefore, if ω_1 is the lowest natural frequency in the real case, by using Rayleigh's principle in the same way as to prove (13.198), we find that

$$\omega_1^2 \geqslant \Omega_1^2 + \Omega_2^2. \tag{13.201}$$

Theorem 6 may be stated formally as follows.

Theorem 6

If a linear system has a stiffness operator $L\{y(z)\}$ that may be expressed as the sum of several separate components $L_1\{y(z)\}$, $L_2\{y(z)\}$, $L_3\{y(z)\}$, ..., and the lowest natural frequencies of the system with each of these partial stiffnesses alone are Ω_1, Ω_2, Ω_3, ..., respectively, then if ω_1 is the lowest natural frequency of the combined system,

$$\omega_1^2 \geqslant \Omega_1^2 + \Omega_2^2 + \Omega_3^2 + \ldots \tag{13.202}$$

This result gives a lower bound for the lowest natural frequency. By using Rayleigh's quotient (13.123) in the usual way, an upper bound on the lowest natural frequency is obtained. For problems whose stiffness can be broken down into two (or more) parts and which have exact solutions when there is partial stiffness, it is possible to use theorem 6 to obtain a lower bound and Rayleigh's quotient to obtain an upper bound, and therefore to bracket the lowest natural frequency of a problem.

Chapter 14

Parametric and nonlinear effects

Introduction

All the general methods of calculation in the previous chapters apply for systems described by linear differential equations with constant coefficients. Apart from the discussions of hysteretic damping in Chapters 3 and 11, we have considered only the vibration of linear systems with constant parameters. This broad, general class includes most cases of structural vibration and many vibration problems in mechanical engineering. We have seen that there are general analytical methods and well-developed computer procedures for these problems. But there are also important examples of mechanical vibration when the linear equations have time-varying coefficients or when the equations are nonlinear. We turn now to some of these special problems.

First, we shall consider the solutions of the Mathieu equation which describes the response of a linear oscillator with time-varying stiffness. This is important for two reasons: first, because it describes the behaviour of a number of practical vibration problems, for example the vibration of rotating shafts of non-circular cross-section; secondly, because the Mathieu equation arises during the analysis of the stability of vibration of certain non-linear systems which we come to later. The numerical solution of the general Mathieu equation involves applying the eigenvalue analysis developed in the earlier chapters and leads to general stability charts. These charts are used to show how a system responding to parametric stiffness excitation can become unstable at a number of different excitation frequencies.

In the section on autoparametric systems, we turn to the case when two or more modes of a dynamic system are coupled by small nonlinear terms in such a way that, when one mode is excited externally, the response of this mode provides parametric excitation for another mode. This leads to a discussion of the phenomenon of internal resonance which is important in several fields, including aircraft structural vibration and helicopter rotor dynamics.

The chapter then moves to consider the forced response of a nonlinear oscillator when the stiffness is a nonlinear function of displacement. This is a problem that occurs in many areas of mechanical engineering, and the example of a centrifugal pendulum vibration absorber is worked out in detail at the end of the chapter. The emphasis is on the steady-state forced vibration of an oscillator with small nonlinearity. The stability of forced vibration is investigated by a perturbation approach which leads back to the Mathieu equation and requires the application of the stability charts developed earlier.

The numerical integration technique of Chapter 10 is used to illustrate the so-called nonlinear jump phenomenon when there is a sudden jump in the response of a nonlinear oscillator and to show the chaotic vibration of a heavily nonlinear system.

Lastly, there is a discussion of methods for finding the approximate response of weakly nonlinear systems subjected to periodic excitation; Galerkin's method, the Ritz minimizing method and the method of Krylov and Bogoliubov are compared, and Galerkin's method is applied to the centrifugal pendulum example. When its excitation amplitude exceeds a critical value, the centrifugal pendulum suffers a nonlinear jump and then becomes useless as a vibration absorber.

Parametric stiffness excitation

Any of the mass, damping or stiffness coefficients of a mechanical oscillator may depend on time, but the problem of parametric excitation generally occurs when the stiffness has a time-varying component. Usually this is a harmonic variation, and the equation of motion for a single degree-of-freedom system can then be written as

$$\ddot{y}(t) + 2\zeta\omega\dot{y}(t) + \omega^2(1 + \alpha\cos\Omega t)\, y(t) = 0 \tag{14.1}$$

or, alternatively, as

$$\ddot{y}(t) + 2\zeta\omega\dot{y}(t) + \omega^2 y(t) = -\omega^2\alpha\cos\Omega t\, y(t). \tag{14.2}$$

Because the excitation term $\cos\Omega t$ is modulated by the response $y(t)$, the solution of (14.1) differs markedly from that for a constant-parameter system.

When there is negligible damping, (14.1) becomes the Mathieu equation

$$\ddot{y}(t) + \omega^2(1 + \alpha\cos\Omega t)\, y(t) = 0 \tag{14.3}$$

whose solutions have been studied extensively (see, for example, Haupt [41], McLachlan [56] and Stoker [93]). The equation takes its name from the original paper by E. Mathieu in 1868 [57]. It turns out that the form of the solution $y(t)$ of (14.3) depends on the magnitude of the non-dimensional coefficient α, which we assume to be real, and on the magnitude of the frequency ratio Ω/ω, where Ω is the frequency of parametric excitation and ω is the natural frequency of the system when $\alpha = 0$.

It is convenient to use $(\Omega/\omega)^2$ instead of Ω/ω to avoid using imaginary numbers when there is negative stiffness (so that ω^2 is negative) and we define two new real parameters

$$\delta = (\omega/\Omega)^2 \tag{14.4}$$

and

$$\varepsilon = (\omega/\Omega)^2\alpha. \tag{14.5}$$

We shall now investigate how the solutions of the Mathieu equation (14.3) depend on the values of δ and ε.

Solutions of the Mathieu equation

Because the parametric excitation in (14.3) has period

$$T = 2\pi/\Omega \tag{14.6}$$

there are solutions $y(t)$ of (14.3) which have the property that

$$y(t + T) = \sigma\, y(t) \tag{14.7}$$

where σ is a constant. This is so because, since (14.7) is true for all time t, it follows that

$$\frac{dy}{dt}(t + T) = \sigma\,\frac{dy}{dt}(t) \tag{14.8}$$

and

$$\frac{d^2y}{dt^2}(t + T) = \sigma\,\frac{d^2y}{dt^2}(t). \tag{14.9}$$

Therefore if $y(t)$ satisfies (14.3), then on account of (14.7) and (14.9), so must $y(t + T)$ satisfy (14.3).

Since the Mathieu equation (14.3) is a second-order equation which is linear in y and $\ddot{y}$ and homogeneous (the r.h.s. of the equation being zero), it always has two independent solutions and its general solution is some linear combination of these solutions. Therefore if, for a particular set of parameter values, we can find two solutions which satisfy (14.7) with different values of σ, we have two independent solutions and then we know the general solution subject to arbitrary constants.

If there is a solution for which $|\sigma| > 1$, from (14.7) the response $y(t)$ will grow as time increases and the solution will be unstable. If $|\sigma| < 1$, the response will decrease with time and the solution will be stable. If $|\sigma| = 1$, the response will continue indefinitely without change of amplitude and the solution will also be stable in the sense that the response will be bounded.

We note here that we assume that we are working in the field of complex numbers so that $y(t)$ and σ may both be complex. The physical response in a particular case is then the real part of $y(t)$ or the imaginary part of $y(t)$, whichever the analyst chooses.

The two values of the parameter σ, say σ_1 and σ_2, depend on the values of the parameters Ω/ω and α in the Mathieu equation (14.3), and therefore on the values of δ and ε defined from Ω/ω and α by (14.4) and (14.5). It is shown in the general theory of Mathieu equations that, if a diagram is drawn with δ plotted against ε, there will be continuous regions of this diagram in which both the σ's are real, with $|\sigma_1| > 1$ and $|\sigma_2| < 1$. In these regions the solution with σ_1 is unbounded (and therefore unstable), so that these regions are unstable regions of the diagram. There are also continuous regions for which the combination of δ and ε is such that both the σ's are complex with $|\sigma_1| = |\sigma_2| = 1$. For these regions the solution is bounded (and therefore stable) so that these are stable regions of the diagram. The boundaries between the stable and unstable regions occur at combinations of δ and ε for which the σ's are at the transition between real and complex values with $\sigma_1 = \sigma_2 = \pm 1$. These boundaries can be found as follows.

If $\sigma = +1$, equation (14.7) gives

$$y(t + T) = y(t) \tag{14.10}$$

and the response $y(t)$ must have period T. In that case, we can write $y(t)$ as the Fourier expansion

$$y(t) = a_0 + \sum_{j=1}^{\infty} (a_j \cos j\Omega t + b_j \sin j\Omega t). \tag{14.11}$$

On substituting the periodic solution (14.11) into (14.3) and using the trigonometrical identities

$$2 \cos \Omega t \cos j\Omega t = \cos (1 + j)\, \Omega t + \cos (1 - j)\, \Omega t \tag{14.12}$$

$$2 \cos \Omega t \sin j\Omega t = \sin (1 + j)\, \Omega t - \sin (1 - j)\, \Omega t \tag{14.13}$$

we find that

$$-\sum_{j=1}^{\infty} j^2 (a_j \cos j\Omega t + b_j \sin j\Omega t) + \delta\left[a_0 + \sum_{j=1}^{\infty} (a_j \cos j\Omega t + b_j \sin j\Omega t) \right] +$$

$$+ \varepsilon\left[\frac{a_1}{2} + a_0 \cos \Omega t + \frac{1}{2} \sum_{j=1}^{\infty} (a_{j+1} \cos j\Omega t + b_{j+1} \sin j\Omega t) \right] +$$

$$+ \frac{\varepsilon}{2}\left[\sum_{j=2}^{\infty} (a_{j-1} \cos j\Omega t + b_{j-1} \sin j\Omega t) \right] = 0. \tag{14.14}$$

For this equation to be true for all values of t, the coefficients of the sine and cosine components of each harmonic must be separately zero. The constant terms are zero if

$$\delta a_0 + \frac{\varepsilon}{2} a_1 = 0,$$ (14.15)

the terms in $\cos \Omega t$ are zero if

$$\varepsilon a_0 + (\delta - 1) a_1 + \frac{\varepsilon}{2} a_2 = 0,$$ (14.16)

and the terms in $\cos j\Omega t$, $j \geqslant 2$, are zero if

$$\frac{\varepsilon}{2} a_{j-1} + (\delta - j^2) a_j + \frac{\varepsilon}{2} a_{j+1} = 0.$$ (14.17)

The terms in $\sin \Omega t$ are zero if

$$(\delta - 1) b_1 + \frac{\varepsilon}{2} b_2 = 0,$$ (14.18)

and those in $\sin j\Omega t$, $j \geqslant 2$, are zero if

$$\frac{\varepsilon}{2} b_{j-1} + (\delta - j^2) b_j + \frac{\varepsilon}{2} b_{j+1} = 0.$$ (14.19)

If we consider only the first N harmonics of the periodic response, equations (14.15)–(14.17) can be written in the matrix form

$$\begin{bmatrix} \delta & \varepsilon/2 & & & & & \\ \varepsilon & \delta - 1 & \varepsilon/2 & & & & \\ & \varepsilon/2 & \delta - 4 & \varepsilon/2 & & & \\ & & \varepsilon/2 & \delta - 9 & \varepsilon/2 & & \\ & & & \cdot & \cdot & \cdot & \\ & & & & \cdot & \cdot & \varepsilon/2 \\ & & & & & \varepsilon/2 & \delta - N^2 \end{bmatrix} \begin{bmatrix} a_0 \\ a_1 \\ a_2 \\ a_3 \\ \cdot \\ \cdot \\ a_N \end{bmatrix} = O$$ (14.20)

and equations (14.18), (14.19) in the form

$$\begin{bmatrix} \delta - 1 & \varepsilon/2 & & & & \\ \varepsilon/2 & \delta - 4 & \varepsilon/2 & & & \\ & \varepsilon/2 & \delta - 9 & \varepsilon/2 & & \\ & & \cdot & \cdot & \cdot & \\ & & & \cdot & \cdot & \varepsilon/2 \\ & & & & \varepsilon/2 & \delta - N^2 \end{bmatrix} \begin{bmatrix} b_1 \\ b_2 \\ b_3 \\ \cdot \\ \cdot \\ b_N \end{bmatrix} = O.$$ (14.21)

Consider solving (14.20) to find the coefficients a_j, $j = 0$ to N. In general (14.20) will have only the trivial solution that all the a's are zero. The exception is when the determinant of the left-hand matrix in (14.20) is a zero determinant. Then the a's have a non-trivial solution. Suppose that the value of ε is specified and we choose the value of δ so that, for this combination of δ and ε, the determinant is to be zero. Since δ lies only on the diagonal of the coefficient matrix, it follows that δ must be one of the eigenvalues of the matrix A where, from (14.20),

$$
A = \begin{bmatrix}
0 & -\varepsilon/2 \\
-\varepsilon & 1 & -\varepsilon/2 \\
& -\varepsilon/2 & 4 & -\varepsilon/2 \\
& & \cdot & & \cdot \\
& & & \cdot & & \cdot & -\varepsilon/2 \\
& & & & -\varepsilon/2 & N^2
\end{bmatrix}. \quad (14.22)
$$

Similarly, for specified ε, the values of δ for which (14.21) has a non-trivial solution are the eigenvalues of B where

$$
B = \begin{bmatrix}
1 & -\varepsilon/2 \\
-\varepsilon/2 & 4 & -\varepsilon/2 \\
& -\varepsilon/2 & 9 & -\varepsilon/2 \\
& & \cdot & & \cdot \\
& & & \cdot & & \cdot & -\varepsilon/2 \\
& & & & -\varepsilon/2 & N^2
\end{bmatrix}. \quad (14.23)
$$

When δ is an eigenvalue of (14.22), there is a periodic solution of the Mathieu equation (14.3), of period $T = 2\pi/\Omega$, with only even (cosine) terms, all the sine terms being zero. When δ is an eigenvalue of (14.23), there is a different periodic solution of (14.3), period T, with only odd (sine) terms, all the cosine terms being zero. The values of the coefficients a_j, $j = 0$ to N, are the elements of the eigenvectors of A and those of b_j, $j = 1$ to N, are the elements of the eigenvectors of B. When $\varepsilon = 0$, A and B are both diagonal matrices and, except for the zero eigenvalue of A, they have the same eigenvalues $\delta = 1, 4, 9$, etc. Then the solution with cosine terms may co-exist alongside a solution with sine terms, the relative magnitude of each depending on the initial conditions.

The results of plotting against ε the values of the first four eigenvalues δ of A and B are shown in Fig. 14.1. The reader will see that there are four curves labelled c for cosine and four labelled s for sine. These are the loci of the eigenvalues of A and B respectively. For combinations of parameter values for which δ and ε lie on one of these curves, there is a periodic solution of the Mathieu equation (14.3) with period $T = 2\pi/\Omega$.

Another periodic solution is possible when $\sigma = -1$ in equation (14.7). Then we have

$$
y(t + T) = -y(t) \quad (14.24)
$$

and the response $y(t)$ must have period $2T$. In this case we can write $y(t)$ as the Fourier expansion

$$
y(t) = c_0 + \sum_{j=1}^{\infty}\left(c_j \cos j\,\frac{\Omega}{2}\,t + d_j \sin j\,\frac{\Omega}{2}\,t\right) \quad (14.25)
$$

instead of (14.11). On substituting this new solution into (14.3), using the

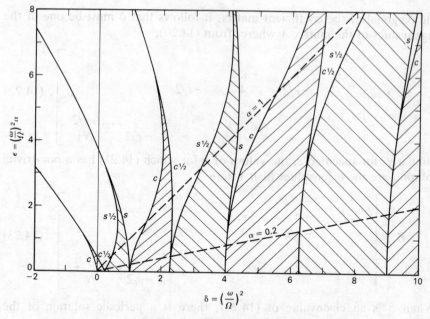

Fig. 14.1 Stable regions (cross-hatched) of the Mathieu equation

$$\frac{d^2y}{dt^2} + \omega^2(1 + \alpha \cos \Omega t)y = 0$$

trigonometrical identities

$$2 \cos \Omega t \cos j \frac{\Omega}{2} t = \cos (1 + j/2) \Omega t + \cos (1 - j/2) \Omega t \quad (14.26)$$

$$2 \cos \Omega t \sin j \frac{\Omega}{2} t = \sin (1 + j/2) \Omega t - \sin (1 - j/2) \Omega t, \quad (14.27)$$

and equating the coefficients of corresponding sine and cosine terms as before, we can find the relationships that must exist between the coefficients c_j, $j = 0$ to ∞, and d_j, $j = 1$ to ∞. As before, these will all be zero unless either δ is an eigenvalue of C or an eigenvalue of D, where

$$C = \begin{bmatrix} 0 & 0 & -\varepsilon/2 & & & & & \\ 0 & 1/4-\varepsilon/2 & 0 & -\varepsilon/2 & & & & \\ -\varepsilon & 0 & 1 & 0 & -\varepsilon/2 & & & \\ & -\varepsilon/2 & 0 & 9/4 & 0 & -\varepsilon/2 & & \\ & & -\varepsilon/2 & 0 & 4 & 0 & -\varepsilon/2 & \\ & & & \cdot & \cdot & \cdot & \cdot & \cdot \\ & & & & \cdot & \cdot & \cdot & \cdot & \cdot \\ & & & & & \cdot & \cdot & \cdot & -\varepsilon/2 \\ & & & & & & \cdot & \cdot & 0 \\ & & & & & & & -\varepsilon/2 & 0 & M^2/4 \end{bmatrix}. \quad (14.28)$$

and

$$D = \begin{bmatrix} 1/4+\varepsilon/2 & 0 & -\varepsilon/2 & & & \\ 0 & 1 & 0 & -\varepsilon/2 & & \\ -\varepsilon/2 & 0 & 9/4 & 0 & -\varepsilon/2 & \\ & -\varepsilon/2 & 0 & 4 & 0 & -\varepsilon/2 \\ & & \cdot & \cdot & \cdot & \cdot \\ & & & & \cdot & \cdot & \cdot & -\varepsilon/2 \\ & & & & & & \cdot & 0 \\ & & & & & -\varepsilon/2 & 0 & M^2/4 \end{bmatrix} \qquad .(14.29)$$

If δ is an eigenvector of C, a solution $y(t)$ exists with only the cosine terms in the expansion (14.25). If δ is an eigenvector of D, $y(t)$ has only sine terms in (14.25). When, for $\varepsilon = 0$, δ is an eigenvalue of both C and D, the solution may have sines or cosines or both together.

It can be seen that the sub-diagonal and super-diagonal elements of C and D are all zero. We shall show next that, as a result, alternate eigenvalues of C are the eigenvalues of A and the remainder are the eigenvalues of E where, if $N = M/2$,

$$E = \begin{bmatrix} 1/4 - \varepsilon/2 & -\varepsilon/2 & & & \\ -\varepsilon/2 & 9/4 & -\varepsilon/2 & & \\ & -\varepsilon/2 & 25/4 & -\varepsilon/2 & \\ & & \cdot & \cdot & \\ & & & \cdot & -\varepsilon/2 \\ & & & -\varepsilon/2 & (2N - 1)^2/4 \end{bmatrix}.$$

$$(14.30)$$

Also alternate eigenvalues of D are the eigenvalues of B and the remainder are the eigenvalues of F where

$$F = \begin{bmatrix} 1/4 + \varepsilon/2 & -\varepsilon/2 & & & \\ -\varepsilon/2 & 9/4 & -\varepsilon/2 & & \\ & -\varepsilon/2 & 25/4 & -\varepsilon/2 & \\ & & \cdot & \cdot & \\ & & & \cdot & -\varepsilon/2 \\ & & & -\varepsilon/2 & (2N - 1)^2/4 \end{bmatrix}.$$

$$(14.31)$$

The proof depends on the fact that the eigenvalues of a matrix are not altered as the result of a similarity transformation. Such a transformation occurs when any two rows are interchanged provided that the same two columns are also interchanged (Problem 14.2). By successively interchanging rows and columns, the odd-numbered rows of C and D can be swept to the top half of the matrix and the even-numbered rows can be swept to the bottom half. The result is that C is found to be similar to the matrix

$$\begin{bmatrix} A & O \\ O & E \end{bmatrix} \qquad (14.32)$$

and **D** is found to be similar to the matrix

$$\begin{bmatrix} F & O \\ O & B \end{bmatrix}. \qquad (14.33)$$

We know already from Chapter 7 that, when a matrix can be partitioned in this way, its eigenvalues are the eigenvalues of the non-zero sub-matrices (see Problem 7.6) and so the eigenvalues of **C** are the eigenvalues of **A** and **E** separately and the eigenvalues of **D** are those of **B** and **F** separately.

The first three eigenvalues δ of each of matrices **E** and **F** are plotted on Fig. 14.1. Those from **E** are for an expansion in terms of the cosine functions in (14.25) and are labelled $c_{\frac{1}{2}}$ because the fundamental harmonic is $\Omega/2$. Those from **F** are for an expansion in terms of the sine functions in (14.25) and these are labelled $s_{\frac{1}{2}}$.

The results in Fig. 14.1 have been calculated using matrices of order 10×10, which is sufficiently large to give results within the accuracy of the diagram for the range of δ and ε covered (Problem 14.3). In Fig. 14.2, the

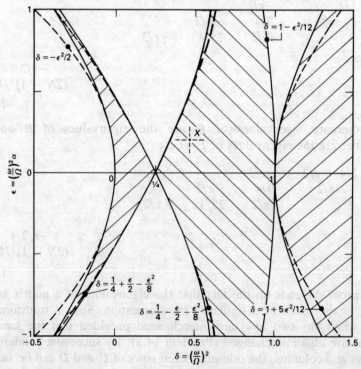

Fig. 14.2 Part of Fig. 14.1 drawn to a larger scale. The results of an approximate calculation of the stability boundaries, for small ε, are shown by the broken-line curves (see pages 434–437)

portion of Fig. 14.1 near the origin is drawn to a larger scale with, this time, negative values as well as positive values of ε being shown. It can be seen that the graph has mirror symmetry about its $\varepsilon = 0$ axis. The reason for this is that changing the sign of the sub-diagonal and super-diagonal elements in A, B, E and F does not alter the determinant of these tri-diagonal matrices (Problem 14.3). Although the first element of E is change from $1/4 - \varepsilon/2$ to $1/4 + \varepsilon/2$, this is the first element of F for positive ε, so that the eigenvalues of E at $-\varepsilon$ are the same as the corresponding eigenvalues of F at $+\varepsilon$ and vice versa. Therefore the $c_{\frac{1}{2}}^{1}$ curve above the axis in Fig. 14.2 is replaced by the $s_{\frac{1}{2}}^{1}$ curve below the $\varepsilon = 0$ axis, and the $s_{\frac{1}{2}}^{1}$ curve above the axis is replaced by the $c_{\frac{1}{2}}^{1}$ curve below the axis.

Stability regions

The curves in Figs 14.1 and 14.2 are the loci of values of δ and ε for which there is a periodic solution (14.7) with $\sigma = \pm 1$. Since from (14.4) negative δ corresponds to $(\omega/\Omega)^2$ being negative, which will be the case if ω^2 is negative, i.e. there is negative stiffness in (14.1), we expect the region to the left of the $\delta = 0$ axis to be unstable. Also, for large δ and therefore large positive stiffness in (14.1), we expect motion to be stable. This is in fact the case generally, and stable regions are shown cross-hatched on Figs 14.1 and 14.2. It is proved in the general theory of Mathieu functions (e.g. Haupt [41]) that stable and unstable regions alternate with $|\sigma| = 1$ in the shaded (stable) regions and $|\sigma| > 1$ (for one of the two values) in the unshaded (unstable) regions. At the boundaries between stable and unstable regions, the two values of σ are the same, with $\sigma_1 = \sigma_2 = \pm 1$. Because of the repeated value of σ it can be shown that, in addition to the periodic solution calculated above, there is also an unbounded solution which tends towards infinity according to the first power of t. Therefore the solutions which occur at the stability boundaries are unstable solutions (except when $\varepsilon = 0$). For $\varepsilon = 0$, it can be seen from Fig. 14.1 that the sine and cosine periodic solutions merge and here the values of σ are $\sigma_1 = +1$, $\sigma_2 = -1$, and σ does not have a repeated value. For $\varepsilon = 0$, the solutions of $y(t)$ are therefore stable (as we know they must be since the Mathieu equation has reduced to an equation with constant coefficients for free, undamped vibration).

Now consider the behaviour of an undamped system defined by (14.3) when the amplitude α of parametric excitation remains constant but the frequency Ω is increased gradually. Suppose that $\alpha = 0.2$, which means that the stiffness fluctuates by $\pm 20\%$ of its mean value. When $\omega/\Omega = \sqrt{10}$, $\delta = 10$ and $\varepsilon = 2$, which is at the right-hand side of Fig. 14.1. As Ω is increased, the operating point on Fig. 14.1 moves inwards towards the origin along the broken line labelled $\alpha = 0.2$. At $\omega/\Omega = 3, 2.5, 2$ and 1.5 approximately, there are narrow regions of instability so that the vibration may be expected to increase in amplitude at $\Omega = \omega/3$, $2\omega/5$, $\omega/2$ and

$2\omega/3$. At $\omega/\Omega = 1$ there is a significant band of instability and another at $\omega/\Omega = 0.5$, so that vibration builds up at $\Omega = \omega$ and at $\Omega = 2\omega$. From Fig. 14.1, we see that at $\omega/\Omega \simeq 1$ the response at the stability boundaries has period $T = 2\pi/\Omega$, (because the boundaries are labelled s and c, denoting the periodic solution (14.11)). Hence the response has a fundamental frequency which is close to the natural frequency ω of the system with $\alpha = 0$. At $\omega/\Omega \simeq 0.5$, the response at the stability boundaries has period $T = 4\pi/\Omega$ (because the boundaries are labelled $c_{\frac{1}{2}}$ and $s_{\frac{1}{2}}$, denoting the periodic solution (14.25)). The fundamental frequency of vibration is therefore $\Omega/2$ which, because $\omega/\Omega \simeq 0.5$, is still close to the natural frequency ω.

When the amplitude of parametric excitation is larger, with $\alpha = 1$, the broken line labelled $\alpha = 1$ on Fig. 14.1 is followed. As the frequency of excitation is increased, the operating point again moves inwards, passing alternately through regions of stability and instability until the origin is reached in a stable region as $\Omega \to \infty$.

By computing the eigenvectors of the matrices A and B we obtain the vector

$$\{a_0, a_1, a_2, a_3, \ldots\}^{\mathrm{T}}$$

from A and the vector

$$\{b_1, b_2, b_3, \ldots\}^{\mathrm{T}}$$

from B, where the a's and b's are the coefficients in the Fourier expansion (14.11). Similarly, by computing the eigenvectors of E and F we obtain the vector

$$\{c_1, c_3, c_5, \ldots\}^{\mathrm{T}}$$

from E and the vector

$$\{d_1, d_3, d_5, \ldots\}^{\mathrm{T}}$$

from F, where the c's and d's are alternate Fourier coefficients from the expansion (14.25). They are alternate coefficients because E and F have been obtained by partitioning the full matrices C and D according to (14.32) and (14.33). The remaining c's are the elements of the eigenvector of A, and the remaining d's are the elements of the eigenvector of B.

By computing the eigenvectors we can therefore find the coefficients of the Fourier expansions of the periodic solutions that occur at the stability boundaries. It turns out (see Problem 14.4) that, for small ε (and therefore for small α), one harmonic predominates at each stability boundary. For $\omega/\Omega = 1/2$ and 1 ($\delta = 1/4$ and 1), the fundamental frequency predominates, which is $\Omega/2 = \omega$ and $\Omega = \omega$, respectively. But for $\omega/\Omega = 3/2$ ($\delta = 9/4$), the third harmonic of the expansion (whose fundamental frequency is $\Omega/2$) is the dominant harmonic, and so the dominant frequency in the response is $3/2\,\Omega = \omega$. For $\omega/\Omega = 2$ ($\delta = 4$), the second harmonic of the expansion whose fundamental frequency is Ω is the dominant harmonic, and so the dominant frequency in this response is $2\Omega = \omega$. These results are summarized in Table 14.1. The conclusion for small α is that, if instability occurs, the predominant frequency of the oscillation that grows without bound is always the natural frequency of the system when $\alpha = 0$.

Table 14.1 Relationship between excitation frequency Ω, natural frequency ω, and the predominant frequency of oscillation at the boundaries of stability for equation (14.3) when α is small

Natural frequency / Excitation frequency ω/Ω	Excitation frequency / Natural frequency Ω/ω	Fundamental frequency at stability boundary	Frequency of dominant harmonic at stability boundary
3	1/3	$\Omega = \omega/3$	$3\Omega = \omega$
5/2	2/5	$\Omega/2 = \omega/5$	$5/2\,\Omega = \omega$
2	1/2	$\Omega = \omega/2$	$2\Omega = \omega$
3/2	2/3	$\Omega/2 = \omega/3$	$3/2\,\Omega = \omega$
1	1	$\Omega = \omega$	$\Omega = \omega$
1/2	2	$\Omega/2 = \omega$	$1/2\,\Omega = \omega$

We have seen that the boundaries of a stable region in the δ versus ε diagram are defined by the combinations of values of δ and ε for which the parameter σ in (14.7) is at the boundary between a real value (in the unstable region) and a complex value whose modulus is unity (in the stable region). For each combination of δ and ε within a stable region there is a pair of complex-conjugate values of σ which characterizes a particular periodic solution of (14.3). For example, in Problem 14.5, a periodic solution of fundamental frequency $\Omega/3$ is investigated by replacing (14.11) by

$$y(t) = a_0 + \sum_{j=1}^{\infty}\left(a_j \cos j\,\frac{\Omega}{3}\,t + b_j \sin j\,\frac{\Omega}{3}\,t\right), \qquad (14.34)$$

substituting this into the equation of motion (14.3), and equating the coefficients of like trigonometric terms. The procedure is the same as above for periodic solutions of fundamental frequency Ω and $\Omega/2$. One such periodic solution is found to occur at the point X in Fig. 14.2. This is at $\varepsilon = 0.2$, $\delta = 0.468$ when there is a solution with only sine terms. By obtaining the eigenvector of the corresponding matrix of coefficients, we find that the amplitudes of the sine terms are as listed in Table 14.2. These results were obtained from a matrix of order 15×15. The terms omitted from Table 14.2 are of order 10^{-8}.

Table 14.2 First 12 terms of the expansion (14.34) when $\varepsilon = 0.2$, $\delta = 0.468$. All the cosine terms are zero

$b_1 = 1.000$	$b_2 = 3.641$	$b_3 =$ zero
$b_4 = 0.076$	$b_5 = 0.158$	$b_6 =$ zero
$b_7 = 0.001$	$b_8 = 0.002$	$b_9 =$ zero
$b_{10} = 1.4 \times 10^{-5}$	$b_{11} = 1.8 \times 10^{-5}$	$b_{12} =$ zero

In Fig. 14.3 this periodic solution to the Mathieu equation (14.3) is shown graphically. In addition to the parametric term $\alpha \cos \Omega t$ and the response $y(t)$, Fig. 14.3 shows also $\ddot{y}(t)$ obtained by differentiating (14.34) and, for comparison, $\omega^2(1 + \alpha \cos \Omega t) \, y(t)$. For

$$\delta = \left(\frac{\omega}{\Omega}\right)^2 = 0.468 \tag{14.35}$$

we have

$$\Omega = 1.46\omega. \tag{14.36}$$

The dominant harmonic in the solution is the second harmonic whose frequency is $2\Omega/3$ which, from (14.36), is

$$(2/3)\Omega = 0.97\omega. \tag{14.37}$$

We see that the system is responding so that its dominant frequency component is close to the system's natural frequency. This is harmonic $2/3$ of the parametric excitation frequency and generally, in the stable regions of Figs 14.1 and 14.2, harmonics of any order p/q of the excitation frequency where p and q are integers prime to each other, can occur somewhere within each stable region. Notice, however, that the amplitude of such periodic solutions is arbitrary and depends on the initial conditions. Because (14.3) is a linear equation, if $y(t)$ is a solution then so will $\eta \, y(t)$ be a solution, where η is any arbitrary multiplier. The magnitude of harmonic b_1 in Table 14.2 is arbitrarily set to unity because the eigenvector program that has been used to compute these figures is a program that normalizes the first element of each eigenvector to unity.

In Problem 14.5, this analysis is examined in more detail and it is shown that there is also a cosine solution at the same values $\varepsilon = 0.2$, $\delta = 0.468$. The coefficients of the cosine solution are

$$a_0 = 0$$
$$a_j = b_j, \; j \text{ odd} \tag{14.38}$$
$$a_j = -b_j, \; j \text{ even}$$

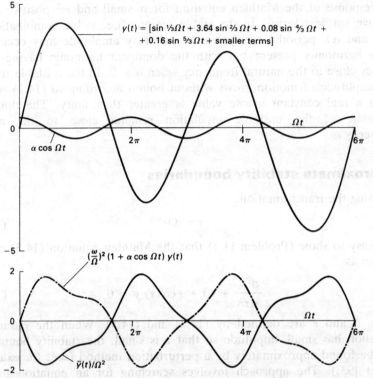

$$y(t) = [\sin \tfrac{1}{3}\Omega t + 3.64 \sin \tfrac{2}{3}\Omega t + 0.08 \sin \tfrac{4}{3}\Omega t + 0.16 \sin \tfrac{5}{3}\Omega t + \text{smaller terms}]$$

$\alpha \cos \Omega t$

$\left(\tfrac{\omega}{\Omega}\right)^2 (1 + \alpha \cos \Omega t) y(t)$

$\ddot{y}(t)/\Omega^2$

Fig. 14.3 Stable solution of $\ddot{y} + \omega^2(1 + \alpha \cos \Omega t)y = 0$ for $\alpha = 0.43$, $\Omega/\omega = 1.46$ (point X on Fig. 14.2)

where the b_j are those for the sine solution listed in Table 14.2. Both solutions can be combined into the complex exponential form

$$y(t) = b_1 e^{i(1/3)\Omega t} - b_2 e^{-i(2/3)\Omega t} + b_4 e^{-i(4/3)\Omega t} - b_5 e^{-i(5/3)\Omega t} + \dots$$

(14.39)

or, alternatively, into

$$y(t) = - b_1 e^{-i(1/3)\Omega t} + b_2 e^{i(2/3)\Omega t} - b_4 e^{-i(4/3)\Omega t} + b_5 e^{i(5/3)\Omega t} - \dots$$

(14.40)

Solution (14.39) satisfies (14.8) with $\sigma = \sigma_1$, and (14.40) satisfies (14.8) with $\sigma = \sigma_2$, where

$$\sigma_{1,2} = - 1/2 \pm \sqrt{3}/2.$$

(14.41)

Notice that the predominant harmonic in this periodic solution is also, from (14.37), close to the natural frequency of the undamped oscillator that is represented by (14.3) when $\alpha = 0$. This is a general characteristic of the response of the Mathieu equation for α small and ω^2 positive (i.e. a positive stiffness term). In the stable regions (i.e. stable combinations of ω/Ω and α), periodic oscillations of arbitrary amplitude may occur with many harmonics present but with the dominant harmonic having a frequency close to the natural frequency when $\alpha = 0$. In the unstable regions, the amplitude of motion grows without bound according to (14.7), with σ being a real constant whose value is greater than unity. The dominant harmonic of the unstable oscillation remains close to the natural frequency ω.

Approximate stability boundaries

By using the transformation

$$\tau = \Omega t \tag{14.42}$$

it is easy to show (Problem 14.1) that the Mathieu equation (14.3) can be written as

$$\frac{d^2 y}{d\tau^2} + (\delta + \varepsilon \cos \tau) y = 0 \tag{14.43}$$

where δ and ε are defined by (14.4) and (14.5). When the parametric excitation has small amplitude so that ε is small, the stability boundaries may be found approximately by a perturbation method (see, for example, Stoker [93]). The approach involves searching for an equation for the stability boundary in the form

$$\delta = f(\varepsilon) \tag{14.44}$$

by expressing $f(\varepsilon)$ as a power series in ε so that

$$\delta = \delta_0 + \varepsilon \delta_1 + \varepsilon^2 \delta_2 + \ldots \tag{14.45}$$

where δ_0, δ_1, δ_2, etc., are constants to be determined. The response $y(\tau)$, which has to be periodic on the stability boundary, is also expressed in a power series with the form

$$y(\tau) = y_0(\tau) + \varepsilon y_1(\tau) + \varepsilon^2 y_2(\tau) + \ldots \tag{14.46}$$

where $y_0(\tau)$, $y_1(\tau)$, $y_2(\tau)$, etc., are unknown functions of τ which also have to be determined.

On substituting (14.45) and (14.46) into (14.43) we find that (14.43) is satisfied to order ε^0 if

$$\ddot{y}_0 + \delta_0 y_0 = 0. \tag{14.47}$$

It is satisfied to order ε^1 if, in addition,

$$\ddot{y}_1 + \delta_0 y_1 = - y_0 \delta_1 - y_0 \cos \tau \tag{14.48}$$

and to order ε^2 if

$$\ddot{y}_2 + \delta_0 y_2 = - y_1 \delta_1 - y_0 \delta_2 - y_1 \cos \tau. \qquad (14.49)$$

We begin with the stability boundary which passes through $\delta = 0$ (see Fig. 14.2). This is the locus of δ and ε for which there are periodic solutions with period of

$$t = 2\pi/\Omega \qquad (14.50)$$

or, with (14.42),

$$\tau = \Omega t = 2\pi. \qquad (14.51)$$

From (14.45) we have $\delta_0 = 0$ and therefore, from (14.47), we find that y_0 is a constant (a term proportional to τ is excluded because we are looking for a periodic solution). In this case (14.48) gives

$$\ddot{y}_1 = - y_0 \delta_1 - y_0 \cos \tau \qquad (14.52)$$

and for y_1 to be periodic the constant term on the r.h.s. of (14.52) must be zero, which requires that $\delta_1 = 0$. Solving (14.52) with $\delta_1 = 0$ gives

$$y_1 = y_0 \cos \tau + c \qquad (14.53)$$

where c is a constant. On substituting into (14.49) we then get

$$\ddot{y}_2 = - y_0 \delta_2 - (y_0 \cos \tau + c) \cos \tau \qquad (14.54)$$

which, using the identity

$$\cos 2\tau = 2 \cos^2 \tau - 1 \qquad (14.55)$$

gives

$$\ddot{y}_2 = - y_0 \delta_2 - \tfrac{1}{2} y_0 - c \cos \tau - \tfrac{1}{2} y_0 \cos 2\tau. \qquad (14.56)$$

The constant term on the r.h.s. of (14.56) must be zero if y_2 is to be a periodic function, and so we find that

$$\delta_2 = - 1/2. \qquad (14.57)$$

Therefore from (14.45), the approximate equation for the stability boundary through $\delta = 0$ is, correct to order ε^2,

$$\delta = - \tfrac{1}{2} \varepsilon^2 \qquad (14.58)$$

which is plotted in Fig. 14.2 for comparison with the exact result. We see that it is very close to the exact result for $\varepsilon \ll 1$ but becomes increasingly inaccurate as the magnitude of ε increases towards unity.

For the stability boundaries through $\delta = 1/4$, the zero-order approximation is, from (14.47),

$$\ddot{y}_0 + 1/4 \, y_0 = 0 \qquad (14.59)$$

whose solution is any linear combination of

$$y_0 = \cos \tau/2 \qquad (14.60)$$

and

$$y_0 = \sin \tau/2. \tag{14.61}$$

We know that one periodic solution consists only of cosines and the other only of sines. Using the cosine solution (14.60) and substituting into (14.48)

$$\ddot{y}_1 + \tfrac{1}{4}y_1 = -(\cos \tau/2)\,\delta_1 - (\cos \tau/2)\cos \tau. \tag{14.62}$$

With the identity

$$2 \cos \tau/2 \cos \tau = \cos(\tau/2) + \cos 3\tau/2 \tag{14.63}$$

we then have

$$\ddot{y}_1 + \tfrac{1}{4}y_1 = -(\delta_1 + 1/2)\cos \tau/2 - \tfrac{1}{2}\cos 3\tau/2. \tag{14.64}$$

The first term on the r.h.s. of (14.64) provides an excitation frequency $1/2$ which is the same as the natural frequency of y_1, and there will be a non-periodic solution $\tau \sin \tau/2$ unless $\delta_1 = -1/2$. In that case, (14.64) becomes

$$\ddot{y}_1 + 1/4y_1 = -\tfrac{1}{2}\cos 3\tau/2 \tag{14.65}$$

whose solution is

$$y_1 = A \cos \tau/2 + B \sin \tau/2 + \tfrac{1}{4}\cos \tfrac{3}{2}\tau. \tag{14.66}$$

This has now to be substituted into the r.h.s. of (14.49) to obtain the equation for $y_2(\tau)$ which must also be a periodic function. Since the r.h.s. must contain no terms with frequency $1/2$ for the same reason as above, it follows that we must have $A = B = 0$ in (14.66), and then (14.49) gives

$$\ddot{y}_2 + 1/4y_2 = \tfrac{1}{4}\cos \tfrac{3}{2}\tau(\tfrac{1}{2} - \cos \tau) - (\cos \tau/2)\,\delta_2. \tag{14.67}$$

Using the identity

$$2\cos \tau \cos 3\tau/2 = \cos \tau/2 + \cos 5\tau/2 \tag{14.68}$$

this gives

$$\ddot{y}_2 + \tfrac{1}{4}y_2 = -(\tfrac{1}{8} + \delta_2)\cos \tau/2 + \tfrac{1}{8}\cos 3\tau/2 - \tfrac{1}{8}\cos 5\tau/2 \tag{14.69}$$

and so, for a periodic response $y_2(\tau)$, it is necessary that $\delta_2 = -1/8$. The equation for the cosine stability boundary through $\delta = 1/4$ is therefore, from (14.45),

$$\delta = \tfrac{1}{4} - \tfrac{1}{2}\,\varepsilon - \tfrac{1}{8}\,\varepsilon^2 \tag{14.70}$$

correct to order ε^2.

The equation for the other stability boundary which passes through $\delta = 1/4$ can be found in the same way. By beginning with (14.61) instead of (14.60), this leads in exactly the same way to the result that (Problem 14.6)

$$\delta = \tfrac{1}{4} + \tfrac{1}{2}\, \varepsilon - \tfrac{1}{8}\, \varepsilon^2. \tag{14.71}$$

For the stability boundaries through $\delta = 1$, we begin with

$$\ddot{y}_0 + y_0 = 0 \tag{14.72}$$

which gives the two solutions

$$y_0 = \cos \tau \tag{14.73}$$

and

$$y_0 = \sin \tau. \tag{14.74}$$

Using the first of these, equation (14.68), and following the same approach as before, gives

$$\delta = 1 + \tfrac{5}{12}\, \varepsilon^2 \tag{14.75}$$

and using the second, equation (14.69), leads to

$$\delta = 1 - \tfrac{1}{12}\, \varepsilon^2, \tag{14.76}$$

both results being correct to order ε^2.

These curves are all shown on Fig. 14.2 for comparison with the exact results. Although the approximate curves diverge from the exact boundaries when the magnitude of ε becomes comparable to unity, for many problems we are concerned only with $\varepsilon \ll 1$. Then the approximate curves provide a good approximation for the exact stability boundaries.

Effect of damping on stability

The stable regions in Figs 14.1 and 14.2 are altered in shape by the presence of damping when the classical Mathieu equation (14.3) is replaced by (14.1). At the stability boundaries we still expect periodic solutions to occur which satisfy (14.7). On substituting the solution of period $T = 2\pi/\Omega$ defined by the Fourier expansion (14.11) into (14.1) and equating the coefficients of the sine and cosine components of each harmonic, we obtain the same equations as before, (14.15) to (14.19), except that if the damping is described by parameter η, where

$$\eta = 2\zeta\omega/\Omega \tag{14.77}$$

then a term ηb_1 has to be added to (the l.h.s. of) (14.16), $\eta j b_j$ has to be added to (14.17), $- \eta a_1$ has to be added to (14.18) and $- \eta j a_j$ has to be added to (14.19).

The solution of the cosine coefficients a_j, $j = 0$ to ∞, is now coupled to the solution of the sine coefficients and the reader can check (Problem 14.7) that, for specified values of ε and η, δ is given by the eigenvalues of the $(2N + 1) \times (2N + 1)$ matrix G defined by

$$G = \begin{bmatrix} A & X \\ Y & B \end{bmatrix} \tag{14.78}$$

where A is defined by (14.22) and B by (14.23). X is an $(N + 1) \times N$ matrix which is null except for the elements in the diagonal to its lower right corner that are $- \eta, - 2\eta, \ldots, - N\eta$, in order from the top. Y is an $N \times (N + 1)$ matrix which is null except for the elements in the diagonal to the lower right corner that are $\eta, 2\eta, \ldots, N\eta$, in order from the top.

Similarly, for the periodic solution with period $T = 4\pi/\Omega$ defined by the odd-numbered terms in the Fourier expansion (14.25), the solution for the cosine coefficients is also coupled by damping to the solution for the sine coefficients and it can be shown (Problem 14.7) that, for specified ε and η, δ must be an eigenvalue of the $2N \times 2N$ matrix H defined by,

$$H = \begin{bmatrix} E & V \\ W & F \end{bmatrix} \tag{14.79}$$

where E is defined by (14.30) and F by (14.31). V is a diagonal matrix whose diagonal elements are $- \eta/2, - 3\eta/2, - 5\eta/2, \ldots, - (2N - 1)$ $\eta/2$, in order from the top, and W is the same except that all the elements are positive instead of negative.

In Fig. 14.4, the stability boundaries for the damped case when $\eta = 0.1$ are plotted for comparison with the undamped case of Fig. 14.2. For positive δ, which means positive stiffness so that the natural frequency ω is real, the unstable regions are diminished in size by the presence of damping. Therefore, for positive stiffness, damping always has a stabilizing effect. If the amplitude of the parametric excitation, represented by α in equation (14.1), is small, then ε may be small enough that the solution is always stable whatever the value of (positive) δ. The left-hand stability boundary in Fig. 14.4, which is in the region of the graph where δ is negative, is moved a very small amount from its former position, decreasing the area of the stable region slightly, but the change is too small to show on Fig. 14.4.

Because ω/Ω changes as δ changes, constant η defined by (14.77) does not imply constant damping ratio ζ. To the right-hand side of Fig. 14.4, ω/Ω increases so that ζ decreases. As the origin is approached, ω/Ω decreases and so ζ increases. At the centre of the main instability region at $\delta = 1/4$ in Fig. 14.4, $\omega/\Omega = 1/2$. From (14.77), the damping ratio is then $\zeta = 0.1$ when $\eta = 0.1$.

For greater damping, the stable regions are extended, with the V-shaped regions of instability being pushed farther away from the $\varepsilon = 0$ axis, but the basic shape of Fig. 14.4 being retained. The unstable regions to the right of the diagram move away from the $\varepsilon = 0$ axis and diminish in size progressively faster as ω/Ω increases, so that instabilities for low frequencies of parametric excitation (Ω small) do not occur in the damped case.

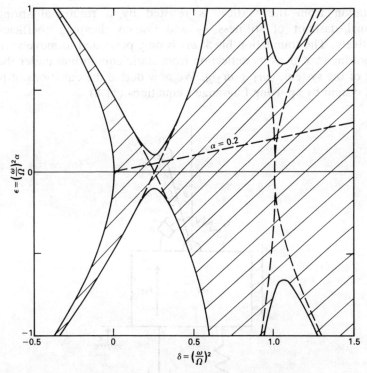

Fig. 14.4 Stable region (cross-hatched) of the damped Mathieu equation

$$\frac{d^2y}{dt^2} + 2\zeta\omega \frac{dy}{dt} + \omega^2(1 + \alpha \cos \Omega t)y = 0$$

for the case when

$$\eta = 2\zeta\left(\frac{\omega}{\Omega}\right) = 0.1$$

Autoparametric systems

In this section we shall consider a system with two modes of vibration, in which, because of nonlinear coupling between the modes, vibration in one externally-excited mode acts as parametric excitation for vibration in the other mode. Such a system is said to be *autoparametric*. Autoparametric systems have the important property that the frequency of the principal harmonic of vibration in the autoparametrically-excited mode will often be different from the frequency of vibration in the externally-excited mode.

The system we shall study is shown in Fig. 14.5. It consists of an initially vertical pendulum supported on a foundation block which can move vertically in response to the externally-applied vertical force $F(t)$. The foundation block has mass m_1 and is itself supported on a fixed base by a linear spring of stiffness k_1 and a linear viscous damper of damping coefficient c_1. The pendulum has length l and concentrated mass m_2, and its rotation from the vertical is resisted by a rotational spring and rotational dashpot of stiffness k_2 and viscous damping coefficient c_2, respectively. The foundation block m_1 is only permitted to move vertically, and coordinate x gives its deflection from static equilibrium under the total weight of the system, $(m_1 + m_2)g$. We now derive the equations of motion of this system by applying Lagrange's equations (11.8).

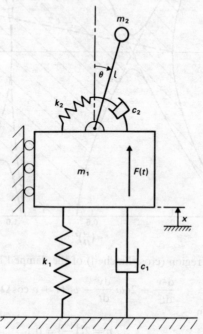

Fig. 14.5 Two-degree-of-freedom autoparametric system

The potential energy, V, of the system is the strain energy of the two springs plus the gravitational potential energy of the two masses. If x_0 is the initial static deflection (downwards) of spring k_1, defined so that

$$(m_1 + m_2) g = k_1 x_0 \tag{14.80}$$

the net deflection after upwards movement x is $x_0 - x$, so that the potential energy of k_1 is

$$\tfrac{1}{2}k_1(x_0 - x)^2.$$

Hence

$$V = \tfrac{1}{2}k_1(x_0 - x)^2 + \tfrac{1}{2}k_2\theta^2 + m_1gx + m_2g(x + l\cos\theta). \tag{14.81}$$

The velocity of mass m_2 is the vector combination of $\dot{x}$ upwards, and $l\dot{\theta}$ perpendicular to the pendulum, so that

$$v^2 = (\dot{x} - l\dot{\theta}\sin\theta)^2 + (l\dot{\theta}\cos\theta)^2$$
$$= \dot{x}^2 - 2\dot{x}l\dot{\theta}\sin\theta + l^2\dot{\theta}^2. \tag{14.82}$$

Therefore the total kinetic energy of the system is

$$T = \tfrac{1}{2}m_1\dot{x}^2 + \tfrac{1}{2}m_2(\dot{x}^2 - 2\dot{x}l\dot{\theta}\sin\theta + l^2\dot{\theta}^2). \tag{14.83}$$

The generalized force Q_1 is defined so that $Q_1\delta x$ is the work done on the system by all the non-conservative forces when x changes by δx but θ remains constant. Hence

$$Q_1\delta x = F(t)\delta x - c_1\dot{x}\delta x \tag{14.84}$$

and so

$$Q_1 = F(t) - c_1\dot{x}. \tag{14.85}$$

Similarly,

$$Q_2 = -c_2\dot{\theta}. \tag{14.86}$$

From Chapter 11, Lagrange's equations (11.8) are

$$\frac{d}{dt}\left(\frac{\partial T}{\partial \dot{x}}\right) - \frac{\partial T}{\partial x} + \frac{\partial V}{\partial x} = Q_1 \tag{14.87}$$

and

$$\frac{\partial}{\partial t}\left(\frac{\partial T}{\partial \dot{\theta}}\right) - \frac{\partial T}{\partial \theta} + \frac{\partial V}{\partial \theta} = Q_2 \tag{14.88}$$

and, on substituting for V and T from (14.81) and (14.83) and using (14.85) and (14.86), we find that the two coupled equations of motion are

$$(m_1 + m_2)\,\ddot{x} + c_1\dot{x} + k_1x = F(t) + m_2l(\ddot{\theta}\sin\theta + \dot{\theta}^2\cos\theta) \tag{14.89}$$

and

$$m_2l^2\ddot{\theta} + c_2\dot{\theta} + k_2\theta - m_2gl\sin\theta - m_2l\ddot{x}\sin\theta = 0. \tag{14.90}$$

When x and θ are very small, so that terms of order 2 and higher in x and θ and their derivatives can be neglected, (14.89) and (14.90) give

$$(m_1 + m_2)\,\ddot{x} + c_1\dot{x} + k_1x = F(t) \tag{14.91}$$

and

$$m_2l^2\ddot{\theta} + c_2\dot{\theta} + (k_2 - m_2\,gl)\,\theta = 0. \tag{14.92}$$

Then $x(t)$ and $\theta(t)$ describe two independent linear modes. There is no coupling between these modes so that small-amplitude motion in each mode can go on independently of motion in the other mode. For convenience we shall call ω_1 and ω_2 the undamped natural frequencies and ζ_1 and ζ_2 the damping ratios of these two modes. On dividing (14.91) by $(m_1 + m_2)$ and (14.92) by m_2l^2 we can then put the equations in the standard form

$$\ddot{x} + 2\zeta_1\omega_1\dot{x} + \omega_1^2 x = \frac{F(t)}{m_1 + m_2} \tag{14.93}$$

$$\ddot{\theta} + 2\zeta_2\omega_2\dot{\theta} + \omega_2^2\theta = 0 \tag{14.94}$$

where

$$\omega_1^2 = k_1/(m_1 + m_2); \quad \omega_2^2 = (k_2 - m_2gl)/m_2l^2$$
$$2\zeta_1\omega_1 = c_1/(m_1 + m_2); \quad 2\zeta_2\omega_2 = c_2/m_2l^2. \tag{14.95}$$

Now consider the result of retaining second-order terms in the small quantities x and θ and their derivatives, but neglecting third- and higher-order terms. Then (14.89) and (14.90) give, using (14.95),

$$\ddot{x} + 2\zeta_1\omega_1\dot{x} + \omega_1^2 x = \frac{F(t)}{m_1 + m_2} + \frac{m_2l}{m_1 + m_2}\frac{d}{dt}(\theta\dot{\theta}) \tag{14.96}$$

and

$$\ddot{\theta} + 2\zeta_2\omega_2\dot{\theta} + \omega_2^2\theta = \frac{\ddot{x}\theta}{l}. \tag{14.97}$$

To this, higher, accuracy the two modes are coupled by nonlinear terms. Vertical motion is now coupled to rotational motion of the pendulum and vice versa. We shall now explore the effect of this inter-modal coupling.

Consider the case when $m_1 \gg m_2$, so that the coupling term on the r.h.s. of (14.96) becomes negligible. Also, let $F(t)$ be harmonic excitation at frequency Ω and of such magnitude that the steady response of the foundation block is given by

$$x(t) = X\cos\Omega t \tag{14.98}$$

where X is the constant (real) amplitude of $x(t)$. In this case

$$\ddot{x}(t) = -X\Omega^2\cos\Omega t \tag{14.99}$$

and (14.97) becomes

$$\ddot{\theta} + 2\zeta_2\omega_2\dot{\theta} + \left(\omega_2^2 + \frac{X}{l}\Omega^2\cos\Omega t\right)\theta = 0 \tag{14.100}$$

or, on putting

$$\alpha = \frac{X}{l}\left(\frac{\Omega}{\omega_2}\right)^2, \tag{14.101}$$

$$\ddot{\theta} + 2\zeta_2\omega_2\dot{\theta} + \omega_2^2(1 + \alpha\cos\Omega t)\,\theta = 0 \tag{14.102}$$

which is the standard damped Mathieu equation (14.1).

Figure 14.4 shows the stable regions for this equation for the case when $\eta = 2\zeta_2\omega_2/\Omega = 0.1$. For other values of damping the picture is similar except that the stability boundaries are nearer to the $\varepsilon = 0$ axis for smaller damping and farther away for larger damping. For ω_2^2 positive and α small enough, motion is always stable whatever the frequency of excitation. If the pendulum is pulled to one side and released, it recovers its vertical position after executing a damped oscillation at approximately its natural frequency ω_2. When the amplitude of parametric excitation, represented by the magnitude of α in (14.102), increases, the slope of the α = constant line in Fig. 14.4 increases until it just touches the bottom of the V-shaped region of instability at $(\omega_2/\Omega)^2 \simeq 1/4$. If the excitation frequency Ω is approximately twice the natural frequency ω_2, so that $(\omega_2/\Omega)^2 \simeq 1/4$, then the pendulum may execute a constant-amplitude oscillation which, according to the theory of the Mathieu equation given previously, is at approximately its natural frequency ω_2 (which is half the excitation frequency, Ω). For other excitation frequencies at this critical value of α, the pendulum's motion, if displaced, will still be a damped oscillatory recovery of its initial vertical position.

For further increase in the amplitude of parametric excitation, the α = constant line in Fig. 14.4 crosses an unstable region at $(\omega_2/\Omega)^2 \simeq 1/4$. Then there will be a range of excitation frequencies near $\Omega \simeq 2\omega_2$ for which the pendulum's amplitude of oscillation grows without bound. For a still steeper α = constant line on Fig. 14.4, two unstable regions will be crossed and then there is a second unstable range of frequencies near $\Omega \simeq \omega_2$. For both unstable regions we know from the theory of the Mathieu equation that the unstable response will be an oscillation of growing amplitude whose principal harmonic has a frequency close to the pendulum's natural frequency ω_2. For other frequencies of excitation outside the unstable ranges, the pendulum's response to an initial displacement will still be a decaying oscillation with a major frequency component at approximately its natural frequency.

We can summarise this behaviour, which is for the case when $m_1 \gg m_2$, as follows. When the foundation mode is excited by steady-state harmonic forcing of constant amplitude and frequency Ω it responds at this frequency. If the amplitude of the response $x(t) = X \sin \Omega t$ is sufficient, the pendulum mode will be excited autoparametrically at approximately its natural frequency ω_2 when $\Omega \simeq 2\omega_2$ and again (for greater amplitude X) when $\Omega \simeq \omega_2$. If X is large enough and the pendulum's damping small enough, autoparametric excitation can also occur when the α = constant line crosses other unstable regions in the larger Mathieu stability chart of Fig. 14.1.

Internal resonance

The above results hold on the assumption that motion of the pendulum does not perturb vibration of its relatively massive foundation (see Fig. 14.5). Next we shall investigate what effect the term

$$\frac{\mathrm{d}}{\mathrm{d}t}(\theta \, \dot{\theta})$$

on the r.h.s. of equation (14.96) may have on the response of the foundation block.

Suppose that the foundation block is excited at a frequency close to its natural frequency ω_1 and that the pendulum is also vibrating. We know from the Mathieu theory explained earlier in this chapter that, for small α defined by (14.101), if $\theta(t)$ vibrates it will do so with a fundamental frequency close to ω_2. Let such a steady-state response be

$$\theta(t) = \Theta \sin \omega_2 t. \tag{14.103}$$

Then

$$\theta\dot\theta = \Theta^2 \omega_2 \sin \omega_2 t \cos \omega_2 t = \tfrac{1}{2}\Theta^2 \omega_2 \sin 2\omega_2 t \tag{14.104}$$

and

$$\frac{d}{dt}(\theta\,\dot\theta) = \Theta^2 \omega_2^2 \cos 2\omega_2 t. \tag{14.105}$$

As a result the r.h.s. of (14.96) has a harmonic term of frequency $2\omega_2$. This will cause $x(t)$ to respond significantly if the foundation mode is excited at a frequency near to its resonant frequency ω_1, that is if

$$2\omega_2 \simeq \omega_1. \tag{14.106}$$

In other words, the foundation mode will be most sensitive to inputs from the pendulum mode when the foundation's natural frequency is about twice the pendulum's natural frequency.

But we have seen already from Fig. 14.4 that the pendulum's maximum tendency towards instability occurs when $\omega_2/\Omega \simeq 1/2$, where ω_2 is the pendulum's natural frequency and Ω is the frequency of its parametric excitation. Since in this example autoparametric excitation comes from $x(t)$ (see equation (14.97)), Ω is the same as the frequency of oscillation of the foundation block, which we have assumed is close to its natural frequency, so that

$$\Omega \simeq \omega_1. \tag{14.107}$$

Hence the pendulum's mode is most sensitive to motion of the foundation block when

$$\omega_2 \simeq \Omega/2 \simeq \omega_1/2, \tag{14.108}$$

which is the same as (14.106). The condition for the pendulum to be most sensitive to its foundation is therefore the same as for the foundation to be most sensitive to the pendulum. This is called an *internal resonance* condition and internal resonance is said to occur when, for the system in Fig. 14.5, the two natural frequencies of the modes are related so that the pendulum's natural frequency ω_2 is half the natural frequency of the foundation ω_1.

At the second unstable region in Fig. 14.4, $\Omega \simeq \omega_2$. The foundation mode is still sensitive to the pendulum mode when $\omega_1 \simeq 2\omega_2$, but the pendulum mode is now most sensitive to the foundation mode when $\omega_1 \simeq \omega_2$. Because these two conditions are different, there is not a second internal resonance to correspond to the second unstable region in Fig. 14.4.

When there is an internal resonance condition, small-amplitude excitation at the natural frequency of the externally-excited mode (in this example the foundation mode) causes autoparametric excitation of a nonlinearly coupled mode (in this example the pendulum mode) at the same or at a different frequency, and vibration of the second mode reacts back to reinforce the external excitation. Provided that there is sufficient damping, stable periodic motion of the coupled system may occur. But, under conditions of internal resonance, an increased amplitude of external excitation may lead to the unstable growth of oscillations which build up in amplitude until eventually the system destroys itself or additional non-linear terms come into play to limit the final amplitude.

Vibration problems with non-linear coupling between modes are important in several fields, for example helicopter blade dynamics and aircraft flutter, and there is considerable literature on the subject (see, for example, references [3], [40], [47] and [48]).

Nonlinear jump phenomena

Consider the steady-state periodic response of the single-degree-of-freedom system for which

$$\ddot{y}(t) + 2\zeta\omega_0\dot{y}(t) + \omega_0^2 y(t) + \gamma y^3(t) = X \cos \Omega t. \tag{14.109}$$

This equation is called *Duffing's equation* after the author of the first significant publication on its solution [21]. When $\gamma = 0$, there is no nonlinearity and the usual harmonic solution applies for steady-state forced vibration at frequency Ω. When $\gamma > 0$, which is the case for a hardening spring, or $\gamma < 0$ for a softening spring, a periodic solution with period $T = 2\pi/\Omega$ is still possible, but this is no longer a pure harmonic and higher frequency components are included. The usual case we are interested in is the response of a lightly-damped oscillator near resonance, and we shall now seek an approximate solution for this case. We assume that the nonlinearity is small and that there is small damping and small-amplitude excitation. Under these conditions, equation (14.109) can be modified to

$$\ddot{y}(t) + \varepsilon 2\zeta\omega_0\dot{y}(t) + \omega_0^2 y(t) + \varepsilon\gamma y^3(t) = \varepsilon X \cos(\Omega t + \delta) \tag{14.110}$$

where ε is a small, positive non-dimensional parameter for which $\varepsilon \ll 1$. The constant phase angle δ has been added to the excitation so that the solution can be written as

$$y(t) = A \cos \Omega t + \varepsilon y_1(t) + \varepsilon^2 y_2(t) + \dots \tag{14.111}$$

where we shall confirm shortly that $A \cos \Omega t$ is the correct zero-order term. Also, since we are considering the forced response for excitation frequencies close to the natural frequency of the linear system, it is possible to put

$$\Omega = \omega_0 + \varepsilon\omega_1 + \varepsilon^2\omega_2 + \ldots \tag{14.112}$$

The next step is to substitute these expansions (14.111) and (14.112) into (14.110) and to equate the terms in like powers of ε in the same way that we did to obtain an approximate solution for Mathieu's equation. However, before we do, it is hepful to change the independent variable in (14.110) from Ωt to θ where

$$\theta = \Omega t. \tag{14.113}$$

With this substitution, (14.110) becomes

$$\Omega^2\ddot{y}(\theta) + \varepsilon 2\zeta\Omega\omega_0\dot{y}(\theta) + \omega_0^2 y(\theta) + \varepsilon\gamma y^3(\theta) = \varepsilon X \cos(\theta + \delta) \tag{14.114}$$

where the differentiation dot now means $d/d\theta$, and (14.111) can be changed to

$$y(\theta) = A \cos \theta + \varepsilon y_1(\theta) + \varepsilon^2 y_2(\theta) + \ldots \tag{14.115}$$

Now, substituting in (14.114) for $y(\theta)$ from (14.115) and for Ω from (14.112) and collecting terms, the zero-order terms all cancel, and the terms to order ε^1 are

$$\omega_0^2\ddot{y}_1 - 2\omega_0\omega_1 A \cos \theta - 2\zeta\omega_0^2 A \sin \theta + \omega_0^2 y_1 + \gamma A^3 \cos^3 \theta$$
$$= X \cos(\theta + \delta). \tag{14.116}$$

Using the identities

$$\cos^3 \theta = \tfrac{3}{4} \cos \theta + \tfrac{1}{4} \cos 3\theta \tag{14.117}$$

and

$$\cos(\theta + \delta) = \cos \theta \cos \delta - \sin \theta \sin \delta \tag{14.118}$$

we then find, on collecting terms, that

$$\ddot{y}_1 + y_1 = \left(2\frac{\omega_1}{\omega_0} A - \frac{3}{4}\frac{\gamma}{\omega_0^2} A^3 + \frac{X}{\omega_0^2} \cos \delta\right)\cos \theta +$$
$$+ \left(2\zeta A - \frac{X}{\omega_0^2} \sin \delta\right)\sin \theta - \frac{1}{4}\frac{\gamma}{\omega_0^2} A^3 \cos 3\theta. \tag{14.119}$$

Following the same argument as for the approximate Mathieu solution, the terms in $\cos \theta$ and $\sin \theta$ on the r.h.s. of (14.119) must be zero because otherwise the solution $y_1(\theta)$ cannot be periodic and would have a term which increases without bound. Therefore, from (14.119), we find that

$$2\frac{\omega_1}{\omega_0} A - \frac{3}{4}\frac{\gamma}{\omega_0^2} A^3 = -\frac{X}{\omega_0^2} \cos \delta \tag{14.120}$$

and

$$2\zeta A = \frac{X}{\omega_0^2} \sin \delta. \tag{14.121}$$

On squaring and adding these equations to eliminate the phase angle δ, we then obtain

$$(2\zeta A)^2 + \left(2\frac{\omega_1}{\omega_0} A - \frac{3}{4}\frac{\gamma}{\omega_0^2} A^3\right)^2 = \left(\frac{X}{\omega_0^2}\right)^2 \tag{14.122}$$

which is a relation between the amplitude A of the zero-order response

$$y_0(t) = A \cos \theta = A \cos \Omega t, \tag{14.123}$$

the first-order difference $\varepsilon\omega_1$ between the frequency of excitation Ω and the linear natural frequency ω_0, the linear damping ratio $\varepsilon\zeta$ and the amplitude of excitation εX.

For given damping ratio and excitation amplitude, equation (14.122) can be used to find how the amplitude of the response A (to order ε^0) depends on the frequency of excitation Ω (to order ε^1). Because we are concerned with the response at resonance, a first-order change of frequency is associated with a zero-order change of amplitude. On solving for ω_1, we find that

$$\frac{\varepsilon\omega_1}{\omega_0} = \frac{3}{8}\frac{\varepsilon\gamma A^2}{\omega_0^2} \pm \sqrt{\left(\frac{\varepsilon X}{2A\omega_0^2}\right)^2 - (\varepsilon\zeta)^2}. \tag{14.124}$$

Using (14.112) to give Ω/ω_0 to order ε^1 according to

$$\frac{\Omega}{\omega_0} = 1 + \frac{\varepsilon\omega_1}{\omega_0} \tag{14.125}$$

we can then plot Ω/ω_0 against A. It is usual to plot amplitude upwards against frequency on a horizontal base and, to make the results non-dimensional, we plot $A\omega_0^2/\varepsilon X$ against Ω/ω_0 for a fixed value of the non-dimensional nonlinearity $\varepsilon\gamma(\varepsilon X)^2/\omega_0^6$ and for a fixed value of the damping ratio $\varepsilon\zeta$. In Fig. 14.6(a), which is for the case when the magnitude of the non-dimensional nonlinearity is $\varepsilon\gamma(\varepsilon X)^2/\omega_0^6 = 0.008$, three different curves are shown for the following three values of the damping ratio, $\varepsilon\zeta = 0.05$, 0.1 and 0.2. These are similar to the corresponding curves in the linear case (see Fig. 1.2(a)), except that the resonant peaks are now bent over to the right. The 'backbone' of the diagram, shown by the broken line in Fig. 14.6(a), defines the relationship between the natural frequency and the amplitude for free, undamped vibrations. In the example shown in Fig. 14.6, the stiffness increases with deflection because $\varepsilon\gamma$ is positive, and therefore the natural frequency increases as the amplitude increases. This is characteristic of any system with a hardening spring. For a softening spring, the natural frequency decreases with increasing amplitude and the resonant peaks bend over to the left.

The equation for the backbone can be derived from (14.124) by taking

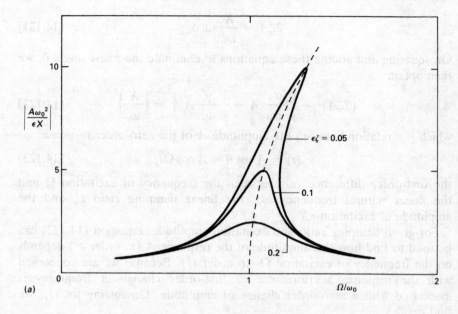

(a)

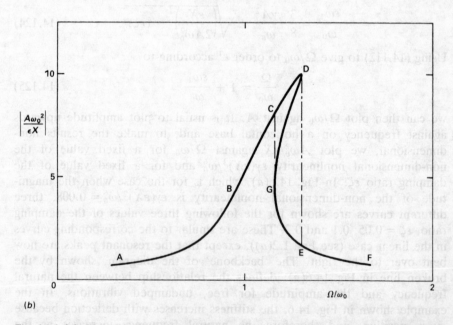

(b)

Fig. 14.6 (*a*) Non-dimensional amplitude of the periodic response of Duffing's oscillator (14.110) plotted against frequency ratio when the magnitude of the nonlinear stiffness term is $\varepsilon\gamma(\varepsilon X)^2/\omega_0^6 = 0.008$. (*b*) Nonlinear jumps from D to E and from G to C when the damping ratio is $\varepsilon\zeta = 0.05$, and the magnitude of the nonlinearity is the same as in Fig. 14.6(*a*)

the case of no damping $\varepsilon\zeta = 0$ and no excitation $\varepsilon X = 0$, when

$$\frac{\varepsilon\omega_1}{\omega_0} = \frac{3}{8}\frac{\varepsilon\gamma A^2}{\omega_0^2} \qquad (14.126)$$

or, in terms of the non-dimensional groupings,

$$\frac{\varepsilon\omega_1}{\omega_0} = \frac{3}{8}\left(\frac{\varepsilon\gamma(\varepsilon X)^2}{\omega_0^6}\right)\left(\frac{A\omega_0^2}{\varepsilon X}\right)^2 = 0.003\left(\frac{A\omega_0^2}{\varepsilon X}\right)^2 \qquad (14.127)$$

when $\varepsilon\gamma(\varepsilon X)^2/\omega_0^6 = 0.008$. This is the equation of the backbone curve shown in Fig. 14.6(a).

The bending of the resonance curves, to the right for a hardening spring and to the left for a softening spring, gives an important new property for the periodic response of a lightly-damped system with nonlinear stiffness. Suppose that, for constant-amplitude harmonic excitation, the frequency of excitation Ω is slowly increased from zero. With reference to Fig. 14.6(b), the steady amplitude of vibration increases as resonance is approached, with the operating point moving from A to B to C and eventually to D when peak amplitude is reached. Once the position of vertical tangency of the response curve has been reached, further increase in frequency causes the operating point to jump from D to E. There is then a sudden decrease in the amplitude of oscillation and, when steady conditions again prevail, there will have been a large reduction in the amplitude of the system's response. On further increase in frequency the operating point moves to point F, with the amplitude decreasing progressively as the excitation frequency moves further away from resonance.

On slowly reducing the excitation frequency, the operating point on Fig. 14.6(b) moves back from F to E and then to G. At the point of vertical tangency of this part of the response curve, further reduction in frequency causes a sudden upward jump in the amplitude of oscillation to point C. The operating point then retraces its former path, but in the reverse direction, moving back through B and A as the amplitude progressively decreases.

These sudden changes in the amplitude of steady forced vibration are characteristic of systems with nonlinear springs. For a hardening spring, the response is like that shown in Fig. 14.6(b), and the nonlinear jump downwards in amplitude which occurs from D to E on increasing frequency is greater than the nonlinear jump upwards which occurs from G to C on decreasing frequency. For a softening spring, when the resonance peaks bend over to the left, the reverse is the case. The nonlinear jump upwards in amplitude as frequency increases is smaller than the jump downwards which occurs on decreasing the frequency.

It will be seen that sections D–G of the response curve in Fig. 14.6(b) cannot be reached by slowly changing the frequency of oscillation from a frequency above or below resonance. We shall show in the next section that, although there is a periodic solution for any point on the response curve in Fig. 14.6(*b*), this solution describes an unstable solution for combinations of amplitude and frequency defined by the curve from D to G.

The results in Figs 14.6(*a*) and (*b*) are for the amplitude of the zero-order term in the expansion (14.111). When the first-order term $y_1(t)$ is calculated from (14.119), it can be shown that the change to the zero-order solution is negligible if the nonlinearity and damping have the magnitudes for which Figs 14.6 have been drawn (see Problem 14.8).

Stability of forced vibration with nonlinear stiffness

Let $y(t) = y(t + 2\pi/\Omega)$ be a periodic solution of Duffing's equation (14.110) and consider a small deviation from this solution $\Delta y(t)$. On replacing $y(t)$ in (14.110) by $y(t) + \Delta y(t)$ and neglecting powers of $\Delta y(t)$ higher than the first, we find that

$$\Delta \ddot{y} + \varepsilon 2 \zeta \omega_0 \Delta \dot{y} + \omega_0^2 \, \Delta y + \varepsilon \gamma 3 y^2 \Delta y = 0 \tag{14.128}$$

because all the zero-order terms cancel. From the previous section, the solution of Duffing's equation is

$$y(t) = A \cos \Omega t \tag{14.129}$$

to a first approximation, and so

$$y^2(t) = A^2 \cos^2 \Omega t = \frac{A^2}{2} (1 + \cos 2\Omega t). \tag{14.130}$$

On substituting this result into (14.128) we obtain

$$\Delta \ddot{y} + \varepsilon 2 \zeta \omega_0 \Delta \dot{y} + (\omega_0^2 + \tfrac{3}{2}\varepsilon\gamma A^2 + \tfrac{3}{2}\varepsilon\gamma A^2 \cos 2\Omega t)\Delta y = 0 \tag{14.131}$$

which is a Mathieu equation of the standard form (14.1). The forcing frequency Ω in (14.1) is replaced by 2Ω in (14.131) and, by comparing the two equations,

$$\omega^2 = \omega_0^2 + \tfrac{3}{2}\varepsilon\gamma A^2 \tag{14.132}$$

and

$$\omega^2 \alpha = \tfrac{3}{2}\varepsilon\gamma A^2 \tag{14.133}$$

so that

$$\alpha = \tfrac{3}{2}\varepsilon\gamma A^2/\omega_0^2 + 0(\varepsilon^2). \tag{14.134}$$

We are interested in whether the solution of (14.131) is stable or unstable. This depends where the combination of values of α and $(\omega/2\Omega)^2$ plots on the Mathieu stability chart, Fig. 14.4. If α is small enough, the slope of the $\alpha = $ constant line through the origin will be small enough that no unstable regions of Fig. 14.4 are intersected and then motion is always stable. But if α is larger, then, if there is only small damping, the $\alpha = $ constant line crosses the lowest region of instability close to $(\omega/2\Omega)^2 = \frac{1}{4}$. Under these circumstances, for a range of values of the excitation frequency 2Ω, (14.131) has an unstable response and the periodic solution of Duffing's equation is not stable, at least to the accuracy of the approximate solution.

For negligible damping, we can find the limits of this unstable range as follows. The equations of the two stability boundaries of Matheiu's equation which pass through $(\omega/\Omega)^2 = \frac{1}{4}$ on Fig. 14.4 are given by (14.70) and (14.71) and, neglecting terms in ε^2, these are

$$\delta = \tfrac{1}{4} \pm \varepsilon/2. \tag{14.135}$$

The relationship between δ and ε on an $\alpha = $ constant line is

$$\delta = \varepsilon/\alpha. \tag{14.136}$$

Eliminating ε between (14.135) and (14.136), we find that the values of δ when the lines intersect are

$$\delta = \frac{1}{4 \pm 2\alpha} \tag{14.137}$$

as shown in Fig. 14.7. Hence we see that there will be instability when the frequency of excitation, which is 2Ω in equation (14.131), is such that

$$\frac{1}{4 + 2\alpha} \leqslant \delta \leqslant \frac{1}{4 - 2\alpha} \tag{14.138}$$

where

$$\delta = \left(\frac{\omega}{2\Omega}\right)^2. \tag{14.139}$$

The lower limit in (14.138) gives Ω_1 where

$$\left(\frac{\omega}{2\Omega_1}\right)^2 = \frac{1}{4 + 2\alpha} \tag{14.140}$$

from which

$$\Omega_1 = \omega\left(1 + \frac{\alpha}{2}\right)^{1/2} = \omega\left(1 + \frac{\alpha}{4}\right) + 0(\varepsilon^2) \tag{14.141}$$

since from (14.134) α has order ε^1. Similarly, the other limit is

$$\Omega_2 = \omega\left(1 - \frac{\alpha}{4}\right) + 0(\varepsilon^2). \tag{14.142}$$

On substituting for α from (14.134), we then find that the limits are, to order ε^1,

$$\Omega_1 = \omega\left(1 + \frac{3}{8}\varepsilon\gamma\frac{A^2}{\omega_0^2}\right) \tag{14.143}$$

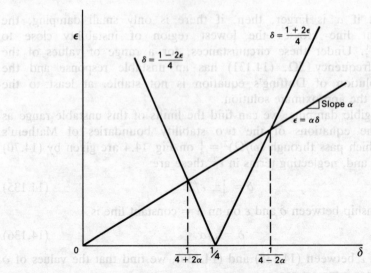

Fig. 14.7 Detail of the stability boundaries of the Mathieu equation close to $\delta = 1/4$ and their intersection by an $\alpha = $ constant line

and

$$\Omega_2 = \omega\left(1 - \frac{3}{8}\,\varepsilon\gamma\,\frac{A^2}{\omega_0^2}\right). \tag{14.144}$$

From (14.132)

$$\frac{\omega}{\omega_0} = \left(1 + \frac{3}{2}\,\varepsilon\gamma\,\frac{A^2}{\omega_0^2}\right)^{1/2} = \left(1 + \frac{3}{4}\,\varepsilon\gamma\,\frac{A^2}{\omega_0^2}\right) + 0(\varepsilon^2) \tag{14.145}$$

and, on substituting for ω in (14.143) and (14.144), we then get

$$\frac{\Omega_1}{\omega_0} = \frac{\Omega_1}{\omega}\left(\frac{\omega}{\omega_0}\right) = \left(1 + \frac{3}{8}\,\varepsilon\gamma\,\frac{A^2}{\omega_0^2}\right)\left(1 + \frac{3}{4}\,\varepsilon\gamma\,\frac{A^2}{\omega_0^2}\right)$$

$$= 1 + \frac{9}{8}\,\varepsilon\gamma\,\frac{A^2}{\omega_0^2} \tag{14.146}$$

and, similarly,

$$\frac{\Omega_2}{\omega_0} = 1 + \frac{3}{8}\,\varepsilon\gamma\,\frac{A^2}{\omega_0^2} \tag{14.147}$$

both again to order ε^1.

These two equations (14.146) and (14.147) are plotted on an amplitude-versus-frequency graph in Fig. 14.8. From (14.125) and (14.126), we see that Ω_2/ω_0 is identical with the graph's backbone that we obtained previously. Ω_1/ω_0 is a new line which curves away to the right more rapidly than the backbone. Periodic solutions with zero damping which fall between these two stability boundaries are unstable. Therefore, for no damping, the response curve on the right of the backbone describes unstable periodic solutions until it reaches the Ω_1/ω_0 line defined by equation (14.146). Problem 14.9 is concerned with proving that the point of intersection occurs where the response curve is at its point of vertical tangency.

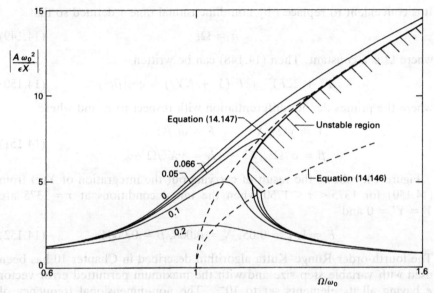

Fig. 14.8 Periodic response curves for Duffing's equation (14.110) for the case when $\varepsilon\gamma(\varepsilon X)^2/\omega_0^6 = 0.008$ with the unstable sections of these curves deleted. Curves are shown for zero damping and for damping ratios $\varepsilon\zeta = 0.05, 0.066, 0.1$ and 0.2

When damping is present, the position is more complicated and the unstable regions of the Mathieu chart shrink away from their boundaries for zero damping, as shown in Fig. 14.4. In that case the stability boundary in Fig. 14.8 also shrinks away from the boundaries for no damping, and the broken lines in Fig. 14.8 are replaced by the continuous line. Its coordinates have been found numerically by carrying out a similar analysis to that for the undamped case, but taking the damped Mathieu stability chart instead of the undamped chart, using different charts for different amounts of damping. To the accuracy of the calculation, the continuous line passes through the points of vertical tangency of the periodic response curves. Within the shaded area to the right of the line, steady periodic oscillations of the nonlinear system represented by Duffing's equation are unstable and break down to the alternative second solution which is possible for the same excitation frequency.

Numerical integration: chaotic response

The unstable behaviour of a nonlinear oscillator when accelerated slowly through its resonant frequency can be demonstrated by integrating the response of Duffing's equation numerically. If the frequency of excitation is increased linearly with time, the equation is

$$\ddot{y} + 2\zeta\omega_0\dot{y} + \omega_0^2 y + \gamma y^3 = X\cos(\alpha t^2). \tag{14.148}$$

It is convenient to replace t by non-dimensional time τ defined so that

$$\tau = \Omega t \tag{14.149}$$

where Ω is a constant. Then (14.148) can be written

$$Y'' + 2\zeta F Y' + F^2(Y + NY^3) = \cos(\beta\tau^2) \tag{14.150}$$

where the primes denote differentiation with respect to τ, and where

$$Y = y\Omega^2/X, \qquad F = \omega_0/\Omega$$
$$\beta = \alpha/\Omega^2, \qquad N = \gamma X^2/\Omega^4\omega_0^2. \tag{14.151}$$

Figure 14.9 shows the result of carrying out the integration of $Y(\tau)$ from (14.150) for $1375 < \tau < 1750$ when the initial conditions at $\tau = 1375$ are $Y = Y' = 0$ and

$$F = 1, \zeta = 0.05, N = 0.008, \beta = 0.0004. \tag{14.152}$$

The fourth-order Runge–Kutta algorithm described in Chapter 10 has been used with variable step size and with the maximum permitted error vector e having all its elements set to 10^{-5}. The non-dimensional frequency of excitation is, from (14.150),

$$\frac{d}{d\tau}(\beta\tau^2) = 2\beta\tau \tag{14.153}$$

and increases from 1.1 at $\tau = 1375$ to 1.4 at $\tau = 1750$. The system passes through resonance between these limiting times (see Fig. 14.8), and the sudden reduction in amplitude as a result of a nonlinear jump can be clearly seen in Fig. 14.9. Because the frequency of excitation is continuously changing, the maximum amplitude of response does not reach the limiting steady-state value of $1/2\zeta = 10$ (see Fig. 14.8) but is only approximately 85% of the steady-state amplitude. This result should be compared with the corresponding result for the linear case, which is shown in Fig. 3.14 for a higher rate of acceleration, $\beta = 0.0025$ instead of $\beta = 0.0004$, as here.

When the nonlinearity is small and there is small damping, we have seen that the response of Duffing's oscillator to harmonic excitation is dominated by the resonant behaviour of the system. Its response is then very close to harmonic. However, when there is large-amplitude excitation of an oscillator with pronounced nonlinearity, the response becomes much more complicated. Many different responses are possible, depending on the

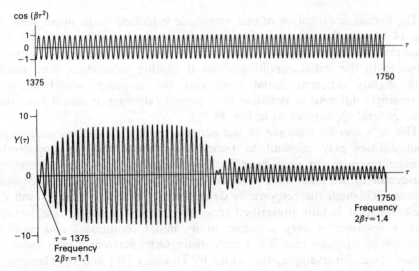

Fig. 14.9 Response of Duffing's oscillator (14.150) with small damping and non-linearity when the frequency of excitation is slowly accelerated through resonance. The parameter values are listed as equation (14.152). The excitation is shown in the upper view and is switched on to any initially dormant system at $\tau = 1375$

equations and the parameter values. For some combinations, several different periodic solutions may be possible, depending on the initial conditions. For other combinations of parameters, the periodicity is lost, as shown in Fig. 14.10. This is the integrated response of

$$Y'' + 2\zeta FY' + F^2(Y + NY^3) = \cos \tau \qquad (14.154)$$

for $0 < \tau < 20\pi$ when the initial conditions are $Y = Y' = 0$ at $\tau = 0$. The parameter values are

$$F = 0.01, \ \zeta = 2.5, \ N = 4 \times 10^6 \qquad (14.155)$$

so that (14.154) reads

$$Y'' + 0.05Y' + 10^{-4}Y + 400Y^3 = \cos \tau. \qquad (14.156)$$

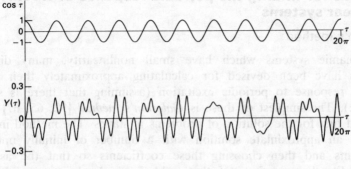

Fig. 14.10 Chaotic response of the nonlinear oscillator (14.156), with its harmonic excitation shown for comparison

The harmonic excitation of unit amplitude is plotted in the upper view in Fig. 14.10 with the corresponding response below. It can be seen that the response no longer has any obvious periodicity. Furthermore, it is very sensitive to the initial conditions, and if another calculation were made with slightly different initial conditions the response would become increasingly different in detail as time passed (although it would have the same general appearance as in Fig. 14.10).

This is a specific example of the general result that systems with large nonlinearities may respond to periodic excitation with an apparently random response. In such cases, motion fluctuates from one extreme of movement to the other in a random manner that has been called *chaotic motion*. Although the response is deterministic because it is the result of excitation that is fully prescribed (and may be just a simple sine wave), such a response is very sensitive to its initial conditions, and motion becomes so irregular that it is hardly distinguishable from a truly random process (see, for example, the books by Devaney [19] and by Thompson and Stewart [98] and the papers by Ueda [103, 104, 105] and by Ueda *et al.* [106, 107]).

When they are plotted on a phase-plane diagram (in which velocity is plotted against displacement), the trajectories of chaotic responses for different initial conditions follow different orbital paths. However, after a few initial orbits, all orbits are found to lie within the same envelope. When the trajectories are sampled periodically at the period of the excitation, each data point has a displacement and velocity which always plots as a point within a preferred region of the phase plane. It has been found that this preferred region often has a rather strange shape, and this has led to the term *strange attractor* or *chaotic attractor* to describe the chaotic response of a nonlinear system, the term attractor referring to the attraction of the periodically sampled data points to preferred regions of the phase plane.

Methods for finding the periodic response of weakly nonlinear systems

Galerkin's method

For dynamic systems which have small nonlinearity, many different methods have been devised for calculating approximately their steady periodic response to periodic excitation (assuming that there is such a response). The simplest of these is *Galerkin's method* [32, 65, 67] which was used first for the solution of problems in statics. The method involves guessing an approximate solution with a number of initially unknown coefficients and then choosing these coefficients so that the assumed solution fits the equations of the problem as closely as possible. The method of finding the unknown coefficients is as follows. The assumed solution is substituted into the equations. Because this solution is not exact, the equations are not satisfied exactly and each equation has a residual error. Various weighted averages of the residual errors are then set to zero, with enough averages being calculated to provide the same number of independent equations as there are arbitrary coefficients. These equations are then solved to find the 'best' values of the unknown coefficients.

For vibration problems which have a periodic response, the response is expressed in the form

$$y(t) = a\,\rho(t) \tag{14.157}$$

where, for N equations, one for each degree of freedom, $y(t)$ is the $N \times 1$ displacement-response vector, $\rho(t)$ is an $M \times 1$ vector of M periodic functions and a is an $N \times M$ matrix of unknown coefficients. On substituting (14.157) into the equations of motion, there will be N residual errors, each of which is a function of t. Let these be given by $E_j(t)$, $j = 1$ to N. Then, if $\phi(t)$ is an $M \times 1$ vector of weighting functions, the coefficients a are chosen to be the solutions of

$$\int_0^T E_j(t)\,\phi(t)\,\mathrm{d}t = O, j = 1 \text{ to } N \tag{14.158}$$

where T is the period. Usually the weighting functions $\phi(t)$ are chosen to be the same as the trial functions $\rho(t)$, and then the unknown coefficients are the solutions of

$$\int_0^T E_j(t)\,\rho(t)\,\mathrm{d}t = O, j = 1 \text{ to } N. \tag{14.159}$$

When the weighting functions are chosen in this way, the Galerkin method is sometimes called the Ritz averaging method, a name given to it by Klotter [52] because basic equations of the form (14.159) were stated (but not exploited) by Ritz [87].

Galerkin's method is easy to apply and its application to a practical problem is shown later.

Ritz's method

Provided that the equations of motion are derived by using Lagrange's equations (see Chapter 11), Galerkin's method produces an approximation which is the same as that obtained by using the *Ritz minimizing method* [52, 67, 87, 108]. In this alternative method, the equations of motion are expressed as a variational problem using Hamilton's principle (see, for example, Crandall *et al.* [16]), and the necessary minimization is carried out approximately to choose the unknown coefficients in (14.157). The initial formulation is the variational equation

$$\delta\int_{t_1}^{t_2}\left[L + \sum_{j=1}^{N} Q_j y_j\right]\mathrm{d}t = 0 \tag{14.160}$$

where L is the Lagrangian, defined as $L = \mathcal{T} - V$, where $\mathcal{T}$ is the kinetic energy and V is the potential energy of the system, Q_j is the jth non-conservative generalized force defined as described in Chapter 11, and t_1 and t_2 are arbitrary instants of time t. The operator δ. denotes the change in the integral brought about by any arbitrary small change in any or all of the displacement–time histories for the different coordinates, provided that the correct relationship is satisfied at $t = t_1$ and $t = t_2$ (i.e. that the varied path coincides with the actual path at these instants) and that the varied path is continuous. It is understood that the variational operator is not applied to the generalized forces Q_j. Expressing this result in another way, the integral in (14.160) has to be a minimum for any admissible variation in the path of motion during which the forces Q_j are held constant. We shall see below that this variational statement leads directly to Lagrange's equations of motion.

In the Ritz minimizing method an assumed approximate solution (14.157) is substituted into (14.160). The kinetic and potential energies $\mathcal{T}$ and V, and the generalized forces Q_j, $j = 1$ to N, are calculated for the assumed solution which has $N \times M$ arbitrary coefficients. The integral

$$I = \int_0^T \left[L(y, \dot{y}) + \sum_{j=1}^{N} Q_j y_j \right] \mathrm{d}t \qquad (14.161)$$

can then in principle be calculated, integrating over the span of one period, T, and the unknown coefficients a_{jr}, $j = 1$ to N, $r = 1$ to M, are chosen so that this integral has its minimum value, i.e. so that

$$\frac{\partial I}{\partial a_{jr}} = 0 \qquad (14.162)$$

for all the $N \times M$ a's. Note that the non-conservative forces are regarded as constants for this calculation and they are not differentiated although their constant values depend on the assumed time history (14.157).

Consider the result of this procedure. First suppose that the y_j are varied in a general manner. Then, carrying out the variation process according to the rules of the calculus of variations, we have

$$\delta L = \sum_{j=1}^{N} \left(\frac{\partial L}{\partial \dot{y}_j} \delta \dot{y}_j + \frac{\partial L}{\partial y_j} \delta y_j \right). \qquad (14.163)$$

The integration

$$\int_{t_1}^{t_2} \frac{\partial L}{\partial \dot{y}_j} \delta \dot{y}_j \, \mathrm{d}t \qquad (14.164)$$

can be carried out by parts after putting

$$\delta \dot{y}_j = \frac{\mathrm{d}}{\mathrm{d}t} \delta y_j \qquad (14.165)$$

and gives

$$\int_{t_1}^{t_2} \frac{\partial L}{\partial \dot{y}_j} \delta \dot{y}_j \, dt = - \int_{t_1}^{t_2} \frac{d}{dt} \left(\frac{\partial L}{\partial \dot{y}_j} \right) \delta y_j \, dt \qquad (14.166)$$

since an admissible variation δy_j has to be zero at $t = t_1$ and $t = t_2$ (see Crandall *et al.* [16]). Using the results (14.163) and (14.165), the application of Hamilton's principle therefore gives, from (14.160),

$$\int_{t_1}^{t_1} \sum_{j=1}^{N} \left[-\frac{d}{dt} \left(\frac{\partial L}{\partial \dot{y}_j} \right) + \frac{\partial L}{\partial y_j} + Q_j \right] \delta y_j \, dt = 0. \qquad (14.167)$$

Since the δy_j are arbitrary, each term in square brackets must separately be zero, thus leading to Lagrange's equations (11.8)*. However, suppose that this final step is not taken. Instead, the approximate solution (14.157) is substituted into (14.167). Then (14.167) can no longer be satisfied for arbitrary variations δy_j. According to the Ritz minimizing method, the unknown coefficients in a are chosen so that (14.167) is satisfied for a series of special cases. In each case, δy_j is zero for all $j = 1$ to N and all $r = 1$ to M except for one combination of j and r for which

$$\delta y_j = \delta a_{jr} \rho_r(t). \qquad (14.168)$$

This gives $N \times M$ different integrals which are evaluated with the time span of each integral covering one period of the periodic response, for example $t_1 = 0$ to $t_2 = T$. Values of the coefficients in the $N \times M$ matrix a are therefore obtained by solving the $N \times M$ simultaneous equations which derive from

$$\int_0^T \left[-\frac{d}{dt} \left(\frac{\partial L}{\partial \dot{y}_j} \right) - \frac{\partial L}{\partial y_j} + Q_j \right] \rho_r(t) \, dt = 0 \begin{cases} r = 1 \text{ to } M \\ j = 1 \text{ to } N \end{cases} \qquad (14.169)$$

where the terms in square brackets are the result of substituting the assumed solution (14.157) into (14.167). This is the residual error which has been called $E_j(t)$, and so (14.169) is identical with (14.159). Hence, provided that two conditions are satisfied, Galerkin's method and the Ritz minimizing method give identical results. The first condition is that the equations used in Galerkin's method must be in the form derived from Lagrange's equations (themselves derived from Hamilton's principle). The second condition is that the assumed solutions must have the same form in both cases, and the weighting functions used in the Galerkin method must be the same as the time functions in the assumed solution.

In order for δy_j to be an admissible variation in Hamilton's principle, δy_j must be zero at the start and at end of the interval, at $t = t_1$ and $t = t_2$. However, in the Ritz minimizing method the functions $\rho_r(t)$,

---

*Since V is a function only of position,

$$\frac{\partial L}{\partial \dot{y}_j} \equiv \frac{\partial (\mathcal{T} - V)}{\partial \dot{y}_j} \equiv \frac{\partial \mathcal{T}}{\partial \dot{y}_j}.$$

Note that the letter $\mathcal{T}$, which denotes kinetic energy, replaces T used in Chapter 11.

$r = 1$ to M, do not need to be separately zero at the beginning and end of the period of integration at $t = 0$ and $t = T$. Provided that all these functions are periodic in t with period T and are zero somewhere, then an admissible variation in the path of motion is obtained by giving any parameter a_{jr} an increment δa_{jr}. The period of integration for each variation process may be thought of as being adjusted so that $\rho_r(t)$ is zero at the beginning and end of the interval for which a_{jr} is the varied coefficient.

Krylov and Bogoliubov's method

A third method of calculating the steady periodic response of a nonlinear system is to take a special case of the more general method of slowly varying amplitude and phase. This is usually known as the method of *Krylov and Bogoliubov* (K & B for short) [53] which has been developed by Bogoliubov and Mitropolsky [11]. For forced vibration near resonance, when the forcing frequency is close to one of the linear natural frequencies, the method is as follows. Consider for simplicity a system with only one degree of freedom with small nonlinearity whose equation may be written as

$$\ddot{y} + \omega^2 y = \varepsilon f(y, \dot{y}, \Omega t) \tag{14.170}$$

where $|\varepsilon| \ll 1$. The natural frequency when $\varepsilon = 0$ is ω and the fundamental frequency of periodic excitation is Ω, where $\Omega \simeq \omega$. The K & B method develops a solution of (14.170) in the form

$$y = a \cos(\Omega t + \theta) + \varepsilon u_1(t) + \varepsilon^2 u_2(t) + \dots \tag{14.171}$$

where
$$\frac{da}{dt} = \varepsilon A_1(a, \theta) + \varepsilon^2 A_2(a, \theta) + \dots \tag{14.172}$$

and
$$\frac{d\theta}{dt} = (\omega - \Omega) + \varepsilon B_1(a, \theta) + \varepsilon^2 B_2(a, \theta) + \dots \tag{14.173}$$

On substituting for y in (14.170) from (14.171), we get

$$\frac{d^2a}{dt^2}\cos(\Omega t + \theta) - 2\frac{da}{dt}\sin(\Omega t + \theta)\left(\Omega + \frac{d\theta}{dt}\right) -$$
$$- a\cos(\Omega t + \theta)\left(\Omega + \frac{d\theta}{dt}\right)^2 - a\sin(\Omega t + \theta)\frac{d^2\theta}{dt^2} + \varepsilon\frac{d^2u_1}{dt^2} + \dots$$
$$+ \omega^2 a\cos(\Omega t + \theta) + \omega^2\varepsilon u_1 + \dots$$
$$= \varepsilon f[a\cos(\Omega t + \theta), -a\omega\sin(\Omega t + \theta), \Omega t] + 0(\varepsilon^2). \tag{14.174}$$

The r.h.s. of (14.174) is the first term of a Taylor expansion of the r.h.s. of (14.170) as a function of y and $\dot{y}$ since, to order ε^0,

$$y = a\cos(\Omega t + \theta) \tag{14.175}$$

and, on differentiating (14.175),

$$\dot{y} = -a(\Omega + \dot{\theta})\sin(\Omega t + \theta) = -a\omega\sin(\Omega t + \theta) \qquad (14.176)$$

from (14.173).

By differentiating (14.172)

$$\frac{d^2a}{dt^2} = \varepsilon \frac{\partial A_1}{\partial a} \frac{da}{dt} + \varepsilon \frac{\partial A_1}{\partial \theta} \frac{d\theta}{dt} + 0(\varepsilon^2) \qquad (14.177)$$

and, substituting for

$$\frac{da}{dt}$$

from (14.172) and for

$$\frac{d\theta}{dt}$$

from (14.173)

$$\frac{d^2a}{dt^2} = \varepsilon \frac{\partial A_1}{\partial \theta}(\omega - \Omega) + 0(\varepsilon^2). \qquad (14.178)$$

Similarly,

$$\frac{d^2\theta}{dt^2} = \varepsilon \frac{\partial B_1}{\partial \theta}(\omega - \Omega) + 0(\varepsilon^2). \qquad (14.179)$$

Substituting for

$$\frac{da}{dt}, \frac{d\theta}{dt}, \frac{d^2a}{dt^2} \text{ and } \frac{d^2\theta}{dt^2}$$

in (14.174) from (14.172), (14.173), (14.178) and (14.179), then gives

$$\varepsilon\cos(\Omega t + \theta)\left[(\omega - \Omega)\frac{\partial A_1}{\partial \theta} - 2\omega a B_1\right] -$$
$$- \varepsilon\sin(\Omega t + \theta)\left[(\omega - \Omega) a \frac{\partial B_1}{\partial \theta} + 2\omega A_1\right] + \varepsilon\left[\frac{d^2 u_1}{dt^2} + \omega^2 u_1\right]$$
$$= \varepsilon f[a\cos(\Omega t + \theta), -a\omega\sin(\Omega t + \theta), \Omega t] + 0(\varepsilon^2). \qquad (14.180)$$

The assumed solution (14.171)–(14.173) therefore automatically satisfies (14.170) to order ε^0. However there is a condition.

The choice of A_1 and B_1 is determined by the requirement that u_1 must not be infinite or very large. This requires that there shall be no terms on the r.h.s. of (14.180) which are harmonic with frequency at or close to ω. If there are, as a result of the terms

$$\left[\frac{d^2 u_1}{dt^2} + \omega^2 u_1\right]$$

on the l.h.s. of (14.180), $u_1(t)$ will respond like an undamped oscillator excited near resonance, and u_1 will have a very large (or infinite) solution.

The term $f[a\cos(\Omega t + \theta), -a\omega\sin(\Omega t + \theta), \Omega t]$ on the r.h.s. of (14.180) is periodic in $(\Omega t + \theta)$ because $\cos(\Omega t + \theta)$ and $\sin(\Omega t + \theta)$ are circular functions, and it is periodic in Ωt because the excitation is periodic. Since we are assuming that $\Omega \simeq \omega$ and that $\dot{\theta}$ is small, the whole function is nearly periodic in ωt. Assuming that it is periodic in ωt, its fundamental component can be calculated approximately as follows. Defining

$$\rho = \Omega t + \theta, \tag{14.181}$$

then, from (14.173),

$$\rho \simeq \omega t \tag{14.182}$$

where the accuracy of approximation during any one period is of $0(\varepsilon)$. From (14.181) we can write

$$f[a\cos(\Omega t + \theta), -a\omega\sin(\Omega t + \theta), \Omega t] = f(a\cos\rho, -a\omega\sin\rho, \rho - \theta)$$

$$\tag{14.183}$$

and assuming that $\rho = \omega t$ and that the phase angle θ does not change much in a single period of the oscillation, Fourier analysis gives (Problem 14.9) the coefficient of the fundamental cosine term as

$$\frac{1}{\pi}\int_0^{2\pi} [f(a\cos\rho, -a\omega\sin\rho, \rho - \theta)]\cos\rho\,d\rho \tag{14.184}$$

and the coefficient of the fundamental sine term as

$$\frac{1}{\pi}\int_0^{2\pi} [f(a\cos\rho, -a\omega\sin\rho, \rho - \theta)]\sin\rho\,d\rho \tag{14.185}$$

and both these terms must be zero if $u_1(t)$ is not to be very large or infinite. The K & B recipe for choosing the unknown functions $A_1(a, \theta)$ and $B_1(a, \theta)$ in (14.180) is therefore to select these so that the fundamental terms (14.184) and (14.185) disappear from the r.h.s. of (14.180). Hence $A_1(a, \theta)$ and $B_1(a, \theta)$ must be the solutions of the simultaneous equations

$$(\omega - \Omega)\frac{\partial A_1}{\partial\theta} - 2\omega a B_1 = \frac{1}{\pi}\int_0^{2\pi} [f(a\cos\rho, -a\omega\sin\rho, \rho - \theta)]\cos\rho\,d\rho$$

$$\tag{14.186}$$

$$(\omega - \Omega)\frac{\partial B_1}{\partial\theta} + 2\omega A_1 = -\frac{1}{\pi}\int_0^{2\pi} [f(a\cos\rho, -a\omega\sin\rho, \rho - \theta)]\sin\rho\,d\rho.$$

Having chosen A_1 and B_1 in this way, (14.180) may in principle be solved to find the unknown function $u_1(t)$.

In the same way, a second approximation can be obtained by considering the conditions on $A_2(a, \theta)$ and $B_2(a, \theta)$ that are needed to ensure that $u_2(t)$ is not very large or infinite. This leads to another pair of linear simultaneous partial differential equations for A_2 and B_2 from which these functions can in principle be determined.

If terms of order ε^2 are neglected in (14.172) and (14.173), then the equation of motion (14.170) is satisfied only to order ε^0 (see equation 14.180). This is because, near resonance, a small change in frequency causes a large change in amplitude. Thus if the terms $\varepsilon^2 A_2$ and $\varepsilon^2 B_2$ are neglected, there is no point in retaining the term $\varepsilon u_1(t)$ in the expression for $y(t)$. Therefore to complete the second approximation it is necessary to find $A_2(a, \theta)$ and $B_2(a, \theta)$.

In summary, according to the K & B method, the *first approximation* to the solution of (14.170) is

$$y = a\cos(\Omega t + \theta) \tag{14.187}$$

where

$$\frac{da}{dt} = \varepsilon A_1(a, \theta) \tag{14.188}$$

$$\frac{d\theta}{dt} = (\omega - \Omega) + \varepsilon B_1(a, \theta) \tag{14.189}$$

and the functions A_1 and B_1 are the solutions of the pair of equations (14.186). The *second approximation* is

$$y = a\cos(\Omega t + \theta) + \varepsilon u_1(t) \tag{14.190}$$

where

$$\frac{da}{dt} = \varepsilon A_1(a, \theta) + \varepsilon^2 A_2(a, \theta) \tag{14.191}$$

$$\frac{d\theta}{dt} = (\omega - \Omega) + \varepsilon B_1(a, \theta) + \varepsilon^2 B_2(a, \theta) \tag{14.192}$$

where A_1 and B_1 are determined from (14.186) and A_2 and B_2 are chosen by following a similar approach. After substituting the assumed solution into equation (14.170), A_2 and B_2 are chosen to ensure that no terms of order ε^2 remain that will cause the function $u_2(t)$ to be very large (or infinite).

For many degrees of freedom, the K & B method works in the same way. Only small nonlinear terms are considered, and the method applies only to oscillations at a single predominant frequency which is close to one of the linear natural frequencies. Internal resonances are assumed not to occur, so that the single frequency response is not upset by interference between neighbouring modes. The equations of motion are written in terms of the normal coordinates for the linear case, so that these are

$$\ddot{y}_j + \omega_j^2 y_j = \varepsilon f_j(y_1, y_2, \ldots, y_N, \dot{y}_1, \dot{y}_2, \ldots, \dot{y}_N, \Omega t), \quad j = 1 \text{ to } N. \tag{14.193}$$

The *first approximation* of K & B is

$$y_j = a \cos(\Omega t + \theta) \tag{14.194}$$

$$y_k = 0, \, k = 1 \text{ to } N, \, k \neq j \tag{14.195}$$

$$\frac{da}{dt} = \varepsilon A_1(a, \theta) \tag{14.196}$$

$$\frac{d\theta}{dt} = (\omega_j - \Omega) + \varepsilon B_1(a, \theta) \tag{14.197}$$

where the functions $A_1(a, \theta)$ and $B_1(a, \theta)$ are shown to be the solution of two simultaneous linear differential equations like (14.186). The *second approximation* is

$$y_j = a \cos(\Omega t + \theta) + \varepsilon u_{j1}(t) \tag{14.198}$$

$$y_k = \varepsilon u_{k1}(t), \, k = 1 \text{ to } N, \, k \neq j \tag{14.199}$$

$$\frac{da}{dt} = \varepsilon A_1(a, \theta) + \varepsilon^2 A_2(a, \theta) \tag{14.200}$$

$$\frac{d\theta}{dt} = (\omega_j - \Omega) + \varepsilon B_1(a, \theta) + \varepsilon^2 B_2(a, \theta). \tag{14.201}$$

The function $u_{j1}(t)$ is obtained by substituting for y_j from (14.198) into (14.193) and then solving the equation to order ε^1 that remains for $u_{j1}(t)$. Because of the choice of $A_1(a, \theta)$ and $B_1(a, \theta)$ in the first approximation, there are no terms remaining that will make $u_{j1}(t)$ infinite or very large. The other functions $u_{k1}(t)$, $k = 1$ to N, $k \neq j$, are obtained by solving each of the remaining equations (14.193) to order ε^1 when the assumed approximate solution is substituted in the functions f_j on their right-hand sides. The assumption that there are no internal resonances means that the $u_{k1}(t)$ will not be infinite or very large.

By considering terms to order ε^2, the quantities $A_2(a, \theta)$ and $B_2(a, \theta)$ would be chosen similarly so as to ensure that $u_{j2}(t)$ occurring in the third approximation should not be infinite or very large. Higher-order approximations may be obtained following the same general procedure, although the complexity of the expressions involved makes it rarely expedient to go further than the second approximation and, in most cases, further than the first approximation.

Comparison between the methods of Galerkin and Krylov–Bogoliubov for steady-state vibrations

In the K & B method, steady-state vibrations occur as a special case. The method applies only to weakly nonlinear systems and, when steady-state conditions exist, the frequency of the response is the same as the frequency of the excitation. Since, from (14.194), the frequency of response is

$$\Omega + \frac{d\theta}{dt}$$

(where Ω is the frequency of excitation) it follows that, if there are steady-state forced vibrations,

$$\frac{d\theta}{dt} = 0. \tag{14.202}$$

We shall show now that, if the Galerkin solution and weighting functions are chosen appropriately, the first approximation of Krylov–Bogoliubov gives, for steady-state forced vibrations, a result which is identical with that produced by Galerkin's method. For simplicity we consider a single-degree-of-freedom system, but the same proof holds for the multi-degree-of-freedom case.

From (14.173), when

$$\frac{d\theta}{dt} = 0$$

we have

$$(\omega - \Omega) = 0(\varepsilon) \tag{14.203}$$

and so, to the order of the approximation, equations (14.186) simplify to

$$B_1 = -\frac{1}{2\omega a\pi} \int_0^{2\pi} [f(a\cos\rho, -a\omega\sin\rho, \rho - \theta)]\cos\rho \, d\rho \tag{14.204}$$

$$A_1 = -\frac{1}{2\omega\pi} \int_0^{2\pi} [f(a\cos\rho, -a\omega\sin\rho, \rho - \theta)]\sin\rho \, d\rho.$$

For a steady-state response with constant amplitude,

$$\frac{da}{dt} = 0$$

and so, from (14.172),

$$A_1(a, \theta) = 0. \tag{14.205}$$

Also, because of (14.202), from (14.173)

$$(\omega - \Omega) = -\varepsilon B_1(a, \theta). \tag{14.206}$$

Substituting these results into equations (14.204) then gives

$$(\omega - \Omega) = \frac{1}{2\omega a\pi} \int_0^{2\pi} [\varepsilon f(a\cos\rho, -a\omega\sin\rho, \rho - \theta)]\cos\rho \, d\rho \tag{14.207}$$

$$0 = \int_0^{2\pi} [f(a\cos\rho, -a\omega\sin\rho, \rho - \theta)]\sin\rho \, d\rho.$$

Finally, since $\omega \simeq \Omega$ as we are assuming that the system is excited at a frequency close to its linear resonant frequency,

$$2\omega \simeq \omega + \Omega \tag{14.208}$$

and so (14.207) may be rewritten, within the accuracy of the Krylov–Bogoliubov first approximation, in the form

$$a\pi \left(\Omega^2 - \omega^2\right) + \int_0^{2\pi} [\varepsilon f(a\cos\rho, \, - a\Omega\sin\rho, \, \rho - \theta)]\cos\rho \, d\rho = 0$$

$$\int_0^{2\pi} [\varepsilon f(a\cos\rho, \, - a\Omega\sin\rho, \, \rho - \theta)]\sin\rho \, d\rho = 0 \qquad (14.209)$$

which are two simultaneous equations for the unknown (constant) amplitude a and the unknown (constant) phase angle θ. Notice that the ω in the argument of $f(\ )$ in (14.207) has been replaced by Ω in (14.209). Since $f(a\cos\rho, \, - a\omega\sin\rho, \, \rho - \theta)$ in K & B is the first term of a Taylor expansion in y and $\dot y$ of $f(y, \, \dot y, \, \Omega t)$, with terms of order ε^1 and smaller being neglected, and that, from (14.206), $\omega = \Omega$ to order ε^1, the difference between $f(a\cos\rho, \, - a\omega\sin\rho, \, \rho - \theta)$ and $f(a\cos\rho, \, - a\Omega\sin\rho, \, \rho - \theta)$ is not significant to the order of K & B's first approximation.

Now suppose that the Galerkin method is used for the same problem, with the equation of motion in the same form (14.170) and with an assumed approximate solution

$$y = a\cos(\Omega t + \theta). \qquad (14.210)$$

On expanding the r.h.s., this solution can be written as

$$y = (a\cos\theta)\cos\Omega t + (- a\sin\theta)\sin\Omega t \qquad (14.211)$$

which is in the standard form (14.157). On substituting (14.211) into the equation of motion (14.170), the error function is

$$E(t) =$$

$$a(\omega^2 - \Omega^2)(\cos\theta\cos\Omega t - \sin\theta\sin\Omega t) - \varepsilon f(a\cos\rho, \, -a\Omega\sin\rho, \, \rho - \theta)$$

$$14.212)$$

when ρ is defined, as before, by (14.181). Choosing $\cos\Omega t$ and $\sin\Omega t$ as weighting functions, according to the usual Galerkin recipe, (14.159) then gives

$$\int_0^{2\pi} E(t)\cos\omega t \, d(\Omega t) = 0$$
$$\int_0^{2\pi} E(t)\sin\Omega t \, d(\Omega t) = 0 \qquad (14.213)$$

which, after substituting for $E(t)$ from (14.212) and integrating, lead to the results that

$$- a\pi(\Omega^2 - \omega^2)\cos\theta = \int_0^{2\pi} [\varepsilon f(a\cos\rho, \, - a\Omega\sin\rho, \, \rho - \theta)]\cos(\Omega t) \, d(\Omega t)$$

$$(14.214)$$

and

$$a\pi(\Omega^2 - \omega^2)\sin\theta = \int_0^{2\pi} [\varepsilon f(a\cos\rho, \, - a\Omega\sin\rho, \, \rho - \theta)]\sin(\Omega t) \, d(\Omega t).$$

$$(14.215)$$

But since θ is assumed to be constant, from (14.181), $d(\Omega t) = d\rho$ and so, multiplying (14.214) by $\cos\theta$ and (14.125) by $\sin\theta$ and subtracting gives

$$a\pi(\Omega^2 - \omega^2) + \int_0^{2\pi} [\varepsilon f(a\cos\rho, -a\Omega\sin\rho, \rho - \theta)]\cos\rho \, d\rho = 0$$

(14.216)

and multiplying (14.214) by $\sin\theta$ and (14.125) by $\cos\theta$ and adding gives

$$\int_0^{2\pi} [\varepsilon f(a\cos\rho, -a\Omega\sin\rho, \rho - \theta)]\sin\rho \, d\rho = 0. \qquad (14.217)$$

These two equations (14.216) and (14.217) obtained by Galerkin's method are the same as the corresponding pair of equations (14.209) obtained by K & B's method. We conclude that, for steady-state vibrations (only), the first approximation of the method of Krylov–Bogoliubov produces a result which is the same as that produced by Galerkin's method starting from the same equation of motion (14.170) and using the two-term approximate solution (14.211).

The same conclusion applies for systems with more than one degree of freedom, provided that their equations are written initially in the standard form (14.193) and that the assumed solution for Galerkin's method is the same as that for the first approximation of K & B, namely

$$y_j = (a\cos\theta)\cos\Omega t + (-a\sin\theta)\sin\Omega t$$

$$y_k = 0, \ k = 1 \text{ to } N, \ k \neq j. \qquad (14.218)$$

As already remarked, it is assumed that there are no internal resonances between modes, and consequently that only one linear mode is excited near resonance.

For practical problems, it may be very difficult or impossible to manipulate the equations of motion into the standard algebraic form required for K & B's method. In such cases, it will be necessary to use Galerkin's method on the equations without any prior manipulation. The accuracy of the result that is obtained then depends on how accurate is the assumed response time history. The best approach seems to be to compute by numerical integration a range of typical results and to use these, in conjunction with calculations by Galerkin's method, to identify and plot trends in the excitation-response relationships.

Nonlinear response of a centrifugal pendulum vibration absorber

We finish this chapter with a practical example of a nonlinear vibration problem which has two degrees of freedom. Galerkin's method will be used to determine its amplitude of steady-state forced vibration. There is no damping and so the assumed solution, which has the standard form (14.157), will be taken to be a single periodic function of time $\rho(t)$ with the coefficient matrix having order 2×1. Both coordinates are therefore assumed to have the same time dependence and the unknown coefficients represent their different amplitudes. First we describe the problem and the solution of its linearized equations.

In order to minimize torsional vibration, centrifugal pendulum vibration absorbers may be attached to a rotating assembly. The arrangement for a lightweight reciprocating engine is shown in Fig. 14.11. The operation of such an absorber can be demonstrated by considering the two-degree-of-freedom model in Fig. 14.12(a). The real pendulum has a roller support which acts as a parallel linkage of length $l = d_1 - d_2$ where d_1 and d_2 are the roller diameters in Fig. 14.11. The masses of the rollers are neglected. In Problem 14.10, the equations of motion of the system in Fig. 14.12(a) are derived and are shown to be the same as those of the simple pendulum in Fig. 14.12(b). The moment of inertia of the pendulum I_2 has been lumped with that of the carrier I_1, and the pendulum's point of support has been moved to distance

$$a = b + h \tag{14.219}$$

from the axis of the carrier, where b and h are as defined in Fig. 14.12(a).

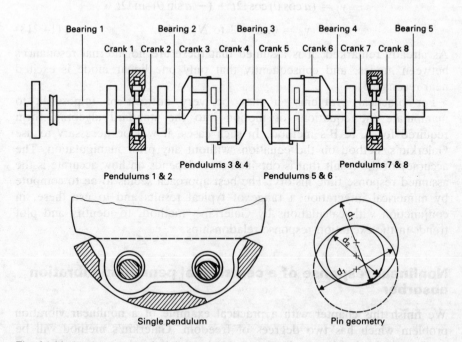

Fig. 14.11 Arrangement of eight centrifugal pendulums of bifilar construction on the crankshaft of a small lightweight engine (from Newland [66]) (*Courtesy of the American Society of Mechanical Engineers*)

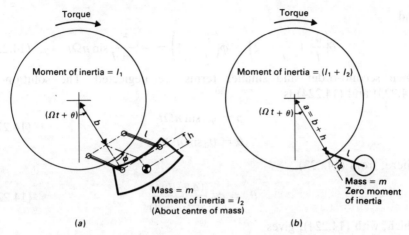

Fig. 14.12 (a) Model of a centrifugal pendulum with bifilar suspension, and (b) its simple pendulum equivalent. Pendulum length $l = (d_1 - d_2)$, where d_1 and d_2 are the roller diameters in Fig. 14.11. The masses of the rollers are neglected. (From Newland [65]) (*Courtesy of the American Society of Mechanical Engineers*)

The carrier is subjected to periodic excitation from the fluctuating loads arising, for example, from a reciprocating engine like that in Fig. 14.11. Suppose that the pendulum is intended to absorb the nth-order torque of angular frequency $n\Omega$, so that

$$F(t) = F_0 \sin n\Omega t. \tag{14.220}$$

This excitation causes a small-amplitude torsional vibration of angular displacement $\theta(t)$ to be superimposed on the steady angular rotation of the carrier at speed Ω and causes the pendulum to respond by moving through angle $\phi(t)$ relative to the carrier. Consider, for simplicity, the operation of a simple pendulum on an inertialess carrier. If the carrier is free to rotate in its bearings and if $\dot{\theta} \ll \Omega$, then the equations of motion are (from Problem 14.10)

$$\ddot{\phi} + \ddot{\theta}\left(1 + \frac{a}{l}\cos\phi\right) + \Omega^2 \frac{a}{l}\sin\phi = 0 \tag{14.221}$$

and

$$\ddot{\theta}\left(\frac{a}{l} + \frac{l}{a} + 2\cos\phi\right) + \ddot{\phi}\left(\frac{l}{a} + \cos\phi\right) - \sin\phi\,\dot{\phi}(2\Omega + \dot{\phi})$$

$$= -\frac{F_0}{mal}\sin n\Omega t. \tag{14.222}$$

The angle ϕ is not necessarily small. If it is small, these equations can be linearized to

$$\ddot{\phi} + \ddot{\theta}\left(1 + \frac{a}{l}\right) + \Omega^2 \frac{a}{l}\phi = 0 \tag{14.223}$$

and

$$\ddot{\theta}\left(\frac{a}{l} + \frac{l}{a} + 2\right) + \ddot{\phi}\left(\frac{l}{a} + 1\right) = -\frac{F_0}{mal}\sin n\Omega t \qquad (14.224)$$

when second-order and smaller terms are neglected. The solution of (14.223) and (14.224) is

$$\phi = \phi_0 \sin n\Omega t$$
$$\theta = \theta_0 \sin n\Omega t \qquad (14.225)$$

where, from (14.223),

$$\theta_0 = \phi_0 \frac{(a - ln^2)}{n^2(a + l)} \qquad (14.226)$$

which, with (14.224), gives

$$\phi_0 \Omega^2 ma(a + l) = F_0. \qquad (14.227)$$

If the pendulum length l is such that

$$l = \frac{a}{n^2} \qquad (14.228)$$

the pendulum is said to be tuned to nth-order excitation. The effective inertia of the pendulum as seen by the carrier is then infinite and the carrier's amplitude of vibration is zero. The pendulum is serving as a perfect vibration absorber. Its amplitude is given by (14.227) and is proportional to the amplitude of the applied torque.

For large-amplitude excitation, the pendulum's amplitude of vibration becomes large and it is then no longer acceptable to linearize its equations of motion. Suppose that we do not linearize, but instead use Galerkin's method to obtain an approximate solution for the nonlinear equations (14.221) and (14.222). Let the trial solution be the linear solution (14.225), where there are two unknown parameters: the amplitudes ϕ_0 and θ_0. On substituting the trial solution into (14.221) we find that there is a residual error

$$E_1(t) = \left[-n^2\Omega^2\phi_0 \sin n\Omega t - n^2\Omega^2\theta_0 \sin n\Omega t\left\{1 + \frac{a}{l}\cos(\phi_0 \sin n\Omega t)\right\} + \right.$$
$$\left. + \Omega^2\frac{a}{l}\sin(\phi_0 \sin n\Omega t)\right] \qquad (14.229)$$

and, substituting into (14.222), there is a second residual error

$$E_2(t) = \left[-n^2\Omega^2\theta_0 \sin n\Omega t\left\{\frac{a}{l} + \frac{l}{a} + 2\cos(\phi_0 \sin n\Omega t)\right\} - \right.$$
$$\left. - n^2\Omega^2\phi_0 \sin n\Omega t\left\{\frac{l}{a} + \cos(\phi_0 \sin n\Omega t)\right\} - \right.$$

$$- \{\sin(\phi_0 \sin n\Omega t)\}(n\Omega\phi_0 \cos n\Omega t)(2\Omega + n\Omega\phi_0 \cos n\Omega t) +$$

$$+ \frac{F_0}{mal} \sin n\Omega t \bigg]. \tag{14.230}$$

According to (14.159), we now have to choose ϕ_0 and θ_0 so that

$$\int_0^{2\pi} E_1(t) \sin n\Omega t \, d(n\Omega t) = 0 \tag{14.231}$$

and

$$\int_0^{2\pi} E_2(t) \sin n\Omega t \, d(n\Omega t) = 0.$$

Since the equations of motion (14.221) and (14.222) are in the form found by applying Lagrange's equations (see Problem 14.10), and the weighting function $\sin n\Omega t$ is the same as the trial function in the approximate solution (14.225), we note that this application of Galerkin's method gives the same result as would be obtained by applying the Ritz minimizing method.

In order to complete the integrations (14.231), it is necessary to use the expansions (see, for example, [39])

$$\cos(\phi_0 \sin \rho) = J_0(\phi_0) + 2J_2(\phi_0) \cos 2\rho + 2J_4(\phi_0) \cos 4\rho + \ldots$$

$$\sin(\phi_0 \sin \rho) = 2J_1(\phi_0) \sin \rho + 2J_3(\phi_0) \sin 3\rho + 2J_5(\phi_0) \sin 5\rho + \ldots \tag{14.232}$$

where $J_m(\phi_0)$ is a Bessel function of the first kind of order m. For $m > 3$, $J_m(\phi_0) \simeq 0$ until ϕ_0 becomes quite large. We are concerned with angles up to about $\phi_0 = 2$ radians (115°), for which value $J_4(\phi_0) = 0.034$ and $J_5(\phi_0) = 0.007$. Hence only the first two terms of each of the series (14.232) need be retained to give reasonable accuracy over quite a wide angle of pendulum motion. With this truncation of the series, and using the identity (Ref. [15])

$$\phi_0[J_1(\phi_0) + J_3(\phi_0)] = 4J_2(\phi_0) \tag{14.232}$$

we find that (Problem 14.10) equations (14.231) lead to the results that

$$\theta_0 \left[1 + \frac{a}{l} \{J_0(\phi_0) - J_2(\phi_0)\} \right] = \left\{ \frac{2}{n^2} \left(\frac{a}{l} \right) J_1(\phi_0) \right\} - \phi_0 \tag{14.234}$$

and

$$\phi_0 \left\{ \frac{l}{a} + J_0(\phi_0) + J_2(\phi_0) \right\} + \theta_0 \left\{ \frac{a}{l} + \frac{l}{a} + 2J_0(\phi_0) - 2J_2(\phi_0) \right\}$$

$$= \frac{F_0}{maln^2\Omega^2}. \tag{14.235}$$

These last two equations (14.234) and (14.235) give the required nonlinear relationship between the pendulum amplitude ϕ_0, the carrier amplitude θ_0 and the magnitude and frequency of the applied torque F_0 and $n\Omega$.

The Bessel functions can be computed (see, for example, Press *et al.* [82], Ch. 6) and it is then a simple task to compute θ_0 from (14.234) and F_0 from (14.235) for a given value of ϕ_0. The relationship between the applied torque amplitude F_0 and pendulum amplitude ϕ_0 can be plotted as shown in Fig. 14.13(*a*) and between applied torque F_0 and carrier-wheel amplitude θ_0 as shown in Fig. 14.13(*b*). Both graphs are for the case when $n = 4$ and $a/l = 17$. Although the pendulum is not exactly in tune because equation (14.228) is not satisfied, these parameters represent a practical case when the pendulum is intentionally detuned slightly. The reason for this detuning is that the pendulum's natural frequency decreases as its amplitude increases, and the pendulum comes into tune at its operating amplitude.

With reference to Fig. 14.13, suppose that the torque amplitude F_0 is slowly increased from zero with the system rotating at constant speed Ω. The operating point on the torque characteristics follows the path OAB (or OA'B' which is the same) until point C is reached, which is at the peak of the curve in each case. A further increase in torque causes a nonlinear jump of the operating point to occur from C to D. There is then a sudden change in the amplitude of the pendulum and a corresponding sudden large increase in the amplitude of the carrier. In both cases there is a change of phase, so that the torque and its response, which were in phase, change to being in anti-phase. Continued increase in torque moves the operating point out towards E; reduction in torque brings the operating point back down the curve to F. In theory, a large-amplitude free vibration can then exist for ever (with no applied torque), but in practice damping will progressively destroy the vibrational energy and the pendulum assembly will return to rest. It appears that the sections C to F' and C' to F are the loci of unstable periodic solutions which cannot be maintained under steady-state conditions (Problem 14.11).

The purpose of a centrifugal pendulum is to reduce the amplitude of vibration of its carrier, if possible to zero. This is achieved if the operating point is at B where the curve in Fig. 14.3(b) crosses over the vertical axis at $\theta_0 = 0$. A problem with practical centrifugal pendulum absorbers occurs if B and C are too close. The increase in torque needed to move from B to C will then be very small and a slight increase in torque over the optimum figure causes the pendulum to make a nonlinear jump in its amplitude of vibration. This stops it operating as a vibration absorber and increases the amplitude of pendulum motion to the extent that mechanical contact may occur between the pendulum mass and its abutment. The resulting impacts have been known to lead to catastrophic failure of the pendulum assembly, with disastrous consequences for an aircraft engine. Design considerations for systems incorporating multiple centrifugal pendulums are discussed in Newland [65, 66].

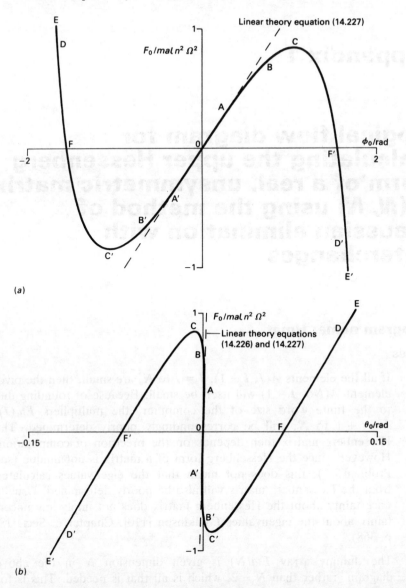

Fig. 14.13 Characteristics of a centrifugal pendulum vibration absorber with $a/l = 17$ when responding to fourth-order excitation, $n = 4$. (a) Shows non-dimensional torque amplitude $F_0/maln^2\Omega^2$ against pendulum amplitude ϕ_0. (b) shows the same torque plotted against carrier amplitude θ_0

Appendix 1

Logical flow diagram for calculating the upper Hessenberg form of a real, unsymmetric matrix $A(N, N)$ using the method of Gaussian elimination with interchanges

Program name: Hmat

Notes

1. If all the elements $A(J, I - 1)$, $J = I$ to N, are small, then the pivot element $A(No, I - 1)$ will itself be small. Because of rounding due to the finite word size of the computer, the multipliers $Eta(J)$, $J = I + 1$ to N, will be correspondingly poorly determined. The Hessenberg matrix then depends on the precision of computation. However, since the Hessenberg form of a matrix is not unique (see Problem 7.1), this does not mean that the eigenvalues calculated from the Hessenberg matrix will also be poorly determined. Usually uncertainty about the Hessenberg matrix does not imply any uncertainty about the eigenvalues (Wilkinson [110], Chapter 6, Sect. 18, p. 368).

2. The dummy array $Eta(N)$ is given dimension N in the above diagram, rather than $N - 2$, which is all that is needed. This is for later convenience in programming. In the version of Basic used by the author, the dimension of $Eta(*)$ must be one of the parameters in the sub-program's list of pass parameters.

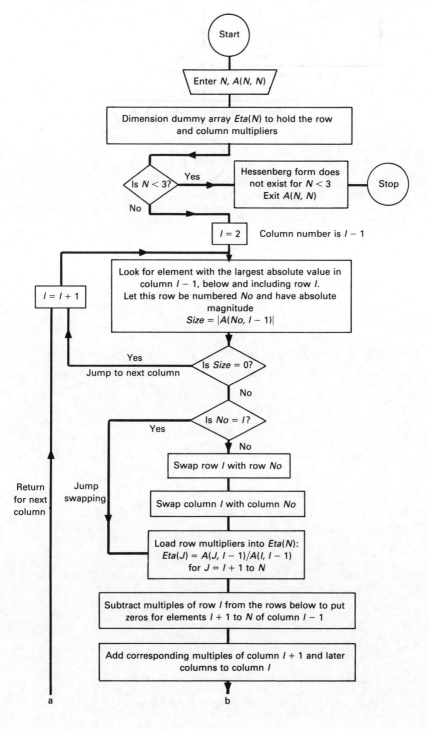

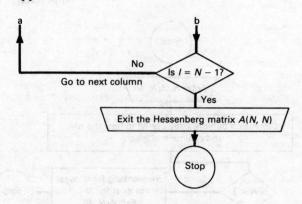

Appendix 2

Logical flow diagram for calculating one iteration of the QR transform

Program name: Qrmat

Notes

1. M is a variable dimension which is fed to this sub-program by the master program. In this context M has no relation to the number of degrees of freedom.

2. The calculation begins by scanning the sub-diagonal elements of the input matrix $A(M, M)$ looking for zeros. An element is defined as being (effectively) zero if its magnitude is less that that of the parameter Error which is specified at the start of the calculation.

3. The sub-diagonal elements are looked at in turn, starting from the element in the bottom row and working upwards. If a sub-diagonal element is found to be zero, the matrix $A(M, M)$ is partitioned as in equation (7.17).

4. Each iteration of the QR algorithm is applied only to the partitioned sub-matrix Y of equation (7.17). This sub-matrix is transformed so that its eigenvalues are swept in order towards the diagonal and its sub-diagonal elements approach zero.

5. Within sub-matrix Y, the algorithm checks whether any two adjacent sub-diagonal elements are small enough for the reduction to begin below the first row of Y. The first row of Y is called row J of the original matrix $A(M, M)$. The row at which reduction begins during each iteration is row Is of $A(M, M)$ which is row $Is - J + 1$ of Y.

6. At the conclusion of the calculation, the whole matrix $A(M, M)$ is returned, including the unprocessed upper sub-matrix X of equation (7.17). This is needed later when all the eigenvalues of Y have been found.

7. The calculation is designed to be repeated until one of the two

lowest sub-diagonal elements becomes zero, after which no further reduction occurs. The matrix $A(M, M)$ must then be deflated, which may be done by the algorithm described in Appendix 3.

8. The measure of effective zero, parameter Error, is set in the program which calls this sub-program. For a computer operating to 12 significant figures, it is suggested that

$$\text{Error} = (\text{Norm of the } A\text{-matrix}) \times 10^{-12}.$$

This is the order of accuracy of the elements of the Hessenberg matrix, which has been generated by transforming the A-matrix. For a calculation which includes transforming A to Hessenberg form, there seems to be no point in making calculations to accuracy greater than the accuracy of individual elements (see Wilkinson [110], p. 526).

However, an alternative strategy for deciding when a quantity is effectively zero is often used. The magnitudes of sub-diagonal elements are compared with the sums of the magnitudes of the adjacent diagonal elements. For a computer with accuracy to 12 significant figures, instead of the criterion

$$\text{Is } A(J, J-1) < \text{Error ?}$$

we would have

$$\text{Is } A(J, J-1) < [|A(J-1, J-1)| + |A(J, J)|] \times 10^{-12}?$$

and, instead of

$$\text{Is } \left| \frac{(|y| + |z|)*A(I, I-1)}{x} \right| < \text{Error ?}$$

we would have

Is

$$\left| \frac{(|y| + |z|)*A(I, I-1)}{x} \right| < [|A(I+1, I+1)| +$$

$$+ |A(I, I)| + |A(I-1, I-1)|] \times 10^{-12}$$

(see Wilkinson and Reinsch [111], p. 366).

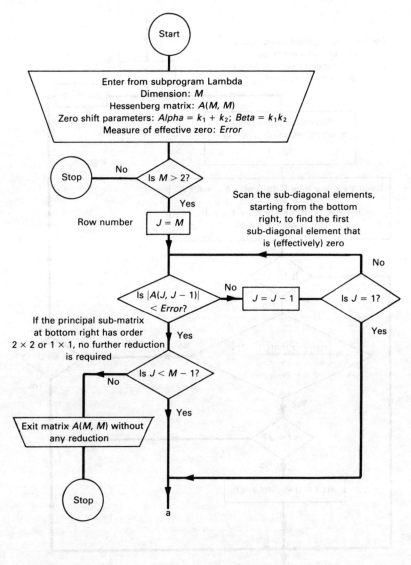

Start

Enter from subprogram Lambda
Dimension: *M*
Hessenberg matrix: *A(M, M)*
Zero shift parameters: *Alpha* = $k_1 + k_2$; *Beta* = $k_1 k_2$
Measure of effective zero: *Error*

Stop ←— No — Is *M* > 2?

Yes

Row number   *J = M*

Scan the sub-diagonal elements, starting from the bottom right, to find the first sub-diagonal element that is (effectively) zero

Is |*A(J, J − 1)*| < *Error*? — No → *J = J − 1* → Is *J* = 1? — No

If the principal sub-matrix at bottom right has order 2 × 2 or 1 × 1, no further reduction is required

Yes

Yes

Is *J* < *M* − 1? — No

Yes

Exit matrix *A(M, M)* without any reduction

Stop

a

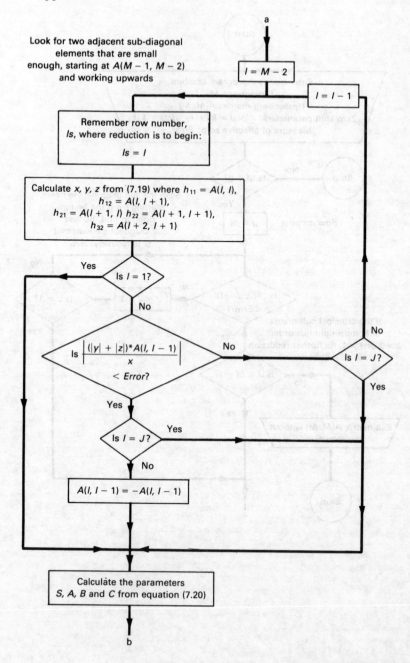

a

Look for two adjacent sub-diagonal elements that are small enough, starting at $A(M - 1, M - 2)$ and working upwards

$I = M - 2$

$I = I - 1$

Remember row number, Is, where reduction is to begin:

$Is = I$

Calculate x, y, z from (7.19) where $h_{11} = A(I, I)$, $h_{12} = A(I, I + 1)$, $h_{21} = A(I + 1, I)$ $h_{22} = A(I + 1, I + 1)$, $h_{32} = A(I + 2, I + 1)$

Is $I = 1$?

Yes

No

Is $\left| \dfrac{(|y| + |z|)*A(I, I - 1)}{x} \right| < Error$?

No

Is $I = J$?

No

Yes

Yes

Is $I = J$?

Yes

No

$A(I, I - 1) = -A(I, I - 1)$

Calculate the parameters S, A, B and C from equation (7.20)

b

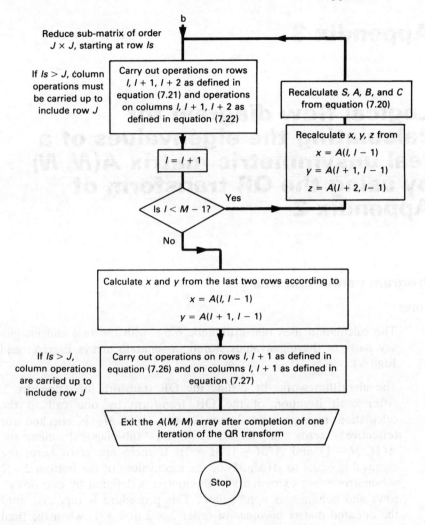

b

Reduce sub-matrix of order
$J \times J$, starting at row *Is*

If *Is > J*, column
operations must
be carried up to
include row *J*

Carry out operations on rows
$I, I + 1, I + 2$ as defined in
equation (7.21) and operations
on columns $I, I + 1, I + 2$ as
defined in equation (7.22)

Recalculate *S, A, B*, and *C*
from equation (7.20)

$I = I + 1$

Recalculate *x, y, z* from
$$x = A(I, I - 1)$$
$$y = A(I + 1, I - 1)$$
$$z = A(I + 2, I - 1)$$

Is $I < M - 1$?

Yes

No

Calculate *x* and *y* from the last two rows according to
$$x = A(I, I - 1)$$
$$y = A(I + 1, I - 1)$$

If *Is > J*,
column operations
are carried up to
include row *J*

Carry out operations on rows
$I, I + 1$ as defined in
equation (7.26) and on columns $I, I + 1$ as defined in
equation (7.27)

Exit the $A(M, M)$ array after completion of one
iteration of the QR transform

Stop

Appendix 3

Logical flow diagram for calculating the eigenvalues of a real unsymmetric matrix $A(N, N)$ by using the QR transform of Appendix 2

Program name: Lambda

Notes

1. The calculation uses real arithmetic only, with the real and imaginary parts of the eigenvalues stored in separate arrays Eigr(N) and Eigi(N).

2. The algorithm works by calling the QR transform of Appendix 2. After each iteration of the QR transform by one call to the calculation in Appendix 2, the matrix $A(M, M)$ is checked for (effective) zeros in its two lowest sub-diagonal elements, $A(M, M - 1)$ and $A(M - 1, M - 2)$. If there are zeros here, the eigenvalue equal to $A(M, M)$ or the eigenvalues of the bottom 2×2 sub-matrix is/are extracted and the matrix is deflated by one or two rows and columns as appropriate. This procedure is repeated until the deflated matrix becomes of order 2×2 or 1×1, when the final eigenvalues are extracted and the calculation stopped.

3. When the QR transform of Appendix 2 is called by the algorithm of Appendix 3, the lowest two sub-diagonal elements are rechecked for zeros as part of the partitioning process in Appendix 2. This redundancy allows the algorithm in Appendix 2 to be used independently of that in Appendix 3 if desired.

4. If the calculation completes 50 iterations of the QR algorithm without extracting all the eigenvalues, the program halts and shows an error message. In that case, different initial values for the zero-shift parameters Alphas and Betas may lead to earlier convergence (see Problem 7.4).

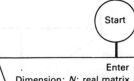

Start

Enter
Dimension: *N*; real matrix **A** as array *A(N, N)*;
Blank arrays *Eigr(N)*, *Eigi(N)*
to hold the real and imaginary
parts of the computed eigenvalues

Dimension the dummy array *Iter(N)*
to hold the cumulative number
of iterations to extract
each of the *N* eigenvalues

Calculate trace [**A**] for later checking

Set the initial values of the
zero-shift parameters *Alpha*
and *Beta*, for example,
Alphas = 0, *Betas* = 0

Calculate the measure of effective zero, *Error*, for example

$$Error = \left| \sum_{j=1}^{N} \sum_{k=1}^{N} a_{jk}^2 \right|^{1/2} \times 10^{-12}$$

Set the initial values:
Mark = 1 (on starting and
following matrix deflation;
otherwise zero)
M = *N* (order of the deflated matrix, initially *N*)
Jj = 0 (eigenvalue number)
Iter = 0 (number of iterations)

Call sub-program Hmat to reduce
A(N, N) to its upper Hessenberg
form required for the QR transform

Call sub-program Hdet to calculate
the determinant of the
Hessenberg matrix **A** in array
A(N, N) for later checking

a

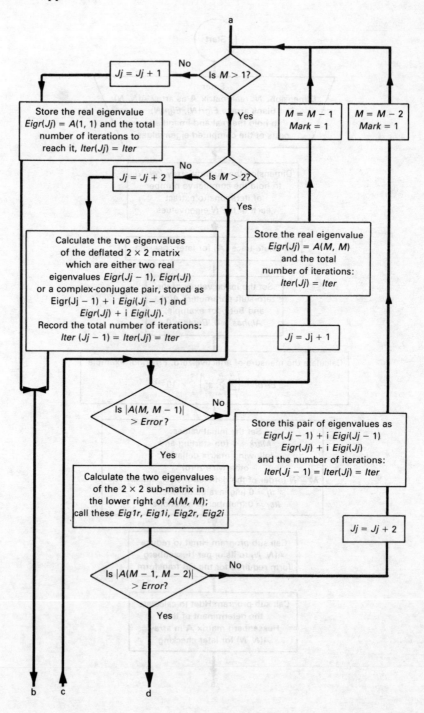

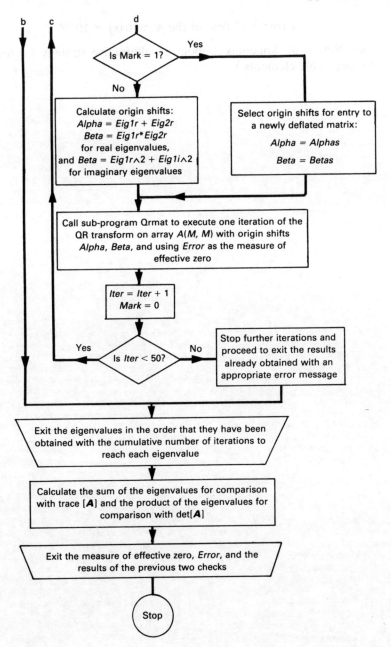

5.   This algorithm decides that a sub-diagonal element is (effectively) zero when its magnitude is less than a small positive quantity Error which is set at the beginning of the calculation. For a computer operating to 12 significant figures, it is suggested that

$$\text{Error} = (\text{Norm of the } A\text{-matrix}) \times 10^{-12}.$$

(See Note 8 of Appendix 2 about an alternative strategy for testing for negligible elements.)

Appendix 4

Logical flow diagram for calculating the determinant of an upper-Hessenberg matrix by Hyman's method

Program name: Hdet

Notes

1. This program calculates the determinant of a real, upper-Hessenberg matrix $A(N,N)$ by applying the logic of equations (7.32), (7.33) and (7.34).

2. When one of the sub-diagonal elements in (7.32) is zero, the matrix is partitioned as in equation (7.17) and the determinants of the sub-matrices X and Y are then calculated separately and multiplied together to obtain the determinant of the full matrix.

3. When a sub-matrix (or the original matrix) has only one term a separate calculation is made to set the determinant of the sub-matrix equal to the single element.

4. The bottom row of a sub-matrix is called row K and this is set to $K = N$ at the beginning of the calculation.

5. The rows of a sub-matrix are called row M where M begins at $M = K$ and is reduced in steps of -1 as the calculation steps up through higher rows of the sub-matrix.

6. After concluding the calculation on a sub-matrix whose first row is row M, K is reset to $M - 1$, and M begins again at K to step through the new sub-matrix.

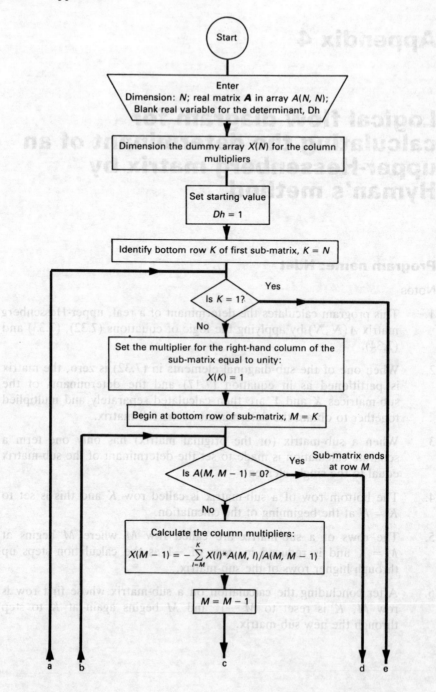

Start

Enter
Dimension: *N*; real matrix **A** in array *A*(*N*, *N*);
Blank real variable for the determinant, Dh

Dimension the dummy array *X*(*N*) for the column
multipliers

Set starting value
Dh = 1

Identify bottom row *K* of first sub-matrix, *K* = *N*

Is *K* = 1?   Yes

No

Set the multiplier for the right-hand column of the
sub-matrix equal to unity:
X(*K*) = 1

Begin at bottom row of sub-matrix, *M* = *K*

Is *A*(*M*, *M* − 1) = 0?   Yes   Sub-matrix ends
at row *M*

No

Calculate the column multipliers:
$$X(M - 1) = - \sum_{I=M}^{K} X(I) * A(M, I)/A(M, M - 1)$$

M = *M* − 1

a   b   c   d   e

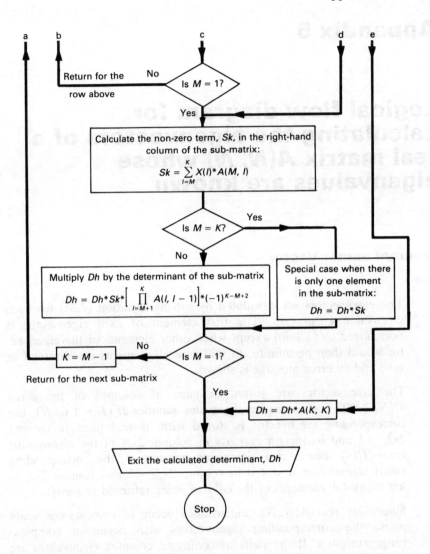

a b   c   d e

Return for the   No
row above ←—————— Is *M* = 1?

                        Yes

Calculate the non-zero term, *Sk*, in the right-hand
column of the sub-matrix:

$$Sk = \sum_{I=M}^{K} X(I)*A(M, I)$$

                        Is *M* = *K*? ——→ Yes

                        No

Multiply *Dh* by the determinant of the sub-matrix   Special case when there
                                                            is only one element
$$Dh = Dh*Sk*\left[\prod_{I=M+1}^{K} A(I, I-1)\right]*(-1)^{K-M+2}$$ in the sub-matrix:
                                                            Dh = *Dh*Sk*

K = *M* − 1 ←—— No Is *M* = 1?

Return for the next sub-matrix

                        Yes

                        Dh = *Dh*A(K, K)*

Exit the calculated determinant, *Dh*

Stop

Appendix 5

Logical flow diagram for calculating the eigenvectors of a real matrix $A(N, N)$ whose eigenvalues are known

Program name: Vector

Notes

1. The eigenvectors are calculated by solving equation (7.35) for each eigenvalue λ, in turn. The first element of each eigenvector is normalized to $(1 + i0)$ except when other elements of the eigenvector would then be infinite. In that case all elements are returned as zero and an error message is shown.

2. The eigenvectors are stored in pairs of columns of the array $U(N, 2*N)$. For a complex eigenvalue number Jj ($Jj = 1$ to N), the corresponding eigenvector is stored with its real parts in column $2*Jj - 1$ and its imaginary parts in column $2*Jj$ of the eigenvector array $U(*)$. For a real eigenvalue number Jj, the corresponding (real) eigenvector is stored in column $2*Jj - 1$ and column $2*Jj$ is left blank (all elements of the column being returned as zeros).

3. Since, for real $A(N, N)$, eigenvalues occur in complex-conjugate pairs, the corresponding eigenvectors also occur in complex-conjugate pairs. If the pairs of conjugate complex eigenvalues are numbered Jj and $Jj + 1$, the complex-conjugate pair of eigenvectors occupy columns $2*Jj - 1$, $2*Jj$, $2*Jj + 1$ and $2*Jj + 2$ of the eigenvector matrix. In this case, elements in columns $2*Jj + 1$ and $2*Jj + 2$ are written in directly from the calculated elements in columns $2*Jj - 1$ and $2*Jj$.

4. The method of solution of equation (7.35) is by Gaussian elimination with interchanges, followed by back substitution. When both the numerator and denominator of an element calculated in this way are (effectively) zero, that element is entered as zero and a message is shown that this element is indeterminate. When only the

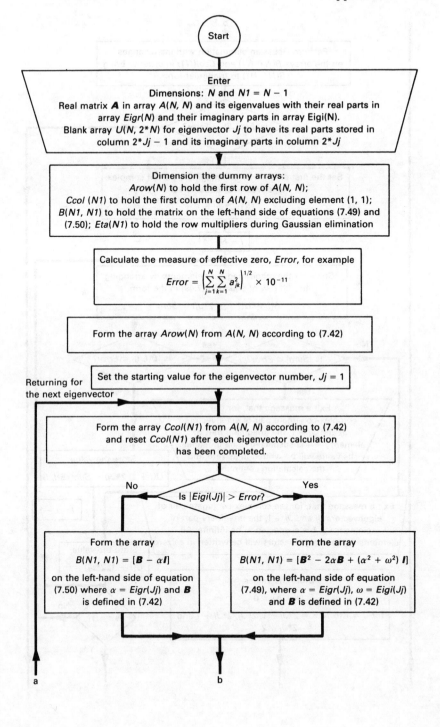

Start

Enter
Dimensions: N and $N1 = N - 1$
Real matrix **A** in array $A(N, N)$ and its eigenvalues with their real parts in
array $Eigr(N)$ and their imaginary parts in array $Eigi(N)$.
Blank array $U(N, 2*N)$ for eigenvector Jj to have its real parts stored in
column $2*Jj - 1$ and its imaginary parts in column $2*Jj$

Dimension the dummy arrays:
$Arow(N)$ to hold the first row of $A(N, N)$;
$Ccol (N1)$ to hold the first column of $A(N, N)$ excluding element $(1, 1)$;
$B(N1, N1)$ to hold the matrix on the left-hand side of equations (7.49) and
(7.50); $Eta(N1)$ to hold the row multipliers during Gaussian elimination

Calculate the measure of effective zero, *Error*, for example

$$Error = \left(\sum_{j=1}^{N} \sum_{k=1}^{N} a_{jk}^2 \right)^{1/2} \times 10^{-11}$$

Form the array $Arow(N)$ from $A(N, N)$ according to (7.42)

Set the starting value for the eigenvector number, $Jj = 1$

Returning for
the next eigenvector

Form the array $Ccol(N1)$ from $A(N, N)$ according to (7.42)
and reset $Ccol(N1)$ after each eigenvector calculation
has been completed.

No   Is $|Eigi(Jj)| > Error$?   Yes

Form the array

$B(N1, N1) = [\textbf{B} - \alpha \textbf{I}]$

on the left-hand side of equation
(7.50) where $\alpha = Eigr(Jj)$ and **B**
is defined in (7.42)

Form the array

$B(N1, N1) = [\textbf{B}^2 - 2\alpha \textbf{B} + (\alpha^2 + \omega^2) \textbf{I}]$

on the left-hand side of equation
(7.49), where $\alpha = Eigr(Jj)$, $\omega = Eigi(Jj)$
and **B** is defined in (7.42)

a

b

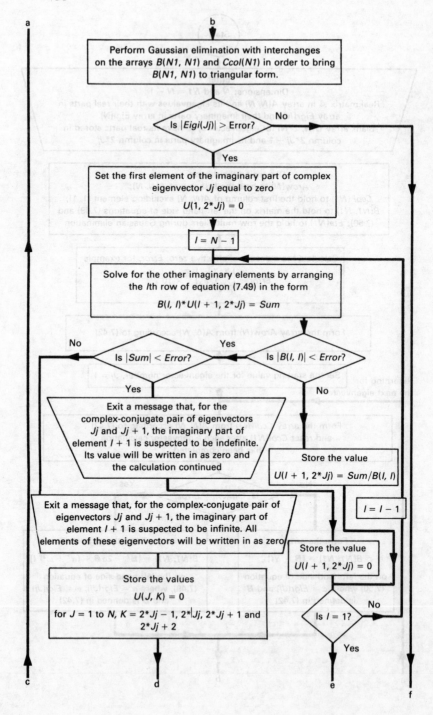

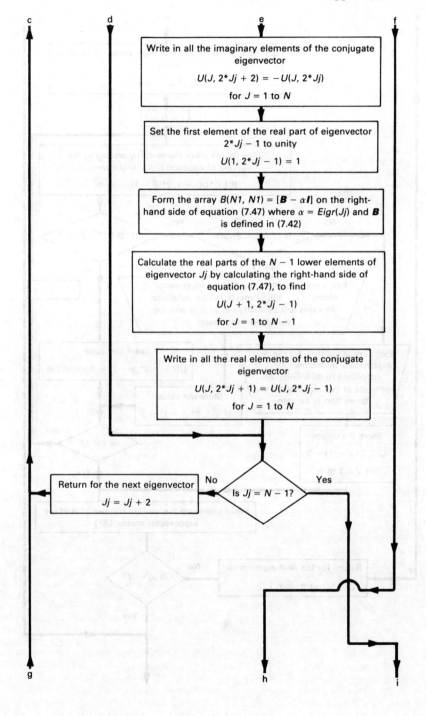

Write in all the imaginary elements of the conjugate eigenvector

$$U(J, 2*Jj + 2) = -U(J, 2*Jj)$$

for $J = 1$ to N

Set the first element of the real part of eigenvector $2*Jj - 1$ to unity

$$U(1, 2*Jj - 1) = 1$$

Form the array $B(N1, N1) = [\mathbf{B} - \alpha\mathbf{I}]$ on the right-hand side of equation (7.47) where $\alpha = Eigr(Jj)$ and $\mathbf{B}$ is defined in (7.42)

Calculate the real parts of the $N - 1$ lower elements of eigenvector Jj by calculating the right-hand side of equation (7.47), to find

$$U(J + 1, 2*Jj - 1)$$

for $J = 1$ to $N - 1$

Write in all the real elements of the conjugate eigenvector

$$U(J, 2*Jj + 1) = U(J, 2*Jj - 1)$$

for $J = 1$ to N

Return for the next eigenvector

$$Jj = Jj + 2$$

No ← Is $Jj = N - 1$? → Yes

c   d   e   f

g   h   i

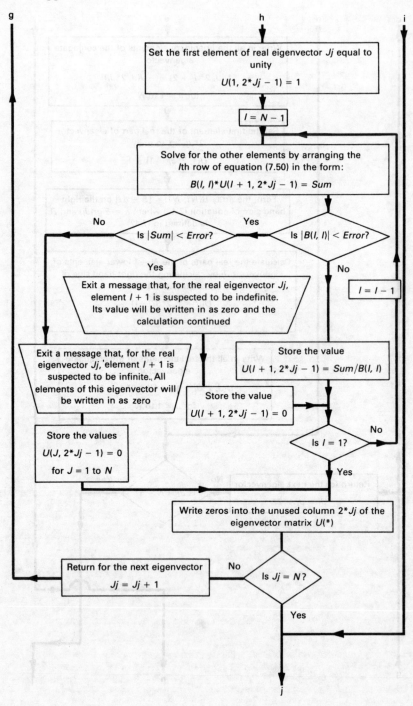

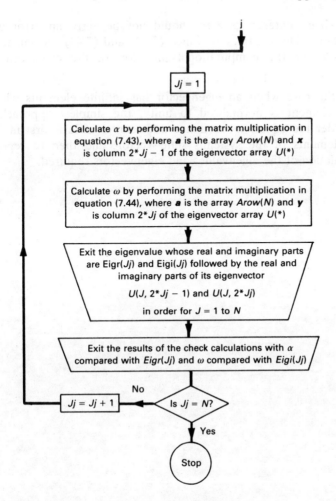

denominator is zero, the element is still entered as zero but a message is shown that the element should be infinite.

5. The measure of effective zero is defined by the positive parameter Error, which is set to a suitable small quantity at the beginning of the calculation. It is desirable for this to be larger than the corresponding small quantity used in the eigenvalue calculation. This ensures that elements of the eigenvector which are indefinite (to the accuracy of the calculation) are always identified.

6. The accuracy of each eigenvector is checked by computing the left-hand sides of (7.43) and (7.44) and comparing these with the real part of the eigenvalue, α, and the imaginary part of the eigenvalue, ω, respectively. When an eigenvector with infinite elements has been returned as zero, or when indefinite elements which

have been entered as zero should not be zero, an error will be apparent. The accuracy to which (7.43) and (7.44) are satisfied is a measure of the computational precision of the eigenvector concerned.

7. For the case when an eigenvector has infinite elements when the first element is normalized to unity, the simplest approach is to re-order the equations so that a different variable is first in the list of elements of the system's state vector, and then to repeat the calculation of the eigenvalues and eigenvectors required.

Appendix 6

Logical flow diagram for calculating the inverse of a complex matrix

Program name: Cinv

Notes

1. The complex matrix to be inverted is entered with its real parts in the array $Ur(N, N)$ and its imaginary parts in the array $Ui(N, N)$. The inverted matrix is returned in the same array. Real arithmetic is used throughout.

2. The method of solution involves Gaussian elimination with interchanges; instead of carrying out back substitution N times (once for each of the N columns), the more compact (but less accurate) method of eliminating the upper triangle of off-diagonal elements is used, as explained in Chapter 7.

3. When the absolute magnitude of the pivot element is less than the quantity taken to be effectively zero, inversion is stopped, and an error message is shown. The magnitude of effective zero can be adjusted as appropriate to the computer being used and the accuracy required.

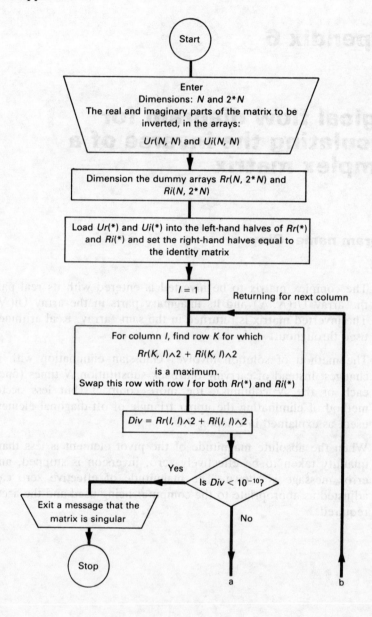

Start

Enter
Dimensions: *N* and 2*N
The real and imaginary parts of the matrix to be
inverted, in the arrays:

Ur(*N*, *N*) and *Ui*(*N*, *N*)

Dimension the dummy arrays *Rr*(*N*, 2*N) and
Ri(*N*, 2*N)

Load *Ur*(*) and *Ui*(*) into the left-hand halves of *Rr*(*)
and *Ri*(*) and set the right-hand halves equal to
the identity matrix

I = 1   Returning for next column

For column *I*, find row *K* for which

Rr(*K*, *I*)∧2 + *Ri*(*K*, *I*)∧2

is a maximum.
Swap this row with row *I* for both *Rr*(*) and *Ri*(*)

Div = *Rr*(*I*, *I*)∧2 + *Ri*(*I*, *I*)∧2

Is *Div* < 10^{-10}?

Yes   No

Exit a message that the
matrix is singular

Stop

a   b

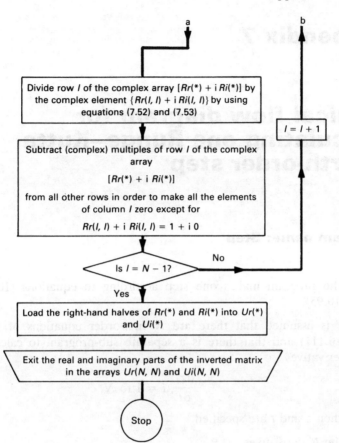

Appendix 7

Logical flow diagram for calculating one Runge–Kutta fourth-order step

Program name: Step

Notes

1. The program makes one step according to equations (10.94) and (10.95).

2. It is assumed that there are N first-order equations of the form (10.111) and that there is a separate sub-program to calculate the derivatives

$$\frac{dz_i}{dt}, i = 1 \text{ to } N,$$

when z and t are specified.

3. The N derivatives

$$\frac{dz_i}{dt}$$

are the elements of the array $Dz(N)$.

4. After one call to the sub-program to calculate slopes, the output from this sub-program is the array $Dz(N)$ whose elements are the elements of the matrix k_1. After a second call, the elements of $Dz(N)$ are the elements of k_2; after a third call they are the elements of k_3; and after a fourth call they are the elements of k_4.

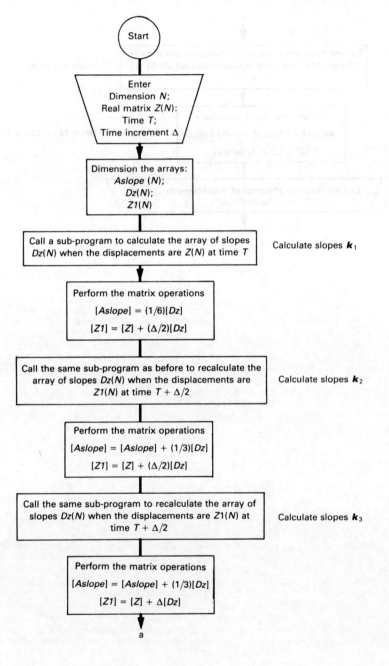

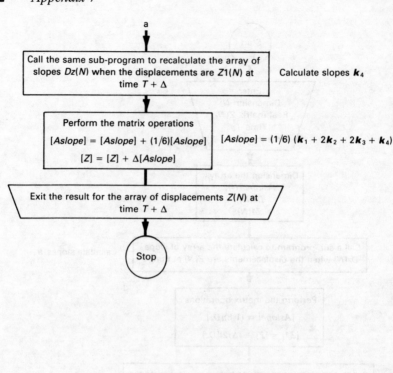

a

Call the same sub-program to recalculate the array of slopes $Dz(N)$ when the displacements are $Z1(N)$ at time $T + \Delta$

Calculate slopes k_4

Perform the matrix operations

$[Aslope] = [Aslope] + (1/6)[Aslope]$

$[Z] = [Z] + \Delta[Aslope]$

$[Aslope] = (1/6) (k_1 + 2k_2 + 2k_3 + k_4)$

Exit the result for the array of displacements $Z(N)$ at time $T + \Delta$

Stop

Problems

Note: Problem numbers are prefixed by the number of the chapter to which they relate.

1.1 Using the result that

$$\frac{d}{dt} \int x(t)\, dt = x(t)$$

show that

$$\frac{d\phi_1(t)}{dt} = e^{-\lambda_1 t} \frac{x(t)}{m}$$

where $\phi_1(t)$ is defined by (1.5). Hence show that if $y(t)$ is given by (1.4), then $\dot{y}(t)$ is given correctly by (1.7).

By substituting for $y(t)$, $\dot{y}(t)$ and $\ddot{y}(t)$, show that (1.4) is the correct general solution for (1.1).

1.2 Show that, if for excitation $x(t) = e^{i\omega t}$ the response is $y(t) = H(i\omega)\, e^{i\omega t}$, the ratio of amplitudes is $|H(i\omega)|$ and the response leads the excitation by angle θ where

$$\tan \theta = \frac{\text{Im}\{H(i\omega)\}}{\text{Re}\{H(i\omega)\}}.$$

Hint. Let $H(i\omega) = X(\omega) + iY(\omega)$, where $X(\omega)$ and $Y(\omega)$ are real. From (1.18), the amplitude of the excitation is one unit. The amplitude of the response is

$$\text{Re}\{(X(\omega) + iY(\omega))e^{i\omega t}\} = X(\omega)\cos \omega t - Y(\omega)\sin \omega t$$

$$= \sqrt{X^2(\omega) + Y^2(\omega)}\, \cos(\omega T + \theta).$$

1.3 Show that, if $\zeta = 1 - \varepsilon$, where $\varepsilon \to 0$, then

$$\sqrt{1 - \zeta^2} = \sqrt{2\varepsilon}\left(1 - \frac{\varepsilon}{4} + \cdots\right).$$

Substitute this result into (1.56) to show that, when $\varepsilon \to 0$, $h(t)$ reduces to (1.60).

1.4 For the case of steady-state harmonic excitation defined by (1.16), use (1.66) to find an expression for the complex frequency-response function $H(i\omega)$ defined by (1.21) for the case when $\zeta = 1$, and check that the result is in agreement with (1.26).

2.1 (i) If

$$X = \log_{10}\left(\frac{\omega}{\omega_N}\right)$$

and

$$Y = \log_{10}[\sqrt{km}|i\omega H(i\omega)|] = Y(X)$$

where $H(i\omega)$ is defined by (2.21), show that

$$Y = -\tfrac{1}{2}\log_{10}[10^{-2X} - (2 - 4\zeta^2) + 10^{2X}].$$

Hence confirm that the graph in Fig. 2.3(b) is symmetrical about the vertical axis at $\omega/\omega_N = 1$.

(ii) Similarly show that the graph in Fig. 2.3(c) is the result of reflecting the graph in Fig. 2.3(a) about the same axis.

2.2 (i) Prove that, when plotted on a polar diagram, the velocity-response function of the system in Fig. 1.1 always forms a perfect circle with its centre on the real axis, whatever the value of the damping. Hence show that the radius of the circle in Fig. 2.5(b) is $1/4\zeta$ which, for $\zeta = 0.1$, gives a radius of 2.5.

(ii) Show from (2.21) and (2.27) that the displacement and acceleration frequency-response functions for the system in Fig. 1.1 are related by

$$kH\left(i\frac{\omega}{\omega_N}\right) = mH_a^*\left(i\frac{\omega_N}{\omega}\right)$$

and hence confirm the similarity between the two polar reponse graphs of Fig. 2.5(a) and (c).

2.3 Consider the limiting form of the displacement frequency-response function defined by (2.21) when the damping ratio $\zeta \to \infty$, and verify that a polar graph for this case is a circle of radius $\tfrac{1}{2}$ with its centre at the point $(\tfrac{1}{2}, i0)$. Compare this result with the graph drawn in Fig. 2.6(a) for the case when $\zeta = 5$.

2.4 (i) For the numerical data given by (2.64), substitute (2.62) into equations (2.58), (2.59), (2.60) for the system shown in Fig. 2.7 and find expressions similar to (2.65) for the displacement frequency response functions $H_2(i\omega)$ and $H_3(i\omega)$.

(ii) Show that, when $H_2(i\omega)$ and $H_3(i\omega)$ are expanded into modal fractions, they give the results (2.86) and (2.87).

2.5 Find the frequency-response functions $H_{11}(i\omega)$, $H_{12}(i\omega)$, $H_{21}(i\omega)$ and $H_{22}(i\omega)$ for each of the four systems in Fig. P2.5(a) to (d). In cases

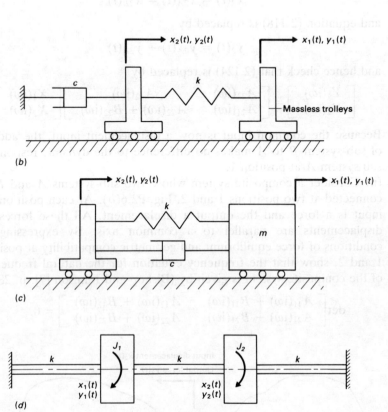

Fig. P2.5

(a) and (d), the inputs $x_1(t)$, $x_2(t)$ are torques and the outputs $y_1(t)$, $y_2(t)$ are angular displacements. In case (b), the inputs are forces and the outputs are displacements. In case (c), $x_1(t)$ is a force and $x_2(t)$ a displacement; $y_1(t)$ is a displacement and $y_2(t)$ a force.

Hint. In each case, to find $H_{11}(i\omega)$ and $H_{21}(i\omega)$, put

$$x_1(t) = e^{i\omega t}, x_2(t) = 0,$$

$$y_1(t) = H_{11}(i\omega)\, e^{i\omega t}, \quad y_2(t) = H_{21}(i\omega)\, e^{i\omega t}.$$

To find $H_{12}(i\omega)$ and $H_{22}(i\omega)$, put

$$x_1(t) = 0, x_2(t) = e^{i\omega t},$$

$$y_1(t) = H_{12}(i\omega)\, e^{i\omega t}, \quad y_2(t) = H_{22}(i\omega)\, e^{i\omega t}.$$

2.6 (i) Consider the composite system shown in Fig. P2.6(a). The input at position 2 is a prescribed displacement $x_2(t)$ and the output $y_2(t)$ is the force required to achieve this displacement. Confirm that equation (2.119) is replaced by

$$x_2(t) = x_{2A}(t) = x_{2B}(t)$$

and equation (2.118) is replaced by

$$y_2(t) = y_{2A}(t) + y_{2B}(t)$$

and hence check that (2.124) is replaced by

$$\begin{bmatrix} Y_1(i\omega) \\ Y_2(i\omega) \end{bmatrix} = \begin{bmatrix} A_{11}(i\omega) & A_{12}(i\omega) \\ A_{21}(i\omega) & A_{22}(i\omega) + B_{22}(i\omega) \end{bmatrix} \begin{bmatrix} X_1(i\omega) \\ X_2(i\omega) \end{bmatrix}.$$

Because the common input is now a displacement input, the addition of sub-system B to A makes no difference to the dynamic response of sub-system A at position 1.

(ii) Consider a composite system whose two sub-systems A and B are connected at two positions 1 and 2, Fig. P2.6(b). At each position, the input is a force and the output a displacement. All these forces and displacements are parallel to a common axis. By expressing the conditions of force equilibrium and geometric compatibility at positions 1 and 2, show that the frequency equation for the natural frequencies of the composite system is given by (Bishop and Johnson [7], p. 28)

$$\det \begin{bmatrix} A_{11}(i\omega) + B_{11}(i\omega) & A_{12}(i\omega) + B_{12}(i\omega) \\ A_{21}(i\omega) + B_{21}(i\omega) & A_{22}(i\omega) + B_{22}(i\omega) \end{bmatrix} = 0.$$

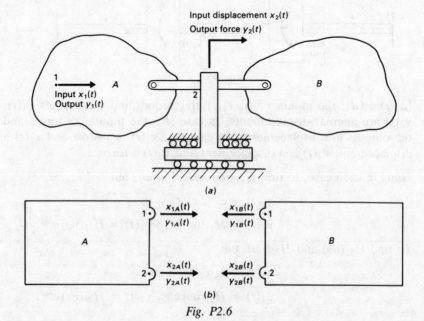

Fig. P2.6

3.1 (i) Investigate the shape of the polar graphs of the displacement, velocity and acceleration responses of a single-degree-of-freedom system with hysteretic damping whose displacement frequency-response function is given by (3.84). Which of these response curves is a perfect circle?

(ii) The polar graph of a frequency-response function $H(i\omega)$ is exactly a circle. If a graph of $|H(i\omega)|$ versus ω has the form shown in Fig. P3.1, find the form of a corresponding graph of $\phi(\omega)$ versus ω, where

$$\tan\phi(\omega) = \frac{-\text{Im}\{H(i\omega)\}}{\text{Re}\{H(i\omega)\}}.$$

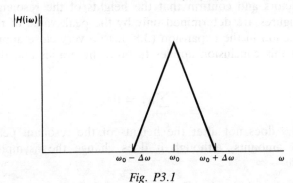

Fig. P3.1

3.2 Investigate the shape of a graph of $|H(i\omega)|$ versus ω where $H(i\omega)$ is defined by the partial fraction expansion (3.83). Assume initially that there is zero damping.

(i) Sketch a graph of $H(i\omega)$ (which is always real for zero damping) versus ω assuming that all the α_k, $k = 1$ to N, are positive.

(ii) Underneath this graph sketch a corresponding graph of $|H(i\omega)|$ versus ω.

(iii) Now consider how graphs (i) and (ii) are modified when some of the α's are negative. Find the conditions under which the zero frequency between ω_k and ω_{k+1} disappears but all the other $N - 2$ zero frequencies remain.

(iv) For $\omega \to \infty$, show that $H(i\omega)$ becomes indistinguishable from

$$-\left(\sum_{k=1}^{N}\alpha_k\right)\bigg/\omega^2 \text{ unless } \sum_{k=1}^{N}\alpha_k = 0,$$

in which case at least one zero frequency will have disappeared.

(v) By writing

$$\frac{\alpha_k}{(i\omega)^2 + \omega_k^2} = -\frac{\alpha_k}{\omega^2}\left(1 + \frac{\omega_k^2}{\omega^2} + \cdots\right)$$

when $\omega \to \infty$, explore the asymptotic behaviour of $H(i\omega)$ when $\omega \to \infty$ for the case when

$$\sum_{k=1}^{N} \alpha_k = 0.$$

(vi) Compare Fig. 3.7(b) with Fig. 3.9. These are both graphs of $|i\omega H(i\omega)|$ versus ω for the case when $N = 6$ and $\tan \psi_k = 0.05$, $k = 1$ to 6. In Fig. 3.7(b), $\alpha_k = 1$, $k = 1$ to 6, while in Fig. 3.9, $\alpha_1 = \alpha_2 = 2$, $\alpha_3 = \alpha_4 = \alpha_5 = \alpha_6 = -1$. Both graphs have been normalized by dividing $|i\omega H(i\omega)|$ by

$$\sum_{k=1}^{6} \alpha_k / \omega_k^2$$

before they have been plotted. Find the values of these different scaling factors and confirm that the heights of the resonant peaks in the two figures are determined only by the peak value of the relevant partial fraction in the expansion (3.83), to a very close approximation. Note that this conclusion applies to both the graphs and that the fact that

$$\sum_{k=1}^{6} \alpha_k = 0$$

for Fig. 3.9 does not alter the heights of the resonant peaks by any significant amounts, although it does change the asymptote of the graph as $\omega \to \infty$.

3.3 Use the general results (1.4), (1.5) and (1.6) to prove that the equation for the build-up of oscillations to resonance of an initially dormant mode is given correctly by equation (3.112).

3.4 Consider how the response of the undamped system represented by

$$\ddot{y} + \omega_N^2 y = x$$

builds up with time if

$$x = X_0 \cos \omega_N t$$

is applied at $t = 0$ when $y = \dot{y} = 0$ by taking the limit of (3.112) when $\zeta \to 0$.

Hint. Expand $e^{-\zeta \omega_N t}$ and $\sqrt{1 - \zeta^2}$ as power series in ζ.

4.1 Show that if the A-matrix defined in (4.6) is substituted into (4.12) and the determinant evaluated, the result is the characteristic equation

$$a_n \lambda^n + a_{n-1} \lambda^{n-1} + \ldots + a_1 \lambda + a_0 = 0$$

which is an nth-order polynomial whose solutions are the n eigenvalues λ_i, $i = 1$ to n.

4.2 Calculate the elements of the last column of U^{-1} when U is the eigenvector matrix defined by (4.17).

Hint. Start with the case $n = 3$ and show that if a, b, c are the elements of the third column, then

$$a + b + c = 0$$
$$\lambda_1 a + \lambda_2 b + \lambda_3 c = 0$$
$$\lambda_1^2 a + \lambda_2^2 b + \lambda_3^2 c = 1.$$

Solve these equations to find a, b and c. Hence deduce the result (4.37) for the general case.

4.3 (i) Show that, for harmonic excitation at frequency ω, the steady-state harmonic velocity response of the system defined by (2.1) is given by

$$\dot{y}(t) = \sum_{j=1}^{n} \frac{\lambda_j B(i\omega)}{a_n(i\omega - \lambda_j)\, \Pi_{k=1}^{n}(\lambda_j - \lambda_k)}\, e^{i\omega t}. \tag{i}$$
$$\scriptstyle k \neq j$$

Hint. Follow the same reasoning as that leading to equation (4.43).

(ii) Starting from

$$\dot{y}(t) = i\omega H(i\omega)\, e^{i\omega t}$$

where $H(i\omega) = B(i\omega)/A(i\omega)$, show from (i) that

$$\frac{1}{A(i\omega)} = \sum_{j=1}^{n} \frac{\lambda_j}{a_n(i\omega)(i\omega - \lambda_j)\, \Pi_{k=1}^{n}(\lambda_j - \lambda_k)}. \tag{ii}$$
$$\scriptstyle k \neq j$$

(iii) Equation (ii) provides an alternative expansion to that given by (4.48). Show similarly that further alternatives are given by

$$\frac{1}{A(i\omega)} = \sum_{j=1}^{n} \frac{(\lambda_j)^r}{a_n(i\omega)^r(i\omega - \lambda_j)\Pi_{k=1}^{n}(\lambda_j - \lambda_k)} \tag{iii}$$
$$\scriptstyle k \neq j$$

provided that the integer $r < n$, where n is the order of $A(i\omega)$.

(iv) For the case when $n = 3$ so that

$$A(i\omega) = a_3(i\omega - \lambda_1)(i\omega - \lambda_2)(i\omega - \lambda_3),$$

verify the correctness of the expansion (iii) when $r = 1$ and when $r = 2$.

4.4 The *minor* M_{jk} of the element a_{jk} in the jth row and kth column of the square matrix a is defined as the determinant of the matrix derived from a by deleting its jth row and kth column. The corresponding *cofactor* C_{jk} is defined as

$$C_{jk} = (-1)^{j+k} M_{jk}. \tag{i}$$

The determinant of an $n \times n$ matrix a can be defined as

$$\det a = \sum_{k=1}^{n} a_{jk} C_{jk} \tag{ii}$$

where j can have any of the values 1 to n. The adjoint matrix of a is defined as

$$\text{adj } a = [C_{kj}] \tag{iii}$$

which is a square matrix of all the cofactors of a with the order of the subscripts reversed. It can be shown (see, for example, Pipes and Hovanessian [81]) that the inverse of a is given by

$$a^{-1} = \frac{\text{adj } a}{\det a}. \tag{iv}$$

If a is a 3×3 matrix, show from (ii) that

$$\det a = a_{11}(a_{22}a_{33} - a_{23}a_{32}) + a_{12}(a_{23}a_{31} - a_{21}a_{33}) +$$
$$+ a_{13}(a_{21}a_{32} - a_{22}a_{31}) \tag{v}$$

and from (iii) that

$$\text{adj } a = \begin{bmatrix} (a_{22}a_{33} - a_{23}a_{32}) & (a_{13}a_{32} - a_{12}a_{33}) & (a_{12}a_{23} - a_{13}a_{22}) \\ (a_{23}a_{31} - a_{21}a_{33}) & (a_{11}a_{33} - a_{13}a_{31}) & (a_{13}a_{21} - a_{11}a_{23}) \\ (a_{21}a_{32} - a_{22}a_{31}) & (a_{12}a_{31} - a_{11}a_{32}) & (a_{11}a_{22} - a_{12}a_{21}) \end{bmatrix}. \tag{vi}$$

Hence show that, if the elements of a are as defined in the r.h.s. of (4.53), the differential equation relating $y_1(t)$ and $x(t)$ in (4.53) is given correctly by (4.57).

5.1 Calculate by hand the exact eigenvalues and eigenvectors of the system defined by (5.11) when $m = k = 1$ and $c = 0$. Hence check that the eigenvector matrix is

$$U = \begin{bmatrix} 1 & 1 & 1 \\ \sqrt{2} & 0 & -\sqrt{2} \\ 1 & 1 & 1 \end{bmatrix}$$

and verify that

$$U^{-1}AU = [\text{diag } \lambda_j]$$

when A is defined by (5.6) and λ_j by (5.9).

5.2 (i) Prepare a computer program to calculate the eigenvalues and eigenvectors of the seven-degree-of-freedom undamped chimney model described in Example 5.2. Check that this gives results in agreement with those quoted in Chapter 5.
(ii) Investigate the behaviour of

$$\det [A - \lambda_1(1 + \varepsilon)I]$$

where ε is a small non-dimensional quantity in the range

$$-5 \times 10^{-7} \leqslant \varepsilon \leqslant 5 \times 10^{-7}$$

and λ_1 is the smallest eigenvalue computed in part (i). Hence determine the sensitivity of this determinant to small changes in λ_1 and obtain an alternative approximation for λ_1. Why is computing λ_1 by this approach likely to lead to an inaccurate result?

(iii) For a conservative system, it will be shown in Chapter 11 that the equations of motion for free vibration can usually be written in the form

$$m\ddot{y} + k\,y = O$$

in which m and k are both symmetric matrices. Show that the non-symmetric mass and stiffness matrices given in (5.16) and (5.17) can be rearranged by re-ordering and combining rows so that they both become symmetrical.

Hint. Begin by reversing the order of rows, and then consider how to add and subtract rows three at a time so that $m_{jk} = 0$ unless $k = j - 1$, j or $j + 1$ and $k_{jk} = 0$ unless $k = j - 2, j - 1, j, j + 1$ or $j + 2$.

5.3 (i) Compute the eigenvalues and eigenvectors of the eight-degree-of-freedom torsional system in Fig. 5.7 for the numerical data listed as equations (5.29).

(ii) Read the last section of Chapter 5 on accuracy and then investigate the accuracy of the computed eigenvalues by comparing the sum of the eigenvalues with the trace of the A-matrix and the product of the eigenvalues with the determinant of the A-matrix.

(iii) Find also the sensitivity of the eigenvalues to small changes in shaft stiffness k.

(iv) Check on the accuracy of the eigenvectors as follows. Let a denote the first row of A. Normalize the eigenvectors so that the first element of each eigenvector is $1 + i\,0$ (if necessary by writing a program to divide each element of the eigenvectors by their first element). Then, if $x + iy$ is the eigenvector corresponding to eigenvalue $\alpha + i\omega$, check to what accuracy $ax = \alpha$ and $ay = \omega$. (These two identities are proved in Chapter 7.)

(v) Reduce both shaft stiffnesses by dividing by 10^6 so that the eigenvalues do not cover such a wide frequency range and investigate how this affects the accuracy of the computed eigenvalues and eigenvectors.

5.4 (i) Let A and B be two complex quantities for which

$$A = Ar + iAi$$

$$B = Br + iBi$$

where the *Ar, Ai, Br* and *Bi* are all real, and show that if $C = AB$, then $C^* = A^*B^*$, where C^* is the complex conjugate of C.

(ii) If the arbitrary constant c_k in (5.60) is

$$c_k = c\, e^{i\theta}$$

where c and θ are real, show that all the elements of $y(t)$ can be represented by a pair of counter-rotating phasors like those shown in Fig. 5.10(c) except that angle ϕ_k is replaced by $\phi_k + \theta$, where ϕ_k is given by (5.65) but θ is the same for all the elements.

5.5 (i) Modify the computer program of Problem 5.2 to include the effect of damping at the chimney's foundation, using the model in Fig. 5.4 and the calculation procedure in Fig. 5.9. For the following parameter values: $l = 6\,\text{m}$, $m = 3 \times 10^3\,\text{kg}$, $k = K = 10^9\,\text{N m/rad}$ and $c = 5.85 \times 10^7\,\text{N m s/rad}$ check the eigenvalues listed in Table 5.5 and calculate all the 14 eigenvectors.

(ii) Draw phasor diagrams for the modes of the chimney and, for the third oscillatory mode, prepare a diagram similar to Fig. 5.15 to show 'snapshots' of a full period of motion of this mode at intervals of 1/8th the period.

5.6 (i) Assuming (*a*) that there is pure rolling (so that if a wheel of radius r has angular velocity about its axle Ω, the centre of the wheel has velocity Ωr in the direction of the plane of the wheel); and (*b*) that the cone-shaped wheels (cone semi-angle α) run on knife-edged rails, show that an unconstrained railway wheelset has a kinematic motion whose frequency and wavelength are given by equations (5.69) and (5.70) provided that the amplitude of motion is small.

(ii) Show that, if the lateral and longitudinal creep forces are given by equation (5.74), the resultant lateral force on a wheelset from creep is given by (5.75) and the resultant yaw-angle couple from creep is given by (5.76) when x and θ are both small.

Hint. Calculate the lateral and longitudinal velocities of the centre of each wheel (*a*) in terms of x, $\dot{x}$, θ and $\dot{\theta}$ and (*b*) in terms of r, V and θ (all the parameters are defined in Fig. 5.16). The difference between the lateral velocities from (*a*) and (*b*) gives the lateral creep velocity, and the difference between the longitudinal velocities from (*a*) and (*b*) gives the longitudinal creep velocity. The lateral and longitudinal forces acting on the wheels at their points of rail contact can then be calculated from (5.74).

(iii) Use the results (5.75) and (5.76) to find the kinematic frequency and wavelength of a massless, rigid two-axle bogie and hence verify the results given in equations (5.71) and (5.72).

Hint. Let y be the lateral deflection of the centre of the bogie from the track centreline and θ be the yaw angle of the bogie, and calculate the lateral deflections of the centres of the two wheelsets in terms of y and θ.

(iv) It is shown in the theory of creep that spin of a rolling wheel about a vertical axis gives rise to a lateral force; also lateral creep gives rise to a spin couple (see, for example, Johnson [50] p. 259). If

u = longitudinal creep velocity,
v = lateral creep velocity,
ω = spin creep angular velocity,
V = forward speed of wheel,
P = longitudinal creep force,
Q = lateral creep force,
M = creep moment about the (vertical) spin axis,
G = shear modulus of elasticity (wheels and rails assumed the same),
and
a = radius of the contact patch (assumed circular),

then (Johnson [50], Appendix 5)

$$\frac{P}{Ga^2} = C_{11}\left(\frac{u}{V}\right)$$

$$\frac{Q}{Ga^2} = C_{22}\left(\frac{v}{V}\right) + C_{23}\left(\frac{\omega a}{V}\right)$$

$$\frac{M}{Ga^3} = C_{32}\left(\frac{v}{V}\right) + C_{33}\left(\frac{\omega a}{V}\right)$$

where

$C_{11} = 4.29$, $C_{22} = 3.73$, $C_{23} = -C_{32} = -1.50$ and $C_{33} = 1.18$.

It can be seen that the longitudinal and lateral creep coefficients C_{11} and C_{22} are similar in magnitude.

The effect of spin creep can be assessed as follows. (a) Calculate the maximum lateral acceleration for the centre of a bogie which is hunting steadily through an amplitude of 5 mm and a wavelength of 17 m when travelling at 50 m/s. Assuming that the mass of the bogie assembly is 5500 kg and that each wheel carries the same lateral force, calculate the maximum lateral creep force at each wheel. (b) For each wheel, calculate the change in spin angular velocity (i.e. the change in that component of the wheel's angular velocity which lies along the normal to the plane of the contact patch) when a wheelset is displaced laterally 5 mm, assuming conical wheels of cone semi-angle 0.05 on knife-edged rails. Hence calculate the change in lateral creep force due to spin. Take $a = 5$ mm and $G = 8 \times 10^{10}$ N/m². (c) Compare the results from parts (a) and (b) and hence comment on the likely effect of spin creep on bogie dynamics. How would this result be affected if the hunting amplitude is large enough for significant flange contact to occur?

(v) Additional wheel-rail forces arise from gravitational stiffness terms. These are illustrated in principle in Fig. P5.6. Calculate the change in magnitude and direction of the wheel–rail forces when a wheelset of weight W is displaced laterally distance x assuming cone-shaped wheels on knife-edged rails. Hence determine an expression for the lateral gravitational stiffness k_g for the wheelset. Calculate also an expression for the (negative) gravitational yaw stiffness c_g which is the result of the changing position and direction of the wheel–rail forces when the wheelset yaws through a small angle θ with x zero.

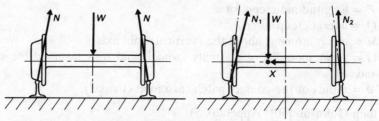

Fig. P5.6 (After Newland [69], courtesy of the American Society of Mechanical Engineers)

Estimate the importance of these gravitational stiffness terms by comparing the magnitudes of $k_g x$ with the creep 'stiffness' term $2f\theta$ in equations (5.77) and (5.79) and by comparing the magnitudes of $c_g\theta$ and the term

$$2f\,\frac{\alpha b}{r}\,x$$

in equations (5.78) and (5.80). Use magnitudes of x and θ for a hunting motion of amplitude 5 mm at a wavelength of 17 m.

Hint. The weight W in Fig. P5.6 is now the weight of the wheelset and the proportion of the weight of the bogie's frame and the car body which is carried on this wheelset. A value of 10 tonnes is suggested. If there is significant relative displacement between the bogie frame and its wheelsets or between the car body and the bogie, then additional gravitational forces arise due to these displacements. These additional forces may be neglected in the above calculations.

5.7 (i) Compute the natural frequencies and mode shapes of the flexible bogie in Fig. 5.16 for the numerical data in equations (5.87) but with the creep coefficient f reduced to zero.
(ii) Now derive the same results analytically by taking advantage of symmetry to identify that there is:

one wheelset yaw mode for which

$$\theta_2 = -\,\theta_1 \text{ and } x_1 = x_2 = y_1 = y_2 = 0;$$

two lateral modes with no yaw for which

$$x_1 = x_2, \ y_1 = y_2 \text{ and } \theta_1 = \theta_2 = 0$$

and three yawing modes for which

$$x_2 = -x_1, \ y_2 = -y_1 \text{ and } \theta_1 = \theta_2.$$

(iii) Compute also the eigenvalues and eigenvectors for the case when f has the value in (5.87) but the velocity V is infinitely large. Note that the c-matrix is now zero, and the calculation procedure in Fig. 5.1 can be used except that the eigenvalues will be complex because the coupling terms

$$2f \frac{\alpha b}{r} x_1$$

in (5.78) and

$$2f \frac{\alpha b}{r} x_2$$

in (5.80) make the system a non-conservative one because these terms cannot be derived from a potential-energy function.

6.1 (i) For a two-degree-of-freedom system defined by (6.3), show that the coefficient of λ^4 in the characteristic equation (6.9) is given by

$$a_4 = \det m.$$

Consider also the corresponding result for three degrees of freedom and hence confirm that (6.10) is true.

(ii) Show that, if $a_0 = 0$ but $a_1 \neq 0$, equation (6.12) may be replaced by the alternative equation

$$a_{2M}\lambda_{2M}\lambda_{2M-1} \ldots \lambda_3\lambda_2 = a_1$$

and hence confirm that, if $a_{2M} = 0$ then one (at least) of the eigenvalues $\lambda_2, \lambda_3, \ldots, \lambda_{2M}$ must be infinite and therefore does not exist.

(iii) Calculate the eigenvalues and eigenvectors of the three-degree-of-freedom systems in Fig. 5.2 for the undamped case when the middle mass is zero. Take $m = 1.0$ kg for the other masses and $k = 1.0$ N/m. Compare the undamped mode shapes with those in Fig. 5.3.

(iv) Also compute the eigenvalues and eigenvectors for the damped case when $m = 1.0$ kg, $c = 0.3$ N s/m, $k = 1.0$ N/m except that the middle mass is reduced to 0.001 kg, and compare your results with those in Table 6.1.

6.2 (i) For example 6.2 in the text, check that, when A, J and W are given by (6.47), (6.51) and (6.60), the similarity transformation

$$W^{-1}AW$$

correctly produces J. Show also that if the arbitrary parameters δ and ε in (6.56) and (6.59) are chosen differently, so that W is different from (6.60), the same result is obtained for J.

(ii) Investigate the effect of changing the mass matrix m in (6.45) to

$$m = \begin{bmatrix} 1 & 0 \\ 0 & \Delta \end{bmatrix}$$

and show that the eigenvalues are then the solutions of

$$(\lambda + 1)^2(\Delta\lambda^2 + \lambda + 1) = 0.$$

Find the eigenvalues and eigenvectors when $\Delta = 0.001$.

Note. Because of the ill-conditioned nature of this problem, with the second of the two equations of motion uncoupled from the first equation, the sub-program Vector in Appendix 5 cannot compute all of the eigenvectors for this example. It finds some of the elements to be indefinite and returns an appropriate warning message. The eigenvector check calculation incorporated in program Vector then shows an error for the eigenvector in question.

6.3 Find the Jordan matrix J and the principal-vector matrix W for a damped two-degrees-of-freedom system for which

$$m = \begin{bmatrix} 1 & 1 \\ 0 & 1 \end{bmatrix}, \quad c = \begin{bmatrix} 2 & 2 \\ 1 & 3 \end{bmatrix}, \quad k = \begin{bmatrix} 2 & 2 \\ 0 & 1 \end{bmatrix}.$$

If the response vector is $y = [y_1, y_2]^T$ and $z = [y_1, y_2, \dot{y}_1, \dot{y}_2]^T$ express the free vibration response $z(t)$ as a series expansion in the three modes of the system (two non-oscillatory modes and one oscillatory mode).

6.4 If A is a real $N \times N$ matrix with a complex-conjugate pair of eigenvalues λ_1, λ_1^* which is repeated, but which has only one pair of independent complex-conjugate eigenvectors, the corresponding Jordan matrix may be written in the form

$$J = \begin{bmatrix} \lambda_1 & 1 & & & & \\ & \lambda_1 & & & & \\ & & \lambda_1^* & 1 & & \\ & & & \lambda_1^* & & \\ & & & & \lambda_5 & \\ & & & & & \lambda_6 \\ & & & & & & \ddots \end{bmatrix} \quad (a)$$

(i) Show that, if $w^{(1)}$ is the independent eigenvector corresponding to λ_1, then $w^{(3)} = w^{(1)*}$ will be its complex conjugate and is the eigenvector corresponding to λ_1^*.

(ii) Show also that the principal vector $w^{(2)}$ is the solution of

$$Aw^{(2)} = w^{(1)} + \lambda_1 w^{(2)}$$

and that, if $w^{(4)}$ is the principal vector corresponding to λ_1^*, then

$$w^{(4)} = w^{(2)*}.$$

(iii) Hence write down an equation for the free response of the first and second oscillatory modes of A in terms of λ_1, $w^{(1)}$, $w^{(2)}$ and two arbitrary constants to be determined by the initial conditions.

Now consider a different case when A has an eigenvalue which is repeated three times but which has only one independent eigenvector so that the Jordan matrix is

$$J = \begin{bmatrix} \lambda_1 & 1 & & & & \\ & \lambda_1 & 1 & & & \\ & & \lambda_1 & & & \\ & & & \lambda_4 & & \\ & & & & \lambda_5 & \\ & & & & & \ddots \end{bmatrix}. \qquad (b)$$

(iv) If the first three columns of the principal-vector matrix W are $w^{(1)}$, $w^{(2)}$, $w^{(3)}$, show that

$$Aw^{(1)} = \lambda_1 w^{(1)}$$

$$Aw^{(2)} = w^{(1)} + \lambda_1 w^{(2)}$$

$$Aw^{(3)} = w^{(2)} + \lambda_1 w^{(3)}.$$

(v) Use the substitution $z = Wq$ to show that the equation of motion $\dot{z} = Az$ may be written as $\dot{q} = Jq$. Hence show that if q_1, q_2, q_3 are the first three elements of q then these satisfy the equations

$$\dot{q}_1 = \lambda_1 q_1 + q_2$$

$$\dot{q}_2 = \lambda_1 q_1 + q_3$$

$$\dot{q}_3 = \lambda_1 q_3.$$

Solve the last of these equations for q_3, using a constant C_3, then solve the second for q_2 and the first for q_1, using constants C_2 and C_1.

Finally, prove that the free-vibration response of a system which has the Jordan matrix in equation (b) above can be expressed in the expanded form

$$z(t) = C_1 e^{\lambda_1 t} w^{(1)} + C_2 e^{\lambda_1 t}(t w^{(1)} + w^{(2)}) +$$

$$+ C_3 e^{\lambda_1 t}(\tfrac{1}{2} t^2 w^{(1)} + t w^{(2)} + w^{(3)}) + C_4 e^{\lambda_4 t} w^{(4)} + \ldots$$

where C_1, C_2, C_3, C_4 are constants depending on the initial conditions.

7.1 (i) If the matrix A_2 in (7.5) is

$$\begin{bmatrix} 5 & 9 & 7 & 4 & 3 & 2 \\ 4 & 5 & 2 & 8 & 1 & 9 \\ 0 & 3 & 4 & 5 & 6 & 7 \\ 0 & 0 & 1 & 2 & 3 & 4 \\ 0 & 0 & 7 & 6 & 5 & 4 \\ 0 & 0 & 3 & 4 & 7 & 3 \end{bmatrix},$$

write a computer program to form the elementary matrix N_4 defined by (7.6) and complete the matrix multiplication $N_4 A_2$. Check that this has the form of (7.7).

(ii) Form the inverse matrix defined by (7.8) and check numerically that $N_4 N_4^{-1} = I$. Then complete the similarity transform $N_4 A_2 N_4^{-1}$ and check that this has the form of (7.9).

(iii) Also form the matrix N_3 defined by (7.10) and check that $N_3 A_2$ overwrites the zeros in the second column of A_2 and that $N_3 A_2 N_3^{-1}$ overwrites the zeros in the third column of $N_3 A_2$.

(iv) Find the elementary matrix N_5 for which $N_5 (N_4 A_2 N_4^{-1})$ has a zero at the bottom of its fourth column and hence complete the similarity transform

$$N_5 (N_4 A_2 N_4^{-1}) N_5^{-1}$$

to find an upper Hessenberg form of the matrix A_2.

(v) Use the sub-program Hmat in Appendix 1 or a similar library program to reduce A_2 to upper-Hessenberg form by an independent calculation and compare the result with that obtained in part (iv). Why may the two results be different?

(vi) Modify the calculation in parts (i) to (iv) so that rows 4 and 5 and then columns 4 and 5 of A_2 are swapped before $N_4 A_2 N_4^{-1}$ is computed, and so that rows 5 and 6 and columns 5 and 6 of the result are swapped before $N_5 (N_4 A_2 N_4^{-1}) N_5^{-1}$ is computed. Compare the result with that obtained from part (iv).

Note. Both the results from parts (iv) and (vi) are valid results for reducing A_2 to Hessenberg form because the Hessenberg form is not unique and depends on the similarity transform used for its calculation.

7.2 (i) Devise a program to check at what positive value of δ your computer records that

$$(1 + \delta) > 1.$$

Hence determine the number of significant decimal figures for which your computer operates and check by printing $1/3$ and $2/3$ to the highest possible accuracy.

(ii) Investigate the effect of round-off errors by calculating $N*(1/3)$ and subtracting $1/3$ from the result N times, where $N = 2, 10, 50$ and

500. For comparison, make the same calculations with 2/3 replacing 1/3.

(iii) Now study the working of the QR algorithm by modifying the program Qrmat in Appendix 2 or a suitable library program so that the *A* matrix is printed out on entry to Qrmat and after each iteration. Use this modified program to calculate the eigenvalues of the following 5×5 matrix:

$$\begin{bmatrix} 0.30 & 0.28 & 0.24 & 0.30 & 0.40 \\ 0.24 & 0.02 & 0.72 & 0.43 & 0.17 \\ 0.57 & 0.78 & 0.13 & 0.37 & 0.85 \\ 0.53 & 0.25 & 0.51 & 0.37 & 0.16 \\ 0.17 & 0.73 & 0.46 & 0.56 & 0.32 \end{bmatrix}.$$

Note that the Hessenberg matrix which is supplied to Qrmat by sub-program Hmat has exact zeros for all its elements below the sub-diagonal, but that these do not remain precisely zero after the QR algorithm is applied because of the round-off error in the QR calculation.

When the QR algorithm is called by the controlling sub-program Lambda (Appendix 3), a zero in the sub-diagonal line is assumed to have been reached whenever the magnitude of a sub-diagonal element is less than

$$\left(\sum_{j=1}^{N} \sum_{k=1}^{N} a_{jk}^2 \right)^{1/2} \eta$$

which, if $\eta = 10^{-10}$ for this problem comes out to be 2.24×10^{-10} approximately. Follow through the results of successive iterations of the QR algorithm to see how the original *A*-matrix evolves towards upper-triangular form (except for 2×2 sub-matrices centred on the diagonal line when the eigenvalues are complex) and compare your results with those quoted for the same problem in the example calculation in Chapter 7.

7.3 (i) Find the mass, damping and stiffness matrices for the system shown in Fig. P7.3, where y_1 and y_2 represent the displacement of the masses from their static equilibrium positions.

(ii) For the case when

$$m_1 = 80 \times 10^3 \text{ kg}, m_2 = 8 \times 10^3 \text{ kg}$$

$$k_1 = 5 \times 10^7 \text{ N/m}, k_2 = 8 \times 10^7 \text{ N/m}$$

$$c_1 = 8 \times 10^6 \text{ N s/m}, c_2 = 8 \times 10^4 \text{ N s/m}$$

$$c_3 = 0$$

write a master program similar to that in Fig. 5.9 to calculate the eigenvalues and eigenvectors of the system.

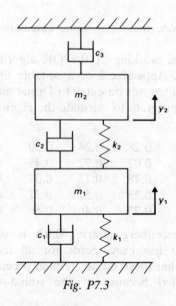

Fig. P7.3

(iii) In order to extract the eigenvalues, subprogram Lambda (Appendix 3) searches for zeros in the sub-diagonal of the transformed A-matrix. A zero is identified when the absolute magnitude of an element is less than the quantity

$$\text{Error} = \left(\sum_{j=1}^{N} \sum_{k=1}^{N} a_{jk}^2 \right)^{1/2} \eta$$

where η is a multiplier which is set at 10^{-12} in Appendix 3. Investigate the effect of altering η (or the comparable quantity for the program you are using) to (a) 10^{-14}, (b) 10^{-20} and (c) 10^{-60}.

Notice that no purpose is achieved by reducing η beyond a certain point, which is determined by the word size (number of significant digits) of the computer concerned. To the contrary, accuracy may be lost because more iterations of the QR algorithm are required by Lambda, and every iteration involves many calculations, all of which are only as accurate as the number of significant figures allows.

7.4 Use the program Lambda in Appendix 3 (or a similar library program for the QR transform) to calculate the eigenvalues of the following test matrices (Wilkinson [110], p. 539):

$$(i) \quad A = \begin{bmatrix} 0 & 0 & 0 & 0 & -1 \\ 1 & 0 & 0 & 0 & 0 \\ 0 & 1 & 0 & 0 & -1 \\ 0 & 0 & 1 & 0 & -1 \\ 0 & 0 & 0 & 1 & 0 \end{bmatrix}$$

$$(ii) \quad A = \begin{bmatrix} 0 & -1 & -1 & 0 & -1 \\ 1 & 0 & 0 & 0 & 0 \\ 0 & 1 & 0 & 0 & 0 \\ 0 & 0 & 1 & 0 & 0 \\ 0 & 0 & 0 & 1 & 0 \end{bmatrix}$$

$$(iii) \quad A = \begin{bmatrix} -1 & -1 & -1 & -1 & -1 \\ 1 & 0 & 0 & 0 & 0 \\ 0 & 1 & 0 & 0 & 0 \\ 0 & 0 & 1 & 0 & 0 \\ 0 & 0 & 0 & 1 & 0 \end{bmatrix}.$$

Record the number of iterations of the QR algorithm that are required to extract all the eigenvalues in each case.

It will be found that, in case (iii), the strategy adopted for choosing the zero-shift parameters Alpha and Beta in sub-program Lambda (Appendix 3) does not lead to the QR transform converging. However, if the starting values of Alpha and Beta in program Lambda are changed from

$$\text{Alphas} = 0, \text{ Betas} = 0$$

to, for example,

$$\text{Alphas} = 1, \text{ Betas} = 1/4$$

then the program converges in 10 iterations.

7.5 (i) Use the computer programs in Appendices 3 and 5 (or similar library programs) to compute the eigenvalues and eigenvectors of the 4×4 matrix

$$A = \begin{bmatrix} -5 & -9 & -7 & -2 \\ 1 & 0 & 0 & 0 \\ 0 & 1 & 0 & 0 \\ 0 & 0 & 1 & 0 \end{bmatrix}.$$

(ii) Compare your answers with exact values worked out by hand calculation.

(iii) Investigate the sensitivity of the computed eigenvalues to small changes in the elements of A. Hence confirm that changes of order ε in its elements make changes of order $\varepsilon^{1/3}$ in the multiple eigenvalues of A (Wilkinson [110], p. 542). An error of order, for example, 10^{-12} introduced by the finite word size of a computer therefore causes changes of order 10^{-4} in the multiple eigenvalues.

7.6 (i) Consider how Hyman's method for calculating the determinant of an upper-Hessenberg matrix is altered when one of the sub-diagonal elements $h_{j,j-1}$ is zero. Check that the form of the matrix (7.32) is changed to

$$
\begin{matrix}
\text{row } j \\
\text{when } j = 5, \\
N = 7 \longrightarrow
\end{matrix}
\begin{bmatrix}
h_{11} & h_{12} & \times & \times & \times & \times & k_1 \\
h_{21} & h_{22} & \times & \times & \times & \times & 0 \\
0 & h_{32} & h_{33} & \times & \times & \times & 0 \\
0 & 0 & h_{43} & \times & \times & \times & 0 \\
0 & 0 & 0 & 0 & h_{jj} & \times & k_j \\
0 & 0 & 0 & 0 & h_{65} & h_{66} & 0 \\
0 & 0 & 0 & 0 & 0 & h_{N,N-1} & 0
\end{bmatrix}
$$

and that the multiplier x_{j-1} in equations (7.34) is now arbitrary.

(ii) The value of a determinant is not changed by adding a multiple of one row to another row. Use this property to demonstrate that the determinant of an upper-Hessenberg matrix for which $h_{j,j-1} = 0$ is the product of the determinant of the upper principal sub-matrix of order $(j - 1) \times (j - 1)$ and the determinant of the lower principal sub-matrix of order $(N - j + 1) \times (N - j + 1)$. Generalize this result to prove that, for the matrix T' defined by (7.17),

$$\det T' = \det X \det Y.$$

Hint. Consider how to transform the matrix to triangular form by subtracting multiples of each row from the row below.

7.7 (i)Using real arithmetic only, prepare a computer sub-program to multiply together two complex matrices and display the result. Let the matrices be $U(N1, N2)$, $V(N2, N3)$ and $W(N1, N3)$, where $UV = W$. Express the real and imaginary parts of $U(N1, N2)$ in the two separate arrays $Ur(N1, N2)$ and $Ui(N1, N2)$, respectively, and similarly for V and W.

(ii) Write a master program to make the calculation

$$UV = W$$

where

$$
U = \begin{bmatrix}
1 + i3 & 2 & 3 \\
4 & 5 - i2 & 6 \\
7 & 6 & 4
\end{bmatrix}
\text{ and } V = \begin{bmatrix}
1 + i \\
1 \\
1 - i2
\end{bmatrix}
$$

by calling the sub-program from part (i).

(iii) Now add to the master program a calculation of U^{-1} by calling a sub-program like Cinv in Appendix 6, and use the result to evaluate $U^{-1}W$ to check that V is regained correctly.

7.8 The inverse iteration method is an accurate and powerful method of calculating the eigenvector u_j of a matrix A whose eigenvalue is known to be approximately s_j. If x^{n-1} is the $(n - 1)$th approximation of u_j, the next approximation is calculated from the formula

$$x^{(n)} = (A - s_j I)^{-1} x^{(n-1)}. \tag{i}$$

(i) If the initial approximation for the eigenvector required, $x^{(0)}$, is a linear combination of the true eigenvectors of A, so that

$$x^{(0)} = \sum_{k=1}^{N} c_k u_k \tag{ii}$$

prove that the result of one iteration is

$$x^{(1)} = \sum_{k=1}^{N} \frac{c_k}{(\lambda_k - s_j)} u_k. \tag{iii}$$

Hence show that, provided that the initial approximation $x^{(0)}$ has some contribution from the required eigenvector (so that $c_j \neq 0$) and that the eigenvalues are distinct and reasonably well separated, $x^{(n)}$ will converge to u_j.

Hint. Substitute for $x^{(1)}$ in equation (i) from equation (iii).

(ii) To implement this algorithm numerically, equation (i) in the form

$$(A - s_j I) x^{(n)} = x^{(n-1)}$$

can be solved for the elements of $x^{(n)}$ by Gaussian elimination with row interchanges. Because $(A - s_j I)$ is an almost singular matrix (its determinant would be zero if s_j were the exact eigenvalue), rounding errors required special consideration. When $(A - s_j I)$ has been reduced to triangular form, some of the pivots (i.e. the diagonal elements) will be very small. In one procedure, nearly zero pivots are replaced by a small positive quantity (say ε) and the calculation continued as if ε were the correct pivot (Wilkinson and Reinsch [111], II/18, p. 435).

Investigate this procedure for the case when A is only a 2×2 matrix and show that the ratio of the two elements of $x^{(n)}$ becomes independent of ε in the limit when $\varepsilon \to 0$. Note that the magnitude of these elements approaches infinity and so the elements of $x^{(n)}$ must be scaled down before proceeding with the next iteration. The same conclusions apply for matrices larger than 2×2 and very often only one or two iterations are needed to find U_j to working accuracy.

8.1 (i) Prove that if U is the $2M \times 2M$ eigenvector matrix for the M-degree-of-freedom system whose A matrix is defined by (8.2), then

$$U = \begin{bmatrix} U_{\text{upper}} \\ U_{\text{upper}}[\text{diag } \lambda_j] \end{bmatrix}$$

where U_{upper} is the upper half of U of dimension $M \times 2M$ and $[\text{diag } \lambda_j]$ is the $2M \times 2M$ diagonal matrix of eigenvalues, λ_j, $j = 1$ to $2M$.

Hint. Begin with the equivalent set of equations (8.4) with $F = O$ and show that, if $u^{(r)}$ is the rth column of U corresponding to λ_r, then

$$u^{(r)} = \begin{bmatrix} u_{\text{upper}}^{(r)} \\ \lambda_r u_{\text{upper}}^{(r)} \end{bmatrix}$$

where the vector $u_{\text{upper}}^{(r)}$ indicates the upper M elements of $u^{(r)}$.

(ii) Prove also that if W is the $2M \times 2M$ matrix of principal vectors for the case when A has multiple eigenvalues, that W may be partitioned in the same way so that

$$W = \begin{bmatrix} W_{\text{upper}} \\ W_{\text{upper}}[\text{diag } \lambda_j] \end{bmatrix}.$$

(iii) If the inverse eigenvector matrix U is partitioned into right-hand and left-hand halves, so that

$$U^{-1} = [U_{\text{left}}^{-1} \quad U_{\text{right}}^{-1}]$$

prove that

$$U_{\text{left}}^{-1} U_{\text{upper}} + U_{\text{right}}^{-1} U_{\text{upper}} [\text{diag } \lambda_j] = I.$$

8.2 (i) If the matrix X can be partitioned into two diagonal blocks X_1 and X_2 so that

$$X = \begin{bmatrix} X_1 & O \\ O & X_2 \end{bmatrix}$$

show that

$$X^{-1} = \begin{bmatrix} X_1^{-1} & O \\ O & X_2^{-1} \end{bmatrix}.$$

(ii) Hence show that if a Jordan matrix J has the form

$$J = \begin{bmatrix} C_r & O & O \\ O & C_s & O \\ O & O & C_t \end{bmatrix}$$

where C_r, C_s and C_t are Jordan sub-matrices as defined in Chapter 6, then

$$[i\omega I - J]^{-1} = \begin{bmatrix} [i\omega I - C_r]^{-1} & O & O \\ O & [i\omega I - C_s]^{-1} & O \\ O & O & [i\omega I - C_t]^{-1} \end{bmatrix}.$$

(iii) Prove that

$$[i\omega I - C_1]^{-1} = 1/(i\omega - \lambda)$$

$$[i\omega I - C_2]^{-1} = \begin{bmatrix} 1/(i\omega - \lambda) & 1/(i\omega - \lambda)^2 \\ 0 & 1/(i\omega - \lambda) \end{bmatrix}$$

$$[i\omega I - C_3]^{-1} = \begin{bmatrix} 1/(i\omega - \lambda) & 1/(i\omega - \lambda)^2 & 1/(i\omega - \lambda)^3 \\ 0 & 1/(i\omega - \lambda) & 1/(i\omega - \lambda)^2 \\ 0 & 0 & 1/(i\omega - \lambda) \end{bmatrix}$$

where $C_1 = [\lambda]$

$$C_2 = \begin{bmatrix} \lambda & 1 \\ 0 & \lambda \end{bmatrix}$$

$$C_3 = \begin{bmatrix} \lambda & 1 & 0 \\ 0 & \lambda & 1 \\ 0 & 0 & \lambda \end{bmatrix}$$

are Jordan sub-matrices of orders 1, 2 and 3.

(iv) Hence show that, if J is a diagonal matrix except for a sub-matrix C_2 in its upper left-hand corner, then instead of (8.39),

$$H_{rs}(i\omega) = \sum_{j=1}^{2M} w_{rj} \frac{1}{(i\omega - \lambda_j)} s_{js} + w_{r1} \frac{1}{(i\omega - \lambda_1)^2} s_{2s}$$

where the extra term arises from the contribution of $1/(i\omega - \lambda_1)^2$ in $[i\omega I - J]^{-1}$.

Hint. Take a simple case, for example $M = 2$, so that

$$J = \begin{bmatrix} \lambda_1 & 1 & 0 & 0 \\ 0 & \lambda_2 & 0 & 0 \\ 0 & 0 & \lambda_3 & 0 \\ 0 & 0 & 0 & \lambda_4 \end{bmatrix}$$

where $\lambda_2 = \lambda_1$, and then generalize the result.

(v) Show also that, if the super-diagonal element of unity in J occurs in row k and column $(k + 1)$, then

$$H_{rs}(i\omega) = \sum_{j=1}^{2M} w_{rj} \frac{1}{(i\omega - \lambda_j)} s_{js} + w_{rk} \frac{1}{(i\omega - \lambda_k)^2} s_{k+1,s}.$$

(vi) Prove that the corresponding result when the Jordan submatrix C_2 is replaced by C_3, with the first row of C_3 being row k of the complete Jordan matrix, is

$$H_{rs}(i\omega) = \sum_{j=1}^{2M} w_{rj} \frac{1}{(i\omega - \lambda_j)} s_{js} + w_{rk} \frac{1}{(i\omega - \lambda_k)^2} s_{k+1,s}$$
$$+ w_{rk} \frac{1}{(i\omega - \lambda_k)^3} s_{k+2,s} + w_{r,k+1} \frac{1}{(i\omega - \lambda_k)^2} s_{k+2,s}.$$

8.3 Figure P8.3 is a diagrammatic view of a dynamic testing apparatus. The specimen to be tested is a resilient block which is sandwiched between the loading mass m_2 and the inertia block foundation m_1. In order to find the equivalent dynamic stiffness k_2 and damping c_2 of the specimen, the loading mass is subjected to a vertical harmonic force $x e^{i\omega t}$ by an electromagnetic shaker (not shown). Assume that there are only vertical vibrations of the masses m_1 and m_2, and let y_1 and y_2 be the displacements of these masses from their positions of static equilibrium.

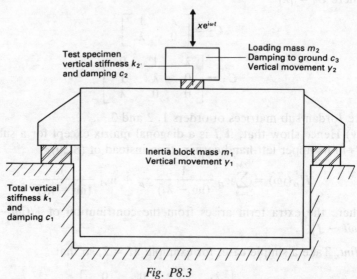

Fig. P8.3

(i) Find the mass, damping and stiffness matrices in terms of m_1, m_2, the stiffness and damping coefficients of the foundation system k_1, c_1, and of the specimen k_2, c_2, and the damping coefficient c_3 between m_2 and the ground. *Note* The same matrices were calculated in Problem 7.3(i), see Fig. P7.3.

(ii) For the following parameter values, calculate by hand the matrix $[(i\omega)^2 m + (i\omega)c + k]$ and use a suitable computer program to compute its inverse

$$m_1 = 80 \times 10^3 \text{ kg}, \qquad m_2 = 8 \times 10^3 \text{ kg}$$
$$k_1 = 5 \times 10^7 \text{ N/m}, \qquad k_2 = 8 \times 10^7 \text{ N/m}$$
$$c_1 = 4 \times 10^5 \text{ N s/m}, \qquad c_2 = 1.5 \times 10^5 \text{ N s/m}$$
$$c_3 = 2 \times 10^4 \text{ N s/m}, \qquad \omega = 100 \text{ rad/s}.$$

(iii) Hence find the amplitudes of the displacement, velocity and acceleration of the two masses when the amplitude of the excitation at $\omega = 100$ rad/s is $x = 500$ N.

(iv) Use equations (8.101) to compute a graph of $|i\omega H_{22}(i\omega)|$ versus ω, over a frequency range 0 to 200 rad/s. Compare the frequencies of the resonant peaks with corresponding values of

$$\sqrt{\frac{k_1}{m_1}} \quad \text{and} \quad \sqrt{\frac{k_2}{m_2}},$$

and comment on the differences.

(v) Compute the eigenvalues and eigenvectors of the system. Then use the calculation procedure in Fig. 8.1 to repeat the computation required for the graph in part (iv). Check that your results agree and compare the time of computation by the two different methods.

8.4 If the Jordan matrix J is diagonal except for a block of order 4, show that (8.146) remains true provided that this includes a new 4×4 sub-matrix of the form shown in (8.149).

Hint. Write down the equations for $q_r(t)$, $q_{r+1}(t)$, $q_{r+2}(t)$, $q_{r+3}(t)$ for unit impulsive excitation defined by (8.124), and follow the same approach as used in the text for the derivation of equations (8.137) and (8.139). Alternatively, apply the general result (8.170) and expand e^{tJ} according to (8.157).

8.5 (i) Show that, if

$$X = \begin{bmatrix} Y & O \\ O & Z \end{bmatrix},$$

where Y and Z are both square matrices, then

$$X^n = \begin{bmatrix} Y^n & O \\ O & Z^n \end{bmatrix}$$

where n is an arbitrary integer.

(ii) Show that the M coupled second-order equations (8.1) can always be written in the form

$$\dot{q} = Jq + W_{\text{right}}^{-1} m^{-1} x(t)$$

where

$$q(t) = W^{-1} z(t)$$

in the usual notation. If $\phi_k(t)$ is the kth row of $W_{\text{right}}^{-1} m^{-1} x(t)$, show that, if row k of J does not have a unit element in the super-diagonal line, then

$$q_k(t) = e^{\lambda_k t} \int e^{-\lambda_k t} \phi_k(t) \, dt + e^{\lambda_k t} C_k$$

where C_k is a constant of integration.

(iii) If J has a diagonal block

$$\begin{bmatrix} \lambda_k & 1 \\ 0 & \lambda_k \end{bmatrix}$$

occupying rows k and $(k + 1)$, prove that

$$q_k(t) = e^{\lambda_k t} \int dt \, e^{-\lambda_k t} \phi_{k+1}(t) \, dt + t \, e^{\lambda_k t} C_{k+1} + e^{\lambda_k t} \int e^{-\lambda_k t} \phi_k(t) \, dt + e^{\lambda_k t} C_k.$$

(iv) After integrating by parts, show that the result of part (iii) becomes

$$q_k(t) = e^{\lambda_k t}\int [e^{-\lambda_k t}\phi_k(t) - t\,e^{-\lambda_k t}\phi_{k+1}(t)]\,dt +$$
$$+ te^{\lambda_k t}\int e^{-\lambda_k t}\phi_{k+1}(t)\,dt + e^{\lambda_k t}C_k + t\,e^{\lambda_k t}C_{k+1}.$$

(v) Use the result in (8.166) for e^{tJ} when

$$J = \begin{bmatrix} \lambda_k & 1 \\ 0 & \lambda_k \end{bmatrix}$$

to prove that the result in part (iv) for $q_k(t)$ may be combined with the corresponding result for $q_{k+1}(t)$ to give

$$\begin{bmatrix} q_k \\ q_{k+1} \end{bmatrix} = e^{tJ}\int e^{-tJ}\begin{bmatrix} \phi_k(t) \\ \phi_{k+1}(t) \end{bmatrix}dt + e^{tJ}\begin{bmatrix} C_k \\ C_{k+1} \end{bmatrix}$$

and hence check that, in the general case,

$$q(t) = e^{tJ}\int e^{-tJ}W_{\text{right}}^{-1}m^{-1}x(t)\,dt + e^{tJ}C$$

thereby confirming equations (8.187).

9.1 If the Fourier transform of $f(t)$ is defined as

$$F(\omega) = \int_{-\infty}^{\infty} f(t)\,e^{-i\omega t}\,dt,$$

find the Fourier transforms of

(i) $f(t) = e^{-at}, 0 \leqslant t < \infty$
      $= 0, -\infty < t < 0$;

(ii) $f(t) = 0, 0 < t < \infty$
       $= e^{at}, -\infty < t \leqslant 0$;

(iii) $f(t) = e^{-a|t|}, -\infty < t < \infty$;

(iv) $f(t) = e^{-at}, 0 < t < \infty$
       $= -e^{at}, -\infty < t < 0$;

(v) $f(t) = e^{-at^2}, -\infty < t < \infty$;

(vi) $f(t) = a\sin\omega_0 t, -T < t < T$
       $= 0$ elsewhere;

(vii) $f(t) = a\sin\omega_0 t, -\infty < t < \infty$.

9.2 (i) For the system shown in Fig. P9.2 find the impulse-response function $h(t)$. Take $x(t)$ to be the excitation and $y(t)$ the response.

(ii) If $x(t) = x_0$ for $-T \leqslant t \leqslant T$

$\qquad = 0$ elsewhere,

find $y(t)$ by the superposition method.

(iii) If $x(t) = x_0 \cos \omega_0 t$ for all t, find $y(t)$ by the superposition method.

(iv) Find the frequency-response function $H(i\omega)$ for the system in Fig. P9.2 by taking the Fourier transform of the $h(t)$ obtained in part (i).

(v) Find the response $y(t)$ in part (iii) by using $H(i\omega)$.

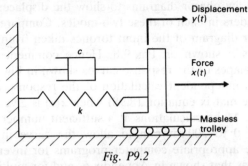

Fig. P9.2

9.3 (i) Check that the frequency-response function $H_{T1}(i\omega)$ found in Example 8.1, equation (8.67) can be derived from the corresponding impulse-response function $h_{T1}(i\omega)$ found in Example 8.3, equation (8.117) by using the Fourier transform relation (9.49).

(ii) Consider calculating (8.67) from (8.117) by using the inverse transform relation (9.50). It is not necessary to evaluate the integral, which requires knowledge of the theory of contour integration (see, for example, Ref. [49], Ch. 12), but the reader should be aware that the integration is possible.

9.4 (i) Show that the result (9.45) may be obtained directly from the convolution integral in its form (9.30).

(ii) By following the method used to derive (9.12) from (9.6), prove that

$$\int_{-\infty}^{\infty} \delta''(t - t_0)x(t)\,dt = x''(t = t_0).$$

(iii) By writing (9.2) as

$$x(t) = \int_{-\infty}^{\infty} X(i\Omega)\,e^{i\Omega t}\,d\Omega$$

and substituting this $x(t)$ into (9.1), show that (9.20) allows the integrations to be made provided that the integration over t can be taken before the integration over Ω. Hence show that, subject to the proviso that the order of integration may be reversed, (9.1) and (9.2) can be shown to be a transform pair.

Note. There is a general theorem that the orders of integration and/or summation may be interchanged in an expression in which convergence is retained when each term is replaced by its modulus. It appears that this condition will be satisfied for all physically realizable functions in vibration theory.

9.5 (i) Compute the 22 eigenvalues and eigenvectors of the 11-degree-of-freedom torsional system shown in Fig. 9.7 for the numerical data listed in (9.93).

(ii) Investigate the mode shapes for the first and second oscillatory modes and draw phasor diagrams to show the displacements at the six pairs of cylinders in each of these two modes. Compare these diagrams with a phasor diagram of the input torques taken from (9.98) for each of the orders n shown on Fig. 9.8. Hence comment on the relative heights and shapes of the response curves shown in Fig. 9.8.

(iii) Make an independent calculation of the response curve for $n = 6$ by solving the matrix equation (8.98) when $x(t)$ is given by (9.96) with $T_6 = 3$ kN m. Make calculations at a sufficient number of values of Ω in the range 0 to 500 rev/min to allow the curve in Fig. 9.8 to be checked. Use appropriate computer programs for inverting a complex matrix, such as that shown in Appendix 6, and for multiplying complex matrices, such as that developed for Problem 7.7.

10.1 (i) Show that if $X(i\omega)$ is the Fourier transform of $x(t)$, then $X(i\omega)\,e^{-i\omega T}$ is the Fourier transform of $x(t - T)$.

(ii) Let $x(t) = x(t + T)$ be a periodic function and show that this may be represented by the infinite series

$$x(t) = \sum_{k=-\infty}^{\infty} x_k(t)$$

where $x_k(t) = 0$ except between $kT < x < (k + 1)T$ when $x_k(t) = x(t)$. Hence show that, if

$$X_0(i\omega) = \frac{1}{2\pi}\int_0^T x(t)\,e^{-i\omega t}\,dt$$

then

$$X(i\omega) = \sum_{k=-\infty}^{\infty} e^{-i\omega kT} X_0(i\omega).$$

(iii) Now use the identity

$$\sum_{k=-\infty}^{\infty} \delta\left(\omega - \frac{2\pi k}{T}\right) = \frac{T}{2\pi}\sum_{m=-\infty}^{\infty} e^{-i\omega mT}$$

(Lighthill [55], Sect. 5.4) to show that if

$$X(i\omega) = \sum_{k=-\infty}^{\infty} X_k \delta(\omega - 2\pi k/T)$$

then

$$X_k = \frac{2\pi}{T} X_0\left(i\,\frac{2\pi k}{T}\right) = \frac{1}{T}\int_0^T x(t)\,e^{-i2\pi kt/T}\,dt$$

in agreement with (10.2).

10.2 (i) Use equation (10.2) to find the Fourier coefficients for a periodic function $x(t)$ which is a square wave of amplitude $\pm a$ and period T, and for which a change of level occurs from $-a$ to $+a$ at $t = 0$.

(ii) Use the FFT computer programs listed in Appendix 2 of *Random Vibrations and Spectral Analysis* (Newland [64]), which calculates the approximate Fourier coefficients according to (10.14), to find approximate values of X_k, $k = 0$ to 63, when

$$x_r = \begin{cases} a \text{ for } r = 0, 1, 2, \ldots, 31 \\ -a \text{ for } r = 32, 33, \ldots, 63. \end{cases}$$

(iii) Compare the answers to parts (i) and (ii) and explain why the coefficients X_k have a real component (for k odd) when calculated from (ii) but not when calculated from (i).

10.3 (i) Prove that (10.14) and (10.15) are a transform pair by substituting from (10.14) into (10.15) after changing the variable integer from r to s in (10.14) to avoid confusion with the r in (10.15).

Hint. Interchange the order of summation and consider how the value of

$$\sum_{k=0}^{N-1} e^{-i2\pi k(s-r)/N}$$

depends on $(s-r)$.

(ii) Prove Parseval's theorem in the three forms of equations (10.23), (10.24) and (10.25).

Hints. For (10.23), begin by substituting for X_k and X_k^* from (10.14) using index r for X_k and s for X_k^*.
For (10.24), proceed similarly except use (10.16) for X_k.
For (10.25), use (10.18) for $X(i\omega)$ and apply equation (9.20).

10.4 Prove that, if

$$m\ddot{y} + c\dot{y} + k\,y = x$$

represent M coupled second-order equations, the relationship between the first element y_1 of y and the first element x_1 of the excitation vector x has the form of equation (10.53), where

$$n = 2M \text{ and } m = 2(M-1).$$

10.5 (i) Find how equations (10.74) and (10.75) are modified when

$$\left(\frac{dz}{dt}\right)_{t\,=\,t_r}$$

is represented by a backward difference rather than a forward difference as in (10.73).

(ii) Hence show that, if the matrix A in (10.72) has eigenvalues all of which have real parts which are negative, then a finite-difference approximation of (10.72) based on backward differences always gives a result which is stable whatever the size of the interval Δ.

(iii) For a nonlinear problem defined by equation (10.111), show that the finite difference approximation is

$$z_{i,r+1} = z_{i,r} + \Delta f_i(z_r, t_r), \quad i = 1 \text{ to } N$$

when the derivative is expressed as a simple forward difference, but is

$$z_{i,r+1} - \Delta f_i(z_{r+1}, t_{r+1}) = z_{i,r}, \quad i = 1 \text{ to } N$$

when the derivative is expressed as a backward difference. Hence confirm that, when backward differences are used, each step requires a nonlinear equation to be solved, whereas, for forward differences, each step requires just one substitution of known values of z_r and t_r.

11.1 Use Lagrange's equations (11.8) to derive the equations of motion of the seven-degree-of-freedom chimney in Fig. 5.4 and hence check that the equations for this system derived by direct application of Newton's laws in Example 5.2 of Chapter 5 are correct.

Hint (i). In calculating the potential energy it is necessary to find the loss of height of the centre of mass of each rigid link. If θ is the angle made with the vertical by a link of length l, then the vertical space occupied by this link is $l \cos \theta$. Use this result for all the links, expressing the θ's in terms of the lateral displacements (assumed small) of the ends of the links.

Hint (ii). Compare the equations derived above with the symmetric equations obtained in Problem 5.2(iii).

11.2 (i) Show that, if there is only one generalized force x_1 applied at coordinate y_1 in the direction of y_1, the strain energy of the system in Fig. 11.1 is

$$U = \tfrac{1}{2}\alpha_{11}x_1^2;$$

that if there are two forces x_1 and x_2, the energy is

$$U = \tfrac{1}{2}[\alpha_{11}x_1^2 + \alpha_{12}x_1x_2 + \alpha_{21}x_2x_1 + \alpha_{22}x_2^2];$$

and that, if there are three forces x_1, x_2, x_3, the energy is

$$U = \tfrac{1}{2}[\alpha_{11}x_1^2 + \alpha_{12}x_1x_2 + \alpha_{13}x_1x_3 + \alpha_{21}x_2x_1 + \alpha_{22}x_2^2 + \alpha_{23}x_2x_3$$
$$+ \alpha_{31}x_3x_1 + \alpha_{32}x_3x_2 + \alpha_{33}x_3^2].$$

Hence confirm that equation (11.28) is correct.

(ii) Starting from equations (11.59) and (11.60), find

$$\frac{\partial T}{\partial \dot{y}_2} \text{ and } \frac{\partial V}{\partial y_3}$$

for the case when $M = 3$ and hence confirm that equations (11.70) and (11.71) are correct.

11.3 (i) Let the real, symmetric matrix A have an eigenvalue λ and corresponding eigenvector x so that

$$Ax = \lambda x.$$

Assume that x is complex and let x^{*T} denote the transpose of the complex conjugate of x. On pre-multiplying by x^{*T} we get

$$x^{*T}Ax = \lambda x^{*T}x.$$

The scalar $x^{*T}x$ is necessarily real. By taking the transpose of the complex conjugate of $x^{*T}Ax$ (which is also a scalar), show that $x^{*T}Ax$ must be real, and hence that the eigenvalues λ of a real, symmetric matrix A are always real.

(ii) Using the result that each distinct eigenvalue has only one eigenvector, show by taking the complex conjugate of $Ax = \lambda x$ that, if A and λ are real then x must also be real.

(iii) Prove that a necessary and sufficient condition for A to be positive definite is for all its eigenvalues to be positive. *Hint* Start from equation (11.79) where R is an orthogonal matrix. Define $y = Rx$ so that

$$y^T A y = x^T R^T A R x$$
$$= x^T [\text{diag } \lambda_j] x$$
$$= \sum_j \lambda_j x_j^2$$

from which the result follows when the λ_j are all positive.

11.4 (i) If $Q(i\omega)$ is the Fourier transform of $q(t)$, show that $i\omega Q(i\omega)$ is the Fourier transform of $\dot{q}(t)$.

Hint. Integrate by parts and assume that $q(t) \to 0$ for $|t| \to \infty$.

(ii) Take Fourier transforms of both sides of equation (11.157), using the above result, and hence show that (11.167) is true when $H_j(i\omega)$ is given by (11.166).

(iii) Find the Fourier transforms of $q(t) = e^{i\Omega t}$ and $\dot{q}(t) = i\Omega e^{i\Omega t}$ and hence show that the result in part (i) applies also when $q(t)$ is any periodic function of t.

Hint. Use equation (9.20).

11.5 (i) Show that, if m is positive semi-definite but k is positive definite, so that some of the natural frequencies ω_j are infinite, the eigenvector matrix U may be normalized so that

$$U^\mathrm{T} k\, U = I$$

and

$$U^\mathrm{T} m\, U = [\mathrm{diag}\ 1/\omega_j^2].$$

(ii) Hence show that, in this case, (11.163) is replaced by

$$h_j(t) = \frac{\omega_j}{\sqrt{1 - \zeta_j^2}} e^{-\zeta_j \omega_j t} \sin \omega_j \sqrt{1 - \zeta_j^2}\ t,\ t > 0$$

and (11.166) is replaced by

$$H_j(i\omega) = \frac{\omega_j^2}{(i\omega)^2 + 2\zeta_j \omega_j (i\omega) + \omega_j^2}.$$

(iii) Subject to the above amendments, show that (11.161) and (11.169) are still true and confirm that equation (11.169) is the Fourier transform of equation (11.161).

Hint. Begin by altering the upper limit of the integral to infinity by using (9.26) instead of (9.25).

11.6 For an undamped M-degree-of-freedom system whose equations of motion are

$$m\ddot{y}(t) + k\, y(t) = x(t) \qquad (a)$$

where m and k are real and symmetric and m is positive definite, the (displacement) eigenvector matrix U is normalized so that

$$U^\mathrm{T} m\, U = \bar{m} I. \qquad (b)$$

The system is subjected to constant-amplitude harmonic excitation at frequency ω and has steady-state response $y\, e^{i\omega t}$. A change in a parameter of the system is made which causes a small change Δk in the stiffness matrix k. As a result, the response to the same excitation changes by Δy.
(i) Show that

$$[k - \omega^2 m]\Delta y = -\Delta k\, y \qquad (c)$$

when second-order terms are neglected.
(ii) If the corresponding change in an eigenvector y_i can be expressed as

$$\Delta y_i = \sum_{j=1}^{N} \alpha_j y_j \qquad (d)$$

where the α_j are all small quantities so that

$$\alpha_j \ll 1$$

show that the corresponding change in natural frequency is given by

$$\bar{m}\Delta(\omega_i^2) = y_i^T \Delta k \, y_i \qquad (e)$$

and confirm that

$$\bar{m}(\omega_i^2 - \omega_j^2)\alpha_j = y_j^T \Delta k \, y_i, \, j \neq i. \qquad (f)$$

(iii) By using the result that the eigenvectors must be normalized to satisfy (b), show that if the α_j are in general quantities of order ε, then α_i will be of order ε^2.

Comment. Notice that equation (e) enables an estimate to be made of the changes in natural frequencies arising from any arbitrary change in a system's stiffnesses. Equation (f) enables the coefficients α_j to be calculated and therefore the corresponding changes in the system's mode shapes can also be estimated.

11.7 An undamped system with M degrees of freedom has mass and stiffness matrices m and k of order $M \times M$.
(i) Show that the natural frequencies are given by ω_j, $j = 1$ to M, where ω_j^2 are the M roots of the polynomial defined by

$$\det[-\omega^2 m + k] = 0.$$

(ii) The motion of one of the masses m_r of the system is completely defined by its (absolute) displacement y_r which is the rth element of the $M \times 1$ displacement vector y. If this mass is clamped, check that the rth equation of motion of the set of M equations is deleted and that the mass and stiffness matrices of the modified system can be obtained by deleting the rth row and rth column of the former m and k matrices.
(iii) From the result for part (ii), show that the natural frequencies of the modified system are given by Ω_k^2, $k = 1$ to $M - 1$ where Ω_k^2 are the $M - 1$ roots of the polynomial defined by

$$D_{rr} = 0$$

where the determinant D_{rr} is the rr-minor of

$$\det[-\omega^2 m + k].$$

(iv) Hence show that the frequency response function $H_{rr}(i\omega)$ for the original system, for an input force applied to m_r and for output displacement y_r, is given by

$$H_{rr}(i\omega) = \frac{1}{k} \frac{\left(1 - \dfrac{\omega^2}{\Omega_1^2}\right)\left(1 - \dfrac{\omega^2}{\Omega_2^2}\right) \cdots \left(1 - \dfrac{\omega^2}{\Omega_{M-1}^2}\right)}{\left(1 - \dfrac{\omega^2}{\omega_1^2}\right)\left(1 - \dfrac{\omega^2}{\omega_2^2}\right) \cdots \cdots \left(1 - \dfrac{\omega^2}{\omega_M^2}\right)}$$

where k is the static stiffness measured at the coordinate x_r. How is this result modified if $k = 0$? Take the total effective mass of the system to be $\bar{m}$.

(v) A four-cylinder reciprocating engine carries a flywheel at one end of the crankshaft. The effective moment of inertia of the flywheel and crankshaft taken together is 2 kg m^2. When the flywheel is fixed, the natural frequencies of torsional oscillation are 34.7, 100.0, 153.2 and 187.9 Hz; when the flywheel is free the natural frequencies are 46.5, 104.4, 154.8 and 188.3 Hz. Assuming that the system can be represented by a number of rigid discs connected by light elastic shafts, sketch the torsional frequency response measured at the flywheel (angular displacement output/torque input).

(vi) A generator of moment of inertia 4 kg m^2 is to be driven by the engine through a light elastic shaft rigidly coupled to the flywheel at one end and to the generator at the other. Find the torsional stiffness of the shaft in order that the lowest natural frequency of the combined system shall be 30 Hz and estimate the second lowest natural frequency.

Reminder. The cofactor of b_{jk} in $\det \boldsymbol{B}$ is $(-1)^{j+k}$ multiplied by the minor determinant D_{jk} which is the determinant of the $(M - 1) \times (M - 1)$ matrix obtained by deleting the jth row and the kth column of $\boldsymbol{B}$.

Hint. For part (vi), use equation (2.141).

12.1 Prove that the equation of free undamped vibration of the following systems (i) to (iv) can be written in the standard form

$$m(z) \frac{\partial^2}{\partial t^2} y(z, t) + L\{y(z, t)\} = 0$$

where $L\{y(z, t)\}$ is given by equation (12.19) to (12.22) respectively.

System (i): small lateral vibrations of a stretched string under tension T.

System (ii): longitudinal vibration of a slender elastic column of constant modulus E and cross-sectional area A.

System (iii): small lateral vibrations of an Euler beam of constant stiffness EI.

System (iv): small lateral vibrations of a flat, thin isotropic plate of constant stiffness D defined by equation (12.23).

Note. Readers unfamiliar with the theory of bending of thin plates, needed for part (iv), will find a concise explanation in Chapter 8 of Timoshenko and Gere [100].

12.2 Show that when the series expansion (12.26) is substituted into the general differential equation (12.25) then, because of (12.14) and

(12.15), the individual modal coordinates $q_j(t)$, $j = 1$ to ∞, are the solutions of (12.27) where the modal bandwidth $2\zeta_j\omega_j$ of mode j is given by equation (12.28).

Check that, if $\beta = 0$ but $\alpha \neq 0$, the proportional bandwidth $\Delta\omega_j/\omega_j$ is inversely proportional to ω_j and the modal Q-factor (see Table 3.1) increases in proportion to ω_j. Also check that if $\alpha = 0$ but $\beta \neq 0$, $\Delta\omega_j/\omega_j$ is proportional to ω_j and Q_j is inversely proportional to ω_j.

12.3 Use the following standard result (see, for example Jolley [51], series 810)

$$\frac{2\theta}{1 - \theta^2} + \frac{2\theta}{3^2 - \theta^2} + \frac{2\theta}{5^2 - \theta^2} + \dots \infty =$$

$$= \frac{\pi}{2}\tan\frac{\pi\theta}{2}$$

to prove that the two alternative expressions (12.98) and (12.99) for $H(L, L, i\omega)$ for an undamped elastic column are identical expressions.

12.4 Derive the equations of motion for the system shown in Fig. P12.4, where the inputs $x_1(t)$ and $x_2(t)$ are a force and a displacement, respectively, and the outputs $y_1(t)$ and $y_2(t)$ are a displacement and a force, respectively. Compare these equations with the standard matrix equation (11.76) derived in Chapter 11 for the small-amplitude vibration of a system with fixed supports.

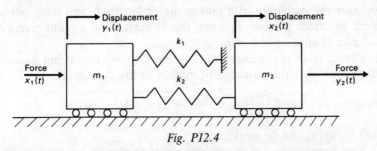

Fig. P12.4

12.5 Investigate how the analysis of the elastic column in Fig. 12.5(a) is modified if the equation of motion (12.103) is replaced by

$$m\frac{\partial^2 y}{\partial t^2} - c\frac{\partial}{\partial t}\left(\frac{\partial^2 y}{\partial z^2}\right) - EA\frac{\partial^2 y}{\partial z^2} = 0.$$

Check that equation (12.109) is replaced by

$$\frac{d^2 Y}{dz^2} + \left(\frac{\omega^2\rho}{E + i\mu\omega}\right)Y = 0$$

and make appropriate corresponding changes in the analysis that leads to equation (12.128) for the frequency response of the column (tension force at height z as output and displacement of the lower

end of the column as input). Hence compute and plot the corresponding version of Fig. 12.6 for the same data as before and
$c/A = 1.87 \times 10^6$ kg m^{-1}s^{-1}, where $m = \rho A$.

12.6 (i) If the amplitude of the upper end of the elastic column in
Fig. 12.5(a) is Y, calculate the amplitude of the reaction force at its
lower end when the column has zero damping and there is free
vibration. Hence confirm that an undamped column acts as a perfect
vibration absorber for harmonic force excitation at its lower end if the
excitation frequency is a natural frequency of the column for the case
when the lower end of the column is fixed.
(ii) Calculate the resonant frequencies for longitudinal vibration of an
undamped elastic column of length L, elastic modulus E and density
ρ when both ends of the column are free. Compare these frequencies
with those for a fixed–free column given by equation (12.51).

12.7 Find the displacement transmissibility (displacement output/
displacement input) (i) from the ground to the base and (ii) from the
ground to the top of the flexible column on a resilient base in
Fig. 12.11 in the limiting case when $\omega \to \infty$. Assume that the
column's equation is (12.166) and that $\eta \neq 0$.

Hint. Begin by showing that when $\eta\omega \to \infty$, $\lambda_1 = \alpha(1 + i)$ where
$\alpha = (\rho\omega/2E\eta)^{1/2}$, and then calculate the corresponding asymptotic
form of (12.121).

12.8 Consider the dynamics of a taut string of length L and mass per unit
length m under tension T, when this is excited by a point transverse
load $x(a, t)$ applied at $z = a$.
(i) If $y(z, t)$ is the transverse displacement of the string (assumed
small) show that the equation of motion of the system is

$$-T\frac{\partial^2 y}{\partial z^2} + m\frac{\partial^2 y}{dt^2} = x(a, t)\delta(z - a)$$

when damping can be neglected.
(ii) Find expressions for the displacement frequency-response function
of the string (displacement output at coordinate z/force input at
$z = a$) by substituting

$$x(a, t) = e^{i\omega t}$$
$$y(z, t) = H(z, a, i\omega) e^{i\omega t}$$

into the equation of motion and solving for $H(z, a, i\omega)$ to show that

$$H(z, a, i\omega) = \frac{\sin\left[\omega\sqrt{\frac{m}{T}}(L - a)\right]}{\omega\sqrt{mT} \sin\left[\omega\sqrt{\frac{m}{T}}L\right]} \sin\left[\omega\sqrt{\frac{m}{T}}x\right]$$

for $0 < x < a$

$$= \frac{\sin\left[\omega\sqrt{\frac{m}{T}}a\right]}{\omega\sqrt{mT}\,\sin\left[\omega\sqrt{\frac{m}{T}}L\right]}\,\sin\left[\omega\sqrt{\frac{m}{T}}(L - x)\right]$$

for $a < x < L$.

Note. These results are special cases of the general results when damping is included, which are given in *Random Vibrations and Spectral Analysis* [64], Chapter 16.

(iii) Check that the natural frequencies ω_j and mode shapes $U_j(z)$ are given by

$$\omega_j = j\frac{\pi}{L}\sqrt{\frac{T}{m}}$$

and

$$U_j(z) = \sqrt{\frac{2}{mL}}\,\sin\left(j\frac{\pi z}{L}\right).$$

(iv) Consider the response that occurs when the string is excited at one of its natural frequencies but the point of application of the force $x(a, t)$ is at a node. For example, take the third mode so that $\omega = \omega_3$ and let $a = L/3$. How does the string respond? By considering $H(z, a, i\omega)$ when $a = L/3$ and $\omega = \omega_3$, it will be seen that the expressions derived above are indeterminate, taking the form $0/0$. This problem can be overcome by setting $a = L/3$ and $\omega = \omega_3 + \Delta$ when Δ is small, and considering the limit when $\Delta \to 0$.

Check that the shape of the third mode is interrupted by a discontinuity at $z = L/3$ in such a way that the components of transverse force arising from the tension force T in the string on both sides of $z = L/3$ add to equal the magnitude of the externally applied force. Sketch the shape of the deflected string at one extreme of its motion.

(v) Check that an alternative series expansion for $H(z, a, i\omega)$ can be obtained by modal analysis in the form

$$H(z, a, i\omega) = \sum_{j=1}^{\infty} \frac{2\sin\left(j\frac{\pi z}{L}\right)\sin\left(j\frac{\pi a}{L}\right)}{mL[(i\omega)^2 + \omega_j^2]}.$$

(vi) Consider the limiting form of this expression when $a \to L/3$ and $\omega \to \omega_3$. Compute and plot against z the summation

$$\sum_{\substack{j=1 \\ j\neq 3}}^{20} \frac{2\sin\left(j\frac{\pi z}{L}\right)\sin\left(j\frac{\pi}{3}\right)}{mL(\omega_j^2 - \omega_3^2)}$$

and confirm that this gives an approximation for the same deflection curve as obtained in part (iv).

Note. The remaining term $j = 3$ in the summation for

$$H\left(z, \frac{L}{3}, i\omega_3\right)$$

is indeterminate. But it is zero for $\omega \simeq \omega_3$ and, since we do not expect a discontinuity at $\omega = \omega_3$, it is not surprising to find that this term does remain zero in the limit.

12.10 (i) Show from (12.55) that the response of a structure to a moving point load

$$x(z, t) = \delta[z - z_s(t)]x(t)$$

can be expressed in the form

$$y(z, t) = \sum_{j=1}^{\infty} U_j(z) \int_{-\infty}^{t} d\tau\, h_j(t - \tau) U_j[z_s(\tau)]x(\tau).$$

(ii) Hence, by taking the Fourier transform of this result and using (9.49), show that

$$Y(z, i\omega) = \sum_{j=1}^{\infty} U_j(z)H_j(i\omega)\frac{1}{2\pi}\int_{-\infty}^{\infty} d\tau\, e^{-i\omega\tau} U_j[z_s(\tau)]x(\tau).$$

(iii) Starting from (12.183) and (12.190) show also that, in the general three-dimensional case, this result becomes

$$Y(z, i\omega) = \sum_{j=1}^{\infty} H_j(i\omega)\frac{1}{2\pi}\int_{-\infty}^{\infty} d\tau\, e^{-\omega\tau}x(\tau)U_j(z)U_j^T[z_s(\tau)]e_s(\tau)$$

in the nomenclature used in Chapter 12.

(iv) Use the result of part (ii) to calculate $Y(z\, i\omega)$ for a simply-supported Euler beam of length L and mass per unit length m for which

$$U_j(z) = \sqrt{\frac{2}{mL}} \sin\left(j\frac{\pi z}{L}\right)$$

when a constant unit load crosses the beam at speed V. For the mid-point of the beam, $z = L/2$, sketch the components of $Y(z, i\omega)$ against ω for a typical mode j.

(v) Use the inverse discrete Fourier transform to compute and plot $y(L/2, t)$ as a function of time, including only the first three modes of the beam's response for the case when the first three natural frequencies are 50, 200 and 450 rad/s, the modal damping ratios are all 0.01, $L = 1$ m, $m = 1$ kg/m, $V = 2$ m/s and the unit load is 1 N.

13.1 Find expressions for the natural frequencies of an Euler beam defined by (13.1) for the following different end conditions:

(i)   clamped at one end, free at the other;
(ii) clamped at both ends;
(iii) free at both ends;
(iv) clamped at one end, pinned at the other;
(v)   pinned at one end, free at the other.

Hence check that the natural frequencies in cases (ii) and (iii) are the same except for two additional zero natural frequencies in case (iii). Similarly, check that the natural frequencies in case (iv) and (v) are the same except for an additional zero natural frequency in case (v).

Investigate the form of the normal mode functions when $a \to 0$ and hence confirm that there are no zero natural frequencies in case (ii) and case (iv). The results of this problem are illustrated in Fig. 13.1.

13.2 The deflection of the neutral axis of a beam $y(z, t)$ consists of two components $y_1(z, t)$ due to bending deformation and $y_2(z, t)$ due to shearing deformation (see Fig. P13.2(a)), so that

$$y(z, t) = y_1(z, t) + y_2(z, t). \qquad (a)$$

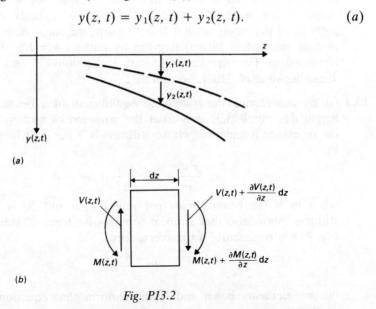

Fig. P13.2

If $M(z, t)$ is the bending moment in the beam, then from the usual beam theory

$$M(z, t) = EI \frac{\partial^2 y_1}{\partial z^2} \qquad (b)$$

where EI is the bending stiffness of the beam. Also, if $V(z, t)$ is the shear force in the beam, then if G is the shear modulus and A is the cross-sectional area of the beam, the mean shear stress is $V(z, t)/A$, and so the shear angle is

$$\frac{\partial y_2(z, t)}{\partial z} = \alpha \frac{V(z, t)}{GA} \tag{c}$$

where α is a non-dimensional factor which relates the shear at the neutral axis to the average shear stress in the cross-section.

(i) Using the sign conventions in Fig. P13.2(b), derive the equations of motion for transverse equilibrium and for rotational equilibrium of the beam element shown in terms of y, M, V, the second moment of area of the beam's cross-section I and its density ρ.

(ii) Substitute for $y_2(t)$ from (a) into (c); then substitute for M and V in the two equations of motion, and eliminate y_1 between them to obtain the final equation of motion of a beam when the effects of rotary inertia and shearing deformation are included. Check that the result agrees with equation (13.61).

(iii) Investigate the value of the non-dimensional factor α for a beam of rectangular cross-section. Check that, according to simple theory, the peak shear stress is 1.5 times the average shear stress, which suggests that α should be 1.5. However, if initially plane cross-sections of the beam are not free to warp, the shear deflection of the neutral axis is less than that given by putting $\alpha = 1.5$. This topic is discussed in Timoshenko [99], Part 1, Sections 39 and 63, and in Timoshenko *et al.* [100], Section 5.12.

13.3 (i) By considering the transverse equilibrium of a beam element of length dz, Fig. P13.3, show that the equation of motion for a beam on an elastic foundation whose stiffness is γ per unit length is given by

$$m \frac{\partial^2 y}{\partial t^2} + EI \frac{\partial^2 y}{\partial z^2} + \gamma y = 0$$

when m is the beam's mass per unit length and EI is its bending stiffness. Show also that an axial compressive force of P in the beam, Fig. P13.3, contributes a transverse force

$$-P \frac{\partial^2 y}{\partial z^2} \, dz$$

on the element shown and hence confirm that equation (13.83) is correct.

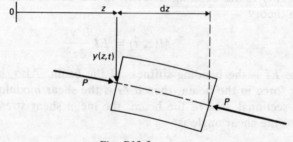

Fig. P13.3

(ii) If the beam is a pipe carrying an incompressible flowing fluid travelling at axial velocity U, check that the transverse velocity of a particle of fluid is

$$\left(\frac{\partial}{\partial t} + U \frac{\partial}{\partial z}\right) y(z, t)$$

and that its transverse acceleration is

$$\left(\frac{\partial}{\partial t} + u \frac{\partial}{\partial z}\right)^2 y(z, t).$$

Hence confirm that the transverse force that the pipe must apply over length dz to the flowing fluid (assumed incompressible) is

$$M \, dz \left(\frac{\partial^2}{\partial t^2} + 2U \frac{\partial^2}{\partial z \partial t} + U^2 \frac{\partial^2}{\partial z^2}\right) y(z, t)$$

where M is the mass of fluid per unit length of the pipe.

(iii) Investigate the travelling wave solution

$$y(z, t) = \sin(kz + \omega t)$$

where k and ω are real and verify that the wave speed c is given by

$$c = \omega/k$$

with the wave travelling in the direction of negative z.

(iv) Substitute this travelling-wave solution into equation (13.85) and verify that k and ω satisfy the dispersion relation

$$EI k^4 - (P + MU^2)k^2 - 2MU \, k\omega - (m + M)\omega^2 + \gamma = 0$$

in agreement with (13.91). Hence verify that ω will be complex if (13.94) is satisfied.

(v) If $\omega = \alpha \pm i\beta$, check that the travelling-wave solution in part (iii) will include an exponentially increasing term of the form

$$e^{\beta t} \sin(kz + \alpha t).$$

Hence confirm that the limiting condition for instability is given by equation (13.100) and that the wave speed is then given by (13.104).

13.4 (i) An initially-straight uniform shaft, whose mass per unit length is m and bending stiffness is EI is subjected to an axial compressive load P. If $y(z)$ is the deflected shape of the shaft in an equilibrium position of steady-state whirling at shaft speed Ω, show that $y(z)$ must satisfy the equation

$$EI \frac{d^4 y}{dz^4} + P \frac{d^2 y}{dz^2} - m\Omega^2 y = 0. \tag{a}$$

(ii) If ω is a natural frequency of bending vibrations of the non-rotating shaft in a natural mode whose deflection is

$$y(z, t) = y(z)\, e^{i\omega t}$$

show that $y(z)$ also satisfies equation (a), after changing Ω for ω.

(iii) Use equation (a) to find an expression for the critical whirling speeds of an infinitely long shaft which is supported by short, equally spaced bearings distance l apart. If the axial load P is proportional to the speed of rotation squared so that

$$P = p\Omega^2$$

show that the critical speeds Ω_n are given by

$$\Omega_n^2 = \frac{n^4\pi^2 P_c}{ml^2 + n^2\pi^2 p}$$

where P_c is the static buckling load of the non-rotating shaft and n is an integer.

(iv) For the case when the shaft is solid with a diameter of 0.3 m and with $m = 555$ kg/m, $E = 2.1 \times 10^{11}$ N/m², and $l = 12$ m, find P_c. Then find Ω_1 in rev/min for the case when $p = 0$ and when p is such that $P = 10^6$ N at $\Omega = 150$ rev/min.

13.5 (i) Show that, if the equation

$$m\ddot{y} + k\,y = \mathbf{0} \tag{a}$$

describes the free vibration of a multi-degree-of-freedom system, its lowest natural frequency ω_1 is defined by

$$\omega_1^2 = \frac{y_1^T k\, y_1}{y_1^T m\, y_1} = \frac{y_1^T m\, y_1}{y^T mk^{-1} m\, y_1} \tag{b}$$

where y_1 is the eigenvector (of displacements) corresponding to ω_1.

If y_1 is not available, but is replaced by the approximation

$$y = y_1 + \varepsilon_2 y_2 + \varepsilon_3 y_3 + \dots \tag{c}$$

and the quotients

$$\alpha^2 = \frac{y^T k\, y}{y^T m\, y} \tag{d}$$

and

$$\beta^2 = \frac{y^T m\, y}{y^T m\, k^{-1} m\, y} \tag{e}$$

are calculated, show that both α and β are upper-bound estimates for ω_1 and that β gives a closer approximation than does α.

(ii) Beginning with the result that the sum of the eigenvalues of a matrix is equal to the trace of the matrix (i.e. the sum of the diagonal elements of the matrix), use equation (a) above as a starting point to demonstrate that a lower-bound estimate for ω_1 is given by

$$\left[\frac{1}{\text{trace } [k^{-1}m]} \right]^{1/2}. \tag{f}$$

Note. The methods of part (i) are versions of Rayleigh's method and that of part (ii) is a version of Dunkerley's method.

(iii) Make three approximate calculations of the lowest natural frequency of the system shown in Fig. P13.5(a) by
(1) Rayleigh's method using equation (d);
(2) Rayleigh's method using equation (e);
(3) Dunkerley's method using equation (f).

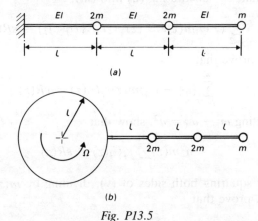

(a)

(b)

Fig. P13.5

Use an assumed deflection curve for the cantilever of the form $y = az^2$. Also, calculate the exact natural frequencies by a suitable computer calculation and compare the approximate and exact results.

(iv) If the system in part (iii) is a model of a turbine blade, which is attached at its root to a hub of radius l that rotates at angular speed Ω as in Fig. P13.5(b), use Rayleigh's method in the form of equation (d) of part (i) to estimate the stiffening effect of the centrifugal field on the lowest natural frequency of the blade (a) for the case when the blade vibrates in an axial plane and (b) for the case when the blade vibrates in a radial plane.

Hint. In each case, calculate the increase of the system's potential energy due to the inwards movement of the masses in the rotor's centrifugal field. The kinetic energy of the masses is then the kinetic energy of motion of the masses relative to the turbine's hub.

13.6 A continuous linear system is defined by

$$m(z) \frac{\partial^2}{\partial t^2} y(z, t) + L\{y(z, t)\} = 0. \tag{i}$$

The approximate normal mode function for the lowest frequency mode, $U(z)$, is given by

$$U(z) = U_1(z) + \varepsilon_2 U_2(z) + \varepsilon_3 U_3(z) + \dots \qquad \text{(ii)}$$

where $U_1(z)$, $U_2(z)$, etc. are the exact normal mode functions for natural frequencies ω_1, ω_2, ..., respectively. At frequency ω_1 the equation of motion is satisfied by $U(z)$ to order ε, so that

$$-\omega_1^2 m(z) U(z) + L\{U(z)\} = \varepsilon R(z) \qquad \text{(iii)}$$

where $R(z)$ is a residual function of zero order and $\varepsilon \ll 1$.
(i) Show that, by substituting (ii) into (iii),

$$\sum_{j=2}^{\infty} (-\omega_1^2 m(z) \varepsilon_j U_j(z) + \varepsilon_j L\{U_j(z)\}) = \varepsilon R(z)$$

and hence prove that

$$\sum_{j=2}^{\infty} (\omega_j^2 - \omega_1^2) m(z) \varepsilon_j U_j(z) = \varepsilon R(z). \qquad \text{(iv)}$$

(ii) By putting $\omega_2^2 - \omega_1^2 = a^2$, show that

$$a^2 m(z) \sum_{j=2}^{\infty} \varepsilon_j U_j(z) < \varepsilon R(z). \qquad \text{(v)}$$

Hence, by squaring both sides of (v), dividing by $m(z)$ and integrating over z, prove that

$$\sum_{j=2}^{\infty} \varepsilon_j^2 < \frac{1}{a^4} 0(\varepsilon^2). \qquad \text{(vi)}$$

(iii) Similarly, multiply both sides of (iv) and (v) together, divide through by $m(z)$ and integrate over z to prove that

$$\sum_{j=2}^{\infty} \varepsilon_j^2 \omega_j^2 < \frac{1}{a^2} 0(\varepsilon^2). \qquad \text{(vii)}$$

(iv) Show that, if $m(z)$ is zero for a sub-region of the complete system, then so is $L\{U_j(z)\}$ for all j, and hence that the integrations in (ii) and (iii) need only be carried out over that part of the system for which $m(z) \neq 0$.
(v) Hence confirm that the general result (13.123) is correct even though the series expansions in (13.118) are infinite in length.

Note. A corresponding general proof in the discrete case is given in Wilkinson [110], pp. 172–3.

13.7 (i) Prove that the integral (13.136) reduces correctly to the alternative form (13.138). Begin by substituting for $(P - pA)$ from (13.128) and consider the integral

$$\int_0^L dz \left[\int_z^L X(\xi) \, d\xi \right] \frac{d^2 U}{dz^2} U$$

where

$$X(\xi) = \left(A \frac{dp}{dz}\right)_{z=\xi}.$$

Integrate by parts using

$$\int u \, dv = uv - \int v \, du$$

where

$$u = \int_z^L X(\xi) \, d\xi.$$

(ii) Prove that the axial translation of section z of the initially-straight cantilever shaft in Fig. 13.3 is given by

$$\frac{1}{2} \int_0^z \left(\frac{dU}{dz}\right)^2_{z=\xi} d\xi$$

when the centreline of the shaft deflects to the position defined by $U(z)$. Hence verify by an energy calculation that the increase in potential energy of the extruder shaft of Fig. 13.3 due to deflection in its pressure field is given by the integral (13.138).

(iii) Use the result of part (i) of Problem 13.1 to check equation (13.154).

13.8 (i) Consider applying Rayleigh's quotient (13.111) to calculate an approximation for the second natural frequency ω_2 of a system with M degrees of freedom by using the approximate displacement vector

$$y = \varepsilon_1 y_1 + y_2 + \varepsilon_3 y_3 + \ldots + \varepsilon_M y_M.$$

Prove, by obtaining a result that corresponds to (13.118), that the approximation for ω_2 is correct to order ε^2 but that the result may be greater than or less than the true value. Compare this conclusion with the result of a calculation of ω_1 using the assumed vector (13.112) when the result is always greater than the true value.

(ii) Examine the Rayleigh–Ritz method of calculation to confirm that, when approximations for ω_1 and ω_2 are calculated together, both the results are upper-bound estimates for the true values. Check that the result (13.183) always produces a lowest natural frequency that is more accurate than the corresponding result (13.187) calculated by Rayleigh's method. Can the same be said about the second natural frequency?

(iii) Confirm that (13.174) and (13.175) may be written in the form

$$q_1(A_{11} - \omega^2 B_{11}) + q_2(A_{12} - \omega^2 B_{12}) = 0$$
$$q_1(A_{21} - \omega^2 B_{21}) + q_2(A_{22} - \omega^2 B_{22}) = 0$$

and hence that the Rayleigh–Ritz method reduces to a standard eigenvalue problem of the form

$$B^{-1}Aq = \omega^2 q.$$

The analysis of an undamped continuous system can thereby be reduced to the analysis of the eigensystem of an $M \times M$ matrix where M is the number of arbitrary real parameters included in the trial solution (13.161).

14.1 (i) By using the transformation

$$\tau = \Omega t,$$

show that Mathieu's equation (14.3) can be written in the standard form

$$\frac{d^2 y}{d\tau^2} + (\delta + \varepsilon \cos \tau)y = 0$$

where δ and ε are defined by (14.4) and (14.5).

(ii) When $\varepsilon = 0$, find the values of δ for which (*a*) periodic solutions are possible with period $2\pi/n$, $n = 1, 2, 3, \ldots$, and (*b*) periodic solutions are possible with period $4\pi/m$, $m = 1, 3, 5, \ldots$. Compare these results with those plotted in Fig. 14.1.

(iii) Also for $\varepsilon = 0$, check that, for each value of δ, there are always two independent stable periodic solutions if $\delta > 0$, there is always an unstable solution if $\delta < 0$, and that if $\delta = 0$ there is an unstable solution which tends to infinity according to the first power of τ.

14.2 (i) Show that if a matrix A is pre-multiplied by N, where N is an identity matrix except for rows j and k and columns j and k which are of the form

	col. j	col. k
row j	0	1
row k	1	0

then the rows j and k of A are interchanged.

(ii) Check that $N^2 = I$ so that N is its own inverse and hence show that, if A is post-multiplied by N^{-1}, columns j and k of A are interchanged.

(iii) Hence confirm that the similarity transformation

$$NAN^{-1}$$

involves interchanging rows j and k and then columns j and k, in this or the reverse order.

(iv) Use this transformation to demonstrate that

$$\begin{bmatrix} a_{11} & 0 & a_{13} & 0 & 0 & 0 \\ 0 & a_{22} & 0 & a_{24} & 0 & 0 \\ a_{31} & 0 & a_{33} & 0 & a_{35} & 0 \\ 0 & a_{42} & 0 & a_{44} & 0 & a_{46} \\ 0 & 0 & a_{53} & 0 & a_{55} & 0 \\ 0 & 0 & 0 & a_{64} & 0 & a_{66} \end{bmatrix}$$

is similar to

$$\begin{bmatrix} \begin{array}{ccc|ccc} a_{11} & a_{13} & 0 & & & \\ a_{31} & a_{33} & a_{35} & & \boldsymbol{O} & \\ 0 & a_{53} & a_{55} & & & \\ \hline & & & a_{22} & a_{24} & 0 \\ & \boldsymbol{O} & & a_{42} & a_{44} & a_{46} \\ & & & 0 & a_{64} & a_{66} \end{array} \end{bmatrix}.$$

14.3 (i) Compute the eigenvalues and eigenvectors of the A matrix defined by equation (14.22) for $\varepsilon = 0.5$ and N successively 4, 9 and 15. Investigate how the accuracy of the eigenvalues and eigenvectors depends on N.

(ii) Prove that the value of the determinant of a tri-diagonal matrix is not altered if the sign of all the super-diagonal and sub-diagonal elements is reversed. Hence show that the stability diagram of ε against δ for a Mathieu equation has mirror symmetry about the axis $\varepsilon = 0$.

14.4 Compute the eigenvalues δ for $\varepsilon = 1$ for each of matrices A, B, E and F defined by (14.22), (14.23), (14.30) and (14.31) taking the order of the matrices to be 10×10. Compute also the corresponding eigenvectors and hence show that the frequency of the dominant harmonic at each stability boundary is close to the natural frequency ω, in agreement with Table 14.1. Note that accurate eigenvectors can only be obtained for the small eigenvalues ($\delta < 9$, approximately) with matrices of this order.

14.5 (i) By substituting the periodic expansion

$$y(t) = \sum_{j=1}^{\infty} b_j \sin j \, \frac{\Omega}{3} t$$

into the Mathieu equation (14.3), using the identity

$$2 \cos \Omega t \sin(j\eta \, \Omega t) = \sin(1 + j\eta) \Omega t - \sin(1 - j\eta) \Omega t,$$

and equating like terms, show that for chosen ε defined by (14.5), the values of δ defined by (14.4) are the eigenvalues of

$$
\begin{bmatrix}
1/9 & \varepsilon/2 & 0 & -\varepsilon/2 & & & & \\
\varepsilon/2 & 4/9 & 0 & 0 & -\varepsilon/2 & & & \\
0 & 0 & 1 & 0 & 0 & -\varepsilon/2 & & \\
-\varepsilon/2 & 0 & 0 & 16/9 & 0 & 0 & -\varepsilon/2 & \\
 & -\varepsilon/2 & 0 & 0 & 25/9 & 0 & & \\
 & & \cdot & \cdot & \cdot & \cdot & \cdot & -\varepsilon/2 \\
 & & & \cdot & & \cdot & \cdot & 0 \\
 & & & & \cdot & & \cdot & 0 \\
 & & & & & -\varepsilon/2 & 0 & 0 & N^2/9
\end{bmatrix}
$$

(ii) Compute these eigenvalues when $N = 15$ and $\varepsilon = 0.2$. Compute the eigenvector which corresponds to the eigenvalue $\delta = 0.468$ (approximately). Check that the results agree with those listed in Table 14.2.

(iii) The solution can be written

$$
y(t) = b_1 \, e^{i(1/3)\Omega t} - b_2 \, e^{-i(2/3)\Omega t} + b_4 \, e^{i(4/3)\Omega t} - b_5 \, e^{-i(5/3)\Omega t} + \ldots
$$

where $y(t)$ is complex and the physical response is understood to be $\mathrm{Im}\{y(t)\}$. Show that

$$
y(t + T) = \sigma_1 y(t)
$$

where

$$
T = \frac{2\pi}{(\Omega/3)} = \frac{6\pi}{\Omega}
$$

and

$$
\sigma_1 = e^{i(2/3)\pi} = -\tfrac{1}{2} + i\sqrt{3}/2.
$$

(iv) Check independently that

$$
y(t) = b_1 \cos \tfrac{1}{3}\Omega t - b_2 \cos \tfrac{2}{3}\Omega t + b_4 \cos \tfrac{4}{3}\Omega t - b_5 \cos \tfrac{5}{3}\Omega t + \ldots
$$

is a solution of (14.3), by substituting this solution using the identity

$$
2 \cos \Omega t \cos(j\eta\, \Omega t) = \cos(1 + j\eta)\Omega t + \cos(1 - j\eta)\Omega t
$$

and equating like terms to obtain the matrix

$$
\begin{bmatrix}
1/9 & -\varepsilon/2 & -\varepsilon/2 & & & & \\
-\varepsilon/2 & 4/9 & 0 & -\varepsilon/2 & & & \\
-\varepsilon/2 & 0 & 16/9 & 0 & -\varepsilon/2 & & \\
 & -\varepsilon/2 & 0 & 25/9 & 0 & -\varepsilon/2 & \\
 & & -\varepsilon/2 & 0 & 4 & 0 & -\varepsilon/2 \\
 & & & \cdot & \cdot & \cdot & \cdot \\
 & & & & \cdot & & \cdot & -\varepsilon/2 \\
 & & & & & & \cdot & 0 \\
 & & & & & & -\varepsilon/2 & 0 & N^2/9
\end{bmatrix}
$$

(v) Check that the solution in part (iii) can also be written as

$$y(t) = -b_1 e^{-i(1/3)\Omega t} + b_2 e^{i(2/3)\Omega t} - b_4 e^{-i(4/3)\Omega t} + b_5 e^{i(5/3)\Omega t} - \cdots$$

where the physical response is again $\text{Im}\{y(t)\}$ and hence show we can also put

$$y(t + T) = \sigma_2 y(t)$$

where T is as before, and

$$\sigma_2 = e^{-i(2/3)\pi} = -1/2 - i\sqrt{3}/2.$$

14.6 By following the analysis that leads to equations (14.58) and (14.70) for two of the approximate stability boundaries on Fig. 14.2, prove that the equations for the three other approximate stability boundaries are given correctly by (14.71), (14.75) and (14.76).

14.7 (i) Show that equation (14.1) is satisfied by the first N terms of the periodic solution (14.11) provided that the Fourier coefficients a_j, $j = 0$ to N, b_j, $j = 1$ to N, satisfy the equation

$$Gz = \delta z$$

where

$$z = \{a_0, a_1, a_2, \ldots, a_N, b_1, b_2, \ldots, b_N\}^{\text{T}}.$$

and G is defined by (14.78).

(ii) Show also that (14.1) is satisfied by the odd-numbered terms in the expansion (14.25) provided that the Fourier coefficients c_j and d_j, $j = 1, 3, 5, \ldots (2N - 1)$, satisfy the equation

$$Hy = \delta y$$

where

$$y = \{c_1, c_3, c_5, \ldots, c_{2N-1}, d_1, d_3, d_5, \ldots, d_{2N-1}\}^{\text{T}}$$

and H is defined by (14.79).

(iii) Compute the eigenvalues of G and H for $N = 7$, $\varepsilon = 1$, $\eta = 0.1$, and check that G has only three real eigenvalues and H has only two real eigenvalues for this combination of parameter values. Compare these results with the eigenvalues plotted in Fig. 14.1 for $\eta = 0$ (the zero damping case).

14.8 (i) Find to order ε^1 the periodic response of the damped Duffing oscillator defined by (14.110) by solving equation (14.119) subject to (14.120) and (14.121) and for the initial conditions that $y(t) = A$ and $\dot{y}(t) = 0$ at $t = 0$.

(ii) Also find the phase difference δ between the excitation and the zero-order response $A \cos \Omega t$. Sketch δ against Ω/ω_0 for $\varepsilon \zeta = 0.05$, 0.1, 0.2 for comparison with the corresponding curves in Fig. 1.2(b).

14.9 For the Duffing oscillator defined by (14.110) with $\gamma > 0$, prove that, for zero damping, the periodic responses represented by the section of the resonance curve to the left of the backbone, equation (14.127), are always stable. Show also that, for the section of the resonance curve to the right of the backbone, the limit of stability is at the point at which the tangent to the resonance curve has infinite slope.

14.10 (i) If Θ is the total angle of rotation of the carrier in Fig. 14.12(a), show that the centre of mass of the pendulum has the velocity components given in Fig. P14.10. Hence prove that the total kinetic energy of the system is

$$T = \tfrac{1}{2}(I_1 + I_2)\dot{\Theta}^2 + \tfrac{1}{2}m[\dot{\Theta}^2(b + h)^2 + (\dot{\Theta} + \dot{\phi})^2 l^2 +$$
$$+ 2\dot{\Theta}(\dot{\Theta} + \dot{\phi})l(b + h)\cos\phi].$$

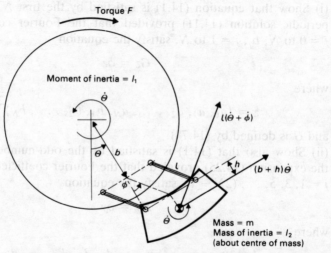

Fig. P14.10 (From Newland [65], courtesy of the American Society of Mechanical Engineers)

(ii) Show that Lagrange's equations (11.8) for this example are

$$\frac{\mathrm{d}}{\mathrm{d}t}\left(\frac{\partial T}{\partial \dot{\Theta}}\right) - \frac{\partial T}{\partial \Theta} = -F$$

and

$$\frac{\mathrm{d}}{\mathrm{d}t}\left(\frac{\partial T}{\partial \dot{\phi}}\right) - \frac{\partial T}{\partial \phi} = 0$$

and hence prove that the equations of motion of the system in Fig. 14.12(a) are

$$\ddot{\Theta}[I_1 + I_2 + m(b + h)^2 + ml^2 + 2ml(b + h)\cos\phi] +$$
$$+ \ddot{\phi}[ml^2 + m(b + h)l\cos\phi] - m(b + h)l\sin\phi \,\dot{\phi}(2\dot{\Theta} + \dot{\phi}) = -F$$

and

$$\ddot{\phi} + \ddot{\Theta}\left[1 + \frac{(b + h)}{l}\cos\phi\right] + \dot{\Theta}^2\frac{(b + h)}{l}\sin\phi = 0.$$

(iii) When

$$\Theta = \Omega t + \theta$$

where Ω is constant and $\dot{\theta} \ll \Omega$ show that, by putting $\dot{\Theta} = \Omega$ and $a = b + h$, these equations simplify to

$$\ddot{\theta}[I_1 + I_2 + m(a^2 + l^2 + 2la\cos\phi)] + \ddot{\phi}[ml(l + a\cos\phi)] -$$
$$- mal\sin\phi\,\dot{\phi}(2\Omega + \dot{\phi}) = -F$$

and

$$\ddot{\phi} + \ddot{\theta}\left[1 + \frac{a}{l}\cos\phi\right] + \Omega^2\frac{a}{l}\sin\phi = 0.$$

Hence confirm that equations (14.221) and (14.222) are correct.
(iv) Find expressions for the errors $E_1(t)$ and $E_2(t)$ when the approximate solution (14.225) is substituted into equations (14.221) and (14.222) and then apply Galerkin equations (14.231) to obtain the response equations (14.234) and (14.235).

14.11 (i) From Figs. 14.13, sketch graphs of the modulus of the applied torque when plotted against (*a*) pendulum amplitude ϕ_0 and (*b*) carrier amplitude θ_0. How are these graphs likely to be changed when the pendulum has a small amount of damping?
(ii) Find how the equations of motion derived in Problem 14.10 are modified if the pendulum is damped so that its rotation relative to the carrier is subjected to a linear viscous restraining couple of magnitude $c\dot{\phi}$.
(iii) Consider how Galerkin's method may be applied to obtain an approximate solution for steady-state harmonically-excited vibration in the damped case. Suggest possible trial functions for Galerkin's method.

Answers to selected problems

2.4 (i) $H_2(i\omega) = \dfrac{1}{(i\omega)^4 + 4(i\omega)^2 + 2}$

$H_3(i\omega) = \dfrac{1}{(i\omega)^6 + 6(i\omega)^4 + 10(i\omega)^2 + 4}$

2.5 (a) $\dfrac{1}{k} - \dfrac{1}{J\omega^2}, \quad -\dfrac{1}{J\omega^2}, \quad -\dfrac{1}{J\omega^2}, \quad \dfrac{1}{J\omega^2}$

(b) $\dfrac{1}{k} + \dfrac{1}{ci\omega}, \quad \dfrac{1}{ci\omega}, \quad \dfrac{1}{ci\omega}, \quad \dfrac{1}{ci\omega}$

(c) $\dfrac{1}{-m\omega^2 + ci\omega + k}, \quad \dfrac{ci\omega + k}{-m\omega^2 + ci\omega + k},$

$\dfrac{ci\omega + k}{-m\omega^2 + ci\omega + k}, \quad \dfrac{-m\omega^2(ci\omega + k)}{-m\omega^2 + ci\omega + k}$

(d) $(-J_2\omega^2 + 2k)/D, \quad k/D, \quad k/D, \quad (-J_1\omega^2 + 2k)/D,$

where $D = (-J_1\omega^2 + 2k)(-J_2\omega^2 + 2k) - k^2$

3.1 (i) The displacement response is part of a perfect circle.

(ii) $\phi(\omega) = 0$, for $\omega \leqslant \omega_0 - \Delta\omega$

$= \pi/2$ for $\omega = \omega_0$

$= \pi$ for $\omega \geqslant \omega_0 + \Delta\omega$.

3.2 (iii) There is no zero between ω_k and ω_{k+1} if α_r is positive for $r \leqslant k$ and negative for $r > k$. This may be seen by adding the separate modal responses.

(v) When $\Sigma\alpha_k = 0$,

$$H(i\omega) \underset{\omega \to \infty}{=} -\frac{1}{\omega^4} \sum \alpha_k\omega_k^2 - \frac{2}{\omega^6} \sum \alpha_k\omega_k^4 + \ldots .$$

The high-frequency response then decreases at least according to ω^{-4}.

(vi) For Fig. 3.7(b),

$$\sum \alpha_k/\omega_k{}^2 = 0.3034$$

and for Fig. 3.9,

$$\sum \alpha_k/\omega_k{}^2 = 0.5666.$$

For the second resonant mode only, from (3.92),

$$20 \log_{10} \frac{5}{(1.25)(0.3034)} = 22.4 \text{ dB}$$

and, from (3.96),

$$20 \log_{10} \frac{5}{(1.25)(0.5666)} = 23.0 \text{ dB}$$

which check closely with Figs. 3.7(*b*) and 3.9.

3.3 $$\phi_1(t) = \left(\frac{X}{m}\right) \frac{1}{(i\omega_N - i\omega_N \sqrt{1 - \zeta^2} + \zeta\omega_N)} e^{(\zeta\omega_N + i\omega_N - i\omega_N \sqrt{(1-\zeta^2)})t}$$

$$\phi_2(t) = \left(\frac{X}{m}\right) \frac{1}{(i\omega_N + i\omega_N \sqrt{1 - \zeta^2} + \zeta\omega_N)} e^{(\zeta\omega_N + i\omega_N + i\omega_N \sqrt{(1-\zeta^2)})t}$$

5.1 The eigenvalues are $2 - \sqrt{2}, 2, 2 + \sqrt{2}$

$$U^{-1} = \begin{bmatrix} 1/4 & 1/2\sqrt{2} & 1/4 \\ 1/2 & 0 & -1/2 \\ 1/4 & -1/2\sqrt{2} & 1/4 \end{bmatrix}$$

5.2 (ii) Using $\lambda_1 = 46.793,466,725,700$, the determinant changes from 9.07×10^{26} at $\varepsilon = -5 \times 10^{-7}$ to -7.27×10^{26} at $\varepsilon = 5 \times 10^{-7}$. The determinant should be zero when $\varepsilon = 0$. However, calculating $A(K, K) - \lambda_1$ involves subtracting a number of order (10^1) from one of order (10^5) or greater. At least four figures of λ_1 are lost in the process. Also, inaccuracies arise when numbers of disparate size are added/subtracted when the determinant is evaluated. The result is a significant loss in overall accuracy, and eigenvalues found by hunting for the values of λ for which $\det[A - \lambda I]$ is zero will generally be less accurate than values found by the QR transform or a similar method.
(iii) (*a*) Reverse the order of the rows.
   (*b*) Subtract 2 × row 2 from row 1 and add row 3.
   (*c*) Subtract 2 × row 3 from row 2 and add row 4, and so on.

5.3 (i) The eigenvalues are listed in the text immediately below the data in (5.29). A typical (displacement) eigenvector, for $\lambda_2 = 710.73 \text{ s}^{-2}$, has the following elements (all real):

$$
\begin{bmatrix}
1.000\,00 \\
-0.263\,68 \\
-0.268\,13 \\
-0.271\,85 \\
-0.274\,85 \\
-0.277\,10 \\
-0.278\,60 \\
-0.279\,35
\end{bmatrix}
$$

(ii) Typical results are the following:

The trace of the A-matrix is: $+2.910\,156\,820\,1\,E + 06$.
The sum of the eigenvalues is: $+2.910\,156\,820\,2\,E + 06$.
The determinant of the A-matrix is: $-3.628\,886\,000\,8\,E + 26$.
The product of the eigenvalues is: $-9.488\,349\,102\,1\,E + 29$.

These are when the quantity taken to be effectively zero in the eigenvalue calculation (this is explained in Ch. 7) is $1.49\,E - 04$. Other programs will produce slightly different results. The determinant and the product of eigenvalues should both be zero. The error arises because the zero eigenvalue has been computed as -3.3×10^{-6}.

(iv) In this example we have real eigenvalues (each of which is a natural frequency squared) and real (displacement) eigenvectors. For the second eigenvector (listed above), the check requested gives the following result.

Result of check calculations (eigenvalues from vectors)

Real part	Imaginary part
$+7.107\,344\,882\,6\,E + 02$	$+0.000\,000\,000\,0\,E + 00$
which should agree with input values	
$+7.107\,344\,873\,0\,E + 02$	$+0.000\,000\,000\,0\,E + 00$

Because the A-matrix is ill-conditioned, the agreement will not be so close on all the eigenvectors. The new calculation for part (v) shows how the accuracy is improved when the eigenvalues do not cover such a wide frequency range.

5.5 Eigenvector number 1 is listed in Table 5.5. The third oscillatory mode is described by eigenvalues nos. 6 and 7 in Table 5.5. Eigenvector number 6 is the following.

Real part	Imaginary part
+1.000 E + 00	+0.000 E + 00
+8.487 E − 01	+2.324 E + 00
−3.801 E − 02	+2.105 E + 00
−5.611 E − 01	−7.180 E − 01
−3.857 E − 01	−2.392 E + 00
+8.474 E − 02	−5.213 E − 01
+5.682 E − 01	+3.177 E + 00
−1.836 E + 01	+1.563 E + 02
−3.787 E + 02	+8.995 E + 01
−3.283 E + 02	−4.460 E + 01
+1.225 E + 02	−7.450 E + 01
+3.808 E + 02	−1.635 E + 01
+7.990 E + 01	+2.281 E + 01
−5.069 E + 02	+3.045 E + 01

Result of check calculations (eigenvalues from vectors):

Real part	Imaginary part
−1.835 585 551 9 E + 01	+1.562 574 039 0 E + 02

which should agree with input values

−1.836 134 494 9 E + 01	+1.562 567 774 1 E + 02

For the above calculation the quantity taken to be effectively zero was 1.07 E − 05.

5.6 (i) Consider the single wheelset shown in Fig. 5.16(c). The rolling radii of the two wheels are $r \pm \alpha x$; the rolling angular velocity is $\Omega = V/r$; hence

$$\dot{\theta} = [\Omega(r + \alpha x) - \Omega(r - \alpha x)]/2b = \Omega \frac{\alpha x}{b}.$$

Also, since the wheelset is rolling at yaw angle θ, $\dot{x} = -V\theta$. Combining these two equations by eliminating θ leads to the results stated.
(ii) The derivation required here is given in full in Ref. [69].
(iii) This result is obtained by expressing the condition that the two lateral creep forces and the two creep moments (in yaw) must form an equilibrium set.
(iv) and (v) For cone-shaped wheels, the effects of spin creep and gravitational stiffness are small relative to the effects of the wheelset creep forces. However, when there is a flange contact, so that the effective angle of conicity is increased, spin creep and gravitational stiffness terms become important.

6.1 (iii) $\Omega_1^2 = k/m$, $\Omega_2^2 = 2k/m$, $\Omega_3^2 = \infty$.

$$U = \begin{bmatrix} 1 & 1 & 0 \\ 1 & 0 & 1 \\ 1 & -1 & 0 \end{bmatrix}$$

(iv) $\lambda_{1,2} = -0.075 \pm i\,1.008$

$\lambda_{3,4} = \pm\,i\,1.414$

$\lambda_5 \;\; = -293.2$

$\lambda_6 \;\; = -6.672$

The eigenvector matrix is $U = U_r + iU_i$, where

$$U_r = \begin{bmatrix} 1 & 1 & 1 & 1 & 1 & 1 \\ 0.99 & 0.99 & 0 & 0 & 8.6 \times 10^4 & 46.5 \\ 1 & 1 & -1 & -1 & 1 & 1 \\ -0.075 & -0.075 & 0 & 0 & -2.9 \times 10^2 & -6.67 \\ 0.078 & 0.078 & 0 & 0 & -2.5 \times 10^7 & -310.3 \\ -0.075 & -0.075 & 0 & 0 & -2.9 \times 10^2 & -6.67 \end{bmatrix}$$

and

$$U_i = \begin{bmatrix} 0 & 0 & 0 & 0 & 0 & 0 \\ -0.151 & 0.151 & 0 & 0 & 0 & 0 \\ 0 & 0 & 0 & 0 & 0 & 0 \\ 1.01 & -1.01 & 1.414 & -1.414 & 0 & 0 \\ 1.01 & -1.01 & 0 & 0 & 0 & 0 \\ 1.01 & -1.01 & -1.414 & 1.414 & 0 & 0 \end{bmatrix}$$

6.2 (ii) The eigenvalues are $-1, -1, -1.001, -999$

There is only one eigenvector for $\lambda = -1$, so the three eigenvectors are

$$\begin{bmatrix} 1 & 1 & 1 \\ 0 & -10^{-6} & 999 \\ -1 & -1.001 & -999 \\ 0 & 10^{-6} & -10^6 \end{bmatrix}$$

6.3 (i)

$$J = \begin{bmatrix} -1 & 1 & 0 & 0 \\ 0 & -1 & 0 & 0 \\ 0 & 0 & -1+i & 0 \\ 0 & 0 & 0 & -1-i \end{bmatrix}$$

$$W = \begin{bmatrix} 1 & 0 & 1 & 1 \\ -1 & 0 & -3/5 + i1/5 & -3/5 - i1/5 \\ -1 & 1 & -1+i & -1-i \\ 1 & -1 & 2/5 - i4/5 & 2/5 + i4/5 \end{bmatrix}$$

See Reference [74] for the derivation of J and W.

$$z(t) = C_1 e^{-t} \begin{bmatrix} 1 \\ -1 \\ -1 \\ 1 \end{bmatrix} + C_2 e^{-t} \begin{bmatrix} t \\ -t \\ -t+1 \\ t-1 \end{bmatrix} +$$

$$+ 2\,\mathrm{Re}\left\{ C_3 e^{(-1+i)t} \begin{bmatrix} 1 \\ -3/5 + i\,1/5 \\ -1 + i \\ 2.5 - i\,4/5 \end{bmatrix} \right\}$$

6.4 (iii)

$$z(t) = \mathrm{Re}\{\underbrace{C_1\, e^{\lambda_1 t} w^{(1)}}_{\text{Mode 1}} + \underbrace{C_2\, e^{\lambda_1 t}(t w^{(1)} + w^{(2)})}_{\text{Mode 2}}\}$$

7.3 (ii) -6.7511, -88.151, $-8.0492 \pm i\,102.16$

$$U = \begin{bmatrix} 1 & 1 & 1 \\ 0.9954 & 0.5399 & -8.646 \pm i\,9.635 \\ -6.751 & -88.15 & -8.049 \pm i\,102.2 \\ -6.720 & -47.59 & \underbrace{-914.7 \mp i\,960.8}_{\text{Cols. 3 and 4}} \end{bmatrix}$$

7.4 (i) and (ii) $i\,1,\ -i\,1,\ \dfrac{1}{2} + i\dfrac{\sqrt{3}}{2},\ \dfrac{1}{2} - i\dfrac{\sqrt{3}}{2},\ -1$

(iii) $\dfrac{1}{2} + i\dfrac{\sqrt{3}}{2},\ \dfrac{1}{2} - i\dfrac{\sqrt{3}}{2},\ -\dfrac{1}{2} + i\dfrac{\sqrt{3}}{2},\ -\dfrac{1}{2} - i\dfrac{\sqrt{3}}{2},\ -1$

7.5 The exact eigenvalues are $-1, -1, -1, -2$
The eigenvector for $\lambda = -1$ is $[1, -1, 1, -1]^{\mathrm{T}}$
and for $\lambda = -2$ is $[1, -\frac{1}{2}, \frac{1}{4}, -\frac{1}{8}]^{\mathrm{T}}$

7.7 (ii) $W = \begin{bmatrix} 3 - i\,2 \\ 15 - i\,10 \\ 17 - i\,1 \end{bmatrix}$

8.2 (i) Assume the answer for X^{-1} and demonstrate that $X^{-1}X = I$.

8.3 (iii) $|y_1| = 2.6\ \mu m$, $|y_2| = 21.7\ \mu m$

$|\dot{y}_1| = 0.26\ mm/s$, $|\dot{y}_2| = 2.17\ mm/s$

$|\ddot{y}_1| = 0.03\ g$, $|\ddot{y}_2| = 0.22\ g$.

9.1 (i) $\dfrac{1}{a + i\omega}$ (ii) $\dfrac{1}{a - i\omega}$ (iii) $\dfrac{2a}{a^2 + \omega^2}$

(iv) $\dfrac{-\mathrm{i}\,2\omega}{a^2 + \omega^2}$ (v) $\sqrt{\dfrac{\pi}{a}}\,\mathrm{e}^{-\omega^2/4a}$ after using the standard integral

$$\int_0^\infty \mathrm{e}^{-y^2/2}\,\mathrm{d}y = \sqrt{\dfrac{\pi}{2}}$$

(vi) $\mathrm{i}\,aT\left[\dfrac{\sin(\omega_0 + \omega)T}{(\omega_0 + \omega)T} - \dfrac{\sin(\omega_0 - \omega)T}{(\omega_0 - \omega)T}\right]$

(vii) $\mathrm{i}\,a\pi[\delta(\omega + \omega_0) - \delta(\omega - \omega_0)]$

The last result can be checked by using the inverse Fourier transform (9.2) to verify that $a\sin\omega_0 t$ is regained.

9.2 (i) $h(t) = \dfrac{1}{c}\,\mathrm{e}^{-(k/c)t}$, $t > 0$

(ii) $y(t) = 0$ for $t < -T$

$\quad = \dfrac{x_0}{k}[1 - \mathrm{e}^{-(k/c)(t+T)}]$ for $-T < t < T$

$\quad = \dfrac{x_0}{k}[\mathrm{e}^{-(k/c)(t-T)} - \mathrm{e}^{-(k/c)(t+T)}]$ for $t > T$

(iii) $y(t) = \dfrac{x_0(k\cos\omega_0 t + c\omega_0\sin\omega_0 t)}{k^2 + \omega_0^2 c^2}$

Hint. Begin by putting $x(t - \theta) = \mathrm{Re}[x_0\,\mathrm{e}^{\mathrm{i}\omega(t-\theta)}]$.

(iv) $H(\mathrm{i}\omega) = \dfrac{1}{k + \mathrm{i}\,c\omega}$

10.2 (i) $X_k = \mathrm{i}\dfrac{a}{\pi k}[(-1)^k - 1]$

(ii) An exact solution is $X_k = 0$ for k even

$$= \dfrac{1}{32}\left(1 - \mathrm{i}\cot\dfrac{\pi k}{64}\right)\text{ for }k\text{ odd.}$$

(iii) In part (i), X_k is calculated from an $x(t)$ which is an odd function of t, and so this X_k is purely imaginary. When the square wave is sampled to give the sequence x_r used in part (ii), the x_r is not exactly odd since x_0 is taken as $+a$ (not zero) and x_{32} is taken as $-a$ (not zero). This lack of odd symmetry leads to a small real component in the X_k calculated in part (ii).

10.5 (i) $z_{r+2} = (I - \Delta A)^{-2}z_r + \Delta(I - \Delta A)^{-2}F_{r+1} + \Delta(I - \Delta A)^{-1}F_{r+2}$

and, for no excitation,

$$z_n = (I - \Delta A)^{-n}z_0.$$

(ii) For a diagonal matrix A

$$(I - \Delta A)^{-n} = \left[\text{diag} \frac{1}{(1 - \Delta \lambda_j)^n} \right]$$

which is stable provided that

$$\left| \frac{1}{1 - \Delta \lambda_j} \right| < 1 \text{ for all } \lambda_j.$$

Putting $\lambda_j = -\alpha \pm i\beta$, where α and β are both positive, check that $|1 + \Delta \lambda_j| > 1$, always. If A is not diagonal, the problem may always be transformed by a change of coordinates so that A is diagonal.

11.1 This calculation is given in Reference [72].

11.7 (iii) Let m' and k' be the mass and stiffness matrices obtained by deleting the rth row and rth column of m and k. The $M - 1$ natural frequencies of the clamped system are obtained by finding the ω's for which

$$\det[-\omega^2 m' + k'] = 0.$$

This is called the determinant of the rr minor of $\det[-\omega^2 m + k]$.
(iv) From equation (8.101), for the original (unclamped) system,

$$H(i\omega) = [-\omega^2 m + k]^{-1}.$$

For input r and output r, we want the rrth element of $H(i\omega)$ which, from the rules for finding the elements of the inverse of a matrix, is

$$H_{rr}(i\omega) = \frac{(-1)^{2r} \det[-\omega^2 m' + k']}{\det[-\omega^2 m + k]}.$$

The determinants can be expanded as polynomials of the form

$$\det[-\omega^2 m' + k'] = (\omega^2 - \Omega_1^2)(\omega^2 - \Omega_2^2) \ldots (\omega^2 - \Omega_{M-1}^2)\alpha$$

and

$$\det[-\omega^2 m + k] = (\omega^2 - \omega_1^2)(\omega^2 - \omega_2^2) \ldots (\omega^2 - \omega_M^2)\beta$$

where α and β are constants. The result stated follows. For the case when $\omega_1 = 0$, at very low frequencies the system behaves as a mass $\bar{m}$. Let $k = \Delta k$ (small) and $\omega_1 = \sqrt{\Delta k / \bar{m}}$. Then the factor

$$\frac{1}{k\left(1 - \frac{\omega^2}{\omega_1^2}\right)} \rightarrow -\frac{1}{\Delta k \frac{\omega^2}{\omega_1^2}} = -\frac{1}{\bar{m}\omega^2}.$$

(vi) The shaft/flywheel sub-system has a frequency-response function (angular displacement output/torque input) of the form

$$G(i\omega) = \frac{1}{k} - \frac{1}{J\omega^2}.$$

From (2.141), we want $H(i\omega) + G(i\omega) = 0$ at $\omega = 30(2\pi)$ rad/s. On substituting the numbers, the required $k = 7.65 \times 10^4$ N m/rad. The second natural frequency (obtained by plotting $-G(i\omega)$ on the graph of part (v)) is about 59 Hz.

12.4

$$\begin{bmatrix} m_1 & 0 \\ 0 & 0 \end{bmatrix} \begin{bmatrix} \ddot{y}_1 \\ \ddot{y}_2 \end{bmatrix} + \begin{bmatrix} k_1 + k_2 & 0 \\ k_2 & 1 \end{bmatrix} \begin{bmatrix} y_1 \\ y_2 \end{bmatrix} =$$

$$= \begin{bmatrix} 1 & k_2 \\ 0 & m_2\dfrac{d^2}{dt^2} + k_2 \end{bmatrix} \begin{bmatrix} x_1 \\ x_2 \end{bmatrix}$$

12.6 (i) Obtain expressions for $Y(L, i\omega)$ from (12.123) and for $F(0, i\omega)$ from (12.128). Hence show that

$$\frac{F(0, i\omega)}{Y(L, i\omega)} = -(\alpha + i\beta)kL(\sinh \alpha L \cos \beta L + i \cosh \alpha L \sin \beta L).$$

When there is no damping, from (12.113), $\alpha = 0$, $\beta = \sqrt{\rho/E}\,\omega$, and then

$$\frac{F(0, i\omega)}{Y(L, i\omega)} = \beta kL \sin \beta L.$$

From (12.46), the lowest natural frequency of a column with one end fixed is given by $\beta L = \pi/2$. Hence

$$\frac{F(0, i\omega)}{Y(L, i\omega)} = \beta kL$$

at this frequency. Also, from (12.123), for $\alpha = 0$ and $\beta L = \pi/2$,

$Y(z, i\omega) = \infty$. This is the ratio of the displacement output/displacement input at the foot of the column. Hence the movement of the foot of the column must be zero and the column is acting as a dynamic vibration absorber to prevent motion at its lower end. The same result holds for other natural frequencies.

(ii) $\omega_j = j\dfrac{\pi}{L}\sqrt{\dfrac{E}{\rho}}$

12.8 (iv) Let $\omega = \omega_3 + \Delta$ so that

$$\omega\sqrt{\frac{m}{T}} = \frac{3\pi}{L + \theta}$$

(θ small). Then

$$H\left(z, \frac{L}{3}, \omega_3 + \Delta\right) = \frac{\sin\left(2\pi + \frac{2L}{3}\theta\right)}{\left(\frac{3\pi}{L} + \theta\right)T\sin(3\pi + \theta L)}\sin\frac{3\pi}{L}z$$

which, when $\theta \to 0$, becomes

$$H\left(z, \frac{L}{3}, \omega_3\right) = -\frac{2L}{9\pi T}\sin\frac{3\pi}{L}z, \quad 0 \leqslant z < \frac{L}{3}.$$

Similarly,

$$H\left(z, \frac{L}{3}, \omega_3\right) = \frac{L}{9\pi T}\sin\frac{3\pi}{L}(L - z), \quad \frac{L}{3} < z \leqslant L.$$

(v) Use equation (12.166) with

$$H_j(i\omega) = \frac{1}{(i\omega)^2 + \omega_j^2}, \qquad U_j(z) = \sqrt{\frac{2}{mL}}\sin\left(j\frac{\pi z}{L}\right).$$

(vi) The third mode term becomes, with $\omega = \omega_3 + \Delta$,

$$\frac{\sin\left(\frac{3\pi z}{L}\right)\sin\pi}{mL[\omega_3^2 - (\omega_3 + \Delta)^2]}.$$

It is zero except when $\Delta = 0$, when it is indeterminate. Since the remaining terms in the summation approach a limit smoothly as $\omega \to \omega_3$, we do not expect the third term to suddenly change its value at $\omega = \omega_3$. This conclusion is confirmed by the result of calculating the deflection curve specified, and comparing this with the result of part (iv).

13.1 (i) $\cosh aL \cos aL = -1$, where $a^4 = \dfrac{m\omega_j^2}{EI}$.

(ii)
(iii) $\Big\}$ $\cosh aL \cos al = +1$

(iv)
(v) $\Big\}$ $\tanh aL = \tan aL.$

In cases (ii) and (iii), for $a \to 0$, the normal mode function (13.12) becomes

$$U_j(z) = (A + B + C) + (A - B + D)az + 0(a^2z^2).$$

For case (ii), the conditions at $z = 0$ require $(A + B + C) = 0$ for no deflection, and $(A - B + D) = 0$ for no slope. Hence when $a = 0$, we get $U_j(z) = 0$, and so $a = 0$ cannot be an eigenvalue in case (ii). In the free–free case (iii), the conditions at $z = 0$ require $(A + B - C) = 0$ for no bending moment, and $(A - B - D) = 0$ for no shear force. Hence we get

$$U_j(z) = 2C + 2Daz$$

where C and D are arbitrary. Since D can be infinite, so that Da remains finite when $a = 0$, the eigenvectors are any two different combinations of translation and rotation.

For cases (iv) and (v) a similar analysis can be made to show that case (iv) cannot have $a = 0$ as an eigenvalue. For case (v), the zero eigenvalue corresponds to $U_j(z) = Kz$, where K is arbitrary, which describes rotation about the hinged end.

13.3 This analysis is given in Reference [68].

13.4 (iii) There is whirling if the shaft may rotate in a displaced position $y(z) = e^{\lambda z}$. On substituting into equation (a), we find that

$$y(z) = A \cos \lambda_1 z + B \sin \lambda_1 z + C \cosh \lambda_2 z + D \sinh \lambda_2 z$$

where

$$\lambda_1^2, \, -\lambda_2^2 = \frac{P \mp \sqrt{P^2 + 4EIm\Omega^2}}{2EI}.$$

For zero deflection and zero bending moment at each bearing, there will only be a non-trivial solution for $y(z)$ if

$$(\lambda_1^2 + \lambda_2^2) \sin \lambda_1 l \sinh \lambda_2 l = 0.$$

Since $(\lambda_1^2 + \lambda_2^2) \neq 0$ and $\sinh \lambda_2 l \neq 0$, this requires

$$\sin \lambda_1 l = 0$$

which leads to the result given.
(iv) $P_c = 5.72$ MN, $\Omega_1 = 254$ rev/min, when $p = 0$

$$= 207 \text{ rev/min when } p \text{ is as specified.}$$

13.5 (ii) Show that $1/\omega_j^2$ is an eigenvalue of $-k^{-1}m$.
(iii) If the deflections of the three masses are labelled y_1, y_2, y_3 reading from left to right, from data on beam bending

$$k^{-1} = \frac{l^3}{EI} \begin{bmatrix} 1/3 & 5/6 & 4/3 \\ 5/6 & 8/3 & 14/3 \\ 4/3 & 14/3 & 9 \end{bmatrix}$$

which, on inversion, gives

$$k = \frac{EI}{l^3} \begin{bmatrix} 18.462 & -10.615 & 2.769 \\ -10.615 & 10.154 & -3.692 \\ 2.769 & -3.692 & 1.615 \end{bmatrix}$$

The mass matrix is

$$\boldsymbol{m} = m \begin{bmatrix} 2 & 0 & 0 \\ 0 & 2 & 0 \\ 0 & 0 & 1 \end{bmatrix}.$$

For the assumed deflection curve $y = az^2$, the corresponding approximate eigenvector is $[1 \quad 4 \quad 9]^T$

Hence Rayleigh's method, equation (d), gives $\omega_1 = 0.306 \sqrt{EI/ml^3}$,

Rayleigh's method, equation (e), gives $\omega_1 = 0.264 \sqrt{EI/ml^3}$,

Dunkerley's method, equation (f), gives $\omega_1 = 0.258 \sqrt{EI/ml^3}$.

For comparison, the exact solution is $\omega_1 = 0.263 \sqrt{EI/ml^3}$.

The exact eigenvector is $[1 \quad 3.339 \quad 6.181]^T$ instead of $[1 \quad 4 \quad 9]^T$.

(iv) We have to calculate the additional potential energy due to the inwards movement of the three masses in the centrifugal field. For a deflection curve $y = ax^2$, with motion taking place in an axial plane, a point at position x has an inwards movement (found by integration) of

$$\frac{2}{3} a^2 x^3.$$

The additional potential energy of the three masses because of this movement is

$$\frac{320}{3} m\Omega^2 a^2 l^4.$$

Combining this with the calculation from part (iii), equation (d), we get

$$\omega^2 = \frac{\frac{1}{2}y^T k\,y + \frac{320}{3}m\Omega^2 a^2 l^4}{\frac{1}{2}y^T m\,y}$$

$$= \omega_1^2 + \alpha\Omega^2$$

where $\omega_1 = 0.307 \sqrt{\dfrac{EI}{ml^3}}$ and $\alpha = 1.855$.

For motion in a radial plane (rather than in an axial plane) the radially inwards movement due to deflection is less than before. For the tip of a blade of length l in a hub of radius R, the inwards movement is

$$\frac{2}{3} a^2 l^3 - \frac{1}{2} \frac{a^2 l^4}{(R + l)}.$$

For this condition the revised value of α is $\alpha = 0.855$. Note that it is not convenient to use Rayleigh's quotient in its more accurate equation (e) because only equation (d) can be expressed in the form

$$\frac{\text{Potential energy}}{\text{Reference kinetic energy}}.$$

13.7 This problem is based on the analysis in Reference [70].

13.8 (ii) The approximate natural frequencies are given by equations (13.183) and (13.186). Equation (13.183) is the same as (13.118) except that

$$\varepsilon_2^2 \left(\frac{\omega_2}{\omega_1}\right)^2$$

is omitted from the numerator and ε_2^2 is omitted from the denominator. The new result is more accurate than (13.118). This can be proved by writing $\omega^2 = A/B$ for (13.183) and

$$\omega^2 = \frac{A + a}{B + b}$$

for (13.118). The new result will be more accurate if

$$\frac{A + a}{B + b} > \frac{A}{B}.$$

This will be true if

$$\frac{a}{b} > \frac{A}{B}.$$

Since

$$\frac{a}{b} = \omega_2^2$$

and

$$\frac{A}{B} \simeq \omega_1^2,$$

this is always the case.

Because Rayleigh's method gives a second natural frequency which is not necessarily an upper bound, we cannot say for certain whether or not the approximation calculated by Rayleigh–Ritz will be more accurate than that calculated by Rayleigh's method.

14.8 (i) From (14.119),

$$\ddot{y}_1 + y_1 = -\left(\frac{1}{4}\frac{\gamma A^3}{\omega^2}\right)\cos 3\theta$$

whose solution subject is $y_1 = \dot{y}_1 = 0$ at $\theta = 0$ is

$$y_1 = \frac{1}{32}\left(\frac{\gamma A^3}{\omega_0^2}\right)(-\cos\theta + \cos 3\theta).$$

From (14.111), the response

$$y(\theta) = A\cos\theta + \varepsilon y_1(\theta)$$

to order ε^1.
(ii) From (14.121),

$$\sin\delta = \frac{2\zeta A\omega_0^2}{X} = 2(\varepsilon\zeta)\left(\frac{A\omega_0^2}{\varepsilon X}\right).$$

Using the relationship between $A\omega_0^2/\varepsilon X$ and Ω/ω_0 plotted in Fig. 14.6(a), it is then possible to plot δ against Ω/ω_0 for the values of $\varepsilon\zeta$ given. Equation (14.120) can be used to confirm that $\cos\delta$ is zero and therefore $\delta = \pi/2$ on the backbone of Fig 14.6(a).

14.9 The periodic response is unstable if, for amplitude A, $\Omega_2 < \Omega < \Omega_1$, where Ω = frequency of harmonic excitation and Ω_1, Ω_2 are defined by (14.146) and (14.147). Equation (14.147) is identical with the backbone equation from (14.125) with (14.126). Hence the response curve to the left of the backbone gives stable solutions.

A typical response curve to the right of the backbone is given by (14.125) with (14.124). Vertical tangency occurs where

$$\frac{d}{dA}\left(\frac{\Omega}{\omega_0}\right) = 0$$

which is where, for zero damping,

$$A^3 = \frac{2\varepsilon X}{3\,\varepsilon\gamma}.$$

This is the point of intersection of the response curve with the curve specified by (14.146).

14.10 These calculations are described in detail in Reference [66].

References

1. ACHENBACH, J. D.
   Wave Propagation in Elastic Solids, North-Holland Publishing Company, Amsterdam, 1973.
2. ATHERTON, D. P.
   Nonlinear Control Engineering, Van Nostrand Reinhold, London, 1975.
3. BARR, ALLAN, D. S.
   'Some Developments in Parametric Stability and Nonlinear Vibration', *Proc. Int. Conf. Recent Advances in Structural Dynamics, Inst. Sound Vib. Research, Southampton*, 1980, 545–68.
4. BATHE, KLAUS-JÜRGEN
   Finite Element Procedures in Engineering Analysis, Prentice-Hall, Englewood Cliffs, New Jersey, 1982.
5. BICKLEY, W. G. and THOMPSON, R. S. H. G.
   Matrices—Their Meaning and Manipulation, English Universities Press, London, 1964.
6. BISHOP, R. E. D., GLADWELL, G. M. L. and MICHAELSON, S.
   The Matrix Analysis of Vibration, Cambridge University Press, Cambridge, 1965.
7. BISHOP, R. E. D. and JOHNSON, D. C.
   Mechanics of Vibration, Cambridge University Press, 1960. Reissued with minor revisions, 1979.
8. BISHOP, R. E. D., PRICE, W. G. and TAM, P. K.
   'On Damping of Torsional Vibration in a Propulsion System having a Fluid Drive', *Trans. Instn Marine Engrs* (TM), Vol. 91, 1979, Part 5, 109–23.
9. BISPLINGHOFF, RAYMOND L., ASHLEY, HOLT and HALFMAN, ROBERT L.
   Aeroelasticity, Addison-Wesley, Reading, MA, 1955.
10. BLEVINS, ROBERT, D.
    Flow-Induced Vibration, Van Nostrand Reinhold, New York, 1977.
11. BOGOLIUBOV, N. N. and MITROPOLSKY, J. A.
    Asymptotical Methods in the Theory of Nonlinear Oscillations (in Russian), State Press for Physics and Mathematical Literature, Moscow, 1963. English translation: Hindustan Publishing Co., Delhi, India: U.S. distributor: Gordon and Breach, New York.
12. BRACEWELL, R. N.
    The Fourier Integral and its Applications (2nd edition), McGraw-Hill, New York, 1978.
13. BROGAN, WILLIAM L.
    Modern Control Theory, Prentice-Hall, Inc., New Jersey, 1982.

14. COLLAR, A. R. and SIMPSON, A.
    Matrices and Engineering Dynamics, Ellis Horwood, Chichester, 1987.
15. COLLATZ, L.
    Eigenwertprobleme, Chelsea Publishing Co., New York, 1948.
16. CRANDALL, S. H., KARNOPP, D. C., KURTZ, E. F., JR. and PRIDMORE-BROWN, D. C.
    Dynamics of Mechanical and Electromechanicl Systems, Krieger Publishing Company, alaarr, Florida, 1982.
17. CRANDALL, S. H. and STRANG, W. G.
    'An Improvememt of the Holzer Table Based on a Suggestion of Rayleigh's', *J. Applied Mechanics, Trans. Am. Soc. Mech. Engrs.*, Vol. 24, 1957, 228–30.
18. DEN HARTOG, J. P.
    Mechanical Vibrations (4th edition), McGraw-Hill, New York, 1956. Reprinted by Dover, New York, 1985.
19. DEVANEY, ROBERT L.
    An Introduction to Chaotic Dynamical Systems, The Benjamin/Cummings Publishing Co. Inc., Menlo Park California, 1986.
20. DOWELL, E. H.
    'Observation and Evolution of Chaos for an Autonomous System', *J. Applied Mechanics, Trans Am. Soc. Mech. Engrs.*, Vol 51, 1984, 664–73.
21. DUFFING, G.
    Erzwungene Schwingungen bei Veränderlicher Eigenfrequenz und ihre Technische Bedeutung, F. Vieweg und Sohn, Braunschweig, 1918.
22. DUNCAN, W. J.
    'Galerkin's Method in Mechanics and Differential Equations', R & M. No. 1798. *Technical Report of the Aeronautical Research Committee*, Gt Britain, for the year 1937. HMSO, London, 1939.
23. DUNCAN, W. J.
    'The Principles of the Galerkin Method', R & M. No 1848. *Technical Report of the Aeronautical Research Committee*, Gt Britain, for the year 1938. HMSO, London, 1947.
24. ELLINGTON, J. P. and McCALLION, H.
    'On Running a Machine Through its Resonant Frequency, *J. R. Aeronaut. Soc.*, Vol. 60, 1956, 620.
25. EVAN-IWANOWSKI, R. M.
    Resonance Oscillations in Mechanical Systems, Elsevier, Amsterdam, 1976.
26. EWINS, D. J.
    Modal Testing: Theory and Practice, Research Studies Press, Letchworth and Wiley, New York, 1984.
27. FAWZY, I. and BISHOP, R. E. D.
    'On the Dynamics of Linear Non-Conservative Systems', *Proc. R. Soc. Lond.*, Vol. A352, 1976, 25–40.
28. FRANCIS, J. G. F.
    'The QR Transformation', Parts I & II, *Computer J.*, Vol. 4, 1961, 1962, 265–71 and 332–45.
29. FRANKLIN, JOEL M.
    Matrix Theory, Prentice-Hall, Englewood Cliffs, New Jersey, 1968.
30. FRAZER, R. A., DUNCAN, W. J. and COLLAR, A. R.
    Elementary Matrices and Some Applications to Dynamics and Differential Equations, Cambridge University Press, Cambridge, 1950.
31. GABEL, ROBERT A. and ROBERTS, RICHARD A.
    Signals and Linear Systems (2nd edition) Wiley, New York, 1980.

32. GALERKIN, V. G.
    'Series Solutions of Some Problems of Elastic Equilibrium of Rods and
    Plates' (title translated from the Russian), *Vestnik Ingenerov*, Petrograd,
    No. 19, 1915, 897.
33. GANTMACHER, F. R.
    The Theory of Matrices, English Language Translation by K. A. Hirsch,
    Chelsea Publishing Company, New York, Vol. 1, 1977.
34. GANTMACHER, F. R.
    The Theory of Matrices, English Language Translation by K. A. Hirsch,
    Chelsea Publishing Company, New York, Vol. 2, 1960.
35. GERALD, CURTIS, F. and WHEATLEY, PATRICK, O.
    Applied Numerical Analysis (3rd edition), Addison-Wesley, Reading, MA,
    1984.
36. GORMAN, D. J.
    Free Vibration Analysis of Beams and Shafts, Wiley, New York, 1975.
37. GORMAN, D. J.
    Free Vibration Analysis of Rectangular Plates, Elsevier, New York, 1982.
38. GEAR, C. WILLIAM
    Numerical Initial Value Problems in Ordinary Differential Equations,
    Prentice-Hall, Englewood Cliffs, New Jersey, 1971.
39. GRAY, ANDREW, MATHEWS, G. B. and MacROBERT, P. M.
    A Treatise on Bessel Functions and Their Applications to Physics (2nd
    edition), MacMillan & Co., London, 1952.
40. HATWAI, H., MALLIK, A. K. and GHOSH, A.
    'Forced Nonlinear Oscillations of an Autoparametric System', Parts I and
    II, *J. Applied Mechanics, Trans Am. Soc. Mech. Engrs.*, Vol. 50, 1983,
    657–68.
41. HAUPT, O.
    'Über Lineare Homogene Differentialgleichungen Zweiter Ordnung Mit
    Periodischen Koeffizienten', *Math. Ann. D.*, Vol. 79, 1919, 278.
42. HAYASHI, CHIHIRO
    Nonlinear Oscillations in Physical Systems, Princeton University Press,
    Princeton, New Jersey, 1985. Published originally by McGraw-Hill, New
    York, 1964.
43. HETÉNYI, M.
    Beams on Elastic Foundations, University of Michigan Press, Ann Arbor,
    Michigan, 1946.
44. HOLMES, P. J. and MOON, F. C.
    'Strange Attractors and Chaos in Nonlinear Mechanics', *J. Applied
    Mechanics, Trans Am. Soc. Mech. Engrs.*, Vol. 50, 1983, 1021–32.
45. HOUSEHOLDER, A. S.
    The Theory of Matrices in Numerical Analysis, Blaisdell, New York, 1964.
46. HUEBNER, K. H.
    The Finite Element Method for Engineers, Wiley, New York, 1975.
47. IBRAHIM, R. A.
    'Parametric Vibration', Part III: Current Problems (1), *Shock Vib. Digest*,
    Vol. 10, 1978, 3, 41–57 and Part IV: Current Problems (2), *Shock Vib.
    Digest*, Vol. 10, 1978, 4, 19–47.
48. IBRAHIM, R. A. and BARR, A. D. S.
    'Parametric Vibration', Part I: Mechanics of Linear Problems, *Shock Vib.
    Digest*, Vol. 10, 1978, 1, 15–29. Part II: Mechanics of Nonlinear Problems,
    Shock Vib. Digest, Vol. 10, 1978, 2, 9–24.
49. JEFFREYS, H. and JEFFREYS, B.

Methods of Mathematical Physics (3rd edition), Cambridge University Press, Cambridge, 1956.

50. JOHNSON, K. L.
    Contact Mechanics, Cambridge University Press, Cambridge, 1985.

51. JOLLEY, L. B. W.
    Summation of Series (2nd edition), Dover, 1961.

52. KLOTTER, K.
    'Nonlinear Vibration Problems Treated by the Averaging Method of W. Ritz'. *Proc. 1st U.S. National Congress of Applied Mechanics*, *Am. Soc. Mech. Engrs*, New York, 1952, 125–31.

53. KRYLOV, N. and BOGOLIUBOV, N. N.
    Introduction to Nonlinear Mechanics, Princeton University Press, Princeton, New Jersey, 1943.

54. LEWIS, F. M.
    'Vibration During Acceleration Through a Critical Speed', *Trans Am. Soc. Mech. Engrs* Vol. 54, 1932, 253.

55. LIGHTHILL, M. J.
    Introduction to Fourier Analysis and Generalised Functions, Cambridge University Press, 1958.

56. McLACHLAN, N. W.
    Theory and Application of Mathieu Functions, Clarendon Press, Oxford, 1947.

57. MATHIEU, E.
    Mémoire sur le Mouvement Vibratoire d'une Membrane de Forme Elliptique, *J. de Math. Pures et Appliqués* (J. de Liouville), Vol. 13, 1868, No. 137.

58. MEIROVITCH, L.
    Analytical Methods in Vibrations, Macmillan, New York, 1967.

59. MEIROVITCH, L.
    Elements of Vibration Analysis (2nd edition), McGraw-Hill, New York, 1986.

60. MICKENS, RONALD E.
    An Introduction to Nonlinear Oscillations, Cambridge University Press, Cambridge, 1981.

61. MÜLLER, P. C. and SCHIEHLEN, W. O.
    Linear Vibrations, Martinus Nijhoff, Dordrecht, The Netherlands, 1985.

62. NASHIF, AHID D., JONES, DAVID I. G. and HENDERSON, JOHN P.
    Vibration Damping, John Wiley, New York, 1985.

63. NAYFEH, ALI HASAN and MOOK, DEAN T.
    Nonlinear Oscillations, John Wiley, New York, 1979.

64. NEWLAND, D. E.
    An Introduction to Random Vibrations and Spectral Analysis (2nd edition), Longman, London, 1984. (Distributed in the USA by John Wiley, New York.)

65. NEWLAND, D. E.
    Nonlinear Vibrations: A Comparative Study with Applications to Centrifugal Pendulum Vibration Absorbers, ScD thesis, Massachusetts Institute of Technology, 1963.

66. NEWLAND, D. E.
    'Nonlinear Aspects of the Performance of Centrifugal Pendulum Vibration Absorbers', *J. Engng Ind., Trans Am. Soc. Mech. Engrs*, Series B, Vol. 86, 1964, 257–63.

67. NEWLAND, D. E.

'On the Methods of Galerkin, Ritz and Krylov-Bogoliubov in the Theory of Non-Linear Vibrations', *Int. J. Mech. Sci.*, Vol. 7, 1985, 159–72.

68. NEWLAND, D. E.
'Instability of an Elastically Supported Beam under a Travelling Inertia Load', *J. Mech. Eng. Sci.*, Vol. 12, 1970, 373–4.

69. NEWLAND, D. E.
'Steering a Flexible Railway Truck on Curved Track', *J. Engng Ind. (Trans. Am. Soc. Mech. Engrs, Series B)*, Vol. 91, 1969, 908–18. Reprinted in *Anthology of Rail Vehicle Dynamics*, Guins, S. G. and Tack, C. E. (Eds.), II, Am. Soc. Mech. Engrs, New York, 1972, 219–26.

70. NEWLAND, D. E.
Whirling of a Cantilever Elastic Shaft Subjected to External Pressure, *J. Mech. Engng Sci.*, Vol. 14, 1972, 11–18.

71. NEWLAND, D. E.
Deflection Equation for the Buckling of an Elastic Column Subjected to Surface Pressure, *J. Mech. Engng Sci.*, Vol. 15, 1973, 73–5.

72. NEWLAND, D. E.
'Calculation of the Effect of a Resilient Seating on the Vibration Characteristics of Slender Structures', *Engng Struc.*, Vol. 6, 1984, 307–14.

73. NEWLAND, D. E.
'Factors in the Design of Resilient Seatings for Steel Chimneys and Masts', *Proc. Soc. Envrl Engrs*, Vol. 23, 1984, 3–9.

74. NEWLAND, D. E.
'On the Modal Analysis of Non-Conservative Linear Systems', *J. Sound Vib.*, Vol. 112, 1987, 69–97.

75. NOBLE, B. and DANIEL, JAMES W.
Applied Linear Algebra (2nd edition), Prentice-Hall, Englewood Cliffs, New Jersey, 1977.

76. OPPENHEIM, ALAN V., WILLSKY, ALAN S. and YOUNG, IAN T.
Signals and Systems, Prentice-Hall, Englewood Cliffs, New Jersey, 1983.

77. PAÏDOUSSIS, M. P.
'Flutter of Conservative Systems of Pipes Carrying Incompressible Fluid', *J. Mech. Engng Sci.*, Vol. 17, 1975, 19–25.

78. PAÏDOUSSIS, M. P. and LAITHIER, B. E.
'Dynamics of Timoshenko Beams Conveying Fluid', *J. Mech. Engng Sci.*, Vol. 18, 1976, 210–20.

79. PAPOULIS, ATHANASIOS
The Fourier Integral and its Applications, McGraw-Hill, New York, 1962.

80. PARLETT, BERESFORD, N.
The Symmetric Eigenvalue Problem, Prentice-Hall, Englewood Cliffs, New Jersey, 1980.

81. PIPES, LOUIS A. and HOVANESSIAN, SHAHEN A.
Matrix-Computer Methods in Engineering, Wiley, New York, 1969.

82. PRESS, W. H., FLANNERY, B. P., TEUKOLSKY, S. A. and VETTERLING, W. T.
Numerical Recipes, Cambridge University Press, Cambridge, 1986.

83. RAYLEIGH, J. W. S.
The Theory of Sound (2nd edition), Vols. 1 and 2, Macmillan, 1896. Reprinted by Dover, New York, 1945.

84. REID, J. GARY
Linear System Fundamentals, McGraw-Hill, New York, 1983.

85. RICE, J. R.
Numerical Methods, Software and Analysis, McGraw-Hill, New York, 1983.

86. RITZ, W.
    Gesammelte Werke, Société Suisse de Physique, Gauthier-Villars, Paris, 1911.
87. RITZ, W.
    'Über eine neue Method zur Losung gewisser Variations-probleme der mathematischen Physik', *Crelle's Journal f.d. reine und angew. Math.*, No. 135, 1909, 1–61. This paper is included in ref. [86].
88. SCHMIDT, G. and TONDL, A.
    Non-Linear Vibrations, Cambridge University Press, Cambridge, 1986.
89. SCRUTON, C. and FLINT, A. R.
    'Wind-Excited Oscillations of Structures', *Proc. Instn Civil Engrs*, Vol. 27, 1964, 673–702.
90. SNOWDON, J. C.
    Vibration and Shock in Damped Mechanical Systems, Wiley, New York, 1968.
91. SOUTHWELL, R. V.
    'On the General Theory of Elastic Stability', *Phil. Trans. R. Soc. Lond.*, Vol. A213, 1914, 187.
92. STOER, J. and BULIRSCH, R.
    Introduction to Numerical Analysis, Springer-Verlag, New York, 1980.
93. STOKER, J. J.
    Nonlinear Vibrations in Mechanical and Electrical Systems, Interscience, New York, 1950.
94. STRANG, GILBERT
    Linear Algebra and its Applications, Academic Press, New York, 1976.
95. STRANG, GILBERT
    Introduction to Applied Mathematics, Wellesley-Cambridge Press, Wellesley, MA, 1986.
96. SYNGE, JOHN L. and GRIFFITH, BYRON A.
    Principles of Mechanics (3rd edition), McGraw-Hill, New York, 1959.
97. TEMPLE, G. and BICKLEY, W. G.
    Rayleigh's Principle And Its Applications to Engineering, Oxford University Press, 1933. Republished by Dover, 1956.
98. THOMPSON, J. M. T. and STEWART, H. B.
    Nonlinear Dynamics and Chaos, Wiley, New York, 1986.
99. TIMOSHENKO, S.
    Strength of Materials (3rd edition), Parts I and II, Van Nostrand Reinhold, New York, 1955.
100. TIMOSHENKO, S. P. and GERE, J. M.
    Theory of Elastic Stability (2nd edition), McGraw-Hill, New York, 1961.
101. TIMOSHENKO, S., YOUNG, D. H. and WEAVER, W. JR
    Vibration Problems in Engineering (4th edition), Wiley, New York, 1974.
102. TONDL, ALES
    'On the Interaction Between Self-Excited and Parametric Vibrations', *Monographs and Memoranda No. 25, National Research Institute for Machine Design*, Běchovice, Prague, 1978.
103. UEDA, Y.
    'Randomly Transitional Phenomena in the System Governed by Duffing's Equation', *J. Stat. Phys.*, Vol. 20, 1979, 181–96.
104. UEDA, Y.
    'Explosion of Strange Attractors Exhibited by Duffing's Equation', in *Nonlinear Dynamics*, R. H. G. Helleman (Ed.), New York Academy of Sciences, New York, 1980, 422–34.

105. UEDA, Y.
'Steady Motions Exhibited by Duffing's Equation: a Picture Book of Regular and Chaotic Motions', in *New Approach to Nonlinear Problems in Dynamics*, P. J. Holmes (Ed.), Soc. Indus. Appl. Maths., Philadelphia, 1980, 311–22.

106. UEDA, Y. and AKAMATSU, N.
'Chaotically Transitional Phenomena in the Forced Negative-Response Oscillator', *Trans. Inst. Elec. Electron. Engrs, Circuits Syst.*, Vol. CAS-28, 1980, 217–24.

107. UEDA, Y., AKAMATSU, N. and HAYASHI, C.
'Computer Simulations of Nonlinear Ordinary Differential Equations and Non-periodic Oscillations', *Trans. Inst. Electron. Commun. Engrs, Japan.*, Vol. 56A, 1973, 218–25.

108. VON SANDEN, H.
Praxis der Differential-gleichungen, Walther de Gruyter & Co., Berlin, 1945, 99.

109. WALSHE, D. E. and WOOTTON, L. R.
'Preventing Wind-Induced Oscillations of Structures of Circular Section', *Proc. Instn Civil Engrs*, Vol. 47, 1970, 1–24.

110. WILKINSON, J. H.
The Algebraic Eigenvalue Problem, Clarendon Press, Oxford, 1965.

111. WILKINSON, J. H. and REINSCH, C.
Linear Algebra (Vol. 2 of Handbook for Automatic Computation, F. L. Bauer, Ed.), Springer-Verlag, Berlin, 1971.

112. ZHU, DECHAO and SHI, GUOQUIN
'The Determination of Defectiveness of Linear Structural Dynamic Systems', *Computers and Struct.*, Vol. 30, 1988, 897–899.

113. ZIENKIEWICZ, O. C.
The Finite Element Method (3rd edition), McGraw-Hill, London, 1977.

Summary of main formulae

The *general response* of $m\ddot{y} + c\dot{y} + k\,y = x$ is obtained from $\dot{z} = Az + F$ where

$$z = \begin{bmatrix} y \\ \dot{y} \end{bmatrix}, \quad A = \begin{bmatrix} O & I \\ -m^{-1}k & -m^{-1}c \end{bmatrix}, \quad F = \begin{bmatrix} O \\ m^{-1}x \end{bmatrix}.$$

Ch. 4, (4.49), (4.64), (4.65) and (4.66)

For M degrees of freedom, A has order $2M \times 2M$, z and F have order $2M \times 1$. The eigenvector matrix U is also $2M \times 2M$, each column having M displacements followed by the corresponding M velocities. The general displacement response is

$$y(t) = U_{\text{upper}}[\text{diag } e^{\lambda_j t}]\left[\int [\text{diag } e^{-\lambda_j t}]U_{\text{right}}^{-1}m^{-1}\,x(t)\,dt + C\right],$$

Ch. 4, (4.73) and Ch. 8, (8.11)

The $M \times M$ matrix of displacement frequency-response functions is

$$H(i\omega) = U_{\text{upper}}\left[\text{diag }\frac{1}{i\omega - \lambda_j}\right]U_{\text{right}}^{-1}m^{-1} \tag{8.32}$$

and the $M \times M$ matrix of displacement impulse response functions is

$$h(t) = U_{\text{upper}}[\text{diag } e^{\lambda_j t}]U_{\text{right}}^{-1}m^{-1}, \text{ for } t > 0, \tag{8.110}$$

provided that there are $2M$ independent eigenvectors. Individual elements of $H(i\omega)$ and $h(t)$ can be computed from (8.39) and (8.111), respectively. Results for the case when the eigenvector matrix is defective are given by (8.86), (8.95), (8.144) and (8.145).

Case of symmetric matrices m and k and $c = \alpha m + \beta k$

The eigenvector matrix now has order $M \times M$, each column consisting of M displacements only. When either m or k (or both) is positive definite, there is a complete set of independent eigenvectors. The eigenvalues ω_j^2, $j = 1$ to M, cannot be negative. When the eigenvector matrix U is normalized so that

$$U^T m\, U = I \quad \text{and} \quad U^T k\, U = [\text{diag } \omega_j^2],$$

Ch. 11, (11.116) and (11.126)

Also (11.141) and (11.144)

the normal coordinate vector q is given by

$$\ddot{q} + [\text{diag } 2\zeta_j\omega_j]\dot{q} + [\text{diag } \omega_j^2]q = U^T x \qquad (11.156)$$

provided that

$$U^T c\, U = [\text{diag } 2\zeta_j\omega_j] \qquad (11.155)$$

which will be the case if

$$c = \alpha m + \beta k. \qquad (11.153) \text{ and } (11.154)$$

The $M \times M$ matrix of displacement frequency-response functions is

$$H(i\omega) = U\left[\text{diag}\frac{1}{(i\omega)^2 + 2\zeta_j\omega_j(i\omega) + \omega_j^2}\right]U^T$$

(11.166) and (11.180)

and the $M \times M$ matrix of displacement impulse-response functions is

$$h(t) = U\left[\text{diag}\frac{1}{\omega_j\sqrt{1 - \zeta_j^2}} e^{-\zeta_j\omega_j t}\sin\omega_j\sqrt{1 - \zeta_j^2}\, t\right]U^T, \; t > 0.$$

(11.163) and (11.175)

Individual elements of $H(i\omega)$ and $h(t)$ can be computed from (11.185) and (11.186).

For the *modal analysis of continuous systems* described by

$$m(z)\frac{\partial^2}{\partial t^2}y(z, t) + \alpha m(z)\frac{\partial}{\partial t}y(z, t) + \beta L\left\{\frac{\partial}{\partial t}\{y(z, t)\}\right\} + L\{y(z, t)\} = x(z, t)$$

the modal expansion is

$$y(z, t) = \sum_{j=1}^{\infty} U_j(z)q_j(t)$$

Ch. 12, (12.25) and (12.26)

where the normal mode functions satisfy the boundary conditions and the orthogonality conditions which are

$$\int_R dz\; m(z)U_j(z)U_k(z) = \delta_{jk}, \; j, k = 1 \text{ to } \infty \qquad (12.14)$$

$$\int_R dz\; L\{U_j(z)\}U_k(z) = \omega_j^2\delta_{jk}, \; j, k = 1 \text{ to } \infty. \qquad (12.15)$$

The normal mode solution is

$$\ddot{q}_j + 2\zeta_j\omega_j\dot{q}_j + \omega_j^2 q_j = \int_R U_j(z)\, x(z, t)\, dz \qquad (12.27)$$

where

$$2\zeta_j\omega_j = \alpha + \beta\omega_j^2. \tag{12.28}$$

The natural frequencies and mode shapes $y(z, t) = U_j(z)\,e^{i\omega_j t}$ are the solutions obtained from

$$-\omega_j^2 m(z) U_j(z) + L\{U_j(z)\} = 0. \quad \text{(12.29) and (12.31)}$$

The frequency response at z_r due to a unit harmonic input at z_s is

$$H(z_r, z_s, i\omega) = \sum_{j=1}^{\infty} \frac{U_j(z_r)U_j(z_s)}{(i\omega)^2 + 2\zeta_j\omega_j(i\omega) + \omega_j^2}$$

$$\text{(12.61) and (12.66)}$$

and the impulse response at z_r due to a unit impulse applied at z_s is

$$h(z_r, z_s, t) = \sum_{j=1}^{\infty} U_j(z_r)U_j(z_s)\frac{1}{\omega_j\sqrt{1 - \zeta_j^2}}e^{-\zeta_j\omega_j t}\sin\omega_j\sqrt{1 - \zeta_j^2}\, t,\ t > 0.$$

$$\text{(12.53) and (12.60)}$$

When the scalar response variable $y(z, t)$ is replaced by the three-dimensional vector $y(z, t)$, corresponding results are given by (12.178), (12.183), (12.184) and (12.189) to (12.192).

Index